A History of the Warfare of Science with
Theology in Christendom

A HISTORY OF THE

Warfare of

Science with

Theology

IN CHRISTENDOM

ANDREW DICKSON WHITE

Abridged for the Modern Reader, with a
Preface and Epilogue by
BRUCE MAZLISH

The Free Press, *New York*

To the Memory of
Ezra Cornell
I dedicate this book

Thoughts that great hearts once broke for, we
  Breathe cheaply in the common air.
                              —LOWELL

Discipulus est prioris posterior dies.
                              —PUBLIUS SYRUS

Truth is the daughter of Time.
                              —BACON

The Truth shall make you free.
                    —ST. JOHN, viii, 32

Preface

ANDREW D. WHITE'S book is one of those rare things: a "classic account" of an important revolution in human thought. Because it first appeared in full in 1896, it naturally provokes the spirit of correction and amendment in modern readers, but the main lines of its thesis as well as its massive support of detail still command immense respect and continued reading. No other single work concerning the conflict of science and theology in Christendom has taken its place, and modern scholars such as the historian of science Charles C. Gillispie, and the historian of philosophy John Herman Randall, Jr., agree in awarding to White's book the accolade of "classic account."[1]

To some, the word "classic" all too often means dusty, dead, and outmoded—something to be regarded respectfully from a distance. White's book is not this sort of classic. It is a crisp, clear presentation, and it deals with fascinating materials of contemporary interest. White carries his enormous scholarly apparatus gracefully, and from the sparkle and verve of his style one forgets the amount of written nonsense he had to wade through in order to emerge with his account. He is not above telling a good story; and his recital of the Salem witch trials and of the tribulations of St. Xavier's legends, for example, makes for sheer literary enjoyment.

With all his light touch and good humor, however, White maintains throughout the *History* a driving sense of mission. It is to tell the story of the relations of two—perhaps *the* two—major concerns of the human spirit: science and religion, and the revolution in thought with which he deals is the emancipation of scientific thought from theological stricture.

This is often dealt with today as part of something called the Scientific Revolution. But by "science" White did not mean only the natural sciences. As a glance at his table of contents will reveal, he includes along with astronomy, geography, physics, chemistry, geology, and biology the fields of

[1] Charles Coulston Gillispie, *Genesis and Geology* (Harper Torchbooks, 1959), viii. John Herman Randall, Jr., "The Changing Impact of Darwin on Philosophy," *Journal of the History of Ideas*, XXII, 4, Oct.-Dec. 1961, 436.

archaeology, anthropology, comparative ethnology, history, meteorology, medical science, psychology (individual and mass, but especially the latter), comparative philology, comparative mythology, and political economy—a rather broad use of the term "science." It is clear that by science White meant not specific disciplines, but a certain way, or method, of thinking: a way or method which invokes secular, naturalistic explanations for phenomena rather than divine ones, and which involves observation, construction of hypotheses, and either experiment or renewed observation to check the hypotheses.

White's subject divides into two parts: 1) the emancipation of various areas of study from theology; and 2) the assertion, derived from studies in comparative mythology, philology, etc., that the sacred texts are not to be used to judge scientific thought but rather are to be judged *by* scientific thought. In short, the Bible is literature, not a collection of truths about the material or even social world. (We have come to call this view the "Higher Criticism.") As we shall see shortly, for White this was to increase, not diminish, the wonder of the Bible.

The two parts of White's subject are illuminated for us if we consider the famous statement of St. Augustine, which White cites in a number of places: "Nothing is to be accepted save on the authority of Scripture, since greater is that authority than all the powers of the human mind." This view was the touchstone of the theological world. In the seventeenth century, science attempted only to secure autonomy or equality with Scripture—to claim the authority of science in scientific matters. Thus, Galileo's plea was that

In the discussion of natural problems, we ought not to begin at the authority of places of scripture, but at sensible experiments and necessary demonstrations. For, from the Divine Word, the sacred scripture and nature did both alike proceed. . . . Nature, being inexorable and immutable, and never passing the bounds of the laws assigned her, . . . I conceive that, concerning natural effects, that which either sensible experience sets before our eyes, or necessary demonstrations do prove unto us, ought not, upon any account, be called into question, much less condemned upon the testimony of texts of scripture, which may, under their words, couch senses seemingly contrary thereto. . . . Nor does God less admirably discover himself to us in Nature's actions, than in the Scripture's sacred dictions.[2]

In the nineteenth century, however, science, in the shape of the higher criticism, took to the offensive. Addressing itself to the second part of St. Augustine's statement, it demonstrated that Scripture is not only *not* superior to science but is itself a product of the powers of the human mind. Clearly, the successful execution of this offensive meant the collapse of a whole universe of thought.

Before that event, however, from Augustine to the time of Galileo, theology did not merely claim authority over scientific thought; it disclaimed any value to the subjects attended to by scientific thought. In the words of Eusebius, speaking of scientific investigators: "It is not through ignorance of the things admired by them, but through contempt of their useless labor that we think little of these matters, turning our souls to better things." The same flavor comes through in the well-turned phrase attributed to Cardinal Baronius, "The intention of the Holy Ghost is to teach us how one goes to heaven, not how heaven goes."

In spite of these admonitions, men *were* interested—out of curiosity or motives of utility—in how the heavens go. And scientific thought proved its worth, for example, by aiding navigation at sea; by demonstrating that pestilences were due to natural, remediable, earthly causes—such as bad sanitation—rather than to heavenly exaltations; and—as White shows in a delightful chapter—by saving structures, including church steeples, from destruction by lightning, now no longer a part of God's wrath but a piece of electrical phenomena.

In this respect, modern natural science has been completely victorious. It need no longer convince men of its usefulness, and it pursues its path independent of theological correction. The triumph is complete. It is this triumph which first engaged White's attention, and he gave its historical account in an early version of the present edition, a version called *The Warfare of Science* (1876).

What is missing from the 1876 book is a treatment of mythological thinking. It is this very important—and then, as perhaps still now—controversial element which was added to

[2] Edwin Arthur Burtt, *The Metaphysical Foundations of Modern Physical Science* (London, 1949), 72-73.

the two volumes of 1896, whose essential pages you now hold. The result of this addition was to show that the sacred texts of Christianity represent part of a continuing evolution of man's spiritual beliefs, and are not a fixed, absolute source of authority.

Nevertheless, in spite of this critical approach, White took a positive view of religion. He did not believe the Bible to be a cunningly devised fable of priestcraft, but "fragments of earlier legends, myths, and theologies, accepted in good faith and brought together for the noblest of purposes." This noblest of purposes was the attestation of a "Power in the universe, not ourselves, which makes for righteousness" and for the love of God and of our neighbor.

On the other hand, White's view of theology was negative. Theology, as distinct from religion, is dogmatic and intolerant; it claims knowledge of the physical and social world on grounds of revelation, not scientific thought. Thus, between science and theology there is and must be deadly conflict; between science and religion there is no antagonism. Indeed, only by the defeat of theology can religion—representing what is poetically and spiritually best in man—be preserved in its purity. Hence, White's purpose in writing his *History* was really to emancipate *both* science and religion from theology; or, rather, to give an account of an intellectual revolution already accomplished.

The *History* came about by what almost seems an accident. We can best understand the circumstances of its composition if we place it in the context of White's life and work: a life which involved work as an educator, historian, and diplomat. White was born on November 7, 1832, in central New York; his father was a banker and man of wealth. After education at Geneva College (now Hobart), Yale, semesters at Paris and at Berlin (where, interestingly enough, he had no taste for the teachings of Ranke, the great German historian whose lectures, White claimed, "he could not follow"), and a graduate year at Yale, the young Andrew—he was only twenty-five—went out West to be a Professor of History at the University of Michigan. Here, inspired by European ideas of free inquiry and scientific study (which he contrasted with the rigid, dogmatic narrowness of Yale), he waged the good fight for a broader, more exciting and open presentation of history. By treating it as "a living subject having relations to present questions," and yet imposing rigor and discipline on the work of his students, White emerged as an eminently successful teacher.

About this time, White began to envisage a broader scope for his pedagogical notions. He conceived of a new state university for New York. His ideal university, he declared, "should exclude no sex or color . . . should afford an asylum for *Science*—where truth shall be sought for truth's sake, not stretched or cut exactly to fit Revealed Religion; should foster . . . a Moral Philosophy, History, and Political Economy unwarped to suit present abuses in Politics and Religion. . . ." Along with the liberal arts and natural sciences, agriculture and engineering were to be taught. The realization of his educational ideal, however, had to wait. Involvement in the anti-slavery movement and the cause of the North during the Civil War helped to shelve temporarily his great plan.

Its revivification came about through a curious side step in White's career. Returning from Michigan to Syracuse, his hometown in central New York, White was named by his fellow citizens to the state senate. Here he became the chairman of the committee on education; and, as chairman of this committee, the guardian of the vast landed endowment of the federal Morrill Act of 1862. New York's share was about one million acres, worth around $600,000. By great good fortune, another member of the senate, chairman of its agriculture committee, was Ezra Cornell, possessor of great wealth built up through the electric telegraph. After initial differences, White won Cornell over to his scheme for a new university: so much so that Cornell gave an additional $500,000 and 200 acres of land as a site for the university which would bear his name at Ithaca, New York. At last, White's ideal of un-biased education, offered to all qualified persons, regardless of sect and creed, was a reality. In 1868, Cornell University began classes, with 600 students in attendance. On the in-sistence of Ezra Cornell, White became the first president; he also reserved for himself the chair of history.

The early years of the new university were marked by perils, both financial and spiritual. These difficulties are de-scribed by White in his *Autobiography*. After telling how the financial perils were met, he then explains how picayune, small-minded men, many of them resentful that they had not secured the land-grant money for their own sectarian institu-tions, attacked Cornell University as a hotbed of infidelity and atheism. It is worth reprinting White's statement of how he responded, for his response gradually turned into the present *History:*

> For a long time I stood on the defensive, hoping that the provisions made for the growth of religious life among the students might show that we were not so wicked as we were represented; but, as all this seemed only to embitter our adversaries, I finally determined to take the offensive, and having been invited to deliver a lecture in the great hall of the Cooper Institute at New York, took as my subject "The Battle-fields of Science." In this my effort was to show how, in the supposed interest of religion, earnest and excellent men, for many ages and in many countries, had bitterly opposed various advances in science and in education, and that such opposition had resulted in most evil results, not only to science and education, but to religion. This lecture was published in full, next day, in the "New York Tribune"; extracts from it were widely copied; it was asked for by lecture associations in many parts of the country; grew first into two magazine articles, then into a little book which was widely circulated at home, reprinted in England with a preface by Tyndall, and circulated on the Continent in translations, was then expanded into a series of articles in the "Popular Science Monthly," and finally wrought into my book on "The Warfare of Science with Theology."[3]

We see in this account a number of elements: 1) the accidental growth of the *History,* which partially accounts for its loosely organized and sometimes repetitive form; 2) the original educative purpose of the book—White wrote it as part of his defense of free learning and inquiry; and 3) the "warfare" aspect of the work: the initial "defensive" attitude to "adversaries," and then the passing over to the "offensive." White was in a real fight—his *History,* as at Michigan, was a vital subject in his own life, related to "present questions"— and it is only natural that images of warfare, tourneys, and battles came readily to his pen.

It may also be from his work as a diplomat, concerned with issues of war and peace, that the shape of his book took its origin. Writing what is really intellectual history, he used the forms of the prevalent politically and diplomatically oriented history of his day.[4] His own experience of diplomacy was

[3] Andrew Dickson White, *Autobiography,* 2 Vols. (New York, 1905), I, 425.
[4] White, incidentally, helped found the American Historical Association, in 1884, and served, in fact, as its first president.

extensive and firsthand. Indeed, one is aghast at the amount of activity White packed into his life. From an early year, in 1854, as an attaché of the American Legation in St. Petersburg (where he incidentally developed material for a lecture on "Civilization in Russia"—later turned into an article on "The Rise and Decline of the Serf System in Russia"—reflecting White's anti-slavery feelings), White went on to numerous appointments by Presidents Grant, Hayes, Harrison, Cleveland, McKinley, and Theodore Roosevelt, and to a varied assortment of posts—a commissioner to Santo Domingo (1871); minister to Germany (1879-81); minister to Russia (1892-94), where he met and had long talks, delightfully recorded in the *Autobiography,* and well worth reading, with Tolstoy and with Pobedonostzeff, the great reactionary politician; member of the Venezuela Commission (1895-96): ambassador to Germany (1897-1903); and head of the American delegation to the Hague Conference (1897).

Clearly, White was as much a man of activity as of thought. It is not, therefore, as a pedant but as a fighter for good causes that he wrote the *History.* Yet, passion did not lead to unmitigated partisanship. White was too much the trained historian and scholar for this. The result is an unusual combination of vigor and learning; and it is partly this—as well as the importance of the subject—which makes White's *History* a "classic account" still worth reading.

In a number of ways, White serves as the final point in a line of enlightened thinkers stretching from *philosophes* like Condorcet and Gibbon up through Comte and his positivist followers. All of these thinkers believed in the idea of progress. White, for example, declared that history showed, not the Fall of Man, but his Ascent: "mankind, instead of having fallen from a high intellectual, moral, and religious condition has slowly risen from low and brutal beginnings." So, too, like Gibbon, who, he remarks in the *Autobiography,* marked an "epoch in my development, intellectual and moral," and Condorcet, who in the *Sketch for a Historical Picture of the Progress of the Human Mind* talks of a step in man's development—the eighth—where everywhere "we see reason and authority fighting for supremacy, a battle which prepared and anticipated the triumph of reason," White believed the Ascent to be characterized by a warfare between science and theology.

Basically, then, White's main thesis is not new. We are constantly reminded, in fact, of the encyclopedic treatment of the same theme by the great French positivist, Auguste Comte. And, although White only mentions him a few times, in rather a curious and indirect fashion, the shadow of Comte's law of the three stages (although there are evident differences) stands over the book. As with Comte's *Cours de philosophie positive*, we work through field after field—astronomy, physics, chemistry, geology, biology, psychology—tracing the shift from the theological stage of thought (Comte also has a metaphysical interim) to the scientific stage.

What is new in White are two aspects of his treatment of the grand theme. First, unlike Comte, who traced the change largely in theoretical and abstract terms, White gives a detailed *historical* picture of the fight. He deals with the concrete events. Secondly (and here he is partly joined by Comte), White accords to the Christian religion a much more affirmative position than any of his predecessors. In fact, he includes religion as one of the fields in which man's ascent manifested itself. Thus, history shows

a progress from fetichism, of which so many evidences crop out in the early Jewish worship as shown in the Old Testament Scriptures, through polytheism, when Jehovah was but "a god above all gods," through the period when he was "a jealous God," capricious and cruel, until he is revealed in such inspired utterances as those of the nobler Psalms, the great passages in Isaiah, the sublime preaching of Micah, and, above all, through the ideal given to the world by Jesus of Nazareth.

Surprisingly, after the smoke of battle has cleared, the victory belongs to what White calls "the higher races"—perhaps an infelicitous phrase to our ears today—who have arrived at "the belief in the Universal Father, as best revealed in the New Testament."

This conclusion results, really, from White's belief in "laws governing the evolution of truth in human history," an evolution which is mirrored in the creative works of the spirit: poems, chronicles, legends, myths, and sacred books. Just as there are natural laws governing the evolution of the physical world, so, he believed, there are natural laws governing the growth of the myths and legends which comprise the spiritual world. These natural laws of man's mental evolution entail a development out of myth and theology not only of science but also of religion. White, by viewing religion as growing out of myth, has gone far beyond Condorcet's simple view of religion as priestly imposture; in sum, for White, his *History* validates a mythical, or religious, way to truth—correctly interpreted—as much as it does a logical, or scientific, way.

How does White's book stand up today? As a history of science, we would have to pass two judgments on it. One, we should probably want to take a more "historicist" approach to the subject; that is, instead of snatching our examples of the conflict of science and theology from any time and place, to serve our polemic purpose, we should want to establish a context—a whole period and a given climate of opinion—in which to examine the interrelationship of the two forces. The way in which theology *gave rise* to science would interest us as much as the way in which it obstructed science; as Whitehead has suggested, for example, in his *Science and the Modern World,* the Middle Ages "formed one long training of the intellect of Western Europe in the sense of order." We should want to ask "why" a Galileo in Catholic Italy, when outside of Christendom there is no rise of science as we moderns know it. To say all this is not to condemn White for neglecting this approach; he is writing in the same way as the comparative anthropologists of his time, whom he respected so much: consider those other classics, Frazer's *Golden Bough* or Tylor's *Primitive Culture,* with their comparative rather than holistic or functional approach.

Two, we should demur as to his blanket condemnation of *all* opponents of the bearers of truth, i.e. Copernicus, Galileo, Kepler, etc. The truth, we know today, is and was not so obvious: first-rate scientists, like Tycho Brahe, could object to the Copernican theory on sound, scientific grounds.[5] In

[5] It is interesting, in this connection, to compare White's reaction to a statement by John Henry Newman with our own. The quotation from Newman was: "Scripture says that the sun moves and the earth is stationary, and science that the earth moves and the sun is comparatively at rest. How can we determine which of these opposite statements is the very truth till we know what motion is? If our idea of motion is but an accidental result of our present senses, neither proposition is true and both are true: neither true philosophically; both true for certain practical purposes in the system in which they are respectively found." White's caustic comment was: "There is no utterance more hopelessly skeptical." I, 166.

fact, the weight of evidence often set against the new theories —the actual dropping of balls from a tower showed that unequal bodies, meeting unequal resistance from the air, did *not* fall equally fast.[6]

Having said this, however, we must remind ourselves that the intent of White's book was much broader than that of present-day histories of science. It was, first of all, to establish beyond any reasonable doubt a thesis: that theological organizations cannot argue with science upon scientific grounds; they must restrict themselves to moral and spiritual considerations of the problems and consequences involved in the effect of science upon society. To demonstrate this, White took a very large definition of science—one which included the natural and human sciences—and amassed an enormous array of scholarly data. His effort was unique—and successful; nothing like it has appeared, or been necessary, since the publication of his *History*.

A few words need to be said about this edition. It seemed gratuitous to touch up White's work by adding extensive new footnote references or by pointing out modern-day differences with his positions; in any case, it would be an impossibly large task and would produce another book than White's. Thus, I have restricted myself to a very few suggestions and comments—*engagements* with White's ideas which I could not resist entering into—and have put these in the form of bracketed footnotes. His own footnotes have been kept because they are still a mine of information, and because without them the solidity of his position might not be apparent. Bracketed footnotes refer to sections deleted from this edition.

So, too, I have not attempted any systematic addition to his story, in an effort to bring it up to modern times. Some reflections on the relationship between science and nonscientific authority, and the new form this has taken in the contemporary period, will be found in an epilogue. It will contain merely some general remarks, occasioned by reading White's book, and not be a continuation of his *History*.

As for a justification of this abridgment, that is provided for in White's own work. In his Introduction, he himself tells

[6] We cannot refrain here from citing a book, even though it was published at White's own university, which disproves the story of Galileo's dropping of weights from the Tower of Pisa. See Lane Cooper, *Aristotle, Galileo, and the Tower of Pisa* (Ithaca, 1935).

us that the circumstances surrounding the composition of the *History* led to "some iterations which in the steady quiet of my own library would not have been made." He also tells us that he intended his book "for the general reader." This abridgment, then, is an attempt to remove the iterations indicated in this edition by bracketed headings, while preserving—and perhaps even enhancing—the appeal of the original to the general reader.

BRUCE MAZLISH

CAMBRIDGE, MASSACHUSETTS
February, 1962

Introduction

MY BOOK IS READY for the printer, and as I begin this preface my eye lights upon the crowd of Russian peasants at work on the Neva under my windows. With pick and shovel they are letting the rays of the April sun into the great ice barrier which binds together the modern quays and the old granite fortress where lie the bones of the Romanoff Czars.

This barrier is already weakened; it is widely decayed, in many places thin, and everywhere treacherous; but it is, as a whole, so broad, so crystallized about old boulders, so imbedded in shallows, so wedged into crannies on either shore, that it is a great danger. The waters from thousands of swollen streamlets above are pressing behind it; wreckage and refuse are piling up against it; every one knows that it must yield. But there is danger that it may resist the pressure too long and break suddenly, wrenching even the granite quays from their foundations, bringing desolation to a vast population, and leaving, after the subsidence of the flood, a widespread residue of slime, a fertile breeding-bed for the germs of disease.

But the patient *mujiks* are doing the right thing. The barrier, exposed more and more to the warmth of spring by the scores of channels they are making, will break away gradually, and the river will flow on beneficent and beautiful.

My work in this book is like that of the Russian *mujik* on the Neva. I simply try to aid in letting the light of historical truth into that decaying mass of outworn thought which attaches the modern world to mediæval conceptions of Christianity, and which still lingers among us—a most serious barrier to religion and morals, and a menace to the whole normal evolution of society.

For behind this barrier also the flood is rapidly rising— the flood of increased knowledge and new thought; and this barrier also, though honeycombed and in many places thin, creates a danger—danger of a sudden breaking away, distressing and calamitous, sweeping before it not only outworn creeds and noxious dogmas, but cherished principles and ideals, and even wrenching out most precious religious and moral foundations of the whole social and political fabric.

My hope is to aid—even if it be but a little—in the grad-

21

ual and healthful dissolving away of this mass of unreason, that the stream of "religion pure and undefiled" may flow on broad and clear, a blessing to humanity.

And now a few words regarding the evolution of this book.

It is something over a quarter of a century since I labored with Ezra Cornell in founding the university which bears his honored name.

Our purpose was to establish in the State of New York an institution for advanced instruction and research, in which science, pure and applied, should have an equal place with literature; in which the study of literature, ancient and modern, should be emancipated as much as possible from pedantry; and which should be free from various useless trammels and vicious methods which at that period hampered many, if not most, of the American universities and colleges.

We had especially determined that the institution should be under the control of no political party and of no single religious sect, and with Mr. Cornell's approval I embodied stringent provisions to this effect in the charter.

It had certainly never entered into the mind of either of us that in all this we were doing anything irreligious or unchristian. Mr. Cornell was reared a member of the Society of Friends; he had from his fortune liberally aided every form of Christian effort which he found going on about him, and among the permanent trustees of the public library which he had already founded, he had named all the clergymen of the town—Catholic and Protestant. As for myself, I had been bred a churchman, had recently been elected a trustee of one church college, and a professor in another; those nearest and dearest to me were devoutly religious; and, if I may be allowed to speak of a matter so personal to myself, my most cherished friendships were among deeply religious men and women, and my greatest sources of enjoyment were ecclesiastical architecture, religious music, and the more devout forms of poetry. So far from wishing to injure Christianity, we both hoped to promote it; but we did not confound religion with sectarianism, and we saw in the sectarian character of American colleges and universities, as a whole, a reason for the poverty of the advanced instruction then given in so many of them.

It required no great acuteness to see that a system of control which, in selecting a Professor of Mathematics or Language or Rhetoric or Physics or Chemistry, asked first and

above all to what sect or even to what wing or branch of a
sect he belonged, could hardly do much to advance the moral,
religious, or intellectual development of mankind.

The reasons for the new foundation seemed to us, then, so
cogent that we expected the co-operation of all good citizens,
and anticipated no opposition from any source.

As I look back across the intervening years, I know not
whether to be more astonished or amused at our simplicity.

Opposition began at once. In the State Legislature it confronted us at every turn, and it was soon in full blaze throughout the State—from the good Protestant bishop who proclaimed that all professors should be in holy orders, since to
the Church alone was given the command, "Go, teach all
nations," to the zealous priest who published a charge that
Goldwin Smith—a profoundly Christian scholar—had come
to Cornell in order to inculcate the "infidelity of the *Westminster Review*"; and from the eminent divine who went from
city to city denouncing the "atheistic and pantheistic tendencies" of the proposed education, to the perfervid minister
who informed a denominational synod that Agassiz, the last
great opponent of Darwin, and a devout theist was "preaching Darwinism and atheism" in the new institution.

As the struggle deepened, as hostile resolutions were introduced into various ecclesiastical bodies, as honored clergymen solemnly warned their flocks first against the "atheism,"
then against the "infidelity," and finally against the "indif-
ferentism" of the university, as devoted pastors endeavoured
to dissuade young men from matriculation, I took the defensive, and, in answer to various attacks from pulpits and
religious newspapers, attempted to allay the fears of the public. "Sweet reasonableness" was fully tried. There was established and endowed in the university perhaps the most effective Christian pulpit, and one of the most vigorous branches
of the Christian Association, then in the United States; but
all this did nothing to ward off the attack. The clause in the
charter of the university forbidding it to give predominance
to the doctrines of any sect, and above all the fact that much
prominence was given to instruction in various branches of
science, seemed to prevent all compromise, and it soon became clear that to stand on the defensive only made matters
worse. Then it was that there was borne in upon me a sense
of the real difficulty—the antagonism between the theological
and scientific view of the universe and of education in rela-

tion to it; therefore it was that, having been invited to deliver a lecture in the great hall of the Cooper Institute at New York, I took as my subject *The Battlefields of Science,* maintaining this thesis which follows:

In all modern history, interference with science in the supposed interest of religion, no matter how conscientious such interference may have been, has resulted in the direst evils both to religion and to science, and invariably; and, on the other hand, all untrammelled scientific investigation, no matter how dangerous to religion some of its stages may have seemed for the time to be, has invariably resulted in the highest good both of religion and of science.

The lecture was next day published in the *New York Tribune* at the request of Horace Greeley, its editor, who was also one of the Cornell University trustees. As a result of this widespread publication and of sundry attacks which it elicited, I was asked to maintain my thesis before various university associations and literary clubs; and I shall always remember with gratitude that among those who stood by me and presented me on the lecture platform with words of approval and cheer was my revered instructor, the Rev. Dr. Theodore Dwight Woolsey, at that time President of Yale College.

My lecture grew—first into a couple of magazine articles, and then into a little book called *The Warfare of Science,* for which, when republished in England, Prof. John Tyndall wrote a preface.

Sundry translations of this little book were published, but the most curious thing in its history is the fact that a very friendly introduction to the Swedish translation was written by a Lutheran bishop.

Meanwhile Prof. John W. Draper published his book on *The Conflict between Science and Religion,* a work of great ability, which, as I then thought, ended the matter, so far as my giving it further attention was concerned.

But two things led me to keep on developing my own work in this field: First, I had become deeply interested in it, and could not refrain from directing my observation and study to it; secondly, much as I admired Draper's treatment of the questions involved, his point of view and mode of looking at history were different from mine.

He regarded the struggle as one between Science and Religion. I believed then, and am convinced now, that it was a struggle between Science and Dogmatic Theology.

More and more I saw that it was the conflict between two epochs in the evolution of human thought—the theological and the scientific.

So I kept on, and from time to time published *New Chapters in the Warfare of Science* as magazine articles in *The Popular Science Monthly*. This was done under many difficulties. For twenty years, as President of Cornell University and Professor of History in that institution, I was immersed in the work of its early development. Besides this, I could not hold myself entirely aloof from public affairs, and was three times sent by the Government of the United States to do public duty abroad: first as a commissioner to Santo Domingo, in 1870; afterward as minister to Germany, in 1879; finally, as minister to Russia, in 1892; and was also called upon by the State of New York to do considerable labor in connection with international exhibitions at Philadelphia and at Paris. I was also obliged from time to time to throw off by travel the effects of overwork.

The variety of residence and occupation arising from these causes may perhaps explain some peculiarities in this book which might otherwise puzzle my reader.

While these journeyings have enabled me to collect materials over a very wide range—in the New World, from Quebec to Santo Domingo and from Boston to Mexico, San Francisco, and Seattle, and in the Old World from Trondhjem to Cairo and from St. Petersburg to Palermo—they have often obliged me to write under circumstances not very favorable: sometimes on an Atlantic steamer, sometimes on a Nile boat, and not only in my own library at Cornell, but in those of Berlin, Helsingfors, Munich, Florence, and the British Museum. This fact will explain to the benevolent reader not only the citation of different editions of the same authority in different chapters, but some iterations which in the steady quiet of my own library would not have been made.

It has been my constant endeavour to write for the general reader, avoiding scholastic and technical terms as much as possible and stating the truth simply as it presents itself to me.

That errors of omission and commission will be found here and there is probable—nay, certain; but the substance of the book will, I believe, be found fully true. I am encouraged in this belief by the fact that, of three bitter attacks which this work in its earlier form has already encountered, one was purely declamatory, objurgatory, and hortatory, and the others based upon ignorance of facts easily pointed out.

And here I must express my thanks to those who have aided me. First and above all to my former student and dear friend, Prof. George Lincoln Burr, of Cornell University, to whose contributions, suggestions, criticisms, and cautions I am most deeply indebted; also to my friends U. G. Weatherly, formerly Travelling Fellow of Cornell, and now Assistant Professor in the University of Indiana,—Prof. and Mrs. Earl Barnes and Prof. William H. Hudson, of Stanford University, —and Prof. E. P. Evans, formerly of the University of Michigan, but now of Munich, for extensive aid in researches upon the lines I have indicated to them, but which I could never have prosecuted without their co-operation. In libraries at home and abroad they have all worked for me most effectively, and I am deeply grateful to them.

This book is presented as a sort of *Festschrift*—a tribute to Cornell University as it enters the second quarter-century of its existence, and probably my last tribute.

The ideas for which so bitter a struggle was made at its foundation have triumphed. Its faculty, numbering over one hundred and fifty; its students, numbering but little short of two thousand; its noble buildings and equipment; the munificent gifts, now amounting to millions of dollars, which it has received from public-spirited men and women; the evidences of public confidence on all sides; and, above all, the adoption of its cardinal principles and main features by various institutions of learning in other States, show this abundantly. But there has been a triumph far greater and wider. Everywhere among the leading modern nations the same general tendency is seen. During the quarter-century just past the control of public instruction, not only in America but in the leading nations of Europe, has passed more and more from the clergy to the laity. Not only are the presidents of the larger universities in the United States, with but one or two exceptions, laymen, but the same thing is seen in the old European strongholds of metaphysical theology. At my first visit to Oxford and Cambridge, forty years ago, they were entirely under ecclesiastical control. Now, all this is changed. An eminent member of the present British Government has recently said, "A candidate for high university position is handicapped by holy orders." I refer to this with not the slightest feeling of hostility toward the clergy, for I have none; among them are many of my dearest friends; no one honours their proper work more than I; but the above fact is simply noted as proving the continuance of that evolution which I have endeavoured to describe in this series of monographs—an evolution, indeed, in which the warfare of Theology against Science has been one of the most active and powerful agents. My belief is that in the field left to them—their proper field—the clergy will more and more, as they cease to struggle against scientific methods and conclusions, do work even nobler and more beautiful than anything they have heretofore done. And this is saying much. My conviction is that Science, though it has evidently conquered Dogmatic Theology based on biblical texts and ancient modes of thought, will go hand in hand with Religion; and that, although theological control will continue to diminish, Religion, as seen in the recognition of "a Power in the universe, not ourselves, which makes for righteousness," and in the love of God and of our neighbor, will steadily grow stronger and stronger, not only in the American institutions of learning but in the world at large. Thus may the declaration of Micah as to the requirements of Jehovah, the definition by St. James of "pure religion and undefiled," and, above all, the precepts and ideals of the blessed Founder of Christianity himself, be brought to bear more and more effectively on mankind.

I close this preface some days after its first lines were written. The sun of spring has done its work on the Neva; the great river flows tranquilly on, a blessing and a joy; the *mujiks* are forgotten.

A. D. W.

LEGATION OF THE UNITED STATES, ST. PETERSBURG,
April 14, 1894.

P. S.—Owing to a wish to give more thorough revision to some parts of my work, it has been withheld from the press until the present date.

A. D. W.

CORNELL UNIVERSITY, ITHACA, N. Y.,
August 15, 1895.

Contents

CHAPTER 1

From Creation to Evolution.

CHAPTER 2

Geography

CHAPTER 3

Astronomy

1. *The Old Sacred Theory of the Universe*

CHAPTER 4

From "Signs and Wonders" to Law in the Heavens

1. *The Theological View*

3. *The Invasion of Scepticism*
***

4. *Theological Efforts at Compromise—the Final Victory of Science*

CHAPTER 5

From Genesis to Geology

[1. *Growth of Theological Explanations*]

2. *Efforts to Suppress the Scientific View*
***

3. *The First Great Effort at Compromise, Based on the Flood of Noah*

CHAPTER 6

The Antiquity of Man, Egyptology, and Assyriology

CHAPTER 7

The Antiquity of Man and Prehistoric Archæology

CHAPTER 8

The "Fall of Man" and Anthropology

CHAPTER 9

The "Fall of Man" and Ethnology

[CHAPTER 10

The "Fall of Man" and History]

CHAPTER 11

From "The Prince of the Power of the Air" to Meteorology

4. *Franklin's Lightning-Rod*

[CHAPTER 12

From Magic to Chemistry and Physics]

CHAPTER 13

From Miracles to Medicine

CHAPTER 14

From Fetich to Hygiene

CHAPTER 15

From "Demoniacal Possession" to Insanity

[2. *The Sacred Theory of Language in Its Second Form*]

3. *Breaking Down of the Theological View*

4. *Triumph of the New Science*

5. *Summary*
***

CHAPTER 18

From the Dead Sea Legends to Comparative Mythology

[1. *The Growth of Explanatory Transformation Myths*]
[2. *Mediæval Growth of the Dead Sea Legends*]
[3. *Post-Reformation Culmination of the Dead Sea Legends—*
      Beginnings of a Healthful Scepticism]
[4. *Theological Efforts at Compromise—Triumph of the Scien-*
      tific View]

[CHAPTER 19

From Leviticus to Political Economy]

[1. *Origin and Progress of Hostility to Loans at Interest*]
[2. *Retreat of the Church, Protestant and Catholic*]

CHAPTER 20

From the Divine Oracles to the Higher Criticism

1. *The Older Interpretation*

2. Beginnings of Scientific Interpretation

6. *Reconstructive Force of Scientific Criticism*

A History of the Warfare of Science with
Theology in Christendom

Chapter 1

From Creation to Evolution

1. The Visible Universe

AMONG THOSE MASSES of cathedral sculpture which preserve so much mediæval theology, one frequently recurring group is noteworthy for its presentment of a time-honoured doctrine regarding the origin of the universe.

The Almighty, in human form, sits benignly, making the sun, moon, and stars, and hanging them from the solid firmament which supports the "heaven above" and overarches the "earth beneath."

The furrows of thought on the Creator's brow show that in this work he is obliged to contrive; the knotted muscles upon his arms shows that he is obliged to toil; naturally, then, the sculptors and painters of the mediæval and early modern period frequently represented him as the writers whose conceptions they embodied had done—as, on the seventh day, weary after thought and toil, enjoying well-earned repose and the plaudits of the hosts of heaven.

In these thought-fossils of the cathedrals, and in other revelations of the same idea through sculpture, painting, glass-staining, mosaic work, and engraving, during the Middle Ages and the two centuries following, culminated a belief which had been developed through thousands of years, and which has determined the world's thought until our own time.

Its beginnings lie far back in human history; we find them among the early records of nearly all the great civilizations, and they hold a most prominent place in the various sacred books of the world. In nearly all of them is revealed the conception of a Creator of whom man is an imperfect image, and who literally and directly created the visible universe with his hands and fingers.

Among these theories, of especial interest to us are those which controlled theological thought in Chaldea. The Assyrian inscriptions which have been recently recovered and given to the English-speaking peoples by Layard, George Smith, Sayce, and others, show that in the ancient religions of Chaldea and Babylonia there was elaborated a narrative of the creation which, in its most important features, must have been the source of that in our own sacred books. It has now become perfectly clear that from the same sources which inspired the accounts of the creation of the universe among the Chaldeo-Babylonian, the Assyrian, the Phœnician, and other ancient civilizations came the ideas which hold so prominent a place in the sacred books of the Hebrews. In the two accounts imperfectly fused together in Genesis, and also in the account of which we have indications in the book of Job and in the Proverbs, there is presented, often with the greatest sublimity, the same early conception of the Creator and of the creation—the conception, so natural in the childhood of civilization, of a Creator who is an enlarged human being working literally with his own hands, and of a creation which is "the work of his fingers." To supplement this view there was developed the belief in this Creator as one who, having

> . . . "from his ample palm
> Launched forth the rolling planets into space,"

sits on high, enthroned "upon the circle of the heavens," perpetually controlling and directing them.

From this idea of creation was evolved in time a somewhat nobler view. Ancient thinkers, and especially, as is now found, in Egypt, suggested that the main agency in creation was not the hands and fingers of the Creator, but his *voice*. Hence was mingled with the earlier, cruder belief regarding the origin of the earth and heavenly bodies by the Almighty the more impressive idea that "he spake and they were made" —that they were brought into existence by his *word*.[1]

[1] Among the many mediæval representations of the creation of the universe, I especially recall from personal observation those sculptured above the portals of the cathedrals of Freiburg and Upsala, the paintings on the walls of the Campo Santo at Pisa, and, most striking of all, the mosaics of the Cathedral of Monreale and those in the Cappella Palatina at Palermo. Among peculiarities showing the simplicity of the earlier conception the representation of the repose of the Almighty on the seventh day is very striking. He is shown as seated in almost the exact attitude of the "Weary Mercury" of classic sculpture—bent, and with a very marked expression of fatigue upon his countenance and in the whole disposition of his body.

The Monreale mosaics are pictured in the great work of Gravina,

Among the early fathers of the Church this general view of creation became fundamental; they impressed upon Christendom more and more strongly the belief that the universe was created in a perfectly literal sense by the hands or voice of God. Here and there sundry theologians of larger mind attempted to give a more spiritual view regarding some parts of the creative work, and of these were St. Gregory of Nyssa and St. Augustine. Ready as they were to accept the literal text of Scripture, they revolted against the conception of an actual creation of the universe by the hands and fingers of a Supreme Being, and in this they were followed by Bede and a few others; but the more material conceptions prevailed, and we find these taking shape not only in the sculptures and mosaics and stained glass of cathedrals, and in the illuminations of missals and psalters, but later, at the close of the Middle Ages, in the pictured Bibles and in general literature.

Into the Anglo-Saxon mind this ancient material conception of the creation was riveted by two poets whose works appealed especially to the deeper religious feelings. In the seventh century Cædmon paraphrased the account given in Genesis, bringing out this material conception in the most literal form; and a thousand years later Milton developed out of the various statements in the Old Testament, mingled with a theology regarding "the creative Word" which had been drawn from the New, his description of the creation by the second person in the Trinity, than which nothing could be more literal and material:

---

and the Pisa frescoes in Didron's *Iconographie,* Paris, 1843, p. 598. For an exact statement of the resemblances which have settled the question among the most eminent scholars in favour of the derivation of the Hebrew cosmogony from that of Assyria, see Jensen, *Die Kosmologie der Babylonier,* Strassburg, 1890, pp. 304, 306; also Franz Lukas, *Die Grundbegriffe in den Kosmographien der alten Völker,* Leipsic, 1893, pp. 35-46; also George Smith's *Chaldean Genesis,* especially the German translation with additions by Delitzsch, Leipsic, 1876, and Schrader, *Die Keilinschriften und das Alte Testament,* Giessen, 1883, pp. 1-54, etc. See also Renan, *Histoire du peuple d'Israel,* vol. i, chap. i, *L'antique influence babylonienne.* For Egyptian views regarding creation, and especially for the transition from the idea of creation by the hands and fingers of the Creator to creation by his *voice* and his "word," see Maspero and Sayce, *The Dawn of Civilization,* pp. 145-146.

"He took the golden compasses, prepared
In God's eternal store, to circumscribe
This universe and all created things.
One foot he centred, and the other turned
Round through the vast profundity obscure,
And said, 'Thus far extend, thus far thy bounds:
This be thy just circumference, O world!' "[2]

So much for the orthodox view of the *manner* of creation.
The next point developed in this theologic evolution had
reference to the *matter* of which the universe was made, and
it was decided by an overwhelming majority that no material
substance existed before the creation of the material universe
—that "God created everything out of nothing." Some ven-
turesome thinkers, basing their reasoning upon the first verses
of Genesis, hinted at a different view—namely, that the
mass, "without form and void," existed before the universe;
but this doctrine was soon swept out of sight. The vast majority of the fathers were explicit on this point. Tertullian especially was very severe against those who took any other view
than that generally accepted as orthodox: he declared that,
if there had been any pre-existing matter out of which the
world was formed, Scripture would have mentioned it; that
by not mentioning it God has given us a clear proof that there
was no such thing; and, after a manner not unknown in other
theological controversies, he threatens Hermogenes, who
takes the opposite view, with "the woe which impends on all
who add to or take away from the written word."

St. Augustine, who showed signs of a belief in a pre-existence of matter, made his peace with the prevailing belief by
the simple reasoning that, "although the world has been made
of some material, that very same material must have been
made out of nothing."

In the wake of these great men the universal Church
steadily followed. The Fourth Lateran Council declared that
God created everything out of nothing; and at the present hour
the vast majority of the faithful—whether Catholic or Prot-

[2] For Gregory of Nyssa, Augustine, and the general subject of the
development of an evolution theory among the Greeks, see the
excellent work by Dr. Osborn, *From the Greeks to Darwin*, pp. 33
and following; for Cædmon, see any edition—I have used Bouter-
wek's, Gütersloh, 1854; for Milton, see *Paradise Lost*, book vii,
lines 225-231.

estant—are taught the same doctrine; on this point the syllabus of Pius IX and the Westminster Catechism fully agree.[3]

Having thus disposed of the manner and matter of creation, the next subject taken up by theologians was the *time* required for the great work.

Here came a difficulty. The first of the two accounts given in Genesis extended the creative operation through six days, each of an evening and a morning, with much explicit detail regarding the progress made in each. But the second account spoke of *"the day"* in which "the Lord God made the earth and the heavens." The explicitness of the first account and its naturalness to the minds of the great mass of early theologians gave it at first a decided advantage; but Jewish thinkers, like Philo, and Christian thinkers, like Origen, forming higher conceptions of the Creator and his work, were not content with this, and by them was launched upon the troubled sea of Christian theology the idea that the creation was instantaneous, this idea being strengthened not only by the second of the Genesis legends, but by the great text, "He spake, and it was done; he commanded, and it stood fast"—or, as it appears in the Vulgate and in most translations, "He spake, and they were made; he commanded, and they were created."

As a result, it began to be held that the safe and proper course was to believe literally *both* statements; that in some mysterious manner God created the universe in six days, and yet brought it all into existence in a moment. In spite of the outcries of sundry great theologians, like Ephrem Syrus, that the universe was created in exactly six days of twenty-four hours each, this compromise was promoted by St. Athanasius and St. Basil in the East, and by St. Augustine and St. Hilary in the West.

Serious difficulties were found in reconciling these two views, which to the natural mind seem absolutely contradictory; but by ingenious manipulation of texts, by dexterous play upon phrases, and by the abundant use of metaphysics to dissolve away facts, a reconciliation was effected, and men came at least to believe that they believed in a creation of the

---

[3] For Tertullian, see *Tertullian against Hermogenes,* chaps. xx and xxii; for St. Augustine regarding "creation from nothing," see the *De Genesi contra Manichæos,* lib. i, cap. vi; for St. Ambrose, see the *Hexameron,* lib. i, cap. iv; for the decree of the Fourth Lateran Council, and the view received in the Church to-day, see the article *Creation* in Addis and Arnold's *Catholic Dictionary.*

universe instantaneous and at the same time extended through six days.[4]

Some of the efforts to reconcile these two accounts were so fruitful as to deserve especial record. The fathers, Eastern and Western, developed out of the double account in Genesis, and the indications in the Psalms, the Proverbs, and the book of Job, a vast mass of sacred science bearing upon this point. As regards the whole work of creation, stress was laid upon certain occult powers in numerals. Philo Judæus, while believing in an instantaneous creation, had also declared that the world was created in six days because "of all numbers six is the most productive"; he had explained the creation of the heavenly bodies on the fourth day by "the harmony of the number four"; of the animals on the fifth day by the five senses; of man on the sixth day by the same virtues in the number six which had caused it to be set as a limit to the creative work; and, greatest of all, the rest on the seventh day by the vast mass of mysterious virtues in the number seven.

St. Jerome held that the reason why God did not pronounce the work of the second day "good" is to be found in the fact that there is something essentially evil in the number two, and this was echoed centuries afterward, afar off in Britain, by Bede.

St. Augustine brought this view to bear upon the Church in the following statement: "There are three classes of numbers—the more than perfect, the perfect, and the less than perfect, according as the sum of them is greater than, equal to, or less than the original number. Six is the first perfect number: wherefore we must not say that six is a perfect number because God finished all his works in six days, but that God finished all his works in six days because six is a perfect number."

Reasoning of this sort echoed along through the mediæval Church until a year after the discovery of America, when the *Nuremberg Chronicle* re-echoed it as follows: "The creation of things is explained by the number six, the parts of which, one, two, and three, assume the form of a triangle."

This view of the creation of the universe as instantaneous

[4] For Origen, see his *Contra Celsum,* cap. xxxvi, xxxvii; also his *De Principibus,* cap. v; for St. Augustine, see his *De Genesi contra Manichæos* and *De Genesi ad Litteram, passim;* for Athanasius, see his *Discourses against the Arians,* ii, 48, 49.

and also as in six days, each made up of an evening and a morning, became virtually universal. Peter Lombard and Hugo of St. Victor, authorities of vast weight, gave it their sanction in the twelfth century, and impressed it for ages upon the mind of the Church.

Both these lines of speculation—as to the creation of everything out of nothing, and the reconciling of the instantaneous creation of the universe with its creation in six days —were still further developed by other great thinkers of the Middle Ages.

St. Hilary of Poitiers reconciled the two conceptions as follows: "For, although according to Moses there is an appearance of regular order in the fixing of the firmament, the laying bare of the dry land, the gathering together of the waters, the formation of the heavenly bodies, and the arising of living things from land and water, yet the creation of the heavens, earth, and other elements is seen to be the work of a single moment."

St. Thomas Aquinas drew from St. Augustine a subtle distinction which for ages eased the difficulties in the case: he taught in effect that God created the substance of things in a moment, but gave to the work of separating, shaping, and adorning this creation, six days.[5]

The early reformers accepted and developed the same view, and Luther especially showed himself equal to the occasion. With his usual boldness he declared, first, that Moses "spoke properly and plainly, and neither allegorically nor figura-

[5] For Philo Judæus, see his *Creation of the World,* chap. iii; for St. Augustine on the powers of numbers in creation, see his *De Genesi ad Litteram,* iv, chap. ii; for Peter Lombard, see the *Sententiæ,* lib. ii, dist. xv, 5; and for Hugo of St. Victor, see *De Sacramentis,* lib. i, pars i; also, *Annotat. Elucidat. in Pentateuchum,* cap. v, vi, vii; for St. Hilary, see *De Trinitate,* lib. xii; for St. Thomas Aquinas, see his *Summa Theologica,* quest. lxxxiv, arts. i and ii; the passage in the *Nuremberg Chronicle,* 1493, is in fol. iii; for Bossuet, see his *Discours sur l'Histoire Universelle;* for the sacredness of the number seven among the Babylonians, see especially Schrader, *Die Keilinschriften und das Alte Testament,* pp. 21, 22; also George Smith *et al.;* for general ideas on the occult powers of various numbers, especially the number seven, and the influence of these ideas on theology and science, see my chapter on astronomy. As to mediæval ideas on the same subject, see Detzel, *Christliche Ikonographie,* Freiburg, 1894, pp. 44 and following.

tively," and that therefore "the world with all creatures was created in six days." And he then goes on to show how, by a great miracle, the whole creation was also instantaneous.

Melanchthon also insisted that the universe was created out of nothing and in a mysterious way, both in an instant and in six days, citing the text: "He spake, and they were made."

Calvin opposed the idea of an instantaneous creation, and laid especial stress on the creation in six days: having called attention to the fact that the biblical chronology shows the world to be not quite six thousand years old and that it is now near its end, he says that "creation was extended through six days that it might not be tedious for us to occupy the whole of life in the consideration of it."

Peter Martyr clinched the matter by declaring: "So important is it to comprehend the work of creation that we see the creed of the Church take this as its starting point. Were this article taken away there would be no original sin, the promise of Christ would become void, and all the vital force of our religion would be destroyed." The Westminster divines in drawing up their Confession of Faith specially laid it down as necessary to believe that all things visible and invisible were created not only out of nothing but in exactly six days.

Nor were the Roman divines less strenuous than the Protestant reformers regarding the necessity of holding closely to the so-called Mosaic account of creation. As late as the middle of the eighteenth century, when Buffon attempted to state simple geological truths, the theological faculty of the Sorbonne forced him to make and to publish a most ignominious recantation which ended with these words: "I abandon everything in my book respecting the formation of the earth, and generally all which may be contrary to the narrative of Moses."

Theologians, having thus settled the manner of the creation, the matter used in it, and the time required for it, now exerted themselves to fix its *date*.

The long series of efforts by the greatest minds in the Church, from Eusebius to Archbishop Usher, to settle this point are presented in another chapter.[6] Suffice it here that the general conclusion arrived at by an overwhelming majority of the most competent students of the biblical accounts was that the date of creation was, in round numbers, four thou-

[6] [See Chapter 6.—Ed.]

sand years before our era; and in the seventeenth century, in his great work, Dr. John Lightfoot, Vice-Chancellor of the University of Cambridge, and one of the most eminent Hebrew scholars of his time, declared, as the result of his most profound and exhaustive study of the Scriptures, that "heaven and earth, centre and circumference, were created all together, in the same instant, and clouds full of water," and that "this work took place and man was created by the Trinity on October 23, 4004 B.C., at nine o'clock in the morning."

Here was, indeed, a triumph of Lactantius's method, the result of hundreds of years of biblical study and theological thought since Bede in the eighth century, and Vincent of Beauvais in the thirteenth, had declared that creation must have taken place in the spring. Yet, alas! within two centuries after Lightfoot's great biblical demonstration as to the exact hour of creation, it was discovered that at that hour an exceedingly cultivated people, enjoying all the fruits of a highly developed civilization, had long been swarming in the great cities of Egypt, and that other nations hardly less advanced had at that time reached a high development in Asia.[7]

But, strange at it may seem, even after theologians had thus settled the manner of creation, the matter employed in it, the time required for it, and the exact date of it, there remained virtually unsettled the first and greatest question of all: and this was nothing less than the question, WHO actually created the universe?

Various theories more or less nebulous, but all centred in texts of Scripture, had swept through the mind of the Church. By some theologians it was held virtually that the actual crea-

[7] For Luther, see his *Commentary on Genesis*, 1545, introduction, and his comments on chap. i, verse 12; the quotations from Luther's commentary are taken mainly from the translation by Henry Cole, D. D., Edinburgh, 1858; for Melanchthon, see *Loci Theologici*, in Melanchthon, *Opera*, ed. Bretschneider, vol. xxi, pp. 269, 270, also pp. 637, 638—in quoting the text (Ps. xxiii, 9) I have used, as does Melanchthon himself, the form of the Vulgate; for the citations from Calvin, see his *Commentary on Genesis* (*Opera omnia*, Amsterdam, 1671, tom. i, cap. ii, p. 8); also in the *Institutes*, Allen's translation, London, 1838, vol. i, chap. xv, pp. 126, 127; for Peter Martyr, see his *Commentary on Genesis*, cited by Zöckler, vol. i, p. 690; for the articles in the Westminster Confesssion of Faith, see chap. iv; for Buffon's recantation, see Lyell, *Principles of Geology*, chap. iii, p. 57. For Lightfoot's declaration, see his works, edited by Pitman, London, 1822.

tive agent was the third person of the Trinity, who, in the opening words of our sublime creation poem, "moved upon the face of the waters." By others it was held that the actual Creator was the second person of the Trinity, in behalf of whose agency many texts were cited from the New Testament. Others held that the actual Creator was the first person, and this view was embodied in the two great formulas known as the Apostles' and Nicene Creeds, which explicitly assigned the work to "God the Father Almighty, Maker of heaven and earth." Others, finding a deep meaning in the words "Let *us* make," ascribed in Genesis to the Creator, held that the entire Trinity directly created all things; and still others, by curious metaphysical processes, seemed to arrive at the idea that peculiar combinations of two persons of the Trinity achieved the creation.

In all this there would seem to be considerable courage in view of the fearful condemnations launched in the Athanasian Creed against all who should "confound the persons" or "divide the substance of the Trinity."

These various stages in the evolution of scholastic theology were also embodied in sacred art, and especially in cathedral sculpture, in glass-staining, in mosaic working, and in missal painting.

The creative Being is thus represented sometimes as the third person of the Trinity, in the form of a dove brooding over chaos; sometimes as the second person, and therefore a youth; sometimes as the first person, and therefore fatherly and venerable; sometimes as the first and second persons, one being venerable and the other youthful; and sometimes as three persons, one venerable and one youthful, both wearing papal crowns, and each holding in his lips a tip of the wing of the dove, which thus seems to proceed from both and to be suspended between them.

Nor was this the most complete development of the mediæval idea. The Creator was sometimes represented with a single body, but with three faces, thus showing that Christian belief had in some pious minds gone through substantially the same cycle which an earlier form of belief had made ages before in India, when the Supreme Being was represented with one body but with the three faces of Brahma, Vishnu, and Siva.

But at the beginning of the modern period the older view in its primitive Jewish form was impressed upon Christians by the most mighty genius in art the world has known; for in 1512, after four years of Titanic labour, Michael Angelo uncovered his frescoes within the vault of the Sistine Chapel.

They had been executed by the command and under the sanction of the ruling Pope, Julius II, to represent the conception of Christian theology then dominant, and they remain today in all their majesty to show the highest point ever attained by the older thought upon the origin of the visible universe.

In the midst of the expanse of heaven the Almighty Father —the first person of the Trinity—in human form, august and venerable, attended by angels and upborne by mighty winds, sweeps over the abyss, and, moving through successive compartments of the great vault, accomplishes the work of the creative days. With a simple gesture he divides the light from the darkness, rears on high the solid firmament, gathers together beneath it the seas, or summons into existence the sun, moon, and planets, and sets them circling about the earth.

In this sublime work culminated the thought of thousands of years; the strongest minds accepted it or pretended to accept it, and nearly two centuries later this conception, in accordance with the first of the two accounts given in Genesis, was especially enforced by Bossuet, and received a new lease of life in the Church, both Catholic and Protestant.[8]

But to these discussions was added yet another, which, beginning in the early days of the Church, was handed down the ages until it had died out among the theologians of our own time.

In the first of the biblical accounts light is created and the distinction between day and night thereby made on the first day, while the sun and moon are not created until the fourth day. Masses of profound theological and pseudoscientific

[8] For strange representations of the Creator and of the creation by one, two, or three persons of the Trinity, see Didron, *Iconographie Chrétienne*, pp. 35, 178, 224, 483, 567-580, and elsewhere; also Detzel as already cited. The most naïve of all survivals of the mediæval idea of creation which the present writer has ever seen was exhibited in 1894 on the banner of one of the guilds at the celebration of the four-hundredth anniversary of the founding of the Munich Cathedral. Jesus of Nazareth, as a beautiful boy and with a nimbus encircling his head, was shown turning and shaping the globe on a lathe, which he keeps in motion with his foot. The emblems of the Passion are about him, God the Father looking approvingly upon him from a cloud, and the dove hovering between the two. The date upon the banner was 1727.

reasoning have been developed to account for this—masses so great that for ages they have obscured the simple fact that the original text is a precious revelation to us of one of the most ancient of recorded beliefs—the belief that light and darkness are entities independent of the heavenly bodies, and that the sun, moon, and stars exist not merely to increase light but to "divide the day from the night, to be for signs and for seasons, and for days and for years," and "to rule the day and the night."

Of this belief we find survivals among the early fathers, and especially in St. Ambrose. In his work on creation he tells us: "We must remember that the light of day is one thing and the light of the sun, moon, and stars another—the sun by his rays appearing to add lustre to the daylight. For before sunrise the day dawns, but is not in full refulgence, for the sun adds still further to its splendour." This idea became one of the "treasures of sacred knowledge committed to the Church," and was faithfully received by the Middle Ages. The mediæval mysteries and miracle plays give curious evidences of this: In a performance of the creation, when God separates light from darkness, the stage direction is, "Now a painted cloth is to be exhibited, one half black and the other half white." It was also given more permanent form. In the mosaics of San Marco at Venice, in the frescoes of the Baptistery at Florence and of the Church of St. Francis at Assisi, and in the altar carving at Salerno, we find a striking realization of it—the Creator placing in the heavens two disks or living figures of equal size, each suitably coloured or inscribed to show that one represents light and the other darkness. This conception was without doubt that of the person or persons who compiled from the Chaldean and other earlier statements the accounts of the creation in the first of our sacred books.[9]

[9] For scriptural indications of the independent existence of light and darkness, compare with the first verses of the first chapter of Genesis such passages as Job xxxviii, 19, 24; for the general prevalence of this early view, see Lukas, *Kosmogonie*, pp. 31, 33, 41, 74, and *passim*; for the view of St. Ambrose regarding the creation of light and of the sun, see his *Hexameron*, lib. 4, cap. iii; for an excellent general statement, see Huxley, *Mr. Gladstone and Genesis*, in the *Nineteenth Century*, 1886, reprinted in his *Essays on Controverted Questions*, London, 1892, note, pp. 126 *et seq.*; for the acceptance in the miracle plays of the scriptural idea of light and darkness as independent creations, see Wright, *Essays on Archæological Subjects*, vol. ii, p. 178; for an account, with illustrations,

Thus, down to a period almost within living memory, it was held, virtually "always, everywhere, and by all," that the universe, as we now see it, was created literally and directly by the voice or hands of the Almighty, or by both—out of nothing—in an instant or in six days, or in both—about four thousand years before the Christian era—and for the convenience of the dwellers upon the earth, which was at the base and foundation of the whole structure.

But there had been implanted along through the ages germs of another growth in human thinking, some of them even as early as the Babylonian period. In the Assyrian inscriptions we find recorded the Chaldeo-Babylonian idea of *an evolution* of the universe out of the primeval flood or "great deep," and of the animal creation out of the earth and sea. This idea, recast, partially at least, into monotheistic form, passed naturally into the sacred books of the neighbours and pupils of the Chaldeans—the Hebrews; but its growth in Christendom afterward was checked, as we shall hereafter find, by the more powerful influence of other inherited statements which appealed more intelligibly to the mind of the Church.

Striking, also, was the effect of this idea as rewrought by the early Ionian philosophers, to whom it was probably transmitted from the Chaldeans through the Phœnicians. In the minds of Ionians like Anaximander and Anaximenes it was most clearly developed: the first of these conceiving of the visible universe as the result of processes of evolution, and the latter pressing further the same mode of reasoning, and dwelling on agencies in cosmic development recognised in modern science.

This general idea of evolution in Nature thus took strong hold upon Greek thought and was developed in many ways, some ingenious, some perverse. Plato, indeed, withstood it; but Aristotle sometimes developed it in a manner which reminds us of modern views.

Among the Romans Lucretius caught much from it, extending the evolutionary process virtually to all things.

In the early Church, as we have seen, the idea of a creation

---

of the mosaics, etc., representing this idea, see Tikkanen, *Die Genesis-mosaiken von San Marco,* Helsingfors, 1889, pp. 14 and 16 of text and Plates I and II. Very naïvely the Salerno carver, not wishing to colour the ivory which he wrought, has inscribed on one disk the word "LUX" and on the other "NOX." See also Didron, *Iconographie,* p. 482.

direct, material, and by means like those used by man, was all-powerful for the exclusion of conceptions based on evolution. From the more simple and crude of the views of creation given in the Babylonian legends, and thence incorporated into Genesis, rose the stream of orthodox thought on the subject, which grew into a flood and swept on through the Middle Ages and into modern times. Yet here and there in the midst of this flood were high grounds of thought held by strong men. Scotus Erigena and Duns Scotus, among the schoolmen, bewildered though they were, had caught some rays of this ancient light, and passed on to their successors, in modified form, doctrines of an evolutionary process in the universe.

In the latter half of the sixteenth century these evolutionary theories seemed to take more definite form in the mind of Giordano Bruno, who evidently divined the fundamental idea of what is now known as the "nebular hypothesis"; but with his murder by the Inquisition at Rome this idea seemed utterly to disappear—dissipated by the flames which in 1600 consumed his body on the Campo dei Fiori.

Yet within the two centuries divided by Bruno's death the world was led into a new realm of thought in which an evolution theory of the visible universe was sure to be rapidly developed. For there came, one after the other, five of the greatest men our race has produced—Copernicus, Kepler, Galileo, Descartes, and Newton—and when their work was done the old theological conception of the universe was gone. "The spacious firmament on high"—"the crystalline spheres" —the Almighty enthroned upon "the circle of the heavens," and with his own hands, or with angels as his agents, keeping sun, moon, and planets in motion for the benefit of the earth, opening and closing the "windows of heaven," letting down upon the earth the "waters above the firmament," "setting his bow in the cloud," hanging out "signs and wonders," hurling comets, "casting forth lightnings" to scare the wicked, and "shaking the earth" in his wrath: all this had disappeared.

These five men had given a new divine revelation to the world; and through the last, Newton, had come a vast new conception, destined to be fatal to the old theory of creation, for he had shown throughout the universe, in place of almighty caprice, all-pervading law. The bitter opposition of theology to the first four of these men is well known; but the fact is not so widely known that Newton, in spite of his deeply religious spirit, was also strongly opposed. It was vigorously urged against him that by his statement of the law of gravitation he "took from God that direct action on his works so constantly ascribed to him in Scripture and transferred it to material mechanism," and that he "substituted gravitation for Providence." But, more than this, these men gave a new basis for the theory of evolution as distinguished from the theory of creation.

Especially worthy of note is it that the great work of Descartes, erroneous as many of its deductions were, and, in view of the lack of physical knowledge in his time, must be, had done much to weaken the old conception. His theory of a universe brought out of all-pervading matter, wrought into orderly arrangement by movements in accordance with physical laws—though it was but a provisional hypothesis—had done much to draw men's minds from the old theological view of creation; it was an example of intellectual honesty arriving at errors, but thereby aiding the advent of truths. Crippled though Descartes was by his almost morbid fear of the Church, this part of his work was no small factor in bringing in that attitude of mind which led to a reception of the thoughts of more unfettered thinkers.

Thirty years later came, in England, an effort of a different sort, but with a similar result. In 1678 Ralph Cudworth published his *Intellectual System of the Universe*. To this day he remains, in breadth of scholarship, in strength of thought, in tolerance, and in honesty, one of the greatest glories of the English Church, and his work was worthy of him. He purposed to build a fortress which should protect Christianity against all dangerous theories of the universe, ancient or modern. The foundations of the structure were laid with old thoughts thrown often into new and striking forms; but, as the superstructure arose more and more into view, while genius marked every part of it, features appeared which gave the rigidly orthodox serious misgivings. From the old theories of direct personal action on the universe by the Almighty he broke utterly. He dwelt on the action of law, rejected the continuous exercise of miraculous intervention, pointed out the fact that in the natural world there are "errors" and "bungles," and argued vigorously in favour of the origin and maintenance of the universe as a slow and gradual development of Nature in obedience to an inward principle. The Balaks of seventeenth-century orthodoxy might well condemn this honest Balaam.

Toward the end of the next century a still more profound genius, Immanuel Kant, presented the nebular theory, giving it, in the light of Newton's great utterances, a consistency which it never before had; and about the same time Laplace gave it yet greater strength by mathematical reasonings of wonderful power and extent, thus implanting firmly in modern thought the idea that our own solar system and others—suns, planets, satellites, and their various movements, distances, and magnitudes—necessarily result from the obedience of nebulous masses to natural laws.

Throughout the theological world there was an outcry at once against "atheism," and war raged fiercely. Herschel and others pointed out many nebulous patches apparently gaseous. They showed by physical and mathematical demonstrations that the hypothesis accounted for the great body of facts, and, despite clamour, were gaining ground, when the improved telescopes resolved some of the patches of nebulous matter into multitudes of stars. The opponents of the nebular hypothesis were overjoyed; they now sang pæans to astronomy, because, as they said, it had proved the truth of Scripture. They had jumped to the conclusion that all nebulæ must be alike; that, if *some* are made up of systems of stars, *all* must be so made up; that none can be masses of attenuated gaseous matter, because some are not.

Science halted for a time. The accepted doctrine became this: that the only reason why all the nebulæ are not resolved into distinct stars is that our telescopes are not sufficiently powerful. But in time came the discovery of the spectroscope and spectrum analysis, and thence Fraunhofer's discovery that the spectrum of an ignited gaseous body is non-continuous, with interrupting lines; and Draper's discovery that the spectrum of an ignited solid is continuous, with no interrupting lines. And now the spectroscope was turned upon the nebulæ, and many of them were found to be gaseous. Here, then, was ground for the inference that in these nebulous masses at different stages of condensation—some apparently mere patches of mist, some with luminous centres—we have the process of development actually going on, and observations like those of Lord Rosse and Arrest gave yet further confirmation to this view. Then came the great contribution of the nineteenth century to physics, aiding to explain important parts of the vast process by the mechanical theory of heat.

Again the nebular hypothesis came forth stronger than ever,

and about 1850 the beautiful experiment of Plateau on the rotation of a fluid globe came in apparently to illustrate if not to confirm it. Even so determined a defender of orthodoxy as Mr. Gladstone at last acknowledged some form of a nebular hypothesis as probably true.

Here, too, was exhibited that form of surrendering theological views to science under the claim that science concurs with theology, which we have seen in so many other fields; and, as typical, an example may be given, which, however restricted in its scope, throws light on the process by which such surrenders are obtained. A few years since one of the most noted professors of chemistry in the city of New York, under the auspices of one of its most fashionable churches, gave a lecture which, as was claimed in the public prints and in placards posted in the streets, was to show that science supports the theory of creation given in the sacred books ascribed to Moses. A large audience assembled, and a brilliant series of elementary experiments with oxygen, hydrogen, and carbonic acid was concluded by the Plateau demonstration. It was beautifully made. As the coloured globule of oil, representing the earth, was revolved in a transparent medium of equal density, as it became flattened at the poles, as rings then broke forth from it and revolved about it, and, finally, as some of these rings broke into satellites, which for a moment continued to circle about the central mass, the audience, as well they might, rose and burst into rapturous applause.

Thereupon a well-to-do citizen arose and moved the thanks of the audience to the eminent professor for "this perfect demonstration of the exact and literal conformity of the statements given in Holy Scripture with the latest results of science." The motion was carried unanimously and with applause, and the audience dispersed, feeling that a great service had been rendered to orthodoxy. *Sancta simplicitas!*

What this incident exhibited on a small scale has been seen elsewhere with more distinguished actors and on a broader stage. Scores of theologians, chief among whom of late, in zeal if not in knowledge, has been Mr. Gladstone, have endeavoured to "reconcile" the two accounts in Genesis with each other and with the truths regarding the origin of the universe gained by astronomy, geology, geography, physics, and chemistry. The result has been recently stated by an eminent theologian, the Hulsean Professor of Divinity at the University of Cambridge. He declares, "No attempt at reconciling Genesis with the exacting requirements of modern sciences has ever been known to succeed without entailing a degree of special pleading or forced interpretation to which, in such a question, we should be wise to have no recourse."[10]

The revelations of another group of sciences, though sometimes bitterly opposed and sometimes "reconciled" by theologians, have finally set the whole question at rest. First, there have come the biblical critics—earnest Christian scholars, working for the sake of truth—and these have revealed beyond the shadow of a reasonable doubt the existence of at least two distinct accounts of creation in our book of Genesis, which can sometimes be forced to agree, but which are generally absolutely at variance with each other. These scholars have further shown the two accounts to be not the cunningly devised fables of priestcraft, but evidently fragments of earlier legends, myths, and theologies, accepted in good faith and brought together for the noblest of purposes by those who put in order the first of our sacred books.

Next have come the archæologists and philologists, the de-

[10] For an interesting reference to the outcry against Newton, see McCosh, *The Religious Aspect of Evolution,* New York, 1890, pp. 103, 104; for germs of an evolutionary view among the Babylonians, see George Smith, *Chaldean Account of Genesis,* New York, 1876, pp. 74, 75; for a germ of the same thought in Lucretius, see his *De Natura Rerum,* lib. v, pp. 187-194, 447-454; for Bruno's conjecture (in 1591), see Jevons, *Principles of Science,* London, 1874, vol. ii, p. 299; for Kant's statement, see his *Naturgeschichte des Himmels;* for his part in the nebular hypothesis, see Lange, *Geschichte des Materialismus,* vol. i, p. 266; for value of Plateau's beautiful experiment, very cautiously estimated, see Jevons, vol. ii, p. 36; also Élisée Reclus, *The Earth,* translated by Woodward, vol. i, pp. 14-18, for an estimate still more careful; for a general account of discoveries of the nature of nebulæ by spectroscope, see Draper, *Conflict between Religion and Science;* for a careful discussion regarding the spectra of solid, liquid, and gaseous bodies, see Schellen, *Spectrum Analysis,* pp. 100 *et seq.;* for a very thorough discussion of the bearings of discoveries made by spectrum analysis upon the nebular hypothesis, ibid., pp. 532-537; for a presentation of the difficulties yet unsolved, see an article by Plummer in the *London Popular Science Review* for January, 1875; for an excellent short summary of recent observations and thought on this subject, see T. Sterry Hunt, *Address at the Priestley Centennial,* pp. 7, 8; for an interesting modification of this hypothesis, see Proctor's writings; for a still more recent view see Lockyer's two articles on *The Sun's Place in Nature,* in *Nature* for February 14 and 25, 1895.

voted students of ancient monuments and records; of these are such as Rawlinson, George Smith, Sayce, Oppert, Jensen, Schrader, Delitzsch, and a phalanx of similarly devoted scholars, who have deciphered a multitude of ancient texts, especially the inscriptions found in the great library of Assurbanipal at Nineveh, and have discovered therein an account of the origin of the world identical in its most important features with the later accounts in our own book of Genesis.

These men have had the courage to point out these facts and to connect them with the truth that these Chaldean and Babylonian myths, legends, and theories were far earlier than those of the Hebrews, which so strikingly resemble them, and which we have in our sacred books; and they have also shown us how natural it was that the Jewish accounts of the creation should have been obtained at that remote period when the earliest Hebrews were among the Chaldeans, and how the great Hebrew poetic accounts of creation were drawn either from the sacred traditions of these earlier peoples or from antecedent sources common to various ancient nations.

In a summary which for profound thought and fearless integrity does honour not only to himself but to the great position which he holds, the Rev. Dr. Driver, Professor of Hebrew and Canon of Christ Church at Oxford, has recently stated the case fully and fairly. Having pointed out the fact that the Hebrews were one people out of many who thought upon the origin of the universe, he says that they "framed theories to account for the beginnings of the earth and man"; that "they either did this for themselves or borrowed those of their neighbours"; that "of the theories current in Assyria and Phœnicia fragments have been preserved, and these exhibit points of resemblance with the biblical narrative sufficient to warrant the inference that both are derived from the same cycle of tradition."

After giving some extracts from the Chaldean creation tablets he says: "In the light of these facts it is difficult to resist the conclusion that the biblical narrative is drawn from the same source as these other records. The biblical historians, it is plain, derived their materials from the best human sources available. . . . The materials which with other nations were combined into the crudest physical theories or associated with a grotesque polytheism were vivified and transformed by the inspired genius of the Hebrew historians, and adapted to become the vehicle of profound religious truth."

Not less honourable to the sister university and to himself is the statement recently made by the Rev. Dr. Ryle, Hulsean Professor of Divinity at Cambridge. He says that to suppose that a Christian "must either renounce his confidence in the achievements of scientific research or abandon his faith in Scripture is a monstrous perversion of Christian freedom." He declares: "The old position is no longer tenable; a new position has to be taken up at once, prayerfully chosen, and hopefully held." He then goes on to compare the Hebrew story of creation with the earlier stories developed among kindred peoples, and especially with the pre-existing Assyro-Babylonian cosmogony, and shows that they are from the same source. He points out that any attempt to explain particular features of the story into harmony with the modern scientific ideas necessitates "a non-natural" interpretation; but he says that, if we adopt a natural interpretation, "we shall consider that the Hebrew description of the visible universe is unscientific as judged by modern standards, and that it shares the limitations of the imperfect knowledge of the age at which it was committed to writing." Regarding the account in Genesis of man's physical origin, he says that it "is expressed in the simple terms of prehistoric legend, of unscientific pictorial description."

In these statements and in a multitude of others made by eminent Christian investigators in other countries is indicated what the victory is which has now been fully won over the older theology.

Thus, from the Assyrian researches as well as from other sources, it has come to be acknowledged by the most eminent scholars at the leading seats of Christian learning that the accounts of creation with which for nearly two thousand years all scientific discoveries have had to be "reconciled"— the accounts which blocked the way of Copernicus, and Galileo, and Newton, and Laplace—were simply transcribed or evolved from a mass of myths and legends largely derived by the Hebrews from their ancient relations with Chaldea, rewrought in a monotheistic sense, imperfectly welded together, and then thrown into poetic forms in the sacred books which we have inherited.

On one hand, then, we have the various groups of men devoted to the physical sciences all converging toward the proofs that the universe, as we at present know it, is the result of an evolutionary process—that is, of the gradual working of physical laws upon an early condition of matter; on the other hand, we have other great groups of men devoted to historical, philological, and archæological science whose researches all converge toward the conclusion that our sacred accounts of creation were the result of an evolution from an early chaos of rude opinion.

The great body of theologians who have so long resisted the conclusions of the men of science have claimed to be fighting especially for "the truth of Scripture," and their final answer to the simple conclusions of science regarding the evolution of the material universe has been the cry, "The Bible is true." And they are right—though in a sense nobler than they have dreamed. Science, while conquering them, has found in our Scriptures a far nobler truth than that literal historical exactness for which theologians have so long and so vainly contended. More and more as we consider the results of the long struggle in this field we are brought to the conclusion that the inestimable value of the great sacred books of the world is found in their revelation of the steady striving of our race after higher conceptions, beliefs, and aspirations, both in morals and religion. Unfolding and exhibiting this long-continued effort, each of the great sacred books of the world is precious, and all, in the highest sense, are true. Not one of them, indeed, conforms to the measure of what mankind has now reached in historical and scientific truth; to make a claim to such conformity is folly, for it simply exposes those who make it and the books for which it is made to loss of their just influence.

That to which the great sacred books of the world conform, and our own most of all, is the evolution of the highest conceptions, beliefs, and aspirations of our race from its childhood through the great turning-points in its history. Herein lies the truth of all bibles, and especially of our own. Of vast value they indeed often are as a record of historical outward fact; recent researches in the East are constantly increasing this value; but it is not for this that we prize them most: they are eminently precious, not as a record of outward fact, but as a mirror of the evolving heart, mind, and soul of man. They are true because they have been developed in accordance with the laws governing the evolution of truth in human history, and because in poem, chronicle, code, legend, myth, apologue, or parable they reflect this development of what is best in the onward march of humanity. To say that they are not true is as if one should say that a flower or a tree or a planet is not true; to scoff at them is to scoff at the law of the universe. In welding together into noble form, whether in the book of Genesis, or in the Psalms, or in the book of Job, or elsewhere, the great conceptions of men acting under earlier inspiration, whether in Egypt, or Chaldea, or India, or Persia, the compilers of our sacred books have given to humanity a possession ever becoming more and more precious; and modern science, in substituting a new heaven and a new earth for the old—the reign of law for the reign of caprice, and the idea of evolution for that of creation—has added and is steadily adding a new revelation divinely inspired.

In the light of these two evolutions, then—one of the visible universe, the other of a sacred creation-legend—science and theology, if the master minds in both are wise, may at last be reconciled.[11] A great step in this reconciliation was recently seen at the main centre of theological thought among English-speaking people, when, in the collection of essays entitled *Lux Mundi,* emanating from the college established in these latter days as a fortress of orthodoxy at Oxford, the legendary character of the creation accounts in our sacred books was acknowledged, and when the Archbishop of Canterbury asked, "May not the Holy Spirit at times have made use of myth and legend?"[12]

[11] [In the Introduction, White has seemed to suggest a distinction between Theology—which he equates with Dogmatic Theology—and Religion. However, he does not appear always to hold clearly to this dichotomy, and the reader must interpret White's use of the words theology and religion, therefore, from the context.—Ed.]

[12] For the first citations above made, see *The Cosmogony of Genesis,* by the Rev. S. R. Driver, D. D., Canon of Christ Church and Regius Professor of Hebrew at Oxford, in *The Expositor* for January, 1886; for the second series of citations, see *The Early Narratives of Genesis,* by Herbert Edward Ryle, Hulsean Professor of Divinity at Cambridge, London, 1892. For evidence that even the stiffest of Scotch Presbyterians have now come to discard the old literal biblical narrative of creation and to regard the declaration of the Westminster Confession thereon as a "disproved theory of creation," see Principal John Tulloch, in *Contemporary Review,* March, 1877, on *Religious Thought in Scotland*—especially page 550.

[2. Theological Teachings Regarding the Animals and Man]

3. Theological and Scientific Theories of an Evolution in Animated Nature

We have seen, thus far, how there came into the thinking of mankind upon the visible universe and its inhabitants the idea of a creation virtually instantaneous and complete, and of a Creator in human form with human attributes, who spoke matter into existence literally by the exercise of his throat and lips, or shaped and placed it with his hands and fingers.

We have seen that this view came from far; that it existed in the Chaldeo-Babylonian and Egyptian civilizations, and probably in others of the earliest date known to us; that its main features passed thence into the sacred books of the Hebrews and then into the early Christian Church, by whose theologians it was developed through the Middle Ages and maintained during the modern period.

But, while this idea was thus developed by a succession of noble and thoughtful men through thousands of years, another conception, to all appearance equally ancient, was developed, sometimes in antagonism to it, sometimes mingled with it—the conception of all living beings as wholly or in part the result of a growth process—of an evolution.

This idea, in various forms, became a powerful factor in nearly all the greater ancient theologies and philosophies. For very widespread among the early peoples who attained to much thinking power was a conception that, in obedience to the divine fiat, a watery chaos produced the earth, and that the sea and land gave birth to their inhabitants.

This is clearly seen in those records of Chaldeo-Babylonian thought deciphered in these latter years, to which reference has already been made. In these we have a watery chaos which, under divine action, brings forth the earth and its inhabitants; first the sea animals and then the land animals—the latter being separated into three kinds, substantially as recorded afterward in the Hebrew accounts. At the various stages in the work the Chaldean Creator pronounces it "beautiful," just as the Hebrew Creator in our own later account pronounces it "good."

In both accounts there is placed over the whole creation a solid, concave firmament; in both, light is created first, and the heavenly bodies are afterward placed "for signs and for seasons"; in both, the number seven is especially sacred, giving rise to a sacred division of time and to much else. It may be added that, with many other features in the Hebrew legends evidently drawn from the Chaldean, the account of the creation in each is followed by a legend regarding "the fall of man" and a deluge, many details of which clearly passed in slightly modified form from the Chaldean into the Hebrew accounts.

It would have been a miracle indeed if these primitive conceptions, wrought out with so much poetic vigour in that earlier civilization on the Tigris and Euphrates, had failed to influence the Hebrews, who during the most plastic periods of their development were under the tutelage of their Chaldean neighbours. Since the researches of Layard, George Smith, Oppert, Schrader, Jensen, Sayce, and their compeers, there is no longer a reasonable doubt that this ancient view of the world, elaborated if not originated in that earlier civilization, came thence as a legacy to the Hebrews, who wrought it in a somewhat disjointed but mainly monotheistic form into the poetic whole which forms one of the most precious treasures of ancient thought preserved in the book of Genesis.

Thus it was that, while the idea of a simple material creation literally by the hands and fingers or voice of the Creator became, as we have seen, the starting-point of a powerful stream of theological thought, and while this stream was swollen from age to age by contributions from the fathers, doctors, and learned divines of the Church, Catholic and Protestant, there was poured into it this lesser current, always discernible and at times clearly separated from it—a current of belief in a process of evolution.

The Rev. Prof. Sayce, of Oxford, than whom no English-speaking scholar carries more weight in a matter of this kind, has recently declared his belief that the Chaldeo-Babylonian theory was the undoubted source of the similar theory propounded by the Ionic philosopher Anaximander—the Greek thinkers deriving this view from the Babylonians through the Phœnicians; he also allows that from the same source its main features were adopted into both the accounts given in the first of our sacred books, and in this general view the most eminent Christian Assyriologists concur.

It is true that these sacred accounts of ours contradict each other. In that part of the first or Elohistic account given in

the first chapter of Genesis the *waters* bring forth fishes, marine animals, and birds (Genesis, i, 20); but in that part of
the second or Jehovistic account given in the second chapter
of Genesis both the land animals and birds are declared to
have been created not out of the water, but *"out of the
ground"* (Genesis, ii, 19).

The dialectic skill of the fathers was easily equal to explaining away this contradiction; but the old current of
thought, strengthened by both these legends, arrested their
attention, and, passing through the minds of a succession of
the greatest men of the Church, influenced theological opinion deeply, if not widely, for ages, in favour of an evolution
theory.

But there was still another ancient source of evolution
ideas. Thoughtful men of the early civilizations which were
developed along the great rivers in the warmer regions of the
earth noted how the sun-god as he rose in his fullest might
caused the water and the rich soil to teem with the lesser
forms of life. In Egypt, especially, men saw how under this
divine power the Nile slime brought forth "creeping things
innumerable." Hence mainly this ancient belief that the animals and man were produced by lifeless matter at the divine
command, "in the beginning," was supplemented by the idea
that some of the lesser animals, especially the insects, were
produced by a later evolution, being evoked after the original
creation from various sources, but chiefly from matter in a
state of decay.

This crude, early view aided doubtless in giving germs of a
better evolution theory to the early Greeks. Anaximander,
Empedocles, Anaxagoras, and, greatest of all, Aristotle, as we
have seen, developed them, making their way at times by
guesses toward truths since established by observation. Aristotle especially, both by speculation and observation, arrived
at some results which, had Greek freedom of thought continued, might have brought the world long since to its present
plane of biological knowledge; for he reached something like
the modern idea of a succession of higher organizations from
lower, and made the fruitful suggestion of "a perfecting principle" in Nature.

With the coming in of Christian theology this tendency
toward a yet truer theory of evolution was mainly stopped, but
the old crude view remained, and as a typical example of it
we may note the opinion of St. Basil the Great in the fourth

century. Discussing the work of creation, he declares that, at the command of God, "the waters were gifted with productive power"; "from slime and muddy places frogs, flies, and gnats came into being"; and he finally declares that the same voice which gave this energy and quality of productiveness to earth and water shall be similarly efficacious until the end of the world. St. Gregory of Nyssa held a similar view.

This idea of these great fathers of the Eastern Church took even stronger hold on the great father of the Western Church. For St. Augustine, so fettered usually by the letter of the sacred text, broke from his own famous doctrine as to the acceptance of Scripture and spurned the generally received belief of a creative process like that by which a toymaker brings into existence a box of playthings. In his great treatise on *Genesis* he says: "To suppose that God formed man from the dust with bodily hands is very childish. . . . God neither formed man with bodily hands nor did he breathe upon him with throat and lips."

St. Augustine then suggests the adoption of the old emanation or evolution theory, shows that "certain very small animals may not have been created on the fifth and sixth days, but may have originated later from putrefying matter," argues that, even if this be so, God is still their creator, dwells upon such a potential creation as involved in the actual creation, and speaks of animals "whose numbers the after-time unfolded."

In his great treatise on the *Trinity*—the work to which he devoted the best thirty years of his life—we find the full growth of this opinion. He develops at length the view that in the creation of living beings there was something like a growth—that God is the ultimate author, but works through secondary causes; and finally argues that certain substances are endowed by God with the power of producing certain classes of plants and animals.[13]

[13] For the Chaldean view of creation, see George Smith, *Chaldean Account of Genesis,* New York, 1876, pp. 14, 15, and 64-86; also Lukas, as above; also Sayce, *Religion of the Ancient Babylonians,* Hibbert Lectures for 1887, pp. 371 and elsewhere; as to the fall of man, Tower of Babel, sacredness of the number seven, etc., see also Delitzsch, appendix to the German translation of Smith, pp. 305 *et seq.;* as to the almost exact adoption of the Chaldean legends into the Hebrew sacred account, see all these, as also Schrader, *Die Keilinschriften und das Alte Testament,* Giessen, 1883, early chap-

This idea of a development by secondary causes apart from the original creation was helped in its growth by a theological exigency. More and more, as the organic world was observed, the vast multitude of petty animals, winged creatures, and "creeping things" was felt to be a strain upon the sacred narrative. More and more it became difficult to reconcile the dignity of the Almighty with his work in bringing each of these creatures before Adam to be named; or to reconcile the human limitations of Adam with his work in naming "every living creature"; or to reconcile the dimensions of Noah's ark with the space required for preserving all of them, and the food of all sorts necessary for their sustenance, whether they were admitted by twos, as stated in one scriptural account, or by sevens, as stated in the other.

The inadequate size of the ark gave especial trouble. Origen had dealt with it by suggesting that the cubit was six times greater than had been supposed. Bede explained Noah's ability to complete so large a vessel by supposing that he worked upon it during a hundred years; and, as to the provision of

ters; also article *Babylonia* in the *Encyclopædia Britannica;* as to the similar approval of creation by the Creator in both accounts, see George Smith, p. 73; as to the migration of the Babylonian legends to the Hebrews, see Schrader, Whitehouse's translation, pp. 44, 45; as to the Chaldean belief in a solid firmament, while Schrader in 1883 thought it not proved, Jensen in 1890 has found it clearly expressed—see his *Kosmologie der Babylonier,* pp. 9 *et seq.,* also pp. 304-306, and elsewhere. Dr. Lukas in 1893 also fully accepts this view of a Chaldean record of a "firmament"—see *Kosmologie,* pp. 43, etc.; see also Maspero and Sayce, *The Dawn of Civilization,* and for crude early ideas of evolution in Egypt, see ibid., pp. 156 *et seq.*

For the seven-day week among Chaldeans and rest on the seventh day, and the proof that even the name "Sabbath" is of Chaldean origin, see Delitzsch, *Beigaben zu Smith's Chald. Genesis,* pp. 300 and 306; also Schrader; for St. Basil, see *Hexæmeron* and *Homilies* vii-ix; but, for the steadfastness of Basil's view in regard to the immutability of species, see a Catholic writer on *Evolution and Faith* in the *Dublin Review* for July, 1871, p. 13; for citations of St. Augustine on Genesis, see the *De Genesi contra Manichæos,* lib. ii, cap. 14, in Migne, xxxiv, 188,—lib. v, cap. 5 and cap. 23,— and lib. vii, cap. 1; for the citations from his work on the Trinity, see his *De Trinitate,* lib. iii, cap. 8 and 9, in Migne, xlii, 877, 878; for the general subject very fully and adequately presented, see Osborn, *From the Greeks to Darwin,* New York, 1894, chaps. ii and iii.

food taken into it, he declared that there was no need of a supply for more than one day, since God could throw the animals into a deep sleep or otherwise miraculously make one day's supply sufficient; he also lessened the strain on faith still more by diminishing the number of animals taken into the ark—supporting his view upon Augustine's theory of the later development of insects out of carrion.

Doubtless this theological necessity was among the main reasons which led St. Isidore of Seville, in the seventh century, to incorporate this theory, supported by St. Basil and St. Augustine, into his great encyclopedic work which gave materials for thought on God and Nature to so many generations. He familiarized the theological world still further with the doctrine of secondary creation, giving such examples of it as that "bees are generated from decomposed veal, beetles from horseflesh, grasshoppers from mules, scorpions from crabs," and, in order to give still stronger force to the idea of such transformations, he dwells on the biblical account of Nebuchadnezzar, which appears to have taken strong hold upon mediæval thought in science, and he declares that other human beings had been changed into animals, especially into swine, wolves, and owls.

This doctrine of after-creations went on gathering strength until, in the twelfth century, Peter Lombard, in his theological summary, *The Sentences,* so powerful in moulding the thought of the Church, emphasized the distinction between animals which spring from carrion and those which are created from earth and water; the former he holds to have been created "potentially," the latter "actually."

In the century following, this idea was taken up by St. Thomas Aquinas and virtually received from him its final form. In the *Summa,* which remains the greatest work of mediæval thought, he accepts the idea that certain animals spring from the decaying bodies of plants and animals, and declares that they are produced by the creative word of God either actually or virtually. He develops this view by saying, "Nothing was made by God, after the six days of creation, absolutely new, but it was in some sense included in the work of the six days"; and that "even new species, if any appear, have existed before in certain native properties, just as animals are produced from putrefaction."

The distinction thus developed between creation "causally" or "potentially," and "materially" or "formally," was made much of by commentators afterward. Cornelius a Lapide spread it by saying that certain animals were created not "absolutely," but only "derivatively," and this thought was still further developed three centuries later by Augustinus Eugubinus, who tells us that, after the first creative energy had called forth land and water, light was made by the Almighty, the instrument of all future creation, and that the light called everything into existence.

All this "science falsely so called," so sedulously developed by the master minds of the Church, and yet so futile that we might almost suppose that the great apostle, in a glow of prophetic vision, had foreseen it in his famous condemnation, seems at this distance very harmless indeed; yet, to many guardians of the "sacred deposit of doctrine" in the Church, even so slight a departure from the main current of thought seemed dangerous. It appeared to them like pressing the doctrine of secondary causes to a perilous extent; and about the beginning of the seventeenth century we have the eminent Spanish Jesuit and theologian Suarez denouncing it, and declaring St. Augustine a heretic for his share in it.

But there was little danger to the older idea just then; the main theological tendency was so strong that the world kept on as of old. Biblical theology continued to spin its own webs out of its own bowels, and all the lesser theological flies continued to be entangled in them; yet here and there stronger thinkers broke loose from this entanglement and helped somewhat to disentangle others.[14]

At the close of the Middle Ages, in spite of the devotion

---

[14] For Bede's view of the ark and the origin of insects, see his *Hexæmeron,* i and ii; for Isidore, see the *Etymologiæ,* xi, 4, and xiii, 22; for Peter Lombard, see *Sent.,* lib. ii, dist. xv, 4 (in Migne, cxcii, 682); for St. Thomas Aquinas as to the laws of Nature, see *Summa Theologica,* i, *Quæst.* lxvii, art. iv; for his discussion on Avicenna's theory of the origin of animals, see ibid., *Quæst.* lxxi, vol. i, pp. 1184 and 1185, of Migne's edit.; for his idea as to the word of God being the active producing principle, see ibid., i, *Quæst.* lxxi, art. i; for his remarks on species, see ibid., i, *Quæst.* lxxii, art i; for his ideas on the necessity of the procreation of man, see ibid., i, *Quæst.* lxxii, art. i; for the origin of animals from putrefaction, see ibid., i, *Quæst.* lxxix, art. i, 3; for Cornelius a Lapide on the derivative creation of animals, see his *In Genesim Comment.,* cap. i, cited by Mivart, *Genesis of Species,* p. 282; for a reference to Suarez's denunciation of the view of St. Augustine, see Huxley's *Essays.*

of the Reformed Church to the letter of Scripture, the revival of learning and the great voyages gave an atmosphere in which better thinking on the problems of Nature began to gain strength. On all sides, in every field, men were making discoveries which caused the general theological view to appear more and more inadequate.

First of those who should be mentioned with reverence as beginning to develop again that current of Greek thought which the system drawn from our sacred books by the fathers and doctors of the Church had interrupted for more than a thousand years, was Giordano Bruno. His utterances were indeed vague and enigmatical, but this fault may well be forgiven him, for he saw but too clearly what must be his reward for any more open statements. His reward indeed came— even for his faulty utterances—when, toward the end of the nineteenth century, thoughtful men from all parts of the world united in erecting his statue on the spot where he had been burned by the Roman Inquisition nearly three hundred years before.

After Bruno's death, during the first half of the seventeenth century, Descartes seemed about to take the leadership of human thought: his theories, however superseded now, gave a great impulse to investigation then. His genius in promoting an evolution doctrine as regards the mechanical formation of the solar system was great, and his mode of thought strengthened the current of evolutionary doctrine generally; but his constant dread of persecution, both from Catholics and Protestants, led him steadily to veil his thoughts and even to suppress them. The execution of Bruno had occurred in his childhood, and in the midst of his career he had watched the Galileo struggle in all its stages. He had seen his own works condemned by university after university under the direction of theologians, and placed upon Roman *Index*. Although he gave new and striking arguments to prove the existence of God, and humbled himself before the Jesuits, he was condemned by Catholics and Protestants alike. Since Roger Bacon, perhaps, no great thinker had been so completely abased and thwarted by theological oppression.

Near the close of the same century another great thinker, Leibnitz, though not propounding any full doctrine on evolution, gave it an impulse by suggesting a view contrary to the sacrosanct belief in the immutability of species—that is, to the pious doctrine that every species in the animal kingdom now

exists as it left the hands of the Creator, the naming process
by Adam, and the door of Noah's ark.

His punishment at the hands of the Church came a few
years later, when, in 1712, the Jesuits defeated his attempt
to found an Academy of Science at Vienna. The imperial authorities covered him with honours, but the priests—ruling in
the confessionals and pulpits—would not allow him the privilege of aiding his fellow-men to ascertain God's truths revealed
in Nature.

Spinoza, Hume, and Kant may also be mentioned as among
those whose thinking, even when mistaken, might have done
much to aid in the development of a truer theory had not the
theologic atmosphere of their times been so unpropitious; but
a few years after Leibnitz's death came in France a thinker
in natural science of much less influence than any of these,
who made a decided step forward.

Early in the eighteenth century Benoist de Maillet, a man
of the world, but a wide observer and close thinker upon
Nature, began meditating especially upon the origin of animal
forms, and was led into the idea of the transformation of
species and so into a theory of evolution, which in some important respects anticipated modern ideas. He definitely,
though at times absurdly, conceived the production of existing species by the modification of their predecessors, and
he plainly accepted one of the fundamental maxims of modern
geology—that the structure of the globe must be studied in
the light of the present course of Nature.

But he fell between two ranks of adversaries. On one side,
the Church authorities denounced him as a freethinker; on the
other, Voltaire ridiculed him as a devotee. Feeling that his
greatest danger was from the orthodox theologians, De Maillet
endeavoured to protect himself by disguising his name in the
title of his book, and by so wording its preface and dedica-
tion that, if persecuted, he could declare it a mere sport of
fancy; he therefore announced it as the reverie of a Hindu
sage imparted to a Christian missionary. But this strategy
availed nothing: he had allowed his Hindu sage to suggest
that the days of creation named in Genesis might be long
periods of time; and this, with other ideas of equally fearful
import, was fatal. Though the book was in type in 1735, it
was not published till 1748—three years after his death.

On the other hand, the heterodox theology of Voltaire was
also aroused; and, as De Maillet had seen in the presence of

fossils on high mountains a proof that these mountains were once below the sea, Voltaire, recognising in this an argument for the deluge of Noah, ridiculed the new thinker without mercy. Unfortunately, some of De Maillet's vagaries lent themselves admirably to Voltaire's sarcasm; better material for it could hardly be conceived than the theory, seriously proposed, that the first human being was born of a mermaid.

Hence it was that, between these two extremes of theology, De Maillet received no recognition until, very recently, the greatest men of science in England and France have united in giving him his due. But his work was not lost, even in his own day; Robinet and Bonnet pushed forward victoriously on helpful lines.

In the second half of the eighteenth century a great barrier was thrown across this current—the authority of Linnæus. He was the most eminent naturalist of his time, a wide observer, a close thinker; but the atmosphere in which he lived and moved and had his being was saturated with biblical theology, and this permeated all his thinking.

He who visits the tomb of Linnæus to-day, entering the beautiful cathedral of Upsala by its southern porch, sees above it, wrought in stone, the Hebrew legend of creation. In a series of medallions, the Almighty—in human form—accomplishes the work of each creative day. In due order he puts in place the solid firmament with the waters above it, the sun, moon, and stars within it, the beasts, birds, and plants below it, and finishes his task by taking man out of a little hillock of "the earth beneath," and woman out of man's side. Doubtless Linnæus, as he went to his devotions, often smiled at this childlike portrayal. Yet he was never able to break away from the idea it embodied. At times, in face of the difficulties which beset the orthodox theory, he ventured to favour some slight concessions. Toward the end of his life he timidly advanced the hypothesis that all the species of one genus constituted at the creation one species; and from the last edition of his *Systema Naturæ* he quietly left out the strongly orthodox statement of the fixity of each species, which he had insisted upon in his earlier works. But he made no adequate declaration. What he might expect if he openly and decidedly sanctioned a newer view he learned to his cost; warnings came speedily both from the Catholic and Protestant sides.

At a time when eminent prelates of the older Church were

eulogizing debauched princes like Louis XV, and using the unspeakably obscene casuistry of the Jesuit Sanchez in the education of the priesthood as to the relations of men to women, the modesty of the Church authorities was so shocked by Linnæus's proofs of a sexual system in plants that for many years his writings were prohibited in the Papal States and in various other parts of Europe where clerical authority was strong enough to resist the new scientific current. Not until 1773 did one of the more broad-minded cardinals—Zelanda— succeed in gaining permission that Prof. Minasi should discuss the Linnæan system at Rome.

And Protestantism was quite as oppressive. In a letter to Eloius, Linnæus tells of the rebuke given to science by one of the great Lutheran prelates of Sweden, Bishop Svedberg. From various parts of Europe detailed statements had been sent to the Royal Academy of Science that water had been turned into blood, and well-meaning ecclesiastics had seen in this an indication of the wrath of God, certainly against the regions in which these miracles had occurred and possibly against the whole world. A miracle of this sort appearing in Sweden, Linnæus looked into it carefully and found that the reddening of the water was caused by dense masses of minute insects. News of this explanation having reached the bishop, he took the field against it; he denounced this scientific discovery as "a Satanic abyss" (*abyssum Satanæ*), and declared "The reddening of the water is *not* natural," and "when God allows such a miracle to take place Satan endeavours, and so do his ungodly, self-reliant, self-sufficient, and worldly tools, to make it signify nothing." In face of this onslaught Linnæus retreated; he tells his correspondent that "it is difficult to say anything in this matter," and shields himself under the statement "It is certainly a miracle that so many millions of creatures can be so suddenly propagated," and "it shows undoubtedly the all-wise power of the Infinite."

The great naturalist, grown old and worn with labours for science, could no longer resist the contemporary theology; he settled into obedience to it, and while the modification of his early orthodox view was, as we have seen, quietly imbedded in the final edition of his great work, he made no special effort to impress it upon the world. To all appearance he continued to adhere to the doctrine that all existing species had been created by the Almighty "in the beginning," and that since "the beginning" no new species had appeared.

Yet even his great authority could not arrest the swelling tide; more and more vast became the number of species, more and more incomprehensible under the old theory became the newly ascertained facts in geographical distribution, more and more it was felt that the universe and animated beings had come into existence by some process other than a special creation "in the beginning," and the question was constantly pressing, "By *what* process?"

Throughout the whole of the eighteenth century one man was at work on natural history who might have contributed much toward an answer to this question: this man was Buffon. His powers of research and thought were remarkable, and his gift in presenting results of research and thought showed genius. He had caught the idea of an evolution in Nature by the variation of species, and was likely to make a great advance with it; but he, too, was made to feel the power of theology.

As long as he gave pleasing descriptions of animals the Church petted him, but when he began to deduce truths of philosophical import the batteries of the Sorbonne were opened upon him; he was made to know that "the sacred deposit of truth committed to the Church" was, that "in the beginning God made the heavens and the earth"; and that "all things were made at the beginning of the world." For his simple statement of truths in natural science which are to-day truisms, he was, as we have seen, dragged forth by the theological faculty, forced to recant publicly, and to print his recantation. In this he announced, "I abandon everything in my book respecting the formation of the earth, and generally all which may be contrary to the narrative of Moses."[15]

[15] For Descartes in his relation to the Copernican theory, see Saisset, *Descartes et ses Précurseurs;* also Fouillée, *Descartes,* Paris, 1893, chaps. ii and iii; also other authorities cited in my chapter on Astronomy; for his relation to the theory of evolution, see the *Principes de Philosophie,* 3ème partie, § 45. For De Maillet, see Quatrefages, *Darwin et ses Précurseurs français,* chap. i, citing D'Archiac, *Paléontologie, Stratigraphie,* vol. i; also, Perrier, *La Philosophie zoologique avant Darwin,* chap. vi; also the admirable article, *Evolution,* by Huxley, in *Encyc. Brit.* The title of De Maillet's book is, *Telliamed, ou Entretiens d'un Philosophe indien avec un Missionnaire français sur la Diminution de la Mer,* 1748 and 1756. For Buffon, see the authorities previously given, also the chapter on Geology in this work. For the resistance of both Catholic and Protestant authorities to the Linnæan system and ideas, see

But all this triumph of the Chaldeo-Babylonian creation legends which the Church had inherited availed but little.

For about the end of the eighteenth century fruitful suggestions and even clear presentations of this or that part of a large evolutionary doctrine came thick and fast, and from the most divergent quarters. Especially remarkable were those which came from Erasmus Darwin in England, from Maupertuis in France, from Oken in Switzerland, and from Herder, and, most brilliantly of all, from Goethe in Germany.

Two men among these thinkers must be especially mentioned—Treviranus in Germany and Lamarck in France; each independently of the other drew the world more completely than ever before in this direction.

From Treviranus came, in 1802, his work on biology, and in this he gave forth the idea that from forms of life originally simple had arisen all higher organizations by gradual development; that every living creature has a capacity for receiving modifications of its structure from external influences; and that no species had become really extinct, but that each had passed into some other species. From Lamarck came about the same time his *Researches,* and a little later his *Zoölogical Philosophy,* which introduced a new factor into the process of evolution—the action of the animal itself in its efforts toward a development to suit new needs—and he gave as his principal conclusions the following:

1. Life tends to increase the volume of each living body and of all its parts up to a limit determined by its own necessities.

2. New wants in animals give rise to new organs.

3. The development of these organs is in proportion to their employment.

4. New developments may be transmitted to offspring.

His well-known examples to illustrate these views, such as that of successive generations of giraffes lengthening their necks by stretching them to gather high-growing foliage, and of successive generations of kangaroos lengthening and strengthening their hind legs by the necessity of keeping themselves erect while jumping, provoked laughter, but the very

---

Alberg, *Life of Linnæus,* London, 1888, pp. 143-147, and 237. As to the creation medallions at the Cathedral of Upsala, it is a somewhat curious coincidence that the present writer came upon them while visiting that edifice during the preparation of this chapter.

comicality of these illustrations aided to fasten his main conclusion in men's memories.

In both these statements, imperfect as they were, great truths were embodied—truths which were sure to grow.

Lamarck's declaration, especially, that the development of organs is in ratio to their employment, and his indications of the reproduction in progeny of what is gained or lost in parents by the influence of circumstances, entered as a most effective force into the development of the evolution theory.

The next great successor in the apostolate of this idea of the universe was Geoffroy Saint-Hilaire. As early as 1795 he had begun to form a theory that species are various modifications of the same type, and this theory he developed, testing it at various stages as Nature was more and more displayed to him. It fell to his lot to bear the brunt in a struggle against heavy odds which lasted many years.

For the man who now took up the warfare, avowedly for science but unconsciously for theology, was the foremost naturalist then living—Cuvier. His scientific eminence was deserved; the highest honours of his own and other countries were given him, and he bore them worthily. An Imperial Councillor under Napoleon; President of the Council of Public Instruction and Chancellor of the University under the restored Bourbons; Grand Officer of the Legion of Honour, a Peer of France, Minister of the Interior, and President of the Council of State under Louis Philippe; he was eminent in all these capacities, and yet the dignity given by such high administrative positions was as nothing compared to his leadership in natural science. Science throughout the world acknowledged in him its chief contemporary ornament, and to this hour his fame rightly continues. But there was in him, as in Linnæus, a survival of certain theological ways of looking at the universe and certain theological conceptions of a plan of creation; it must be said, too, that while his temperament made him distrust new hypotheses, of which he had seen so many born and die, his environment as a great functionary of state, honoured, admired, almost adored by the greatest, not only in the state but in the Church, his solicitude lest science should receive some detriment by openly resisting the Church, which had recaptured Europe after the French Revolution, and had made of its enemies its footstool—all these considerations led him to oppose the new theory. Amid the plaudits, then, of the foremost churchmen he threw across the path of the evolution doctrines the whole mass of his authority in favour of the old theory of catastrophic changes and special creations.

Geoffroy Saint-Hilaire stoutly withstood him, braving non-recognition, ill-treatment, and ridicule. Treviranus, afar off in his mathematical lecture-room at Bremen, seemed simply forgotten.

But the current of evolutionary thought could not thus be checked: dammed up for a time, it broke out in new channels and in ways and places least expected; turned away from France, it appeared especially in England, where great paleontologists and geologists arose whose work culminated in that of Lyell. Specialists throughout all the world now became more vigorous than ever, gathering facts and thinking upon them in a way which caused the special creation theory to shrink more and more. Broader and more full became these various rivulets, soon to unite in one great stream of thought.

In 1813 Dr. Wells developed a theory of evolution by natural selection to account for varieties in the human race. About 1820 Dean Herbert, eminent as an authority in horticulture, avowed his conviction that species are but fixed varieties. In 1831 Patrick Matthews stumbled upon and stated the main doctrine of natural selection in evolution; and others here and there, in Europe and America, caught an inkling of it.

But no one outside of a circle apparently uninfluential cared for these things: the Church was serene: on the Continent it had obtained reactionary control of courts, cabinets, and universities; in England, Dean Cockburn was denouncing Mary Somerville and the geologists to the delight of churchmen; and the Rev. Mellor Brown was doing the same thing for the edification of dissenters.

In America the mild suggestions of Silliman and his compeers were met by the protestations of the Andover theologians headed by Moses Stuart. Neither of the great English universities, as a rule, took any notice of the innovators save by sneers.

To this current of thought there was joined a new element when, in 1844, Robert Chambers published his *Vestiges of Creation*. The book was attractive and was widely read. In Chambers's view the several series of animated beings, from the simplest and oldest up to the highest and most recent, were the result of two distinct impulses, each given once and for all time by the Creator. The first of these was an impulse imparted to forms of life, lifting them gradually through higher grades; the second was an impulse tending to modify organic substances in accordance with external circumstances; in fact, the doctrine of the book was evolution tempered by miracle—a stretching out of the creative act through all time —a pious version of Lamarck.

Two results followed, one mirth-provoking, the other leading to serious thought. The amusing result was that the theologians were greatly alarmed by the book: it was loudly insisted that it promoted atheism. Looking back along the line of thought which has since been developed, one feels that the older theologians ought to have put up thanksgivings for Chambers's theory, and prayers that it might prove true. The more serious result was that it accustomed men's minds to a belief in evolution as in some form possible or even probable. In this way it was provisionally of service.

Eight years later Herbert Spencer published an essay contrasting the theories of creation and evolution—reasoning with great force in favour of the latter, showing that species had undoubtedly been modified by circumstances; but still only few and chosen men saw the significance of all these lines of reasoning which had been converging during so many years toward one conclusion.

On July 1, 1858, there were read before the Linnæan Society at London two papers—one presented by Charles Darwin, the other by Alfred Russel Wallace—and with the reading of these papers the doctrine of evolution by natural selection was born. Then and there a fatal breach was made in the great theological barrier of the continued fixity of species since the creation.

The story of these papers the scientific world knows by heart: how Charles Darwin, having been sent to the University of Cambridge to fit him for the Anglican priesthood, left it in 1831 to go upon the scientific expedition of the Beagle; how for five years he studied with wonderful vigour and acuteness the problems of life as revealed on land and at sea— among volcanoes and coral reefs, in forests and on the sands, from the tropics to the arctic regions; how, in the Cape Verde and the Galapagos Islands, and in Brazil, Patagonia, and Australia he interrogated Nature with matchless persistency and skill; how he returned unheralded, quietly settled down to his work, and soon set the world thinking over its first published results, such as his book on *Coral Reefs,* and the monograph on the *Cirripedia;* and, finally, how he presented his paper, and followed it up with treatises which made him one of the great leaders in the history of human thought.

The scientific world realizes, too, more and more, the power of character shown by Darwin in all this great career; the faculty of silence, the reserve of strength seen in keeping his great thought—his idea of evolution by natural selection— under silent study and meditation for nearly twenty years, giving no hint of it to the world at large, but working in every field to secure proofs or disproofs, and accumulating masses of precious material for the solution of the questions involved.

To one man only did he reveal his thought—to Dr. Joseph Hooker, to whom in 1844, under the seal of secrecy, he gave a summary of his conclusions. Not until fourteen years later occurred the event which showed him that the fulness of time had come—the letter from Alfred Russel Wallace, to whom, in brilliant researches during the decade from 1848 to 1858, in Brazil and in the Malay Archipelago, the same truth of evolution by natural selection had been revealed. Among the proofs that scientific study does no injury to the more delicate shades of sentiment is the well-known story of this letter. With it Wallace sent Darwin a memoir, asking him to present it to the Linnæan Society: on examining it, Darwin found that Wallace had independently arrived at conclusions similar to his own—possibly had deprived him of fame; but Darwin was loyal to his friend, and his friend remained ever loyal to him. He publicly presented the paper from Wallace, with his own conclusions; and the date of this presentation—July 1, 1858—separates two epochs in the history, not merely of natural science, but of human thought.

In the following year, 1859, came the first instalment of his work in its fuller development—his book on *The Origin of Species.* In this book one at least of the main secrets at the heart of the evolutionary process, which had baffled the long line of investigators and philosophers from the days of Aristotle, was more broadly revealed. The effective mechanism of evolution was shown at work in three ascertained facts: in the struggle for existence among organized beings; in the survival of the fittest; and in heredity. These facts were presented with such minute research, wide observation, patient collation, transparent honesty, and judicial fairness, that they at once commanded the world's attention. It was the outcome of thirty years' work and thought by a worker and thinker of genius, but it was yet more than that—it was the outcome, also, of the work and thought of another man of genius fifty years before. The book of Malthus on the *Principle of Population,* mainly founded on the fact that animals increase in a geometrical ratio, and therefore, if unchecked, must encumber the earth, had been generally forgotten, and was only recalled with a sneer. But the genius of Darwin recognised in it a deeper meaning, and now the thought of Malthus was joined to the new current. Meditating upon it in connection with his own observations of the luxuriance of Nature, Darwin had arrived at his doctrine of natural selection and survival of the fittest.

As the great dogmatic barrier between the old and new views of the universe was broken down, the flood of new thought pouring over the world stimulated and nourished strong growths in every field of research and reasoning: edition after edition of the book was called for; it was translated even into Japanese and Hindustani; the stagnation of scientific thought, which Buckle, only a few years before, had so deeply lamented, gave place to a widespread and fruitful activity; masses of accumulated observations, which had seemed stale and unprofitable, were made alive; facts formerly without meaning now found their interpretation. Under this new influence an army of young men took up every promising line of scientific investigation in every land. Epoch-making books appeared in all the great nations. Spencer, Wallace, Huxley, Galton, Tyndall, Tylor, Lubbock, Bagehot, Lewes, in England, and a phalanx of strong men in Germany, Italy, France, and America gave forth works which became authoritative in every department of biology. If some of the older men in France held back, overawed perhaps by the authority of Cuvier, the younger and more vigorous pressed on.

One source of opposition deserves to be especially mentioned—Louis Agassiz.

A great investigator, an inspired and inspiring teacher, a noble man, he had received and elaborated a theory of animated creation which he could not readily change. In his heart and mind still prevailed the atmosphere of the little Swiss parsonage in which he was born, and his religious and moral nature, so beautiful to all who knew him, was especially repelled by sundry evolutionists, who, in their zeal as neophytes, made proclamations seeming to have a decidedly irreligious if not immoral bearing. In addition to this was the direction his thinking had received from Cuvier. Both these influences combined to prevent his acceptance of the new view.

He was the third great man who had thrown his influence as a barrier across the current of evolutionary thought. Linnæus in the second half of the eighteenth century, Cuvier in the first half, and Agassiz in the second half of the nineteenth —all made the same effort. Each remains great; but not all of them together could arrest the current. Agassiz's strong efforts throughout the United States, and indeed throughout Europe, to check it, really promoted it. From the great museum he had founded at Cambridge, from his summer school at Penikese, from his lecture rooms at Harvard and Cornell, his disciples went forth full of love and admiration for him, full of enthusiasm which he had stirred and into fields which he had indicated; but their powers, which he had aroused and strengthened, were devoted to developing the truth he failed to recognise; Shaler, Verrill, Packard, Hartt, Wilder, Jordan, with a multitude of others, and especially the son who bore his honoured name, did justice to his memory by applying what they had received from him to research under inspiration of the new revelation.

Still another man deserves especial gratitude and honour in this progress—Edward Livingston Youmans. He was perhaps the first in America to recognise the vast bearings of the truths presented by Darwin, Wallace, and Spencer. He became the apostle of these truths, sacrificing the brilliant career on which he had entered as a public lecturer, subordinating himself to the three leaders, and giving himself to editorial drudgery in the stimulation of research and the announcement of results.

In support of the new doctrine came a world of new proofs; those which Darwin himself added in regard to the cross-fertilization of plants, and which he had adopted from embryology, led the way, and these were followed by the discoveries of Wallace, Bates, Huxley, Marsh, Cope, Leidy, Haeckel, Müller, Gaudry, and a multitude of others in all lands.[16]

[16] For Agassiz's opposition to evolution, see the *Essay on Classification,* vol. i, 1857, as regards Lamarck, and vol. iii, 1860, as regards Darwin; also *Silliman's Journal,* July, 1860; also the *Atlantic Monthly,* January, 1874; also his *Life and Correspondence,* vol. ii, p. 647; also Asa Gray, *Scientific Papers,* vol. ii, p. 484. A rem-

4. The Final Effort of Theology

Darwin's *Origin of Species* had come into the theological world like a plough into an ant-hill. Everywhere those thus rudely awakened from their old comfort and repose had swarmed forth angry and confused. Reviews, sermons, books light and heavy, came flying at the new thinker from all sides.

The keynote was struck at once in the *Quarterly Review* by Wilberforce, Bishop of Oxford. He declared that Darwin was guilty of "a tendency to limit God's glory in creation"; that "the principle of natural selection is absolutely incompatible with the word of God"; that it "contradicts the revealed relations of creation to its Creator"; that it is "inconsistent with the fulness of his glory"; that it is "a dishonouring view of Nature"; and that there is "a simpler explanation of the presence of these strange forms among the works of God": that explanation being—"the fall of Adam." Nor did the bishop's efforts end here; at the meeting of the British Association for the Advancement of Science he again disported himself in the tide of popular applause. Referring to the ideas of Darwin, who was absent on account of illness, he congratulated himself in a public speech that he was not descended from a monkey. The reply came from Huxley, who said in substance: "If I had to choose, I would prefer to be a descendant of a humble monkey rather than of a man who employs his knowledge and eloquence in misrepresenting those who are wearing out their lives in the search for truth."

This shot reverberated through England, and indeed through other countries.

The utterances of this the most brilliant prelate of the Anglican Church received a sort of antiphonal response from the leaders of the English Catholics. In an address before the "Academia," which had been organized to combat "science falsely so called," Cardinal Manning declared his abhorrence of the new view of Nature, and described it as "a brutal philosophy—to wit, there is no God, and the ape is our Adam."

---

iniscence of my own enables me to appreciate his deep ethical and religious feeling. I was passing the day with him at Nahant in 1868, consulting him regarding candidates for various scientific chairs at the newly established Cornell University, in which he took a deep interest. As we discussed one after another of the candidates he suddenly said: "Who is to be your Professor of Moral Philosophy? That is a far more important position than all the others."

These attacks from such eminent sources set the clerical fashion for several years. One distinguished clerical reviewer, in spite of Darwin's thirty years of quiet labour, and in spite of the powerful summing up of his book, prefaced a diatribe by saying that Darwin "might have been more modest had he given some slight reason for dissenting from the views generally entertained." Another distinguished clergyman, vice-president of a Protestant institute to combat "dangerous" science, declared Darwinism "an attempt to dethrone God." Another critic spoke of persons accepting the Darwinian views as "under the frenzied inspiration of the inhaler of mephitic gas," and of Darwin's argument as "a jungle of fanciful assumption." Another spoke of Darwin's views as suggesting that "God is dead," and declared that Darwin's work "does open violence to everything which the Creator himself had told us in the Scriptures of the methods and results of his work." Still another theological authority asserted: "If the Darwinian theory is true, Genesis is a lie, the whole framework of the book of life falls to pieces, and the revelation of God to man, as we Christians know it, is a delusion and a snare." Another, who had shown excellent qualities as an observing naturalist, declared the Darwinian view "a huge imposture from the beginning."

Echoes came from America. One review, the organ of the most widespread of American religious sects, declared that Darwin was "attempting to befog and to pettifog the whole question"; another denounced Darwin's views as "infidelity"; another, representing the American branch of the Anglican Church, poured contempt over Darwin as "sophistical and illogical," and then plunged into an exceedingly dangerous line of argument in the following words: "If this hypothesis be true, then is the Bible an unbearable fiction; . . . then have Christians for nearly two thousand years been duped by a monstrous lie. . . . Darwin requires us to disbelieve the authoritative word of the Creator." A leading journal representing the same church took pains to show the evolution theory to be as contrary to the explicit declarations of the New Testament as to those of the Old, and said: "If we have all, men and monkeys, oysters and eagles, developed from an original germ, then is St. Paul's grand deliverance—'All flesh is not the same flesh; there is one kind of flesh of men, another of beasts, another of fishes, and another of birds'—untrue."

Another echo came from Australia, where Dr. Perry, Lord

Bishop of Melbourne, in a most bitter book on *Science and the Bible,* declared that the obvious object of Chambers, Darwin, and Huxley is "to produce in their readers a disbelief of the Bible."

Nor was the older branch of the Church to be left behind in this chorus. Bayma, in the *Catholic World,* declared, "Mr. Darwin is, we have reason to believe, the mouthpiece or chief trumpeter of that infidel clique whose well-known object is to do away with all idea of a God."

Worthy of especial note as showing the determination of the theological side at that period was the foundation of sacro-scientific organizations to combat the new ideas. First to be noted is the "Academia," planned by Cardinal Wiseman. In a circular letter the cardinal, usually so moderate and just, sounded an alarm and summed up by saying, "Now it is for the Church, which alone possesses divine certainty and divine discernment, to place itself at once in the front of a movement which threatens even the fragmentary remains of Christian belief in England." The necessary permission was obtained from Rome, the Academia was founded, and the "divine discernment" of the Church was seen in the utterances which came from it, such as those of Cardinal Manning, which every thoughtful Catholic would now desire to recall, and in the diatribes of Dr. Laing, which only aroused laughter on all sides. A similar effort was seen in Protestant quarters; the "Victoria Institute" was created, and perhaps the most noted utterance which ever came from it was the declaration of its vice-president, the Rev. Walter Mitchell, that "Darwinism endeavours to dethrone God."[17]

[17] For Wilberforce's article, see *Quarterly Review*, July, 1860. For the reply of Huxley to the bishop's speech I have relied on the account given in *Quatrefages,* who had it from Carpenter; a somewhat different version is given in the *Life and Letters of Darwin.* For Cardinal Manning's attack, see *Essays on Religion and Literature,* London, 1865. For the review articles, see the *Quarterly* already cited, and that for July, 1874; also the *North British Review,* May, 1860; also, F. O. Morris's letter in the *Record,* reprinted at Glasgow, 1870; also the *Addresses of Rev. Walter Mitchell* before the Victoria Institute, London, 1867; also Rev. B. G. Johns, *Moses not Darwin, a Sermon,* March 31, 1871. For the earlier American attacks, see *Methodist Quarterly Review,* April, 1871; *The American Church Review,* July and October, 1865, and January, 1866. For the Australian attack, see *Science and the Bible,* by the Right Reverend Charles Perry, D. D., Bishop of Melbourne, London, 1869.

In France the attack was even more violent. Fabre d'Envieu brought out the heavy artillery of theology, and in a long series of elaborate propositions demonstrated that any other doctrine than that of the fixity and persistence of species is absolutely contrary to Scripture. The Abbé Désorges, a former Professor of Theology, stigmatized Darwin as a "pedant," and evolution as "gloomy"; Monseigneur Ségur, referring to Darwin and his followers, went into hysterics and shrieked: "These infamous doctrines have for their only support the most abject passions. Their father is pride, their mother impurity, their offspring revolutions. They come from hell and return thither, taking with them the gross creatures who blush not to proclaim and accept them."

In Germany the attack, if less declamatory, was no less severe. Catholic theologians vied with Protestants in bitterness. Prof. Michelis declared Darwin's theory "a caricature of creation." Dr. Hagermann asserted that it "turned the Creator out of doors." Dr. Schund insisted that "every idea of the Holy Scriptures, from the first to the last page, stands in diametrical opposition to the Darwinian theory"; and, "if Darwin be right in his view of the development of man out of a brutal condition, then the Bible teaching in regard to man is utterly annihilated." Rougemont in Switzerland called for a crusade against the obnoxious doctrine. Luthardt, Professor of Theology at Leipsic, declared: "The idea of creation belongs to religion and not to natural science; the whole superstructure of personal religion is built upon the doctrine of creation"; and he showed the evolution theory to be in direct contradiction to Holy Writ.

But in 1863 came an event which brought serious confusion to the theological camp: Sir Charles Lyell, the most eminent of living geologists, a man of deeply Christian feeling and of exceedingly cautious temper, who had opposed the evolution theory of Lamarck and declared his adherence to the idea of successive creations, then published his work on the *Antiquity of Man*, and in this and other utterances showed himself a complete though unwilling convert to the fundamental ideas of Darwin. The blow was serious in many ways, and especially

---

For Bayma, see the *Catholic World*, vol. xxvi, p. 782. For the Academia, see *Essays* edited by Cardinal Manning, above cited; and for the Victoria Institute, see *Scientia Scientiarum*, by a member of the Victoria Institute, London, 1865.

so in two—first, as withdrawing all foundation in fact from the scriptural chronology, and secondly, as discrediting the creation theory. The blow was not unexpected; in various review articles against the Darwinian theory there had been appeals to Lyell, at times almost piteous, "not to flinch from the truths he had formerly proclaimed." But Lyell, like the honest man he was, yielded unreservedly to the mass of new proofs arrayed on the side of evolution against that of creation.

At the same time came Huxley's *Man's Place in Nature,* giving new and most cogent arguments in favour of evolution by natural selection.

In 1871 was published Darwin's *Descent of Man.* Its doctrine had been anticipated by critics of his previous books, but it made, none the less, a great stir; again the opposing army trooped forth, though evidently with much less heart than before. A few were very violent. The *Dublin University Magazine,* after the traditional Hibernian fashion, charged Mr. Darwin with seeking "to displace God by the unerring action of vagary," and with being "resolved to hunt God out of the world." But most notable from the side of the older Church was the elaborate answer to Darwin's book by the eminent French Catholic physician, Dr. Constantin James. In his work, *On Darwinism, or the Man-Ape,* published at Paris in 1877, Dr. James not only refuted Darwin scientifically but poured contempt on his book, calling it "a fairy tale," and insisted that a work "so fantastic and so burlesque" was, doubtless, only a huge joke, like Erasmus's *Praise of Folly,* or Montesquieu's *Persian Letters.* The princes of the Church were delighted. The Cardinal Archbishop of Paris assured the author that the book had become his "spiritual reading," and begged him to send a copy to the Pope himself. His Holiness, Pope Pius IX, acknowledged the gift in a remarkable letter. He thanked his dear son, the writer, for the book in which he "refutes so well the aberrations of Darwinism." "A system," His Holiness adds, "which is repugnant at once to history, to the tradition of all peoples, to exact science, to observed facts, and even to Reason herself, would seem to need no refutation, did not alienation from God and the leaning toward materialism, due to depravity, eagerly seek a support in all this tissue of fables. . . . And, in fact, pride, after rejecting the Creator of all things and proclaiming man independent, wishing him to be his own king, his own priest, and his own God— pride goes so far as to degrade man himself to the level of the unreasoning brutes, perhaps even of lifeless matter, thus unconsciously confirming the Divine declaration, *When pride cometh, then cometh shame.* But the corruption of this age, the machinations of the perverse, the danger of the simple, demand that such fancies, altogether absurd though they are, should—since they borrow the mask of science—be refuted by true science." Wherefore the Pope thanked Dr. James for his book, "so opportune and so perfectly appropriate to the exigencies of our time," and bestowed on him the apostolic benediction. Nor was this brief all. With it there came a second, creating the author an officer of the Papal Order of St. Sylvester. The cardinal archbishop assured the delighted physician that such a double honour of brief and brevet was perhaps unprecedented, and suggested only that in a new edition of his book he should "insist a little more on the relation existing between the narratives of Genesis and the discoveries of modern science, in such fashion as to convince the most incredulous of their perfect agreement." The prelate urged also a more dignified title. The proofs of this new edition were accordingly all submitted to His Eminence, and in 1882 it appeared as *Moses and Darwin: the Man of Genesis compared with the Man-Ape, or Religious Education opposed to Atheistic.* No wonder the cardinal embraced the author, thanking him in the name of science and religion. "We have at last," he declared, "a handbook which we can safely put into the hands of youth."

Scarcely less vigorous were the champions of English Protestant orthodoxy. In an address at Liverpool, Mr. Gladstone remarked: "Upon the grounds of what is termed evolution God is relieved of the labour of creation; in the name of unchangeable laws he is discharged from governing the world"; and, when Herbert Spencer called his attention to the fact that Newton with the doctrine of gravitation and with the science of physical astronomy is open to the same charge, Mr. Gladstone retreated in the *Contemporary Review* under one of his characteristic clouds of words. The Rev. Dr. Coles, in the *British and Foreign Evangelical Review,* declared that the God of evolution is not the Christian's God. Burgon, Dean of Chichester, in a sermon preached before the University of Oxford, pathetically warned the students that "those who refuse to accept the history of the creation of our first parents according to its obvious literal intention, and are for substituting the modern dream of evolution in its place, cause the entire scheme of man's salvation to collapse." Dr. Pusey also came into the fray with most earnest appeals against the new doctrine, and the Rev. Gavin Carlyle was perfervid on the same side. The Society for Promoting Christian Knowledge published a book by the Rev. Mr. Birks, in which the evolution doctrine was declared to be "flatly opposed to the fundamental doctrine of creation." Even the *London Times* admitted a review stigmatizing Darwin's *Descent of Man* as an "utterly unsupported hypothesis," full of "unsubstantiated premises, cursory investigations, and disintegrating speculations," and Darwin himself as "reckless and unscientific."[18]

But it was noted that this second series of attacks, on the *Descent of Man*, differed in one remarkable respect—so far as England was concerned—from those which had been made over ten years before on the *Origin of Species*. While everything was done to discredit Darwin, to pour contempt upon him, and even, of all things in the world, to make him—the

[18] For the French theological opposition to the Darwinian theory, see Pozzy, *La Terre et le Récit Biblique de la Création*, 1874, especially pp. 353, 363; also, Félix Ducane, *Études sur le Transformisme*, 1876, especially pp. 107 to 119. As to Fabre d'Envieu, see especially his Proposition xliii. For the Abbé Désorges, "former Professor of Philosophy and Theology," see his *Erreurs Modernes*, Paris, 1878, pp. 677 and 595 to 598. For Monseigneur Ségur, see his *La Foi devant la Science Moderne*, sixth ed., Paris, 1874, pp. 23, 34, etc. For Herbert Spencer's reply to Mr. Gladstone, see his *Study of Sociology;* for the passage in the *Dublin Review*, see the issue for July, 1871. For the review in the *London Times*, see *Nature* for April 20, 1871. For Gavin Carlyle, see *The Battle of Unbelief*, 1870, pp. 86 and 171. For the attacks by Michelis and Hagermann, see *Natur und Offenbarung*, Münster, 1861 to 1869. For Schund, see his *Darwin's Hypothese und ihr Verhältniss zu Religion und Moral*, Stuttgart, 1869. For Luthardt, see *Fundamental Truths of Christianity*, translated by Sophia Taylor, second ed., Edinburgh, 1869. For Rougemont, see his *L'Homme et le Singe*, Neuchâtel, 1863 (also in German trans.). For Constantin James, see his *Mes Entretiens avec l'Empéreur Don Pédro sur le Darwinisme*, Paris, 1888, where the papal briefs are printed in full. For the English attacks on Darwin's *Descent of Man*, see the *Edinburgh Review*, July, 1871, and elsewhere; the *Dublin Review*, July, 1871; the *British and Foreign Evangelical Review*, April, 1886. See also *The Scripture Doctrine of Creation*, by the Rev. T. R. Birks, London, 1873, published by the S. P. C. K. For Dr. Pusey's attack, see his *Unscience, not Science, adverse to Faith*, 1878; also, *Darwin's Life and Letters*, vol. ii, pp. 411, 412.

gentlest of mankind, only occupied with the scientific side of the problem—"a persecutor of Christianity," while his followers were represented more and more as charlatans or dupes, there began to be in the most influential quarters careful avoidance of the old argument that evolution—even by natural selection—contradicts Scripture. It began to be felt that this was dangerous ground. The defection of Lyell had, perhaps, more than anything else, started the question among theologians who had preserved some equanimity, *What if, after all, the Darwinian theory should prove to be true?* Recollections of the position in which the Roman Church found itself after the establishment of the doctrines of Copernicus and Galileo naturally came into the minds of the more thoughtful. In Germany this consideration does not seem to have occurred at quite so early a day. One eminent Lutheran clergyman at Magdeburg called on his hearers to choose between Darwin and religion; Delitszch, in his new commentary on Genesis, attempted to bring science back to recognise human sin as an important factor in creation; Prof. Heinrich Ewald, while carefully avoiding any sharp conflict between the scriptural doctrine and evolution, comforted himself by covering Darwin and his followers with contempt; Christlieb, in his address before the Evangelical Alliance at New York in 1873, simply took the view that the tendencies of the Darwinian theory were "toward infidelity," but declined to make any serious battle on biblical grounds; the Jesuit, Father Pesch, in Holland, drew up in Latin, after the old scholastic manner, a sort of general indictment of evolution, of which one may say that it was interesting—as interesting as the display of a troop in chain armour and with cross-bows on a nineteenth-century battlefield.

From America there came new echoes. Among the myriad attacks on the Darwinian theory by Protestants and Catholics two should be especially mentioned. The first of these was by Dr. Noah Porter, President of Yale College, an excellent scholar, an interesting writer, a noble man, broadly tolerant, combining in his thinking a curious mixture of radicalism and conservatism. While giving great latitude to the evolutionary teaching in the university under his care, he felt it his duty upon one occasion to avow his disbelief in it; but he was too wise a man to suggest any necessary antagonism between it and the Scriptures. He confined himself mainly to pointing out the tendency of the evolution doctrine in this form toward agnosticism and pantheism. To those who knew and loved him, and had noted the genial way in which by wise neglect he had allowed scientific studies to flourish at Yale, there was an amusing side to all this. Within a stone's throw of his college rooms was the Museum of Paleontology, in which Prof. Marsh had laid side by side, among other evidences of the new truth, that wonderful series of specimens showing the evolution of the horse from the earliest form of the animal, "not larger than a fox, with five toes," through the whole series up to his present form and size—that series which Huxley declared an absolute proof of the existence of natural selection as an agent in evolution. In spite of the veneration and love which all Yale men felt for President Porter, it was hardly to be expected that these particular arguments of his would have much permanent effect upon them when there was constantly before their eyes so convincing a refutation.

But a far more determined opponent was the Rev. Dr. Hodge, of Princeton; his anger toward the evolution doctrine was bitter: he denounced it as thoroughly "atheistic"; he insisted that Christians "have a right to protest against the arraying of probabilities against the clear evidence of the Scriptures"; he even censured so orthodox a writer as the Duke of Argyll, and declared that the Darwinian theory of natural selection is "utterly inconsistent with the Scriptures," and that "an absent God, who does nothing, is to us no God"; that "to ignore design as manifested in God's creation is to dethrone God"; that "a denial of design in Nature is virtually a denial of God"; and that "no teleologist can be a Darwinian." Even more uncompromising was another of the leading authorities at the same university—the Rev. Dr. Duffield. He declared war not only against Darwin but even against men like Asa Gray, Le Conte, and others, who had attempted to reconcile the new theory with the Bible: he insisted that "evolutionism and the scriptural account of the origin of man are irreconcilable"—that the Darwinian theory is "in direct conflict with the teaching of the apostle, 'All scripture is given by inspiration of God' "; he pointed out, in his opposition to Darwin's *Descent of Man* and Lyell's *Antiquity of Man,* that in the Bible "the genealogical links which connect the Israelites in Egypt with Adam and Eve in Eden are explicitly given." These utterances of Prof. Duffield culminated in a declaration which deserves to be cited as showing that a Presbyterian minister can "deal damnation round the land" *ex cathedra* in a fashion quite equal to that of popes and bishops. It is as follows: "If the development theory of the origin of man," wrote Dr. Duffield in the *Princeton Review,* "shall in a little while take its place—as doubtless it will—with other exploded scientific speculations, then they who accept it with its proper logical consequences will in the life to come have their portion with those who in this life 'know not God and obey not the gospel of his Son.' "

Fortunately, at about the time when Darwin's *Descent of Man* was published, there had come into Princeton University a *"deus ex machina"* in the person of Dr. James McCosh. Called to the presidency, he at once took his stand against teachings so dangerous to Christianity as those of Drs. Hodge, Duffield, and their associates. In one of his personal confidences he has let us into the secret of this matter. With that hard Scotch sense which Thackeray had applauded in his well-known verses, he saw that the most dangerous thing which could be done to Christianity at Princeton was to reiterate in the university pulpit, week after week, solemn declarations that if evolution by natural selection, or indeed evolution at all, be true, the Scriptures are false. He tells us that he saw that this was the certain way to make the students unbelievers; he therefore not only checked this dangerous preaching but preached an opposite doctrine. With him began the inevitable compromise, and, in spite of mutterings against him as a Darwinian, he carried the day. Whatever may be thought of his general system of philosophy, no one can deny his great service in neutralizing the teachings of his predecessors and colleagues—so dangerous to all that is essential in Christianity.

Other divines of strong sense in other parts of the country began to take similar ground—namely, that men could be Christians and at the same time Darwinians. There appeared, indeed, here and there, curious discrepancies: thus in 1873 the *Monthly Religious Magazine* of Boston congratulated its readers that the Rev. Mr. Burr had "demolished the evolution theory, knocking the breath of life out of it and throwing it to the dogs." This amazing performance by the Rev. Mr. Burr was repeated in a very striking way by Bishop Keener before the Œcumenical Council of Methodism at Washington in 1891. In what the newspapers described as an "admirable speech," he refuted evolution doctrines by saying that evolutionists had "only to make a journey of twelve hours from the place where he was then standing to find together the bones of the muskrat, the opossum, the coprolite, and the ichthyosaurus." He asserted that Agassiz—whom the good bishop, like so many others, seemed to think an evolutionist—when he visited these beds near Charleston, declared: "These old beds have set me crazy; they have destroyed the work of a lifetime." And the Methodist prelate ended by saying: "Now, gentlemen, brethren, take these facts home with you; get down and look at them. This is the watch that was under the steam hammer— the doctrine of evolution; and this steam hammer is the wonderful deposit of the Ashley beds."

Exhibitions like these availed little. While the good bishop amid vociferous applause thus made comically evident his belief that Agassiz was a Darwinian and a coprolite an animal, scientific men were recording in all parts of the world facts confirming the dreaded theory of an evolution by natural selection. While the Rev. Mr. Burr was so loudly praised for "throwing Darwinism to the dogs," Marsh was completing his series leading from the five-toed ungulates to the horse. While Dr. Taylor Lewis at Union, and Drs. Hodge and Duffield at Princeton, were showing that if evolution be true the biblical accounts must be false, the indefatigable Yale professor was showing his cretaceous birds, and among them *Hesperornis* and *Ichthyornis* with teeth. While in Germany Luthardt, Schund, and their compeers were demonstrating that Scripture requires a belief in special and separate creations, the *Archæopteryx,* showing a most remarkable connection between birds and reptiles, was discovered. While in France Monseigneur Ségur and others were indulging in diatribes against "a certain Darwin," Gaudry and Filhol were discovering a striking series of "missing links" among the carnivora.

In view of the proofs accumulating in favour of the new evolutionary hypothesis, the change in the tone of controlling theologians was now rapid. From all sides came evidences of desire to compromise with the theory. Strict adherents of the biblical text pointed significantly to the verses in Genesis in which the earth and sea were made to bring forth birds and fishes, and man was created out of the dust of the ground. Men of larger mind like Kingsley and Farrar, with English and American broad churchmen generally, took ground directly in Darwin's favour. Even Whewell took pains to show that there might be such a thing as a Darwinian argument for design in Nature; and the Rev. Samuel Houghton, of the Royal Society, gave interesting suggestions of a divine design in evolution.

Both the great English universities received the new teaching as a leaven: at Oxford, in the very front of the High Church party at Keble College, was elaborated a statement that the evolution doctrine is "an advance in our theological thinking." And Temple, Bishop of London, perhaps the most influential thinker then in the Anglican episcopate, accepted the new revelation in the following words: "It seems something more majestic, more befitting him to whom a thousand years are as one day, thus to impress his will once for all on his creation, and provide for all the countless varieties by this one original impress, than by special acts of creation to be perpetually modifying what he had previously made."

In Scotland the Duke of Argyll, head and front of the orthodox party, dissenting in many respects from Darwin's full conclusions, made concessions which badly shook the old position.

Curiously enough, from the Roman Catholic Church, bitter as some of its writers had been, now came argument to prove that the Catholic faith does not prevent any one from holding the Darwinian theory, and especially a declaration from an authority eminent among American Catholics—a declaration which has a very curious sound, but which it would be ungracious to find fault with—that "the doctrine of evolution is no more in opposition to the doctrine of the Catholic Church than is the Copernican theory or that of Galileo."

Here and there, indeed, men of science like Dawson, Mivart, and Wigand, in view of theological considerations, sought to make conditions; but the current was too strong, and eminent theologians in every country accepted natural selection as at least a very important part in the mechanism of evolution.

At the death of Darwin it was felt that there was but one place in England where his body should be laid, and that this place was next the grave of Sir Isaac Newton in Westminster Abbey. The noble address of Canon Farrar at his funeral was echoed from many pulpits in Europe and America, and theological opposition as such was ended. Occasionally appeared, it is true, a survival of the old feeling: the Rev. Dr. Laing referred to the burial of Darwin in Westminster Abbey as "a proof that England is no longer a Christian country," and added that this burial was a desecration—that this honour was given him because he had been "the chief promoter of the mock doctrine of evolution of the species and the ape descent of man."

Still another of these belated prophets was, of all men, Thomas Carlyle. Soured and embittered, in the same spirit which led him to find more heroism in a marauding Viking or in one of Frederick the Great's generals than in Washington, or Lincoln, or Grant, and which caused him to see in the American civil war only the burning out of a foul chimney, he, with the petulance natural to a dyspeptic eunuch, railed at Darwin as an "apostle of dirt worship."

The last echoes of these utterances reverberated between Scotland and America. In the former country, in 1885, the Rev. Dr. Lee issued a volume declaring that, if the Darwinian view be true, "there is no place for God"; that "by no method of interpretation can the language of Holy Scripture be made wide enough to re-echo the orang-outang theory of man's natural history"; that "Darwinism reverses the revelation of God" and "implies utter blasphemy against the divine and human character of our Incarnate Lord"; and he was pleased to call Darwin and his followers "gospellers of the gutter." In one of the intellectual centres of America the editor of a periodical called *The Christian* urged frantically that "the battle be set in array, and that men find out who is on the Lord's side and who is on the side of the devil and the monkeys."

To the honour of the Church of England it should be recorded that a considerable number of her truest men opposed such utterances as these, and that one of them—Farrar, Archdeacon of Westminster—made a protest worthy to be held in perpetual remembrance. While confessing his own inability to accept fully the new scientific belief, he said: "We should consider it disgraceful and humiliating to try to shake it by an *ad captandum* argument, or by a claptrap platform appeal to the unfathomable ignorance and unlimited arrogance of a prejudiced assembly. We should blush to meet it with an anathema or a sneer."

All opposition had availed nothing; Darwin's work and fame were secure. As men looked back over his beautiful life —simple, honest, tolerant, kindly—and thought upon his great labours in the search for truth, all the attacks faded into nothingness.

There were indeed some dark spots, which as time goes on appear darker. At Trinity College, Cambridge, Whewell, the "omniscient," author of the *History of the Inductive Sciences,* refused to allow a copy of the *Origin of Species* to be placed in the library. At multitudes of institutions under theological control—Protestant as well as Catholic—attempts were made to stamp out or to stifle evolutionary teaching. Especially was this true for a time in America, and the case of the American College at Beyrout, where nearly all the younger professors were dismissed for adhering to Darwin's views, is worthy of remembrance. The treatment of Dr. Winchell at the Vanderbilt University in Tennessee showed the same spirit; one of the truest of men, devoted to science but of deeply Christian feeling, he was driven forth for views which centred in the Darwinian theory.

Still more striking was the case of Dr. Woodrow. He had, about 1857, been appointed to a professorship of Natural Science as connected with Revealed Religion, in the Presbyterian Seminary at Columbia, South Carolina. He was a devoted Christian man, and his training had led him to accept the Presbyterian standards of faith. With great gifts for scientific study he visited Europe, made a most conscientious examination of the main questions under discussion, and adopted the chief points in the doctrine of evolution by natural selection. A struggle soon began. A movement hostile to him grew more and more determined, and at last, in spite of the efforts made in his behalf by the directors of the seminary and by a large and broad-minded minority in the representative bodies controlling it, an orthodox storm, raised by the delegates from various Presbyterian bodies, drove him from his post. Fortunately, he was received into a professorship at the University of South Carolina, where he has since taught with more power than ever before.

This testimony to the faith by American provincial Protestantism was very properly echoed from Spanish provincial Catholicism. In the year 1878 a Spanish colonial man of science, Dr. Chil y Marango, published a work on the Canary Islands. But Dr. Chil had the imprudence to sketch, in his introduction, the modern hypothesis of evolution, and to exhibit some proofs, found in the Canary Islands, of the barbarism of primitive man. The ecclesiastical authorities, under the lead of Bishop Urquinaona y Bidot, at once grappled with this new idea. By a solemn act they declared it *"falsa, impia, scandalosa"*; all persons possessing copies of the work were ordered to surrender them at once to the proper ecclesiastics, and the author was placed under the major excommunication.

But all this opposition may be reckoned among the last

expiring convulsions of the old theologic theory. Even from the new Catholic University at Washington has come an utterance in favour of the new doctrine, and in other universities in the Old World and in the New the doctrine of evolution by natural selection has asserted its right to full and honest consideration. More than this, it is clearly evident that the stronger men in the Church have, in these latter days, not only relinquished the struggle against science in this field, but have determined frankly and manfully to make an alliance with it. In two very remarkable lectures given in 1892 at the parish church of Rochdale, Wilson, Archdeacon of Manchester, not only accepted Darwinism as true, but wrought it with great argumentative power into a higher view of Christianity; and what is of great significance, these sermons were published by the same Society for the Promotion of Christian Knowledge which only a few years before had published the most bitter attacks against the Darwinian theory. So, too, during the year 1893, Prof. Henry Drummond, whose praise is in all the dissenting churches, developed a similar view most brilliantly in a series of lectures delivered before the American Chautauqua schools, and published in one of the most widespread of English orthodox newspapers.

Whatever additional factors may be added to natural selection—and Darwin himself fully admitted that there might be others—the theory of an evolution process in the formation of the universe and of animated nature is established, and the old theory of direct creation is gone forever. In place of it science has given us conceptions far more noble, and opened the way to an argument for design infinitely more beautiful than any ever developed by theology.[19]

[19] For causes of the bitterness shown regarding the Darwinian hypothesis, see Reusch, *Bibel und Natur,* vol. ii, pp. 46 *et seq.* For hostility in the United States toward the Darwinian theory, see, among a multitude of writers, the following: Dr. Charles Hodge, of Princeton, monograph, *What is Darwinism?* New York, 1874; also his *Systematic Theology,* New York, 1872, vol. ii, part 2, *Anthropology;* also *The Light by which we see Light, or Nature and the Scriptures,* Vedder Lectures, 1875, Rutgers College, New York, 1875; also *Positivism and Evolutionism,* in the *American Catholic Quarterly,* October, 1877, pp. 607, 619; and, in the same number, *Professor Huxley and Evolution,* by Rev. A. M. Kirsch, pp. 662, 664; *The Logic of Evolution,* by Prof. Edward F. X. McSweeney, D. D., July, 1879, p. 561; *Das Hexæmeron und die Geologie,* von P. Eirich, Pastor in Albany, N. Y., Lutherischer

Concordia-Verlag, St. Louis, Mo., 1878, pp. 81, 82, 84, 92-94; *Evolutionism respecting Man and the Bible,* by John T. Duffield, of Princeton, January, 1878, *Princeton Review,* pp. 151, 153, 154, 158, 159, 160, 188; *A Lecture on Evolution,* before the Nineteenth Century Club of New York, May 25, 1886, by ex-President Noah Porter, pp. 4, 26-29. For the laudatory notice of the Rev. E. F. Burr's demolition of evolution in his book *Pater Mundi,* see *Monthly Religious Magazine,* Boston, May, 1873, p. 492. Concerning the removal of Rev. Dr. James Woodrow, Professor of Natural Science in the Columbia Theological Seminary, see *Evolution or Not,* art. in the *New York Weekly Sun,* October 24, 1888. For the dealings of Spanish ecclesiastics with Dr. Chil and his Darwinian exposition, see the *Revue d'Anthropologie,* cited in the *Academy* for April 6, 1878; see also the *Catholic World,* xix, 433, *A Discussion with an Infidel,* directed against Dr. Louis Büchner and his *Kraft und Stoff;* also *Mind and Matter,* by Rev. James Tait, of Canada, p. 66 (in the third edition the author bemoans the "horrible plaudits" that "have accompanied every effort to establish man's brutal descent"); also *The Church Journal,* New York, May 28, 1874. For the effort in favour of a teleological evolution, see Rev. Samuel Houghton, F. R. S., *Principles of Animal Mechanics,* London, 1873, preface and p. 156 and elsewhere. For details of the persecution of Drs. Winchell and Woodrow, and of the Beyrout professors, with authorities cited, see my chapter on *The Fall of Man and Anthropology.* For more liberal views among religious thinkers regarding the Darwinian theory, and for efforts to mitigate and adapt it to theological views, see, among the great mass of utterances, the following: Charles Kingsley's letters to Darwin, November 18, 1859, in *Darwin's Life and Letters,* vol. ii, p. 82; Adam Sedgwick to Charles Darwin, December 24, 1859, see ibid., vol. ii, pp. 356-359; the same to Miss Gerard, January 2, 1860, see *Sedgwick's Life and Letters,* vol. ii, pp. 359, 360; the same in *The Spectator,* London, March 24, 1860; *The Rambler,* March, 1860, cited by Mivart, *Genesis of Species,* p. 30; *The Dublin Review,* May, 1860; *The Christian Examiner,* May, 1860; Charles Kingsley to F. D. Maurice in 1863, in Kingsley's *Life,* vol. ii, p. 171; Adam Sedgwick to Livingstone (the explorer), March 16, 1865, in *Life and Letters of Sedgwick,* vol. ii, pp. 410-412; the Duke of Argyll, *The Reign of Law,* New York, pp. 16, 18, 31, 116, 117, 120, 159; Joseph P. Thompson, D. D., LL.D., *Man in Genesis and Geology,* New York, 1870, pp. 48, 49, 82; Canon H. P. Liddon, *Sermons preached before the University of Oxford,* 1871, Sermon III; St. George Mivart, *Evolution and its Consequences, Contemporary Review,* January, 1872; *British and Foreign Evangelical Review,* 1872, article on *The Theory of Evolution; The Lutheran Quarterly,* Gettysburg, Pa., April, 1872, article by Rev. Cyrus Thomas, Assistant, United States Geological Survey, on *The Descent of Man,* pp. 214, 239, 372-376; *The Lutheran Quarterly,* July, 1873, article on *Some Assumptions against Christianity,* by Rev. C. A. Stork, Baltimore, Md., pp. 325, 326; also, in the same number, see a review of Dr. Burr's *Pater Mundi,* pp. 474, 475, and contrast with the review in the *Andover Review* of that period; an article in the *Religious Magazine and Monthly Review,* Boston, on *Religion and Evolution,* by Rev. S. R. Calthrop, September, 1873, p. 200; *The Popular Science Monthly,* January, 1874, article *Genesis, Geology, and Evolution,* by Rev. George Henslow—this article first appeared in his book *Evolution and Religion;* article by Asa Gray, *Nature,* London, June 4, 1874; *Materialism,* by Rev. W. Streissguth, *Lutheran Quarterly,* July, 1875, originally written in German, and translated by J. G. Morris, D. D., pp. 406, 408; *Darwinismus und Christenthum,* von R. Steck, Ref. Pfarrer in Dresden, Berlin, 1875, pp. 5, 6, and 26, reprinted from the *Protestantische Kirchenzeitung,* and issued as a tract by the Protestantenverein; Rev. W. E. Adams, article in the *Lutheran Quarterly,* April, 1879, on *Evolution: Shall it be Atheistic?* John Wood, *Bible Anticipations of Modern Science,* 1880, pp. 18, 19, 22; *Lutheran Quarterly,* January, 1881, *Some Postulates of the New Ethics,* by Rev. C. A. Stork, D. D.; *Lutheran Quarterly,* January, 1882, *The Religion of Evolution as against the Religion of Jesus,* by Prof. W. H. Wynn, Iowa State Agricultural College—this article was republished as a pamphlet; Canon Liddon, prefatory note to sermon on *The Recovery of St. Thomas,* pp. 4, 11, 12, 13, and 26, preached in St. Paul's Cathedral, April 23, 1882; *Lutheran Quarterly,* January, 1882, *Evolution and the Scripture,* by Rev. John A. Earnest, pp. 101, 105; *Glimpses in the Twilight,* by Rev. F. G. Lee, D. D., Edinburgh, 1885, especially pp. 18 and 19; the *Hibbert Lectures* for 1883, by Rev. Charles Beard, pp. 392, 393, *et seq.;* F. W. Farrar, D. D., Canon of Westminster, *The History of Interpretation,* being the *Bampton Lectures* for 1885, pp. 426, 427; Bishop Temple, *Bampton Lectures,* pp. 184-186; article *Evolution,* in the *Dictionary of Religion,* edited by Rev. William Benham, 1887; Prof. Huxley, *An Episcopal Trilogy, Nineteenth Century,* November, 1887—this article discusses three sermons delivered by the Bishops of Carlisle, Bedford, and Manchester, in Manchester Cathedral, during the meeting of the British Association, September, 1887—these sermons were afterward published in pamphlet form under the title *The Advance of Science;* John Fiske, *Darwinism, and other Essays,* Boston, 1888; Harriet Mackenzie, *Evolution illuminating the Bible,* London, 1891, dedicated to Prof. Huxley; H. E. Ryle, Hulsean Professor of Divinity at Cambridge, *The Early Narratives of Genesis,* London, 1892, preface, pp. vii-ix, pp. 7, 9, 11; Rev. G. M. Searle, of the Catholic University, Washington, article in the *Catholic World,* November, 1892, pp. 223, 227, 229, 231. For the statement from Keble College, see Rev. Mr. Illingworth, in *Lux Mundi.* For Bishop Temple, see citation in Laing. For a complete and admirable acceptance of the evolution theory as lifting Christian doctrine and practice to a higher plane, with suggestions for a

[Chapter 2

Geography]

[1. The Form of the Earth]

[2. The Delineation of the Earth]

[3. The Inhabitants of the Earth]

[4. The Size of the Earth]

[5. The Character of the Earth's Surface]

Chapter 3

Astronomy

1. The Old Sacred Theory of the Universe
THE NEXT GREAT SERIES of battles was fought over the relations of the visible heavens to the earth.

In the early Church, in view of the doctrine so prominent in the New Testament, that the earth was soon to be destroyed, and that there were to be "new heavens and a new earth," astronomy, like other branches of science, was generally looked upon as futile. Why study the old heavens and the old earth, when they were so soon to be replaced with something infinitely better? This feeling appears in St. Augustine's famous utterance, "What concern is it to me whether the heavens as

---

new theology, see two *Sermons* by Archdeacon Wilson, of Manchester, S. P. C. K., London, and Young & Co., New York, 1893; and for a characteristically lucid statement of the most recent development of evolution doctrines, and the relations of Spencer, Weismann, Galton, and others to them, see Lester F. Ward's *Address* as President of the Biological Society, Washington, 1891; also, recent articles in the leading English reviews. For a brilliant glorification of evolution by natural selection as a doctrine necessary to the highest and truest view of Christianity, see Prof. Drummond's *Chautauqua Lectures,* published in *The British Weekly,* London, from April 20 to May 11, 1893.

a sphere inclose the earth in the middle of the world or over-hang it on either side?"

As to the heavenly bodies, theologians looked on them as at best only objects of pious speculation. Regarding their nature the fathers of the Church were divided. Origen, and others with him, thought them living beings possessed of souls, and this belief was mainly based upon the scriptural vision of the morning stars singing together, and upon the beautiful appeal to the "stars and light" in the song of the three children—the *Benedicite*—which the Anglican communion has so wisely retained in its Liturgy.

Other fathers thought the stars abiding-places of the angels, and that stars were moved by angels. The Gnostics thought the stars spiritual beings governed by angels, and appointed not to cause earthly events but to indicate them.

As to the heavens in general, the prevailing view in the Church was based upon the scriptural declarations that a solid vault—a "firmament"—was extended above the earth, and that the heavenly bodies were simply lights hung within it. This was for a time held very tenaciously. St. Philastrius, in his famous treatise on heresies, pronounced it a heresy to deny that the stars are brought out by God from his treasure-house and hung in the sky every evening; any other view he declared "false to the Catholic faith." This view also survived in the sacred theory established so firmly by Cosmas in the sixth century. Having established his plan of the universe upon various texts in the Old and New Testaments, and hav-ing made it a vast oblong box, covered by the solid "firma-ment," he brought in additional texts from Scripture to ac-count for the planetary movements, and developed at length the theory that the sun and planets are moved and the "windows of heaven" opened and shut by angels appointed for that purpose.

How intensely real this way of looking at the universe was, we find in the writings of St. Isidore, the greatest leader of orthodox thought in the seventh century. He affirms that since the fall of man, and on account of it, the sun and moon shine with a feebler light; but he proves from a text in Isaiah that when the world shall be fully redeemed these "great lights" will shine again in all their early splendour. But, despite these authorities and their theological finalities, the evolution of scientific thought continued, its main germ being the geocentric doctrine—the doctrine that the earth is the centre, and that the sun and planets revolve about it.[1]

This doctrine was of the highest respectability: it had been developed at a very early period, and had been elaborated until it accounted well for the apparent movements of the heavenly bodies; its final name, "Ptolemaic theory," carried weight; and, having thus come from antiquity into the Christian world, St. Clement of Alexandria demonstrated that the altar in the Jewish tabernacle was "a symbol of the earth placed in the middle of the universe": nothing more was needed; the geocentric theory was fully adopted by the Church and universally held to agree with the letter and spirit of Scripture.[2]

Wrought into this foundation, and based upon it, there was developed in the Middle Ages, mainly out of fragments of Chaldean and other early theories preserved in the Hebrew Scriptures, a new sacred system of astronomy, which became one of the great treasures of the universal Church—the last word of revelation.

Three great men mainly reared this structure. First was the

[1] For passage cited from Clement of Alexandria, see English translation, Edinburgh, 1869, vol. ii, p. 368; also the *Miscellanies,* Book V, cap. vi. For typical statements by St. Augustine, see *De Genesi,* ii, cap. ix, in Migne, *Patr. Lat.,* tome xxxiv, pp. 270, 271. For Origen's view, see the *De Principiis,* lib. i, cap. vii; see also Leopardi's *Errori Populari,* cap. xi; also Wilson's *Selections from the Prophetic Scriptures* in *Ante-Nicene Library,* p. 132. For Philo Judæus, see *On the Creation of the World,* chaps. xviii and xix, and *On Monarchy,* chap. i. For St. Isidore, see the *De Ordine Creaturarum,* cap. v, in Migne, *Patr. Lat.,* lxxxiii, pp. 923-925; also, 1000, 1001. For Philastrius, see the *De Hæresibus,* chap. cxxxiii, in Migne, tome xii, p. 1264. For Cosmas's view, see his *Topographia Christiana,* in Montfauçon, *Col. Nov. Patrum,* ii, p. 150, and elsewhere as cited in my chapter on Geography.

[2] As to the respectability of the geocentric theory, etc., see Grote's *Plato,* vol. iii, p. 257; also Sir G. C. Lewis's *Astronomy of the Ancients,* chap. iii, sec. 1, for a very thoughtful statement of Plato's view, and differing from ancient statements. For plausible elaboration of it, and for supposed agreement of Scripture with it, see Fromundus, *Anti-Aristarchus,* Antwerp, 1631; also Melanchthon's *Initia Doctrinæ Physicæ.* For an admirable statement of the theological view of the geocentric theory, antipodes, etc., see Eicken, *Geschichte und System der mittelalterlichen Weltanschauung,* pp. 618 *et seq.*

unknown who gave to the world the treatises ascribed to Dionysius the Areopagite. It was unhesitatingly believed that these were the work of St. Paul's Athenian convert, and therefore virtually of St. Paul himself. Though now known to be spurious, they were then considered a treasure of inspiration, and an emperor of the East sent them to an emperor of the West as the most worthy of gifts. In the ninth century they were widely circulated in western Europe, and became a fruitful source of thought, especially on the whole celestial hierarchy. Thus the old ideas of astronomy were vastly developed, and the heavenly hosts were classed and named in accordance with indications scattered through the sacred Scriptures.

The next of these three great theologians was Peter Lombard, professor at the University of Paris. About the middle of the twelfth century he gave forth his collection of *Sentences,* or Statements by the Fathers, and this remained until the end of the Middle Ages the universal manual of theology. In it was especially developed the theological view of man's relation to the universe. The author tells the world: "Just as man is made for the sake of God—that is, that he may serve Him, —so the universe is made for the sake of man—that is, that it may serve *him*; therefore is man placed at the middle point of the universe, that he may both serve and be served."

The vast significance of this view, and its power in resisting any real astronomical science, we shall see, especially in the time of Galileo.

The great triad of thinkers culminated in St. Thomas Aquinas—the sainted theologian, the glory of the mediæval Church, the "Angelic Doctor," the most marvellous intellect between Aristotle and Newton; he to whom it was believed that an image of the Crucified had spoken words praising his writings. Large of mind, strong, acute, yet just—even more than just—to his opponents, he gave forth, in the latter half of the thirteenth century, his Cyclopædia of Theology, the *Summa Theologica.* In this he carried the sacred theory of the universe to its full development. With great power and clearness he brought the whole vast system, material and spiritual, into its relations to God and man.[3]

[3] For the beliefs of Chaldean astronomers in revolving spheres carrying sun, moon, and planets, in a solid firmament supporting the celestial waters, and in angels as giving motion to the planets, see Lenormant; also Lethaby, 13-21; also Schröder, Jensen, Lukas,

Thus was the vast system developed by these three leaders of mediæval thought; and now came the man who wrought it yet more deeply into European belief, the poet divinely inspired who made the system part of the world's *life*. Pictured by Dante, the empyrean and the concentric heavens, paradise, purgatory, and hell, were seen of all men; the God Triune, seated on his throne upon the circle of the heavens, as real as the Pope seated in the chair of St. Peter; the seraphim, cherubim, and thrones, surrounding the Almighty, as real as the cardinals surrounding the Pope; the three great orders of angels in heaven, as real as the three great orders, bishops, priests, and deacons, on earth; and the whole system of spheres, each revolving within the one above it, and all moving about the earth, subject to the *primum mobile*, as real as the feudal system of western Europe, subject to the Emperor.[4]

Let us look into this vast creation—the highest achievement of theology—somewhat more closely.

Its first feature shows a development out of earlier theological ideas. The earth is no longer a flat plain inclosed by four walls and solidly vaulted above, as theologians of previous centuries had believed it, under the inspiration of Cosmas; it is no longer a mere flat disk, with sun, moon, and

---

et al. For the contribution of the pseudo-Dionysius to mediæval cosmology, see Dion. Areopagita, *De Cælesti Hierarchia,* vers. Joan. Scoti, in Migne, *Patr. Lat.,* cxxii. For the contribution of Peter Lombard, see Pet. Lomb., *Libr. Sent.,* II, i, 8,—IV, i, 6, 7, in Migne, tome 192. For the citations from St. Thomas Aquinas, see the *Summa,* ed. Migne, especially Pars I, Qu. 70, (tome i, pp. 1174-1184); also Quæstio 47, Art. iii. For good general statement, see Milman, *Latin Christianity,* iv, 191 *et seq.;* and for relation of Cosmas to these theologians of western Europe, see Milman, as above, viii, 228, note.

[4] For the central sun, hierarchy of angels, and concentric circles, see Dante, *Paradiso,* canto xxviii. For the words of St. Thomas Aquinas, showing to Virgil and Dante the great theologians of the Middle Ages, see canto x, and in Dean Plumptre's translation, vol. ii, pp. 56 *et seq.;* also Botta, *Dante,* pp. 350, 351. As to Dante's deep religious feeling and belief in his own divine mission, see J. R. Lowell, *Among my Books,* vol. i, p. 36. For a remarkable series of coloured engravings showing Dante's whole cosmology, see *La Materia della Divina Commedia di Dante dichiarata* in vi tavole, da Michelangelo Caetani, published by the monks of Monte Cassino, to whose kindness I am indebted for my copy.

stars hung up to give it light, as the earlier cathedral sculptors had figured it; it has become a globe at the centre of the universe. Encompassing it are successive transparent spheres, rotated by angels about the earth, and each carrying one or more of the heavenly bodies with it: that nearest the earth carrying the moon; the next, Mercury; the next, Venus; the next, the sun; the next three, Mars, Jupiter, and Saturn; the eighth carrying the fixed stars. The ninth was the *primum mobile,* and inclosing all was the tenth heaven—the Empyrean. This was immovable—the boundary between creation and the great outer void; and here, in a light which no one can enter, the Triune God sat enthroned, the "music of the spheres" rising to Him as they moved. Thus was the old heathen doctrine of the spheres made Christian.

In attendance upon the Divine Majesty, thus enthroned, are vast hosts of angels, who are divided into three hierarchies, one serving in the empyrean, one in the heavens, between the empyrean and the earth, and one on the earth.

Each of these hierarchies is divided into three choirs, or orders; the first, into the orders of Seraphim, Cherubim, and Thrones; and the main occupation of these is to chant incessantly—to "continually cry" the divine praises.

The order of Thrones conveys God's will to the second hierarchy, which serves in the movable heavens. This second hierarchy is also made up of three orders. The first of these, the order of Dominions, receives the divine commands; the second, the order of Powers, moves the heavens, sun, moon, planets, and stars, opens and shuts the "windows of heaven," and brings to pass all other celestial phenomena; the third, the order of Empire, guards the others.

The third and lowest hierarchy is also made up of three orders. First of these are the Principalities, the guardian spirits of nations and kingdoms. Next come Archangels; these protect religion, and bear the prayers of the saints to the foot of God's throne. Finally come Angels; these care for earthly affairs in general, one being appointed to each mortal, and others taking charge of the qualities of plants, metals, stones, and the like. Throughout the whole system, from the great Triune God to the lowest group of angels, we see at work the mystic power attached to the triangle and sacred number three—the same which gave the triune idea to ancient Hindu theology, which developed the triune deities in Egypt, and which transmitted this theological gift to the Christian world, especially through the Egyptian Athanasius.

Below the earth is hell. This is tenanted by the angels who rebelled under the lead of Lucifer, prince of the seraphim—the former favourite of the Trinity; but, of these rebellious angels, some still rove among the planetary spheres, and give trouble to the good angels; others pervade the atmosphere about the earth, carrying lightning, storm, drought, and hail; others infest earthly society, tempting men to sin; but Peter Lombard and St. Thomas Aquinas take pains to show that the work of these devils is, after all, but to discipline man or to mete out deserved punishment.

All this vast scheme had been so riveted into the Ptolemaic view by the use of biblical texts and theological reasonings that the resultant system of the universe was considered impregnable and final. To attack it was blasphemy.

It stood for centuries. Great theological men of science, like Vincent of Beauvais and Cardinal d'Ailly, devoted themselves to showing not only that it was supported by Scripture, but that it supported Scripture. Thus was the geocentric theory embedded in the beliefs and aspirations, in the hopes and fears, of Christendom down to the middle of the sixteenth century.[5]

[5] For the earlier sacred cosmology of Cosmas, with citations from Montfauçon, see the chapter on *Geography* in this work. For the views of the mediæval theologians, see foregoing notes in this chapter. For the passages of Scripture on which the theological part of this structure was developed, see especially Romans viii, 38; Ephesians i, 21; Colossians i, 16, and ii, 15; and innumerable passages in the Old Testament. As to the music of the spheres, see Dean Plumptre's *Dante*, vol. ii, p. 4, note. For an admirable summing up of the mediæval cosmology in its relation to thought in general, see Rydberg, *Magic of the Middle Ages*, chap. i, whose summary I have followed in the main. For striking woodcuts showing the view taken of the successive heavens with their choirs of angels, the earth being at the centre and the spheres about it, and the Almighty on his throne above all, see the *Nuremberg Chronicle*, ff. iv and v; its date is 1493. For charts showing the continuance of this general view down to the beginning of the sixteenth century, see the various editions of the *Margarita Philosophica*, from that of 1503 onward, astronomical part. For interesting statements regarding the trinities of gods in ancient Egypt, see Sharpe, *History of Egypt*, vol. i, pp. 94 and 101. The present writer once heard a lecture in Cairo, from an eminent Scotch Doctor of Medicine, to account for the

2. The Heliocentric Theory

But, on the other hand, there had been planted, long before, the germs of a heliocentric theory. In the sixth century before our era, Pythagoras, and after him Philolaus, had suggested the movement of the earth and planets about a central fire; and, three centuries later, Aristarchus had restated the main truth with striking precision. Here comes in a proof that the antagonism between theological and scientific methods is not confined to Christianity; for this statement brought upon Aristarchus the charge of blasphemy, and drew after it a cloud of prejudice which hid the truth for six hundred years. Not until the fifth century of our era did it timidly appear in the thoughts of Martianus Capella: then it was again lost to sight for a thousand years, until in the fifteenth century, distorted and imperfect, it appeared in the writings of Cardinal Nicholas de Cusa.

But in the shade cast by the vast system which had grown from the minds of the great theologians and from the heart of the great poet there had come to this truth neither bloom nor fruitage.

Quietly, however, the soil was receiving enrichment and the air warmth. The processes of mathematics were constantly improved, the heavenly bodies were steadily observed, and at length appeared, far from the centres of thought, on the borders of Poland, a plain, simple-minded scholar, who first fairly uttered to the modern world the truth—now so commonplace, then so astounding—that the sun and planets do not revolve about the earth, but that the earth and planets revolve about the sun: this man was Nicholas Copernicus.

Copernicus had been a professor at Rome, and even as early as 1500 had announced his doctrine there, but more in the way of a scientific curiosity or paradox, as it had been previously held by Cardinal de Cusa, than as the statement of a system representing a great fact in Nature. About thirty years later one of his disciples, Widmanstadt, had explained it to Clement VII; but it still remained a mere

---

ancient Hindu and Egyptian sacred threes and trinities. The lecturer's theory was that, when Jehovah came down into the garden of Eden and walked with Adam in "the cool of the day," he explained his triune character to Adam, and that from Adam it was spread abroad to the various ancient nations.

hypothesis, and soon, like so many others, disappeared from the public view. But to Copernicus, steadily studying the subject, it became more and more a reality, and as this truth grew within him he seemed to feel that at Rome he was no longer safe. To announce his discovery there as a theory or a paradox might amuse the papal court, but to announce it as a truth—as *the* truth—was a far different matter. He therefore returned to his little town in Poland.

To publish his thought as it had now developed was evidently dangerous even there, and for more than thirty years it lay slumbering in the mind of Copernicus and of the friends to whom he had privately intrusted it.

At last he prepared his great work on the *Revolutions of the Heavenly Bodies,* and dedicated it to the Pope himself. He next sought a place of publication. He dared not send it to Rome, for there were the rulers of the older Church ready to seize it; he dared not send it to Wittenberg, for there were the leaders of Protestantism no less hostile; he therefore intrusted it to Osiander, at Nuremberg.[6]

[6] For germs of heliocentric theory planted long before, see Sir G. C. Lewis; and for a succinct statement of the claims of Pythagoras, Philolaus, Aristarchus, and Martianus Capella, see Hoefer, *Histoire de l'Astronomie,* 1873, p. 107 *et seq.;* also Heller, *Geschichte der Physik,* Stuttgart, 1882, vol. i, pp. 12, 13; also pp. 99 *et seq.* For germs among thinkers of India, see Whewell, vol. i, p. 277; also Whitney, *Oriental and Linguistic Studies,* New York, 1874; *Essay on the Lunar Zodiac,* p. 345. For the views of Vincent of Beauvais, see his *Speculum Naturale,* lib. xvi, cap. 21. For Cardinal d'Ailly's view, see his treatise *De Concordia Astronomicæ Veritatis cum Theologia* (in his *Ymago Mundi* and separately). For general statement of De Cusa's work, see Draper, *Intellectual Development of Europe,* p. 512. For skilful use of De Cusa's view in order to mitigate censure upon the Church for its treatment of Copernicus's discovery, see an article in the *Catholic World* for January, 1869. For a very exact statement, in a spirit of judicial fairness, see Whewell, *History of the Inductive Sciences,* p. 275 and pp. 379, 380. In the latter, Whewell cites the exact words of De Cusa in the *De Docta Ignorantia,* and sums up in these words: "This train of thought might be a preparation for the reception of the Copernican system; but it is very different from the doctrine that the sun is the centre of the planetary system." Whewell says: "De Cusa propounded the doctrine of the motion of the earth more as a paradox than as a reality. We can not consider this as any distinct anticipation of a profound and consistent view of the truth." On De Cusa, see also Heller, vol. i, p. 216. For Aristotle's views,

But Osiander's courage failed him: he dared not launch the new thought boldly. He wrote a grovelling preface, endeavouring to excuse Copernicus for his novel idea, and in this he inserted the apologetic lie that Copernicus had propounded the doctrine of the earth's movement not as a fact, but as a hypothesis. He declared that it was lawful for an astronomer to indulge his imagination, and that this was what Copernicus had done.

---

and their elaboration by St. Thomas Aquinas, see the *De Cælo et Mundo*, sec. xx, and elsewhere in the latter. It is curious to see how even such a biographer as Archbishop Vaughan slurs over the Angelic Doctor's errors. See Vaughan's *Life and Labours of St. Thomas of Aquin*, pp. 459, 460.

As to Copernicus's danger at Rome, the *Catholic World* for January, 1869, cites a speech of the Archbishop of Mechlin before the University of Louvain, to the effect that Copernicus defended his theory at Rome, in 1500, before two thousand scholars; also, that another professor taught the system in 1528, and was made apostolic notary by Clement VIII. All this, even if the doctrines taught were identical with those of Copernicus as finally developed—which is simply not the case—avails nothing against the overwhelming testimony that Copernicus felt himself in danger—testimony which the after-history of the Copernican theory renders invincible. The very title of Fromundus's book, already cited, published within a few miles of the archbishop's own cathedral, and sanctioned expressly by the theological faculty of that same University of Louvain in 1630, utterly refutes the archbishop's idea that the Church was inclined to treat Copernicus kindly. The title is as follows: *Ant-Aristarchus sive Orbis-Terræ Immobilis, in quo decretum S. Congregationis S. R. E. Cardinal. an. M.DC.XVI adversus Pythagorico-Copernicanos editum defenditur*, Antverpiæ, MDCXXXI. L'Épinois, *Galilée*, Paris, 1867, lays stress, p. 14, on the broaching of the doctrine by De Cusa in 1435, and by Widmanstadt in 1533, and their kind treatment by Eugenius IV and Clement VII; but this is absolutely worthless in denying the papal policy afterward. Lange, *Geschichte des Materialismus*, vol. i, pp. 217, 218, while admitting that De Cusa and Widmanstadt sustained this theory and received honours from their respective popes, shows that, when the Church gave it serious consideration, it was condemned. There is nothing in this view unreasonable. It would be a parallel case to that of Leo X, at first inclined toward Luther and others, in their "squabbles with the envious friars," and afterward forced to oppose them. That Copernicus felt the danger, is evident, among other things, by the expression in the preface; *"Statim me explodendum cum tali opinione clamitant."* For dangers at Wittenberg, see Lange, as above, vol. i, p. 217.

Thus was the greatest and most ennobling, perhaps, of scientific truths—a truth not less ennobling to religion than to science—forced, in coming before the world, to sneak and crawl.[7]

On the 24th of May, 1543, the newly printed book arrived at the house of Copernicus. It was put into his hands; but he was on his deathbed. A few hours later he was beyond the reach of the conscientious men who would have blotted his reputation and perhaps have destroyed his life.

Yet not wholly beyond their reach. Even death could not be trusted to shield him. There seems to have been fear of vengeance upon his corpse, for on his tombstone was placed no record of his lifelong labours, no mention of his great discovery; but there was graven upon it simply a prayer: "I ask not the grace accorded to Paul; not that given to Peter; give me only the favour which Thou didst show to the thief on the cross." Not till thirty years after did a friend dare write on his tombstone a memorial of his discovery.[8]

The preface of Osiander, pretending that the book of Copernicus suggested a hypothesis instead of announcing a truth, served its purpose well. During nearly seventy years the Church authorities evidently thought it best not to stir the matter, and in some cases professors like Calganini were

[7] Osiander, in a letter to Copernicus, dated April 20, 1541, had endeavoured to reconcile him to such a procedure, and ends by saying, "*Sic enim placidiores reddideris peripatheticos et theologos quos contradicturos metuis.*" See *Apologia Tychonis* in Kepler's *Opera Omnia,* Frisch's edition, vol. i, p. 246. Kepler holds Osiander entirely responsible for this preface. Bertrand, in his *Fondateurs de l'Astronomie moderne*, gives its text, and thinks it possible that Copernicus may have yielded "in pure condescension toward his disciple." But this idea is utterly at variance with expressions in Copernicus's own dedicatory letter to the Pope, which follows the preface. For a good summary of the argument, see Figuier, *Savants de la Renaissance,* pp. 378, 379; see also citation from Gassendi's *Life of Copernicus,* in Flammarion, *Vie de Copernic,* p. 124. Mr. John Fiske, accurate as he usually is, in his *Outlines of Cosmic Philosophy* appears to have followed Laplace, Delambre, and Petit into the error of supposing that Copernicus, and not Osiander, is responsible for the preface. For the latest proofs, see Menzer's translation of Copernicus's work, Thorn, 1879, notes on pp. 3 and 4 of the appendix.

[8] See Flammarion, *Vie de Copernic,* p. 190.

allowed to present the new view purely as a hypothesis. There were, indeed, mutterings from time to time on the theological side, but there was no great demonstration against the system until 1616. Then, when the Copernican doctrine was upheld by Galileo as a *truth,* and proved to be a truth by his telescope, the book was taken in hand by the Roman curia. The statements of Copernicus were condemned, "until they should be corrected"; and the corrections required were simply such as would substitute for his conclusions the old Ptolemaic theory.

That this was their purpose was seen in that year when Galileo was forbidden to teach or discuss the Copernican theory, and when were forbidden "all books which affirm the motion of the earth." Henceforth to read the work of Copernicus was to risk damnation, and the world accepted the decree.[9] The strongest minds were thus held fast. If they could not believe the old system, they must *pretend* that they believed it;—and this, even after the great circumnavi-

[9] The authorities deciding this matter in accordance with the wishes of Pope Paul V and Cardinal Bellarmine were the Congregation of the Index, or cardinals having charge of the *Index Librorum Prohibitorum.* Recent desperate attempts to fasten the responsibility on them as individuals seem ridiculous in view of the simple fact that their work was sanctioned by the highest Church authority, and required to be universally accepted by the Church. Eleven different editions of the *Index* in my own possession prove this. Nearly all of these declare on their title-pages that they are issued by order of the pontiff of the period, and each is prefaced by a special papal bull or letter. See especially the *Index* of 1664, issued under order of Alexander VII, and that of 1761, under Benedict XIV. Copernicus's statements were prohibited in the *Index* "*donec corrigantur.*" Kepler said that it ought to be worded "*donec explicetur.*" See Bertrand, *Fondateurs de l'Astronomie moderne,* p. 57. De Morgan, pp. 57-60, gives the corrections required by the *Index* of 1620. Their main aim seems to be to reduce Copernicus to the grovelling level of Osiander, making of his discovery a mere hypothesis; but occasionally they require a virtual giving up of the whole Copernican doctrine—e.g., "correction" insisted upon for chap. viii, p. 6. For a scholarly account of the relation of the Prohibitory and Expurgatory Indexes to each other, see Mendham, *Literary Policy of the Church of Rome;* also Reusch, *Index der verbotenen Bücher,* Bonn, 1855, vol. ii, chaps. i and ii. For a brief but very careful statement, see Gebler, *Galileo Galilei,* English translation, London, 1879, chap. i; see also Addis and Arnold's *Catholic Dictionary,* article *Galileo,* p. 8.

gation of the globe had done so much to open the eyes of the world! Very striking is the case of the eminent Jesuit missionary Joseph Acosta, whose great work on the *Natural and Moral History of the Indies,* published in the last quarter of the sixteenth century, exploded so many astronomical and geographical errors. Though at times curiously credulous, he told the truth as far as he dared; but as to the movement of the heavenly bodies he remained orthodox—declaring, "I have seen the two poles, whereon the heavens turn as upon their axletrees."

There was, indeed, in Europe one man who might have done much to check this current of unreason which was to sweep away so many thoughtful men on the one hand from scientific knowledge, and so many on the other from Christianity. This was Peter Apian. He was one of the great mathematical and astronomical scholars of the time. His brilliant abilities had made him the astronomical teacher of the Emperor Charles V; his work on geography had brought him a world-wide reputation; his work on astronomy brought him a patent of nobility; his improvements in mathematical processes and astronomical instruments brought him the praise of Kepler and a place in the history of science: never had a true man better opportunity to do a great deed. When Copernicus's work appeared, Apian was at the height of his reputation and power: a quiet, earnest plea from him, even if it had been only for ordinary fairness and a suspension of judgment, must have carried much weight. His devoted pupil, Charles V, who sat on the thrones of Germany and Spain, must at least have given a hearing to such a plea. But, unfortunately, Apian was a professor in an institution of learning under the strictest Church control—the University of Ingolstadt. His foremost duty was to teach *safe* science—to keep science within the line of scriptural truth as interpreted by theological professors. His great opportunity was lost. Apian continued to maunder over the Ptolemaic theory and astrology in his lecture-room. The attacks on the Copernican theory he neither supported nor opposed; he was silent; and the cause of his silence should never be forgotten so long as any Church asserts its title to control university instruction.[10]

[10] For Joseph Acosta's statement, see the translation of his *History,* published by the Hakluyt Society, chap. ii. For Peter Apian, see Mädler, *Geschichte der Astronomie,* Braunschweig, 1873, vol. i,

Doubtless many will exclaim against the Roman Catholic Church for this; but the simple truth is that Protestantism was no less zealous against the new scientific doctrine. All branches of the Protestant Church—Lutheran, Calvinist, Anglican—vied with each other in denouncing the Copernican doctrine as contrary to Scripture; and, at a later period, the Puritans showed the same tendency.

Said Martin Luther: "People gave ear to an upstart astrologer who strove to show that the earth revolves, not the heavens or the firmament, the sun and the moon. Whoever wishes to appear clever must devise some new system, which of all systems is of course the very best. This fool wishes to reverse the entire science of astronomy; but sacred Scripture tells us that Joshua commanded the sun to stand still, and not the earth." Melanchthon, mild as he was, was not behind Luther in condemning Copernicus. In his treatise on the *Elements of Physics,* published six years after Copernicus's death, he says: "The eyes are witnesses that the heavens revolve in the space of twenty-four hours. But certain men, either from the love of novelty, or to make a display of ingenuity, have concluded that the earth moves; and they maintain that neither the eighth sphere nor the sun revolves. . . . Now, it is a want of honesty and decency to assert such notions publicly, and the example is pernicious. It is the part of a good mind to accept the truth as revealed by God and to acquiesce in it." Melanchthon then cites the passages in the Psalms and Ecclesiastes, which he declares assert positively and clearly that the earth stands fast and that the sun moves around it, and adds eight other proofs of his proposition that "the earth can be nowhere if not in the centre of the universe." So earnest does this mildest of the Reformers become, that he suggests severe measures to restrain such impious teachings as those of Copernicus.[11]

---

p. 141. For evidences of the special favour of Charles V, see Delambre, *Histoire de l'Astronomie au Moyen Age,* p. 390; also Brühns, in the *Allgemeine deutsche Biographie.* For an attempted apology for him, see Günther, *Peter and Philipp Apian,* Prag, 1882, p. 62.

[11] See the *Tischreden* in the Walsch edition of Luther's *Works,* 1743, vol. xxii, p. 2260; also Melanchthon's *Initia Doctrinæ Physicæ.* This treatise is cited under a mistaken title by the *Catholic World,* September, 1870. The correct title is as given above; it will be found in the *Corpus Reformatorum,* vol. xiii (ed. Bretschneider,

While Lutheranism was thus condemning the theory of the earth's movement, other branches of the Protestant Church did not remain behind. Calvin took the lead, in his *Commentary on Genesis,* by condemning all who asserted that the earth is not at the centre of the universe.[12] He clinched the matter by the usual reference to the first verse of the ninety-third Psalm, and asked, "Who will venture to place the authority of Copernicus above that of the Holy Spirit?" Turretin, Calvin's famous successor, even after Kepler and Newton had virtually completed the theory of Copernicus and Galileo, put forth his compendium of theology, in which he proved, from a multitude of scriptural texts, that the heavens, sun, and moon move about the earth, which stands still in the centre. In England we see similar theological efforts, even after they had become evidently futile. Hutchinson's *Moses's Principia,* Dr. Samuel Pike's *Sacred Philosophy,* the writings of Horne, Bishop Horsley, and President Forbes contain most earnest attacks upon the ideas of Newton, such attacks being based upon Scripture. Dr. John Owen, so famous in the annals of Puritanism, declared the Copernican system a "delusive and arbitrary hypothesis, contrary to Scripture"; and even John Wesley declared the new ideas to "tend toward infidelity."[13]

And Protestant peoples were not a whit behind Catholic in following out such teachings. The people of Elbing made themselves merry over a farce in which Copernicus was the main object of ridicule. The people of Nuremberg, a Protestant stronghold, caused a medal to be struck with inscriptions ridiculing the philosopher and his theory.

Halle, 1846), pp. 216, 217. See also Mädler, vol. i, p. 176; also Lange, *Geschichte des Materialismus,* vol. i, p. 217; also Prowe, *Ueber die Abhängigkeit des Copernicus,* Thorn, 1865, p. 4; also note, pp. 5, 6, where text is given in full.

[12] [For a modern debate on Calvin's position toward Copernicus, the interested reader may consult Edward Rosen, "Calvin's Attitude Toward Copernicus," *Journal of the History of Ideas,* XXI, 3 (July, 1960); and Joseph Ratner, "Some Comments on Rosen's 'Calvin's Attitude Toward Copernicus,'" and Edward Rosen, "A Reply to Dr. Ratner," *Ibid.,* XXII, 3 (July-September, 1961).—Ed.]

[13] On the teachings of Protestantism as regards the Copernican theory, see citations in Canon Farrar's *History of Interpretation,* preface, xviii; also Rev. Dr. Shields, of Princeton, *The Final Philosophy,* pp. 60, 61.

Why the people at large took this view is easily understood when we note the attitude of the guardians of learning, both Catholic and Protestant, in that age. It throws
great light upon sundry claims by modern theologians to
take charge of public instruction and of the evolution of
science. So important was it thought to have "sound learning" guarded and "safe science" taught, that in many of
the universities, as late as the end of the seventeenth century, professors were forced to take an oath not to hold the
"Pythagorean"—that is, the Copernican—idea as to the
movement of the heavenly bodies. As the contest went on,
professors were forbidden to make known to students the
facts revealed by the telescope. Special orders to this effect
were issued by the ecclesiastical authorities to the universities and colleges of Pisa, Innspruck, Louvain, Douay, Salamanca, and others. During generations we find the authorities of these universities boasting that the godless doctrines
were kept away from their students. It is touching to hear
such boasts made then, just as it is touching now to hear
sundry excellent university authorities boast that they dis-
courage the reading of Mill, Spencer, and Darwin. Nor
were such attempts to keep the truth from students confined
to the Roman Catholic institutions of learning. Strange as
it may seem, nowhere were the facts confirming the Copernican theory more carefully kept out of sight than at Wittenberg—the university of Luther and Melanchthon. About
the middle of the sixteenth century there were at that centre
of Protestant instruction two astronomers of a very high
order, Rheticus and Reinhold; both of these, after thorough
study, had convinced themselves that the Copernican system was true, but neither of them was allowed to tell this
truth to his students. Neither in his lecture announcements
nor in his published works did Rheticus venture to make
the new system known, and he at last gave up his professorship and left Wittenberg, that he might have freedom to
seek and tell the truth. Reinhold was even more wretchedly humiliated. Convinced of the truth of the new theory,
he was obliged to advocate the old; if he mentioned the
Copernican ideas, he was compelled to overlay them with
the Ptolemaic. Even this was not thought safe enough, and
in 1571 the subject was intrusted to Peucer. He was eminently "sound," and denounced the Copernican theory in

his lectures as "absurd, and unfit to be introduced into the schools."

To clinch anti-scientific ideas more firmly into German Protestant teaching, Rector Hensel wrote a text-book for schools entitled *The Restored Mosaic System of the World,* which showed the Copernican astronomy to be unscriptural.

Doubtless this has a far-off sound; yet its echo comes very near modern Protestantism in the expulsion of Dr. Woodrow by the Presbyterian authorities in South Carolina; the expulsion of Prof. Winchell by the Methodist Episcopal authorities in Tennessee; the expulsion of Prof. Toy by Baptist authorities in Kentucky; the expulsion of the professors at Beyrout under authority of American Protestant divines—all for holding the doctrines of modern science, and in the last years of the nineteenth century.[14]

But the new truth could not be concealed; it could neither be laughed down nor frowned down. Many minds had received it, but within the hearing of the papacy only one tongue appears to have dared to utter it clearly. This new warrior was that strange mortal, Giordano Bruno. He was hunted from land to land, until at last he turned on his pursuers with fearful invectives. For this he was entrapped at Venice, imprisoned during six years in the dungeons of the Inquisition at Rome, then burned alive, and his ashes scattered to the winds. Still, the new truth lived on. Ten years after the martyrdom of Bruno the truth of Copernicus's doctrine was established by the telescope of Galileo.[15]

[14] For treatment of Copernican ideas by the people, see *The Catholic World,* as above; also Melanchthon, *ubi supra;* also Prowe, *Copernicus,* Berlin, 1883, vol. i, p. 269, note; also pp. 279, 280; also Mädler, i, p. 167. For Rector Hensel, see Rev. Dr. Shield's *Final Philosophy,* p. 60. For details of recent Protestant efforts against evolution doctrines, see the chapter on *The Fall of Man and Anthropology* in this work.

[15] For Bruno, see Bartholmèss, *Vie de Jordano Bruno,* Paris, 1846, vol. i, p. 121 and pp. 212 *et seq.*; also Berti, *Vita di Giordano Bruno,* Firenze, 1868, chap. xvi; also Whewell, vol. i, pp. 272, 273. That Whewell is somewhat hasty in attributing Bruno's punishment entirely to the *Spaccio della Bestia Trionfante* will be evident, in spite of Montucla, to any one who reads the account of the persecution in Bartholmèss or Berti; and, even if Whewell be right, the *Spaccio* would never have been written but for Bruno's indignation at ecclesiastical oppression. See Tiraboschi, vol. vii, pp. 466 *et seq.*

Herein was fulfilled one of the most touching of prophecies. Years before, the opponents of Copernicus had said to him, "If your doctrines were true, Venus would show phases like the moon." Copernicus answered: "You are right; I know not what to say; but God is good, and will in time find an answer to this objection." The God-given answer came when, in 1611, the rude telescope of Galileo showed the phases of Venus.[16]

3. The War Upon Galileo

On this new champion, Galileo, the whole war was at last concentrated. His discoveries had clearly taken the Copernican theory out of the list of hypotheses, and had placed it before the world as a truth. Against him, then, the war was long and bitter. The supporters of what was called "sound learning" declared his discoveries deceptions and his announcements blasphemy. Semi-scientific professors, endeavouring to curry favour with the Church, attacked him with sham science;[17] earnest preachers attacked him with perverted Scripture; theologians, inquisitors, congregations of cardinals, and at last two popes dealt with him, and, as was supposed, silenced his impious doctrine forever.[18]

[16] For the relation of these discoveries to Copernicus's work, see Delambre, *Histoire de l'Astronomie moderne, discours préliminaire,* p. xiv; also Laplace, *Système du Monde,* vol. i, p. 326; and for more careful statements, Kepler's *Opera Omnia,* edit. Frisch, tome ii, p. 464. For Copernicus's prophecy, see Cantu, *Histoire Universelle,* vol. xv, p. 473. (Cantu was an eminent Roman Catholic.)

[17] [White appears here to ignore the fact that some reputable professors opposed the Copernican theory on legitimate—whether ultimately correct or not doesn't matter—scientific grounds; for example, the great astronomer, Tycho Brahe, did not espouse the Copernican theory.—Ed.]

[18] A very curious example of this sham science employed by theologians is seen in the argument, frequently used at that time, that, if the earth really moved, a stone falling from a height would fall back of the point immediately below its point of starting. This is used by Fromundus with great effect. It appears never to have occurred to him to test the matter by dropping a stone from the topmast of a ship. Benzenburg has experimentally demonstrated just such an aberration in falling bodies as is mathematically required by the diurnal motion of the earth. See Jevons, *Principles of Science,* pp. 388, 389, second edition, 1877.

I shall present this warfare at some length because, so far as I can find, no careful summary of it has been given in our language, since the whole history was placed in a new light by the revelations of the trial documents in the Vatican Library, honestly published for the first time by L'Épinois in 1867, and since that by Gebler, Berti, Favaro, and others.

The first important attack on Galileo began in 1610, when he announced that his telescope had revealed the moons of the planet Jupiter. The enemy saw that this took the Copernican theory out of the realm of hypothesis, and they gave battle immediately. They denounced both his method and its results as absurd and impious. As to his method, professors bred in the "safe science" favoured by the Church argued that the divinely appointed way of arriving at the truth in astronomy was by theological reasoning on texts of Scripture; and, as to his results, they insisted, first, that Aristotle knew nothing of these new revelations; and, next, that the Bible showed by all applicable types that there could be only seven planets; that this was proved by the seven golden candlesticks of the Apocalypse, by the seven-branched candlestick of the tabernacle, and by the seven churches of Asia; that from Galileo's doctrine consequences must logically result destructive to Christian truth. Bishops and priests therefore warned their flocks, and multitudes of the faithful besought the Inquisition to deal speedily and sharply with the heretic.[19]

In vain did Galileo try to prove the existence of satellites by showing them to the doubters through his telescope: they either declared it impious to look, or, if they did look, denounced the satellites as illusions from the devil. Good Father Clavius declared that "to see satellites of Jupiter, men had to make an instrument which would create them." In vain did Galileo try to save the great truths he had discovered by his letters to the Benedictine Castelli and the Grand-Duchess Christine, in which he argued that literal biblical interpretation should not be applied to science; it was answered that such an argument only made his heresy more detestable; that he was "worse than Luther or Calvin."

The war on the Copernican theory, which up to that

[19] See Delambre on the discovery of the satellites of Jupiter as the turning-point with the heliocentric doctrine. As to its effects on Bacon, see Jevons, p. 638, as above. For argument drawn from the candlestick and the seven churches, see Delambre, p. 20.

time had been carried on quietly, now flamed forth. It was declared that the doctrine was proved false by the standing still of the sun for Joshua, by the declarations that "the foundations of the earth are fixed so firm that they can not be moved," and that the sun "runneth about from one end of the heavens to the other."[20]

But the little telescope of Galileo still swept the heavens, and another revelation was announced—the mountains and valleys in the moon. This brought on another attack. It was declared that this, and the statement that the moon shines by light reflected from the sun, directly contradict the statement in Genesis that the moon is "a great light." To make the matter worse, a painter, placing the moon in a religious picture in its usual position beneath the feet of the Blessed Virgin, outlined on its surface mountains and valleys; this was denounced as a sacrilege logically resulting from the astronomer's heresy.

Still another struggle was aroused when the hated telescope revealed spots upon the sun, and their motion indicating the sun's rotation. Monsignor Elci, head of the University of Pisa, forbade the astronomer Castelli to mention these spots to his students. Father Busaeus, at the University of Innspruck, forbade the astronomer Scheiner, who had also discovered the spots and proposed a *safe* explanation of them, to allow the new discovery to be known there. At the College of Douay and the University of Louvain this discovery was expressly placed under the ban, and this became the general rule among the Catholic universities and colleges of Europe. The Spanish universities were especially intolerant of this and similar ideas, and up to a recent period

[20] For principal points as given, see Libri, *Histoire des Sciences mathématiques en Italie,* vol. iv, p. 211; De Morgan, *Paradoxes,* p. 26, for account of Father Clavius. It is interesting to know that Clavius, in his last years, acknowledged that "the whole system of the heavens is broken down, and must be mended," Cantu, *Histoire Universelle,* vol. xv, p. 478. See Th. Martin, *Galilée,* pp. 34, 208, and 266; also Heller, *Geschichte der Physik,* Stuttgart, 1882, vol. i, p. 366. For the original documents, see L'Épinois, pp. 34 and 36; or, better, Gebler's careful edition of the trial (*Die Acten des Galileischen Processes,* Stuttgart, 1877), pp. 47 *et seq.* Martin's translation seems somewhat too free. See also Gebler, *Galileo Galilei,* English translation, London, 1879, pp. 76-78; also Reusch, *Der Process Galilei's und die Jesuiten,* Bonn, 1879, chaps. ix, x, xi.

their presentation was strictly forbidden in the most important university of all—that of Salamanca.[21]

Such are the consequences of placing the instruction of men's minds in the hands of those mainly absorbed in saving men's souls. Nothing could be more in accordance with the idea recently put forth by sundry ecclesiastics, Catholic and Protestant, that the Church alone is empowered to promulgate scientific truth or direct university instruction. But science gained a victory here also. Observations of the solar spots were reported not only from Galileo in Italy, but from Fabricius in Holland. Father Scheiner then endeavoured to make the usual compromise between theology and science. He promulgated a pseudo-scientific theory, which only provoked derision.

The war became more and more bitter. The Dominican Father Caccini preached a sermon from the text, "Ye men of Galilee, why stand ye gazing up into heaven?" and this wretched pun upon the great astronomer's name ushered in sharper weapons; for, before Caccini ended, he insisted that "geometry is of the devil," and that "mathematicians should be banished as the authors of all heresies." The Church authorities gave Caccini promotion.

Father Lorini proved that Galileo's doctrine was not only heretical but "atheistic," and besought the Inquisition to intervene. The Bishop of Fiesole screamed in rage against the Copernican system, publicly insulted Galileo, and denounced him to the Grand-Duke. The Archbishop of Pisa secretly sought to entrap Galileo and deliver him to the Inquisition at Rome. The Archbishop of Florence solemnly condemned the new doctrines as unscriptural; and Paul V, while petting Galileo, and inviting him as the greatest astronomer of the world to visit Rome, was secretly moving the Archbishop of Pisa to pick up evidence against the astronomer.

But by far the most terrible champion who now appeared was Cardinal Bellarmin, one of the greatest theologians the world has known. He was earnest, sincere, and learned, but insisted on making science conform to Scripture. The weapons which men of Bellarmin's stamp used were purely theological. They held up before the world the dreadful consequences

[21] See Ticknor, *History of Spanish Literature,* vol. iii.

which must result to Christian theology were the heavenly bodies proved to revolve about the sun and not about the earth. Their most tremendous dogmatic engine was the statement that "his pretended discovery vitiates the whole Christian plan of salvation." Father Lecazre declared "it casts suspicion on the doctrine of the incarnation." Others declared, "It upsets the whole basis of theology. If the earth is a planet, and only one among several planets, it can not be that any such great things have been done specially for it as the Christian doctrine teaches. If there are other planets, since God makes nothing in vain, they must be inhabited; but how can their inhabitants be descended from Adam? How can they trace back their origin to Noah's ark? How can they have been redeemed by the Saviour?" Nor was this argument confined to the theologians of the Roman Church; Melanchthon, Protestant as he was, had already used it in his attacks on Copernicus and his school.

In addition to this prodigious theological engine of war there was kept up a fire of smaller artillery in the shape of texts and scriptural extracts.

But the war grew still more bitter, and some weapons used in it are worth examining. They are very easily examined, for they are to be found on all the battlefields of science; but on that field they were used with more effect than on almost any other. These weapons are the epithets "infidel" and "atheist." They have been used against almost every man who has ever done anything new for his fellowmen. The list of those who have been denounced as "infidel" and "atheist" includes almost all great men of science, general scholars, inventors, and philanthropists. The purest Christian life, the noblest Christian character, have not availed to shield combatants. Christians like Isaac Newton, Pascal, Locke, Milton, and even Fénelon and Howard, have had this weapon hurled against them. Of all proofs of the existence of a God, those of Descartes have been wrought most thoroughly into the minds of modern men; yet the Protestant theologians of Holland sought to bring him to torture and to death by the charges of atheism, and the Roman Catholic theologians of France thwarted him during his life and prevented any due honours to him after his death.[22]

22 For various objectors and objections to Galileo by his contemporaries, see Libri, *Histoire des Sciences mathématiques en Italie*, vol. iv, pp. 233, 234; also Martin, *Vie de Galilée*. For Father Le-

These epithets can hardly be classed with civilized weapons. They are burning arrows; they set fire to masses of popular prejudice, always obscuring the real question, sometimes destroying the attacking party. They are poisoned weapons. They pierce the hearts of loving women; they alienate dear children; they injure a man after life is ended, for they leave poisoned wounds in the hearts of those who loved him best—fears for his eternal salvation, dread of the Divine wrath upon him. Of course, in these days these weapons, though often effective in vexing good men and in scaring good women, are somewhat blunted; indeed, they not infrequently injure the assailants more than the assailed. So it was not in the days of Galileo; they were then in all their sharpness and venom.[23]

Yet a baser warfare was waged by the Archbishop of Pisa. This man, whose cathedral derives its most enduring fame from Galileo's deduction of a great natural law from the swinging lamp before its altar, was not an archbishop after the noble mould of Borromeo and Fénelon and Cheverus. Sadly enough for the Church and humanity, he was simply a zealot and intriguer: he perfected the plan for entrapping the great astronomer.

Galileo, after his discoveries had been denounced, had written to his friend Castelli and to the Grand-Duchess Christine two letters to show that his discoveries might be reconciled with Scripture. On a hint from the Inquisition at Rome, the archbishop sought to get hold of these letters and exhibit them as proofs that Galileo had uttered heretical views of theology and of Scripture, and thus to bring him into the clutch of the Inquisition. The archbishop begs Castelli, therefore, to let him see the original letter in the handwriting of Galileo. Castelli declines. The archbishop

---

cazre's argument, see Flammarion, *Mondes imaginaires et mondes réels*, 6e éd., pp. 315, 316. For Melanchthon's argument, see his *Initia*, in *Opera*, vol. iii, Halle, 1846.

[23] For curious exemplification of the way in which these weapons have been hurled, see lists of persons charged with "infidelity" and "atheism," in the *Dictionnaire des Athées*, Paris, [1800]; also Lecky, *History of Rationalism*, vol. ii, p. 50. For the case of Descartes, see Saisset, *Descartes et ses Précurseurs*, pp. 103, 110. For the facility with which the term "atheist" has been applied from the early Aryans down to believers in evolution, see Tylor, *Primitive Culture*, vol. i, p. 420.

then, while, as is now revealed, writing constantly and bitterly to the Inquisition against Galileo, professes to Castelli the greatest admiration of Galileo's genius and a sincere desire to know more of his discoveries. This not succeeding, the archbishop at last throws off the mask and resorts to open attack.

The whole struggle to crush Galileo and to save him would be amusing were it not so fraught with evil. There were intrigues and counter-intrigues, plots and counter-plots, lying and spying; and in the thickest of this seething, squabbling, screaming mass of priests, bishops, archbishops, and cardinals, appear two popes, Paul V and Urban VIII. It is most suggestive to see in this crisis of the Church, at the tomb of the prince of the apostles, on the eve of the greatest errors in Church policy the world has known, in all the intrigues and deliberations of these consecrated leaders of the Church, no more evidence of the guidance or presence of the Holy Spirit than in a caucus of New York politicians at Tammany Hall.

But the opposing powers were too strong. In 1615 Galileo was summoned before the Inquisition at Rome, and the mine which had been so long preparing was sprung. Sundry theologians of the Inquisition having been ordered to examine two propositions which had been extracted from Galileo's letters on the solar spots, solemnly considered these points during about a month and rendered their unanimous decision as follows: *"The first proposition, that the sun is the centre and does not revolve about the earth, is foolish, absurd, false in theology, and heretical, because expressly contrary to Holy Scripture"*; and *"the second proposition, that the earth is not the centre but revolves about the sun, is absurd, false in philosophy, and, from a theological point of view at least, opposed to the true faith."*

The Pope himself, Paul V, now intervened again: he ordered that Galileo be brought before the Inquisition. Then the greatest man of science in that age was brought face to face with the greatest theologian—Galileo was confronted by Bellarmin. Bellarmin shows Galileo the error of his opinion and orders him to renounce it. De Lauda, fortified by a letter from the Pope, gives orders that the astronomer be placed in the dungeons of the Inquisition should he refuse to yield. Bellarmin now commands Galileo, "in the name of His Holiness the Pope and the whole Congregation of the Holy Office, to relinquish altogether the opinion that the sun is the centre of the world and immovable, and that the earth moves, nor henceforth to hold, teach, or defend it in any way whatsoever, verbally or in writing." This injunction Galileo acquiesces in and promises to obey.[24]

This was on the 26th of February, 1616. About a fortnight later the Congregation of the Index, moved thereto, as the letters and documents now brought to light show, by Pope Paul V, solemnly rendered a decree that *"the doctrine of the double motion of the earth about its axis and about the sun is false, and entirely contrary to Holy Scripture"*; and that this opinion must neither be taught nor advocated. The same decree condemned all writings of Copernicus and *"all writings which affirm the motion of the earth."* The great work of Copernicus was interdicted until corrected in accordance with the views of the Inquisition; and the works of Galileo and Kepler, though not mentioned by name at that time, were included among those implicitly condemned as "affirming the motion of the earth."

The condemnations were inscribed upon the *Index;* and, finally, the papacy committed itself as an infallible judge and teacher to the world by prefixing to the *Index* the usual papal bull giving its monitions the most solemn papal sanction. To teach or even read the works denounced or passages condemned was to risk persecution in this world and damnation in the next. Science had apparently lost the decisive battle.

For a time after this judgment Galileo remained in Rome, apparently hoping to find some way out of this difficulty; but he soon discovered the hollowness of the protestations made to him by ecclesiastics, and, being recalled to Flor-

[24] I am aware that the theory proposed by Wohlwill and developed by Gebler denies that this promise was ever made by Galileo, and holds that the passage was a forgery devised later by the Church rulers to justify the proceedings of 1632 and 1633. This would make the conduct of the Church worse, but authorities as eminent consider the charge not proved. A careful examination of the documents seems to disprove it. [For the latest research on these and related matters, see Giorgio de Santillana, *The Crime of Galileo* (University of Chicago Press, 1955).—Ed.]

ence, remained in his hermitage near the city in silence, working steadily, indeed, but not publishing anything save by private letters to friends in various parts of Europe.

But at last a better vista seemed to open for him. Cardinal Barberini, who had seemed liberal and friendly, became pope under the name of Urban VIII. Galileo at this conceived new hopes, and allowed his continued allegiance to the Copernican system to be known. New troubles ensued. Galileo was induced to visit Rome again, and Pope Urban tried to cajole him into silence, personally taking the trouble to show him his errors by argument. Other opponents were less considerate, for works appeared attacking his ideas—works all the more unmanly, since their authors knew that Galileo was restrained by force from defending himself. Then, too, as if to accumulate proofs of the unfitness of the Church to take charge of advanced instruction, his salary as a professor at the University of Pisa was taken from him, and sapping and mining began. Just as the Archbishop of Pisa some years before had tried to betray him with honeyed words to the Inquisition, so now Father Grassi tried it, and, after various attempts to draw him out by flattery, suddenly denounced his scientific ideas as "leading to a denial of the Real Presence in the Eucharist."

For the final assault upon him a park of heavy artillery was at last wheeled into place. It may be seen on all the scientific battlefields. It consists of general denunciation; and in 1631 Father Melchior Inchofer, of the Jesuits, brought his artillery to bear upon Galileo with this declaration: "The opinion of the earth's motion is of all heresies the most abominable, the most pernicious, the most scandalous; the immovability of the earth is thrice sacred; argument against the immortality of the soul, the existence of God, and the incarnation, should be tolerated sooner than an argument to prove that the earth moves."

From the other end of Europe came a powerful echo. From the shadow of the Cathedral of Antwerp, the noted theologian Fromundus gave forth his famous treatise, the *Ant-Aristarchus*. Its very title-page was a contemptuous insult to the memory of Copernicus, since it paraded the assumption that the new truth was only an exploded theory of a pagan astronomer. Fromundus declares that "sacred Scripture fights against the Copernicans." To prove that the sun revolves about the earth, he cites the passage in the

Psalms which speaks of the sun "which cometh forth as a bridegroom out of his chamber." To prove that the earth stands still, he quotes a passage from Ecclesiastes, "The earth standeth fast forever." To show the utter futility of the Copernican theory, he declares that, if it were true, "the wind would constantly blow from the east"; and that "buildings and the earth itself would fly off with such a rapid motion that men would have to be provided with claws like cats to enable them to hold fast to the earth's surface." Greatest weapon of all, he works up, by the use of Aristotle and St. Thomas Aquinas, a demonstration from theology and science combined, that the earth *must* stand in the centre, and that the sun *must* revolve about it.[25] Nor was it merely fanatics who opposed the truth revealed by Copernicus; such strong men as Jean Bodin, in France, and Sir Thomas Browne, in England, declared against it as evidently contrary to Holy Scripture.

4. Victory of the Church Over Galileo

While news of triumphant attacks upon him and upon the truth he had established were coming in from all parts of Europe, Galileo prepared a careful treatise in the form of a dialogue, exhibiting the arguments for and against the Copernican and Ptolemaic systems, and offered to submit to any conditions that the Church tribunals might impose, if they would allow it to be printed. At last, after discussions which extended through eight years, they consented, imposing a humiliating condition—a preface written in accord-

[25] For Father Inchofer's attack, see his *Tractatus Syllepticus*, cited in Galileo's letter to Deodati, July 28, 1634. For Fromundus's more famous attack, see his *Ant-Aristarchus*, already cited, *passim*, but especially the heading of chapter vi, and the argument in chapters x and xi. A copy of this work may be found in the Astor Library at New York, and another in the White Library at Cornell University. For interesting reference to one of Fromundus's arguments, showing, by a mixture of mathematics and theology, that the earth is the centre of the universe, see Quetelet, *Histoire des Sciences mathématiques et physiques,* Bruxelles, 1864, p. 170; also Mädler, *Geschichte der Astronomie,* vol. i, p. 274. For Bodin's opposition to the Copernican theory, see Hallam, *Literature of Europe;* also Lecky. For Sir Thomas Browne, see his *Vulgar and Common Errors,* book iv, chap. v; and as to the real reason for his disbelief in the Copernican view, see Dr. Johnson's preface to his *Life of Browne,* vol. i, p. xix, of his collected works.

ance with the ideas of Father Ricciardi, Master of the Sacred Palace, and signed by Galileo, in which the Copernican theory was virtually exhibited as a play of the imagination, and not at all as opposed to the Ptolemaic doctrine reasserted in 1616 by the Inquisition under the direction of Pope Paul V.

This new work of Galileo—the *Dialogo*—appeared in 1632, and met with prodigious success. It put new weapons into the hands of the supporters of the Copernican theory. The pious preface was laughed at from one end of Europe to the other. This roused the enemy; the Jesuits, Dominicans, and the great majority of the clergy returned to the attack more violent than ever, and in the midst of them stood Pope Urban VIII, most bitter of all. His whole power was now thrown against Galileo. He was touched in two points: first, in his personal vanity, for Galileo had put the Pope's arguments into the mouth of one of the persons in the dialogue and their refutation into the mouth of another; but, above all, he was touched in his religious feelings. Again and again His Holiness insisted to all comers on the absolute and specific declarations of Holy Scripture, which prove that the sun and heavenly bodies revolve about the earth, and declared that to gainsay them is simply to dispute revelation. Certainly, if one ecclesiastic more than another ever seemed *not* under the care of the Spirit of Truth, it was Urban VIII in all this matter.

Herein was one of the greatest pieces of ill fortune that has ever befallen the older Church. Had Pope Urban been broad-minded and tolerant like Benedict XIV, or had he been taught moderation by adversity like Pius VII, or had he possessed the large scholarly qualities of Leo XIII, now reigning, the vast scandal of the Galileo case would never have burdened the Church: instead of devising endless quibbles and special pleadings to escape responsibility for this colossal blunder, its defenders could have claimed forever for the Church the glory of fearlessly initiating a great epoch in human thought.

But it was not so to be. Urban was not merely Pope; he was also a prince of the house of Barberini, and therefore doubly angry that his arguments had been publicly controverted.

The opening strategy of Galileo's enemies was to forbid the sale of his work; but this was soon seen to be unavailing, for the first edition had already been spread throughout Europe. Urban now became more angry than ever, and both Galileo and his works were placed in the hands of the Inquisition. In vain did the good Benedictine Castelli urge that Galileo was entirely respectful to the Church; in vain did he insist that "nothing that can be done can now hinder the earth from revolving." He was dismissed in disgrace, and Galileo was forced to appear in the presence of the dread tribunal without defender or adviser. There, as was so long concealed, but as is now fully revealed, he was menaced with torture again and again by express order of Pope Urban, and, as is also thoroughly established from the trial documents themselves, forced to abjure under threats, and subjected to imprisonment by command of the Pope; the Inquisition deferring in this whole matter to the papal authority. All the long series of attempts made in the supposed interest of the Church to mystify these transactions have at last failed. The world knows now that Galileo was subjected certainly to indignity, to imprisonment, and to threats equivalent to torture, and was at last forced to pronounce publicly and on his knees his recantation, as follows:

"I, Galileo, being in my seventieth year, being a prisoner and on my knees, and before your Eminences, having before my eyes the Holy Gospel, which I touch with my hands, abjure, curse, and detest the error and the heresy of the movement of the earth."[26]

He was vanquished indeed, for he had been forced, in the face of all coming ages, to perjure himself. To complete his dishonour, he was obliged to swear that he would denounce to the Inquisition any other man of science whom he should discover to be supporting the "heresy of the motion of the earth."

[26] For various utterances of Pope Urban against the Copernican theory at this period, see extracts from the original documents given by Gebler. For punishment of those who had shown some favour to Galileo, see various citations, and especially those from the Vatican manuscript, Gebler, p. 216. As to the text of the abjuration, see L'Épinois; also Polacco, *Anticopernicus*, etc., Venice, 1644; and for a discussion regarding its publication, see Favaro, *Miscellanea Galileana*, p. 804. It is not probable that torture in the ordinary sense was administered to Galileo, though it was threatened. See Th. Martin, *Vie de Galilée*, for a fair summing up of the case.

Many have wondered at this abjuration, and on account of it have denied to Galileo the title of martyr. But let such gainsayers consider the circumstances. Here was an old man—one who had reached the allotted threescore years and ten—broken with disappointments, worn out with labours and cares, dragged from Florence to Rome, with the threat from the Pope himself that if he delayed he should be "brought in chains"; sick in body and mind, given over to his oppressors by the Grand-Duke who ought to have protected him, and on his arrival in Rome threatened with torture. What the Inquisition was he knew well. He could remember as but of yesterday the burning of Giordano Bruno in that same city for scientific and philosophic heresy; he could remember, too, that only eight years before this very time De Dominis, Archbishop of Spalatro, having been seized by the Inquisition for scientific and other heresies, had died in a dungeon, and that his body and his writings had been publicly burned.

To the end of his life—nay, after his life was ended—the persecution of Galileo was continued. He was kept in exile from his family, from his friends, from his noble employments, and was held rigidly to his promise not to speak of his theory. When, in the midst of intense bodily sufferings from disease, and mental sufferings from calamities in his family, he besought some little liberty, he was met with threats of committal to a dungeon. When, at last, a special commission had reported to the ecclesiastical authorities that he had become blind and wasted with disease and sorrow, he was allowed a little more liberty, but that little was hampered by close surveillance. He was forced to bear contemptible attacks on himself and on his works in silence; to see the men who had befriended him severely punished; Father Castelli banished; Ricciardi, the Master of the Sacred Palace, and Ciampoli, the papal secretary, thrown out of their positions by Pope Urban, and the Inquisitor at Florence reprimanded for having given permission to print Galileo's work. He lived to see the truths he had established carefully weeded out from all the Church colleges and universities in Europe; and, when in a scientific work he happened to be spoken of as "renowned," the Inquisition ordered the substitution of the word "notorious."[27]

[27] For the substitution of the word "notorious" for "renowned" by order of the Inquisition, see Martin, p. 227.

And now measures were taken to complete the destruction of the Copernican theory, with Galileo's proofs of it. On the 16th of June, 1633, the Holy Congregation, with the permission of the reigning Pope, ordered the sentence upon Galileo, and his recantation, to be sent to all the papal nuncios throughout Europe, as well as to all archbishops, bishops, and inquisitors in Italy; and this document gave orders that the sentence and abjuration be made known "to your vicars, that you and all professors of philosophy and mathematics may have knowledge of it, that they may know why we proceeded against the said Galileo, and recognise the gravity of his error, in order that they may avoid it, and thus not incur the penalties which they would have to suffer in case they fell into the same."[28]

As a consequence, the professors of mathematics and astronomy in various universities of Europe were assembled and these documents were read to them. To the theological authorities this gave great satisfaction. The Rector of the University of Douay, referring to the opinion of Galileo, wrote to the papal nuncio at Brussels: "The professors of our university are so opposed to this fanatical opinion that they have always held that it must be banished from the schools. In our English college at Douay this paradox has never been approved and never will be."

Still another step was taken: the Inquisitors were ordered, especially in Italy, not to permit the publication of a new edition of any of Galileo's works, or of any similar writings. On the other hand, theologians were urged, now that Copernicus and Galileo and Kepler were silenced, to reply to them with tongue and pen. Europe was flooded with these theological refutations of the Copernican system.

To make all complete, there was prefixed to the *Index* of the Church, forbidding "all writings which affirm the motion of the earth," a bull signed by the reigning Pope, which, by virtue of his infallibility as a divinely guided teacher in matters of faith and morals, clinched this condemnation into the consciences of the whole Christian world.

From the mass of books which appeared under the auspices of the Church immediately after the condemnation of Galileo, for the purpose of rooting out every vestige of the hated

[28] For a copy of this document, see Gebler, p. 269. As to the spread of this and similar documents notifying Europe of Galileo's condemnation, see Favaro, pp. 804, 805.

Copernican theory from the mind of the world, two may be taken as typical. The first of these was a work by Scipio Chiaramonti, dedicated to Cardinal Barberini. Among his arguments against the double motion of the earth may be cited the following:

"Animals, which move, have limbs and muscles; the earth has no limbs or muscles, therefore it does not move. It is angels who make Saturn, Jupiter, the sun, etc., turn round. If the earth revolves, it must also have an angel in the centre to set it in motion; but only devils live there; it would therefore be a devil who would impart motion to the earth. . . .

"The planets, the sun, the fixed stars, all belong to one species—namely, that of stars. It seems, therefore, to be a grievous wrong to place the earth, which is a sink of impurity, among these heavenly bodies, which are pure and divine things."

The next, which I select from the mass of similar works, is the *Anticopernicus Catholicus* of Polacco. It was intended to deal a finishing stroke at Galileo's heresy. In this it is declared:

"The Scripture always represents the earth as at rest, and the sun and moon as in motion; or, if these latter bodies are ever represented as at rest, Scripture represents this as the result of a great miracle. . . .

"These writings must be prohibited, because they teach certain principles about the position and motion of the terrestrial globe repugnant to Holy Scripture and to the Catholic interpretation of it, not as hypotheses but as established facts. . . ."

Speaking of Galileo's book, Polacco says that it "smacked of Copernicanism," and that, "when this was shown to the Inquisition, Galileo was thrown into prison and was compelled to utterly abjure the baseness of this erroneous dogma."

As to the authority of the cardinals in their decree, Polacco asserts that, since they are the "Pope's Council" and his "brothers," their work is one, except that the Pope is favoured with special divine enlightenment.

Having shown that the authority of the Scriptures, of popes, and of cardinals is against the new astronomy, he gives a refutation based on physics. He asks: "If we concede the motion of the earth, why is it that an arrow shot into the air falls back to the same spot, while the earth and all things on it have in the meantime moved very rapidly toward the east? Who does not see that great confusion would result from this motion?"

Next he argues from metaphysics, as follows: "The Copernican theory of the earth's motion is against the nature of the earth itself, because the earth is not only cold but contains in itself the principle of cold; but cold is opposed to motion, and even destroys it—as is evident in animals, which become motionless when they become cold."

Finally, he clinches all with a piece of theological reasoning, as follows: "Since it can certainly be gathered from Scripture that the heavens move above the earth, and since a circular motion requires something immovable around which to move, . . . the earth is at the centre of the universe."[29]

But any sketch of the warfare between theology and science in this field would be incomplete without some reference to the treatment of Galileo after his death. He had begged to be buried in his family tomb in Santa Croce; this request was denied. His friends wished to erect a monument over him; this, too, was refused. Pope Urban said to the ambassador Niccolini that "it would be an evil example for the world if such honours were rendered to a man who had been brought before the Roman Inquisition for an opinion so false and erroneous; who had communicated it to many others, and who had given so great a scandal to Christendom." In accordance, therefore, with the wish of the Pope and the orders of the Inquisition, Galileo was buried ignobly, apart from his family, without fitting ceremony, without monument, without epitaph. Not until forty years after did Pierrozzi dare write an inscription to be placed above his bones; not until a hundred years after did Nelli dare transfer his remains to a suitable position in Santa Croce, and erect a monument above them. Even then the old conscientious hostility burst forth: the Inquisition was besought to prevent such honours to "a man condemned for notorious errors"; and that tribunal refused to allow any epitaph to be placed above him which had not been submitted to its censorship. Nor has that old conscientious consistency in hatred yet fully

[29] For Chiaramonti's book and selections given, see Gebler as above, p. 271. For Polacco, see his work as cited, especially Assertiones i, ii, vii, xi, xiii, lxxiii, clxxxvii, and others. The work is in the White Library at Cornell University. The date of it is 1644.

relented: hardly a generation since has not seen some ecclesiastic, like Marini or De Bonald or Rallaye or De Gabriac,
suppressing evidence, or torturing expressions, or inventing
theories to blacken the memory of Galileo and save the
reputation of the Church. Nay, more: there are school histories, widely used, which, in the supposed interest of the
Church, misrepresent in the grossest manner all these transactions in which Galileo was concerned. *Sancta simplicitas!*
The Church has no worse enemies than those who devise
and teach these perversions. They are simply rooting out,
in the long run, from the minds of the more thoughtful
scholars, respect for the great organization which such writings are supposed to serve.[30]

The Protestant Church was hardly less energetic against
this new astronomy than the mother Church. The sacred
science of the first Lutheran Reformers was transmitted as
a precious legacy, and in the next century was made much
of by Calovius. His great learning and determined orthodoxy gave him the Lutheran leadership. Utterly refusing
to look at ascertained facts, he cited the turning back of the
shadow upon King Hezekiah's dial and the standing still
of the sun for Joshua, denied the movement of the earth,
and denounced the whole new view as clearly opposed to
Scripture. To this day his arguments are repeated by sundry orthodox leaders of American Lutheranism.

As to the other branches of the Reformed Church, we
have already seen how Calvinists, Anglicans, and, indeed,
Protestant sectarians generally, opposed the new truth.[31] In
England, among the strict churchmen, the great Dr. South
denounced the Royal Society as "irreligious," and among
the Puritans the eminent John Owen declared that New-

---

[30] For the persecutions of Galileo's memory after his death, see
Gebler and Wohlwill, but especially Th. Martin, p. 243 and chaps.
ix and x. For documentary proofs, see L'Épinois. For a collection
of the slanderous theories invented against Galileo, see Martin,
final chapters and appendix. Both these authors are devoted to the
Church, but, unlike Monsignor Marini, are too upright to resort to
the pious fraud of suppressing documents or interpolating pretended
facts.

[31] For Calovius, see Zoeckler, *Geschichte,* vol. i, pp. 684 and 763.
For Calvin and Turretin, see Shields, *The Final Philosophy,* pp. 60,
61.

ton's discoveries were "built on fallible phenomena and advanced by many arbitrary presumptions against evident testimonies of Scripture." Even Milton seems to have hesitated between the two systems. At the beginning of the eighth book of *Paradise Lost* he makes Adam state the difficulties of the Ptolemaic system, and then brings forward an angel to make the usual orthodox answers. Later, Milton seems to lean toward the Copernican theory, for, referring to the earth, he says:

> "Or she from west her silent course advance
> With inoffensive pace, that spinning sleeps
> On her soft axle, while she faces even
> And bears thee soft with the smooth air along."

English orthodoxy continued to assert itself. In 1724 John Hutchinson, professor at Cambridge, published his *Moses' Principia,* a system of philosophy in which he sought to build up a complete physical system of the universe from the Bible. In this he assaulted the Newtonian theory as "atheistic," and led the way for similar attacks by such Church teachers as Horne, Duncan Forbes, and Jones of Nayland. But one far greater than these involved himself in this view. That same limitation of his reason by the simple statements of Scripture which led John Wesley to declare that, "unless witchcraft is true, nothing in the Bible is true," led him, while giving up the Ptolemaic theory and accepting in a general way the Copernican, to suspect the demonstrations of Newton. Happily, his inborn nobility of character lifted him above any bitterness or persecuting spirit, or any imposition of doctrinal tests which could prevent those who came after him from finding their way to the truth.

But in the midst of this vast expanse of theologic error signs of right reason began to appear, both in England and America. Noteworthy is it that Cotton Mather, bitter as was his orthodoxy regarding witchcraft, accepted, in 1721, the modern astronomy fully, with all its consequences.

In the following year came an even more striking evidence that the new scientific ideas were making their way in England. In 1722 Thomas Burnet published the sixth edition of his *Sacred Theory of the Earth.* In this he argues, as usual, to establish the scriptural doctrine of the earth's stability; but in his preface he sounds a remarkable warning. He mentions the great mistake into which St. Augustine led the Church regarding the doctrine of the antipodes, and says, "If within a few years or in the next generation it should prove as certain and demonstrable that the earth is moved, as it is now that there are antipodes, those that have been zealous against it, and engaged the Scripture in the controversy, would have the same reason to repent of their forwardness that St. Augustine would now, if he were still alive."

Fortunately, too, Protestantism had no such power to oppose the development of the Copernican ideas as the older Church had enjoyed. Yet there were some things in its warfare against science even more indefensible. In 1772 the famous English expedition for scientific discovery sailed from England under Captain Cook. Greatest by far of all the scientific authorities chosen to accompany it was Dr. Priestley. Sir Joseph Banks had especially invited him. But the clergy of Oxford and Cambridge interfered. Priestley was considered unsound in his views of the Trinity; it was evidently suspected that this might vitiate his astronomical observations; he was rejected, and the expedition crippled.

The orthodox view of astronomy lingered on in other branches of the Protestant Church. In Germany even Leibnitz attacked the Newtonian theory of gravitation on theological grounds, though he found some little consolation in thinking that it might be used to support the Lutheran doctrine of consubstantiation.

In Holland the Calvinistic Church was at first strenuous against the whole new system, but we possess a comical proof that Calvinism even in its strongholds was powerless against it; for in 1642 Blaeu published at Amsterdam his book on the use of globes, and, in order to be on the safe side, devoted one part of his work to the Ptolemaic and the other to the Copernican scheme, leaving the benevolent reader to take his choice.[32]

[32] For the attitude of Leibnitz, Hutchinson, and the others named toward the Newtonian theory, see Lecky, *History of England in the Eighteenth Century,* chap. ix. For John Wesley, see his *Compendium of Natural Philosophy, being a Survey of the Wisdom of God in the Creation,* London, 1784. See also Leslie Stephen, *Eighteenth Century,* vol. ii, p. 413. For Owen, see his *Works,* vol. xix, p. 310. For Cotton Mather's view, see *The Christian Philosopher,* London,

Nor have efforts to renew the battle in the Protestant Church been wanting in these latter days. The attempt in the Church of England, in 1864, to fetter science, which was brought to ridicule by Herschel, Bowring, and De Morgan; the assemblage of Lutheran clergy at Berlin, in 1868, to protest against "science falsely so called," are examples of these. Fortunately, to the latter came Pastor Knak, and his denunciations of the Copernican theory as absolutely incompatible with a belief in the Bible, dissolved the whole assemblage in ridicule.

In its recent dealings with modern astronomy the wisdom of the Catholic Church in the more civilized countries has prevented its yielding to some astounding errors into which one part of the Protestant Church has fallen heedlessly.

Though various leaders in the older Church have committed the absurd error of allowing a text-book and sundry review articles to appear which grossly misstate the Galileo episode, with the certainty of ultimately undermining confidence in her teachings among her more thoughtful young men, she has kept clear of the folly of continuing to tie her instruction, and the acceptance of our sacred books, to an adoption of the Ptolemaic theory.

Not so with American Lutheranism. In 1873 was published in St. Louis, at the publishing house of the Lutheran Synod of Missouri, a work entitled *Astronomische Unterredung,* the author being well known as a late president of a Lutheran Teachers' Seminary.

No attack on the whole modern system of astronomy could be more bitter. On the first page of the introduction the author, after stating the two theories, asks, "Which is right?" and says: "It would be very simple to me which is right, if it were only a question of human import. But the wise and truthful God has expressed Himself on this matter in the Bible. The entire Holy Scripture settles the question that the earth is the principal body *(Hauptkörper)* of the universe, that it stands fixed, and that sun and moon only serve to light it."

The author then goes on to show from Scripture the

1721, especially pp. 16 and 17. For the case of Priestley, see Weld, *History of the Royal Society,* vol. ii, p. 56, for the facts and the admirable letter of Priestley upon this rejection. For Blaeu, see his *L'Usage des Globes,* Amsterdam, 1642.

folly, not only of Copernicus and Newton, but of a long line of great astronomers in more recent times. He declares: "Let no one understand me as inquiring first where truth is to be found—in the Bible or with the astronomers. No; I know that beforehand—that my God never lies, never makes a mistake; out of his mouth comes only truth, when he speaks of the structure of the universe, of the earth, sun, moon, and stars. . . .

"Because the truth of the Holy Scripture is involved in this, therefore the above question is of the highest importance to me. . . . Scientists and others lean upon the miserable reed *(Rohrstab)* that God teaches only the order of salvation, but not the order of the universe."

Very noteworthy is the fact that this late survival of an ancient belief based upon text-worship is found, not in the teachings of any zealous priest of the mother Church, but in those of an eminent professor in that branch of Protestantism which claims special enlightenment.[33]

Nor has the warfare against the dead champions of science been carried on by the older Church alone.

On the 10th of May, 1859, Alexander von Humboldt was buried. His labours had been among the glories of the century, and his funeral was one of the most imposing that Berlin had ever seen. Among those who honoured themselves by their presence was the prince regent, afterward the Emperor William I; but of the clergy it was observed that none were present save the officiating clergyman and a few regarded as unorthodox.[34]

5. Results of the Victory Over Galileo

We return now to the sequel of the Galileo case.

Having gained their victory over Galileo, living and dead, having used it to scare into submission the professors of astronomy throughout Europe, conscientious churchmen

[33] For the amusing details of the attempt in the English Church to repress science, and of the way in which it was met, see De Morgan, *Paradoxes,* p. 42. For Pastor Knak and his associates, see the *Revue des Deux Mondes,* 1868. Of the recent Lutheran works against the Copernican astronomy, see especially the *Astronomische Unterredung zwischen einem Liebhaber der Astronomie und mehreren berühmten Astronomer der Neuzeit,* by J. C. W. L., St. Louis, 1873.
[34] See Brühns and Lassell, *Life of Humboldt,* London, 1873, vol. ii, p. 411.

exulted. Loud was their rejoicing that the "heresy," the "infidelity," the "atheism" involved in believing that the earth revolves about its axis and moves around the sun had been crushed by the great tribunal of the Church, acting in strict obedience to the expressed will of one Pope and the written order of another. As we have seen, all books teaching this hated belief were put upon the *Index* of books forbidden to Christians, and that *Index* was prefaced by a bull enforcing this condemnation upon the consciences of the faithful throughout the world, and signed by the reigning Pope.

The losses to the world during this complete triumph of theology were even more serious than at first appears: one must especially be mentioned. There was then in Europe one of the greatest thinkers ever given to mankind—René Descartes. Mistaken though many of his reasonings were, they bore a rich fruitage of truth. He had already done a vast work. His theory of vortices—assuming a uniform material regulated by physical laws—as the beginning of the visible universe, though it was but a provisional hypothesis, had ended the whole old theory of the heavens with the vaulted firmament and the direction of the planetary movements by angels, which even Kepler had allowed. The scientific warriors had stirred new life in him, and he was working over and summing up in his mighty mind all the researches of his time. The result would have made an epoch in history. His aim was to combine all knowledge and thought into a *Treatise on the World,* and in view of this he gave eleven years to the study of anatomy alone. But the fate of Galileo robbed him of all hope, of all courage; the battle seemed lost; he gave up his great plan forever.[35]

But ere long it was seen that this triumph of the Church was in reality a prodigious defeat. From all sides came proofs that Copernicus and Galileo were right; and although Pope Urban and the Inquisition held Galileo in strict seclusion, forbidding him even to *speak* regarding the double mo-

[35] For Descartes's discouragement, see Humboldt, *Cosmos,* London, 1851, vol. iii, p. 21; also Lange, *Geschichte des Materialismus,* English translation, vol. i, pp. 248, 249, where the letters of Descartes are given, showing his despair, and the relinquishment of his best thoughts and works in order to preserve peace with the Church: also Saisset, *Descartes et ses Précurseurs,* pp. 100 *et seq.*; also Jolly, *Histoire du Mouvement intellectuel au XVIe Siècle,* vol. i, p. 390.

tion of the earth; and although this condemnation of "all books which affirm the motion of the earth" was kept on the *Index;* and although the papal bull still bound the *Index* and the condemnations in it on the consciences of the faithful; and although colleges and universities under Church control were compelled to teach to old doctrine—it was seen by clear-sighted men everywhere that this victory of the Church was a disaster to the victors.

New champions pressed on. Campanella, full of vagaries as he was, wrote his *Apology for Galileo,* though for that and other heresies, religious and political, he seven times underwent torture.

And Kepler comes: he leads science on to greater victories. Copernicus, great as he was, could not disentangle scientific reasoning entirely from the theological bias: the doctrines of Aristotle and Thomas Aquinas as to the necessary superiority of the circle had vitiated the minor features of his system, and left breaches in it through which the enemy was not slow to enter; but Kepler sees these errors, and by wonderful genius and vigour he gives to the world the three laws which bear his name, and this fortress of science is complete.[36] He thinks and speaks as one inspired. His battle is severe. He is solemnly warned by the Protestant Consistory of Stuttgart "not to throw Christ's kingdom into confusion with his silly fancies," and as solemnly ordered to "bring his theory of the world into harmony with Scripture": he is sometimes abused, sometimes ridiculed, sometimes imprisoned. Protestants in Styria and Würtemberg, Catholics in Austria and Bohemia, press upon him; but Newton, Halley, Bradley, and other great astronomers follow, and to science remains the victory.[37]

[36] [For further treatments of Kepler, here rather thinly dealt with, see Max Caspar, *Johannes Kepler* (Stuttgart, 1948; also recently translated into English, paper edition, Collier Books, 1961) as well as the provocative book by Arthur Koestler, *The Watershed: A Biography of Johannes Kepler* (Doubleday Anchor, 1960).—Ed.]
[37] For Campanella, see Amabile, *Fra Tommaso Campanella,* Naples, 1882, especially vol. iii; also Libri, vol. iv, pp. 149 *et seq.* Fromundus, speaking of Kepler's explanation, says, *"Vix teneo ebullientem risum."* This is almost equal to the *New York Church Journal,* speaking of John Stuart Mill as "that small sciolist," and of the preface to Dr. Draper's great work as "chippering." How a journal, generally so fair in its treatment of such subjects, can con-

Yet this did not end the war. During the seventeenth century, in France, after all the splendid proofs added by Kepler, no one dared openly teach the Copernican theory, and Cassini, the great astronomer, never declared for it. In 1672 the Jesuit Father Riccioli declared that there were precisely forty-nine arguments for the Copernican theory and seventy-seven against it. Even after the beginning of the eighteenth century—long after the demonstrations of Sir Isaac Newton—Bossuet, the great Bishop of Meaux, the foremost theologian that France has ever produced, declared it contrary to Scripture.

Nor did matters seem to improve rapidly during that century. In England, John Hutchinson, as we have seen, published in 1724 his *Moses' Principia* maintaining that the Hebrew Scriptures are a perfect system of natural philosophy, and are opposed to the Newtonian system of gravitation; and, as we have also seen, he was followed by a long list of noted men in the Church. In France, two eminent mathematicians published in 1748 an edition of Newton's *Principia;* but, in order to avert ecclesiastical censure, they felt obliged to prefix to it a statement absolutely false. Three years later, Boscovich, the great mathematician of the Jesuits, used these words: "As for me, full of respect for the Holy Scriptures and the decree of the Holy Inquisition, I regard the earth as immovable; nevertheless, for simplicity in explanation I will argue as if the earth moves; for it is proved that of the two hypotheses the appearances favour this idea."

In Germany, especially in the Protestant part of it, the war was even more bitter, and it lasted through the first half of the eighteenth century. Eminent Lutheran doctors of divinity flooded the country with treatises to prove that the Copernican theory could not be reconciled with Scripture. In the theological seminaries and in many of the universities where clerical influence was strong they seemed to sweep all before them;

descend to such weapons, is one of the wonders of modern journalism. For the persecution of Kepler, see Heller, *Geschichte der Physik,* vol. i, pp. 281 *et seq.*; also Reuschle, *Kepler und die Astronomie,* Frankfurt a. M., 1871, pp. 87 *et seq.*; also Prof. Sigwart, *Kleine Schriften,* pp. 211 *et seq.* There is poetic justice in the fact that these two last-named books come from Würtemberg professors. See also *The New-Englander* for March, 1884, p. 178.

and yet at the middle of the century we find some of the clearest-headed of them aware of the fact that their cause was lost.[38]

In 1757 the most enlightened perhaps in the whole line of the popes, Benedict XIV, took up the matter, and the Congregation of the *Index* secretly allowed the ideas of Copernicus to be tolerated. Yet in 1765 Lalande, the great French astronomer, tried in vain at Rome to induce the authorities to remove Galileo's works from the *Index*. Even at a date far within our own nineteenth century the authorities of many universities in Catholic Europe, and especially those in Spain, excluded the Newtonian system. In 1771 the greatest of them all, the University of Salamanca, being urged to teach physical science, refused, making answer as follows: "Newton teaches nothing that would make a good logician or metaphysician; and Gassendi and Descartes do not agree so well with revealed truth as Aristotle does."

Vengeance upon the dead also has continued far into our own century. On the 5th of May, 1829, a great multitude assembled at Warsaw to honour the memory of Copernicus and to unveil Thorwaldsen's statue of him.

Copernicus had lived a pious, Christian life; he had been beloved for unostentatious Christian charity; with his religious belief no fault had ever been found; he was a canon of the Church at Frauenberg, and over his grave had been written the most touching of Christian epitaphs. Naturally, then, the people expected a religious service; all was understood to be arranged for it; the procession marched to the church and waited. The hour passed, and no priest appeared; none could be induced to appear. Copernicus, gentle, charitable, pious, one of the noblest gifts of God to religion as well as to science, was evidently still under the ban. Five years after

[38] For Cassini's position, see Henri Martin, *Histoire de France,* vol. xiii, p. 175. For Riccioli, see Daunou, *Études Historiques,* vol. ii, p. 439. For Bossuet, see Bertrand, p. 41. For Hutchinson, see Lyell, *Principles of Geology,* p. 48. For Wesley, see his work, already cited. As to Boscovich, his declaration, mentioned in the text, was in 1746, but in 1785 he seemed to feel his position in view of history, and apologized abjectly: Bertrand, pp. 60, 61. See also Whewell's notice of Le Sueur and Jacquier's introduction to their edition of Newton's *Principia.* For the struggle in Germany, see Zoeckler, *Geschichte der Beziehungen zwischen Theologie und Naturwissenschaft,* vol. ii, pp. 45 *et seq.*

that, his book was still standing on the *Index* of books prohibited to Christians.

The edition of the *Index* published in 1819 was as inexorable toward the works of Copernicus and Galileo as its predecessors had been; but in the year 1820 came a crisis. Canon Settele, Professor of Astronomy at Rome, had written an elementary book in which the Copernican system was taken for granted. The Master of the Sacred Palace, Anfossi, as censor of the press, refused to allow the book to be printed unless Settele revised his work and treated the Copernican theory as merely a hypothesis. On this Settele appealed to Pope Pius VII, and the Pope referred the matter to the Congregation of the Holy Office. At last, on the 16th of August, 1820, it was decided that Settele might teach the Copernican system as established, and this decision was approved by the Pope. This aroused considerable discussion, but finally, on the 11th of September, 1822, the cardinals of the Holy Inquisition graciously agreed that "the printing and publication of works treating of the motion of the earth and the stability of the sun, in accordance with the general opinion of modern astronomers, is permitted at Rome." This decree was ratified by Pius VII, but it was not until thirteen years later, in 1835, that there was issued an edition of the *Index* from which the condemnation of works defending the double motion of the earth was left out.

This was not a moment too soon, for, as if the previous proofs had not been sufficient, each of the motions of the earth was now absolutely demonstrated anew, so as to be recognised by the ordinary observer. The parallax of fixed stars, shown by Bessel as well as other noted astronomers in 1838, clinched forever the doctrine of the revolution of the earth around the sun, and in 1851 the great experiment of Foucault with the pendulum showed to the human eye the earth in motion around its own axis. To make the matter complete, this experiment was publicly made in one of the churches at Rome by the eminent astronomer, Father Secchi, of the Jesuits, in 1852—just two hundred and twenty years after the Jesuits had done so much to secure Galileo's condemnation.[39]

[39] For good statements of the final action of the Church in the matter, see Gebler; also Zoeckler, ii, 352. See also Bertrand, *Fondateurs de l'Astronomie moderne*, p. 61; Flammarion, *Vie de Copernic*, chap. ix. As to the time when the decree of condemnation was re-

6. The Retreat of the Church after Its Victory Over Galileo

* * *

Nothing is more unjust than to cast especial blame for all this resistance to science upon the Roman Church. The Protestant Church, though rarely able to be so severe, has been more blameworthy. The persecution of Galileo and his compeers by the older Church was mainly at the beginning of the seventeenth century; the persecution of Robertson Smith, and Winchell, and Woodrow, and Toy, and the young professors at Beyrout, by various Protestant authorities, was near the end of the nineteenth century. Those earlier persecutions by Catholicism were strictly in accordance with principles held at that time by all religionists, Catholic and Protestant, throughout the world; these later persecutions by Protestants were in defiance of principles which all Protestants to-day hold or pretend to hold, and none make louder claim to hold them than the very sects which persecuted these eminent Christian men of our day, men whose crime was that they were intelligent enough to accept the science of their time, and honest enough to acknowledge it.

Most unjustly, then, would Protestantism taunt Catholicism for excluding knowledge of astronomical truths from Euro-

---

pealed, there have been various pious attempts to make it earlier than the reality. Artaud, p. 307, cited in an apologetic article in the *Dublin Review,* September, 1865, says that Galileo's famous dialogue was published in 1714, at Padua, entire, and with the usual approbations. The same article also declares that in 1818 the ecclesiastical decrees were repealed by Pius VII in full Consistory. Whewell accepts this; but Cantu, an authority favourable to the Church, acknowledges that Copernicus's work remained on the *Index* as late as 1835 (Cantu, *Histoire universelle,* vol. xv, p. 483); and with this Th. Martin, not less favourable to the Church, but exceedingly careful as to the facts, agrees; and the most eminent authority of all, Prof. Reusch, of Bonn, in his *Der Index der verbotenen Bücher,* Bonn, 1885, vol. ii, p. 396, confirms the above statement in the text. For a clear statement of Bradley's exquisite demonstration of the Copernican theory by reasonings upon the rapidity of light, etc., and Foucault's exhibition of the rotation of the earth by the pendulum experiment, see Hoefer, *Histoire de l'Astronomie,* pp. 492 et seq. For more recent proofs of the Copernican theory, by the discoveries of Bunsen, Bischoff, Benzenburg, and others, see Jevons, *Principles of Science.*

pean Catholic universities in the seventeenth and eighteenth centuries, while real knowledge of geological and biological and anthropological truth is denied or pitifully diluted in so many American Protestant colleges and universities in the nineteenth century.

Nor has Protestantism the right to point with scorn to the Catholic *Index,* and to lay stress on the fact that nearly every really important book in the last three centuries has been forbidden by it, so long as young men in so many American Protestant universities and colleges are nursed with "ecclesiastical pap" rather than with real thought, and directed to the works of "solemnly constituted impostors," or to sundry "approved courses of reading," while they are studiously kept aloof from such leaders in modern thought as Darwin, Spencer, Huxley, Draper, and Lecky.

It may indeed be justly claimed by Protestantism that some of the former strongholds of her bigotry have become liberalized; but, on the other hand, Catholicism can point to the fact that Pope Leo XIII, now happily reigning, has made a noble change as regards open dealing with documents. The days of Monsignor Marini, it may be hoped, are gone. The Vatican Library, with its masses of historical material, has been thrown open to Protestant and Catholic scholars alike, and this privilege has been freely used by men representing all shades of religious thought.

As to the older errors, the whole civilized world was at fault, Protestant as well as Catholic. It was not the fault of religion; it was the fault of that short-sighted linking of theological dogmas to scriptural texts which, in utter defiance of the words and works of the Blessed Founder of Christianity, narrow-minded, loud-voiced men are ever prone to substitute for religion. Justly is it said by one of the most eminent among contemporary Anglican divines, that "it is because they have mistaken the dawn for a conflagration that theologians have so often been foes of light."[40]

[40] For an exceedingly striking statement, by a Roman Catholic historian of genius, as to the *popular* demand for persecution and the pressure of the lower strata in ecclesiastical organizations for cruel measures, see Balmès's *Le Protestantisme comparé au Catholicisme,* etc., fourth edition, Paris, 1855, vol. ii. Archbishop Spaulding has something of the same sort in his *Miscellanies.* L'Épinois, *Galilée,* pp. 22 *et seq.,* stretches this as far as possible to save the reputation of the Church in the Galileo matter. As to the various

Chapter 4

From "Signs and Wonders" to Law in the Heavens

1. The Theological View

FEW THINGS in the evolution of astronomy are more suggestive than the struggle between the theological and the scientific doctrine regarding comets—the passage from the conception of them as fire-balls flung by an angry God for the purpose of scaring a wicked world, to a recognition of them as natural in origin and obedient to law in movement. Hardly anything throws a more vivid light upon the danger of wresting texts of Scripture to preserve ideas which observation and thought have superseded, and upon the folly of arraying ecclesiastical power against scientific discovery.[1]

Out of the ancient world had come a mass of beliefs regarding comets, meteors, and eclipses; all these were held to be signs displayed from heaven for the warning of mankind. Stars and meteors were generally thought to presage happy events, especially the births of gods, heroes, and great men. So firmly rooted was this idea that we constantly find among

branches of the Protestant Church in England and the United States, it is a matter of notoriety that the smug, well-to-do laymen, whether elders, deacons, or vestrymen, are, as a rule, far more prone to heresy-hunting than are their better educated pastors. As to the cases of Messrs. Winchell, Woodrow, Toy, and the professors at Beyrout, with details, see the chapter in this series on *The Fall of Man and Anthropology*. Among Protestant historians who have been recently allowed full and free examination of the treasures in the Vatican Library, and even those involving questions between Catholicism and Protestantism, are Von Sybel, of Berlin, and Philip Schaff, of New York. It should be added that the latter went with commendatory letters from eminent prelates of the Catholic Church in Europe and America. For the closing citation, see Canon Farrar, *History of Interpretation,* p. 432.

[1] The present study, after its appearance in the *Popular Science Monthly* as a "new chapter in the Warfare of Science," was revised and enlarged to nearly its present form, and read before the American Historical Association, among whose papers it was published, in 1887, under the title of *A History of the Doctrine of Comets*.

the ancient nations traditions of lights in the heavens preceding the birth of persons of note. The sacred books of India show that the births of Crishna and of Buddha were announced by such heavenly lights.[2] The sacred books of China tell of similar appearances at the births of Yu, the founder of the first dynasty, and of the inspired sage, Lao-tse. According to the Jewish legends, a star appeared at the birth of Moses, and was seen by the Magi of Egypt, who informed the king; and when Abraham was born an unusual star appeared in the east. The Greeks and Romans cherished similar traditions. A heavenly light accompanied the birth of Æsculapius, and the births of various Cæsars were heralded in like manner.[3]

The same conception entered into our Christian sacred books. Of all the legends which grew in such luxuriance and beauty about the cradle of Jesus of Nazareth, none appeals more directly to the highest poetic feeling than that given by one of the evangelists, in which a star, rising in the east, conducted the wise men to the manger where the Galilean peasant-child—the Hope of Mankind, the Light of the World— was lying in poverty and helplessness.

Among the Mohammedans we have a curious example of the same tendency toward a kindly interpretation of stars and meteors, in the belief of certain Mohammedan teachers that

[2] For Crishna, see Cox, *Aryan Mythology,* vol. ii, p. 133; the *Vishnu Purana* (Wilson's translation), book v, chap. iv. As to lights at the birth, or rather at the conception, of Buddha, see Bunsen, *Angel Messiah,* pp. 22, 23; Alabaster, *Wheel of the Law* (illustrations of Buddhism), p. 102; Edwin Arnold, *Light of Asia;* Bp. Bigandet, *Life of Gaudama,* the Burmese Buddha, p. 30; Oldenberg, *Buddha* (English translation), part i, chap. ii.

[3] For Chinese legends regarding stars at the birth of Yu and Lao-tse, see Thornton, *History of China,* vol. i, p. 137; also Pingré, *Cométographie,* p. 245. Regarding stars at the births of Moses and Abraham, see Calmet, *Fragments,* part viii; Baring-Gould, *Legends of Old Testament Characters,* chap. xxiv; Farrar, *Life of Christ,* chap. iii. As to the Magi, see Higgins, *Anacalypsis;* Hooykaas, Ort, and Kuenen, *Bible for Learners,* vol. iii. For Greek and Roman traditions, see Bell, *Pantheon,* s. v. *Æsculapius* and *Atreus;* Gibbon, *Decline and Fall,* vol. i, pp. 151, 590; Farrar, *Life of Christ* (Amer. ed.), p. 52; Cox, *Tales of Ancient Greece,* pp. 41, 61, 62; Higgins, *Anacalypsis,* vol. i, p. 322; also Suetonius, *Caes.,* Julius, p. 88, Claud., p. 463; Seneca, *Nat. Quaest.,* vol. i, p. 1; Virgil, *Ecl.,* vol. ix, p. 47; as well as Ovid, Pliny, and others.

meteoric showers are caused by good angels hurling missiles to drive evil angels out of the sky.

Eclipses were regarded in a very different light, being supposed to express the distress of Nature at earthly calamities. The Greeks believed that darkness overshadowed the earth at the deaths of Prometheus, Atreus, Hercules, Æsculapius, and Alexander the Great. The Roman legends held that at the death of Romulus there was darkness for six hours. In the history of the Cæsars occur portents of all three kinds; for at the death of Julius the earth was shrouded in darkness, the birth of Augustus was heralded by a star, and the downfall of Nero by a comet. So, too, in one of the Christian legends clustering about the crucifixion, darkness overspread the earth from the sixth to the ninth hour. Neither the silence regarding it of the only evangelist who claims to have been present, nor the fact that observers like Seneca and Pliny, who, though they carefully described much less striking occurrences of the same sort and in more remote regions, failed to note any such darkness even in Judea, have availed to shake faith in an account so true to the highest poetic instincts of humanity.

This view of the relations between Nature and man continued among both Jews and Christians. According to Jewish tradition, darkness overspread the earth for three days when the books of the Law were profaned by translation into Greek. Tertullian thought an eclipse an evidence of God's wrath against unbelievers. Nor has this mode of thinking ceased in modern times. A similar claim was made at the execution of Charles I; and Increase Mather thought an eclipse in Massachusetts an evidence of the grief of Nature at the death of President Chauncey, of Harvard College. Archbishop Sandys expected eclipses to be the final tokens of woe at the destruction of the world, and traces of this feeling have come down to our own time. The quaint story of the Connecticut statesman who, when his associates in the General Assembly were alarmed by an eclipse of the sun, and thought it the beginning of the Day of Judgment, quietly ordered in candles, that he might in any case be found doing his duty, marks probably the last noteworthy appearance of the old belief in any civilized nation.[4]

[4] For Hindu theories, see Alabaster, *Wheel of the Law,* II. For Greek and Roman legends, see Higgins, *Anacalypsis,* vol. i, pp. 616, 617; also Suetonius, *Caes.,* Julius, p. 88, Claud., p. 46; Seneca, *Quaest. Nat.,* vol. i, p. 1, vol. vii, p. 17; Pliny, *Hist. Nat.,* vol. ii,

In these beliefs regarding meteors and eclipses there was little calculated to do harm by arousing that superstitious terror which is the worst breeding-bed of cruelty. Far otherwise was it with the belief regarding comets. During many centuries it gave rise to the direst superstition and fanaticism. The Chaldeans alone among the ancient peoples generally regarded comets without fear, and thought them bodies wandering as harmless as fishes in the sea; the Pythagoreans alone among philosophers seem to have had a vague idea of them as bodies returning at fixed periods of time; and in all antiquity, so far as is known, one man alone, Seneca, had the scientific instinct and prophetic inspiration to give this idea definite shape, and to declare that the time would come when comets would be found to move in accordance with natural law. Here and there a few strong men rose above the prevailing superstition. The Emperor Vespasian tried to laugh it down, and insisted that a certain comet in his time could not betoken his death, because it was hairy, and he bald; but such scoffing produced little permanent effect, and the prophecy of Seneca was soon forgotten. These and similar isolated utterances could not stand against the mass of opinion which upheld the doctrine that comets are "signs and wonders."[5]

The belief that every comet is a ball of fire flung from the

p. 25; Tacitus, *Ann.*, vol. xiv, p. 22; Josephus, *Antiq.*, vol. xiv, p. 12; and the authorities above cited. For the tradition of the Jews regarding the darkness of three days, see citation in Renan, *Histoire du Peuple Israël,* vol. iv, chap. iv. For Tertullian's belief regarding the significance of an eclipse, see the *Ad Scapulam,* chap. iii, in Migne, *Patrolog. Lat.,* vol. i, p. 701. For the claim regarding Charles I, see a sermon preached before Charles II, cited by Lecky, *England in the Eighteenth Century,* vol. i, p. 65. Mather thought, too, that it might have something to do with the death of sundry civil functionaries of the colonies: see his *Discourse concerning Comets,* 1682. For Archbishop Sandys's belief, see his eighteenth sermon (in *Parker Soc. Publications*). The story of Abraham Davenport has been made familiar by the poem of Whittier.

[5] For terror caused in Rome by comets, see Pingré, *Cométographie,* pp. 165, 166. For the Chaldeans, see Wolf, *Geschichte der Astronomie,* p. 10 *et seq.,* and p. 181 *et seq.*; also Pingré, chap. ii. For the Pythagorean notions, see citation from Plutarch in Costard, *History of Astronomy,* p. 283. For Seneca's prediction, see Guillemin, *World of Comets* (translated by Glaisher), pp. 4, 5; also Watson, *On Comets,* p. 126. For this feeling in antiquity generally, see the preliminary chapters of the two works last cited.

right hand of an angry God to warn the grovelling dwellers of earth was received into the early Church, transmitted through the Middle Ages to the Reformation period, and in its transmission was made all the more precious by supposed textual proofs from Scripture. The great fathers of the Church committed themselves unreservedly to it. In the third century Origen, perhaps the most influential of the earlier fathers of the universal Church in all questions between science and faith, insisted that comets indicate catastrophes and the downfall of empires and worlds. Bede, so justly revered by the English Church, declared in the eighth century that "comets portend revolutions of kingdoms, pestilence, war, winds, or heat"; and John of Damascus, his eminent contemporary in the Eastern Church, took the same view. Rabanus Maurus, the great teacher of Europe in the ninth century, an authority throughout the Middle Ages, adopted Bede's opinion fully. St. Thomas Aquinas, the great light of the universal Church in the thirteenth century, whose works the Pope now reigning commends as the centre and source of all university instruction, accepted and handed down the same opinion. The sainted Albert the Great, the most noted genius of the mediæval Church in natural science, received and developed this theory. These men and those who followed them founded upon scriptural texts and theological reasonings a system that for seventeen centuries defied every advance of thought.[6]

The main evils thence arising were three: the paralysis of self-help, the arousing of fanaticism, and the strengthening of ecclesiastical and political tyranny. The first two of these evils —the paralysis of self-help and the arousing of fanaticism— are evident throughout all these ages. At the appearance of a comet we constantly see all Christendom, from pope to peasant, instead of striving to avert war by wise statesmanship, instead of striving to avert pestilence by observation and reason, instead of striving to avert famine by skilful economy, whining before fetiches, trying to bribe them to remove these signs of God's wrath, and planning to wreak this supposed wrath of God upon misbelievers.

[6] For Origen, see his *De Princip.*, vol. i, p. 7; also Maury, *Lég. Pieuses,* p. 203, note. For Bede and others, see *De Nat.,* vol. xxiv; Joh. Dam., *De Fid. Or.,* vol. ii, p. 7; Maury, *La Magie et l'Astronomie,* pp. 181, 182. For Albertus Magnus, see his *Opera,* vol. i, tr. iii, chaps. x, xi. Among the texts of Scripture on which this belief rested was especially Joel ii, 30, 31.

As to the third of these evils—the strengthening of ecclesiastical and civil despotism—examples appear on every side. It was natural that hierarchs and monarchs whose births were announced by stars, or whose deaths were announced by comets, should regard themselves as far above the common herd, and should be so regarded by mankind; passive obedience was thus strengthened, and the most monstrous assumptions of authority were considered simply as manifestations of the Divine will. Shakespeare makes Calphurnia say to Cæsar:

"When beggars die, there are no comets seen;
The heavens themselves blaze forth the death of princes."

Galeazzo, the tryant of Milan, expressing satisfaction on his deathbed that his approaching end was of such importance as to be heralded by a comet, is but a type of many thus encouraged to prey upon mankind; and Charles V, one of the most powerful monarchs the world has known, abdicating under fear of the comet of 1556, taking refuge in the monastery of San Yuste, and giving up the best of his vast realms to such a scribbling bigot as Philip II, furnishes an example even more striking.[7]

But for the retention of this belief there was a moral cause. Myriads of good men in the Christian Church down to a recent period saw in the appearance of comets not merely an exhibition of "signs in the heavens" foretold in Scripture, but also Divine warnings of vast value to humanity as incentives to repentance and improvement of life—warnings, indeed, so precious that they could not be spared without danger to the moral government of the world. And this belief in the portentous character of comets as an essential part of the Divine government, being, as it was thought, in full accord with Scripture, was made for centuries a source of terror to humanity. To say nothing of examples in the earlier periods, comets in the tenth century especially increased the distress of all Europe. In the middle of the eleventh century a comet was thought to accompany the death of Edward the Confessor and to presage the Norman conquest; the traveller in

[7] For Cæsaer, see Shakespeare, *Julius Cæsar*, act ii, sc. 2. For Galeazzo see Guillemin, *World of Comets*, p. 19. For Charles V, see Prof. Wolf's essay in the *Monatschrift des wissenschaftlichen Vereins*, Zürich, 1857, p. 228.

France to-day may see this belief as it was then wrought into the Bayeux tapestry.[8]

Nearly every decade of years throughout the Middle Ages saw Europe plunged into alarm by appearances of this sort, but the culmination seems to have been reached in 1456. At that time the Turks, after a long effort, had made good their footing in Europe. A large statesmanship or generalship might have kept them out; but, while different religious factions were disputing over petty shades of dogma, they had advanced, had taken Constantinople, and were evidently securing their foothold. Now came the full bloom of this superstition. A comet appeared. The Pope of that period, Calixtus III, though a man of more than ordinary ability, was saturated with the ideas of his time. Alarmed at this monster, if we are to believe the contemporary historian, this infallible head of the Church solemnly "decreed several days of prayer for the averting of the wrath of God, that whatever calamity impended might be turned from the Christians and against the Turks." And, that all might join daily in this petition, there was then established that midday Angelus which has ever since called good Catholics to prayer against the powers of evil. Then, too, was incorporated into a litany the plea, "From the Turk and the comet, good Lord, deliver us." Never was papal intercession less effective; for the Turk has held Constantinople from that day to this, while the obstinate comet, being that now known under the name of Halley, has returned imperturbably at short periods ever since.[9]

[8] For evidences of this widespread terror, see chronicles of Raoul Glaber, Guillaume de Nangis, William of Malmesbury, Florence of Worcester, Ordericus Vitalis, *et al., passim,* and the *Anglo-Saxon Chronicle* (in the *Rolls Series*). For very thrilling pictures of this horror in England, see Freeman, *Norman Conquest,* vol. iii, pp. 640-644, and *William Rufus,* vol. ii, p. 118. For the Bayeux tapestry, see Bruce, *Bayeux Tapestry Elucidated,* plate vii and p. 86; also Guillemin, *World of Comets,* p. 24. There is a large photographic copy, in the South Kensington Museum at London, of the original, wrought, as is generally believed, by the wife of William the Conqueror and her ladies, and still preserved in the town museum at Bayeux.

[9] The usual statement is, that Calixtus excommunicated the comet by a bull, and this is accepted by Arago, Grant, Hoefer, Guillemin, Watson, and many historians of astronomy. Hence the parallel made on a noted occasion by President Lincoln. No such bull, however, is to be found in the published *Bullaria,* and that establishing

But the superstition went still further. It became more and more incorporated into what was considered "scriptural science" and "sound learning." The encyclopedic summaries, in which the science of the Middle Ages and the Reformation period took form, furnish abundant proofs of this.

Yet scientific observation was slowly undermining this structure. The inspired prophecy of Seneca had not been forgotten. Even as far back as the ninth century, in the midst of the sacred learning so abundant at the court of Charlemagne and his successors, we find a scholar protesting against the accepted doctrine. In the thirteenth century we have a mild question by Albert the Great as to the supposed influence of comets upon individuals; but the prevailing theological current was too strong, and he finally yielded to it in this as in so many other things.

So, too, in the sixteenth century, we have Copernicus refusing to accept the usual theory, Paracelsus writing to Zwingli against it, and Julius Cæsar Scaliger denouncing it as "ridiculous folly."[10]

At first this scepticism only aroused the horror of theologians and increased the vigour of ecclesiastics; both asserted the theological theory of comets all the more strenuously as based on scriptural truth. During the sixteenth century France felt the influence of one of her greatest men on the side of this superstition. Jean Bodin, so far before his time in political theories, was only thoroughly abreast of it in religious the-

---

the *Angelus* (as given by Raynaldus in the *Annales Eccl.*) contains no mention of the comet. But the authority of Platina (in his *Vitæ Pontificum,* Venice, 1479, *sub* Calistus III), who was not only in Rome at the time, but, when he wrote his history, archivist of the Vatican, is final as to the Pope's attitude. Platina's authority was never questioned until modern science had changed the ideas of the world. The recent attempt of Pastor (in his *Geschichte der Päpste*) to pooh-pooh down the whole matter is too evident an evasion to carry weight with those who know how even the most careful histories have to be modified to suit the views of the censorship at Rome.

[10] As to encyclopedic summaries, see Vincent of Beauvais, *Speculum Naturale,* and the various editions of Reisch's *Margarita Philosophica.* For Charlemagne's time, see Champion, *La Fin du Monde,* p. 156; Leopardi, *Errori Populari,* p. 165. As to Albert the Great's question, see Heller, *Geschichte der Physik,* vol. i, p. 188. As to scepticism in the sixteenth century, see Champion, *La Fin du Monde,* pp. 155, 156; and for Scaliger, Dudith's book, cited below.

ories: the same reverence for the mere letter of Scripture which made him so fatally powerful in supporting the witch-craft delusion, led him to support this theological theory of comets—but with a difference: he thought them the souls of men, wandering in space, bringing famine, pestilence, and war.

Not less strong was the same superstition in England. Based upon mediæval theology, it outlived the revival of learning. From a multitude of examples a few may be selected as typical. Early in the sixteenth century Polydore Virgil, an ecclesiastic of the unreformed Church, alludes, in his *English History,* to the presage of the death of the Emperor Constantine by a comet as to a simple matter of fact; and in his work on prodigies he pushes this superstition to its most extreme point, exhibiting comets as preceding almost every form of calamity.

In 1532, just at the transition period from the old Church to the new, Cranmer, paving the way to his archbishopric, writes from Germany to Henry VIII, and says of the comet then visible: "What strange things these tokens do signify to come hereafter, God knoweth; for they do not lightly appear but against some great matter."

Twenty years later Bishop Latimer, in an Advent sermon, speaks of eclipses, rings about the sun, and the like, as signs of the approaching end of the world.[11]

In 1580, under Queen Elizabeth, there was set forth an "order of prayer to avert God's wrath from us, threatened by the late terrible earthquake, to be used in all parish churches." In connection with this there was also commended to the faithful "a godly admonition for the time present"; and among the things referred to as evidence of God's wrath are comets, eclipses, and falls of snow.

This view held sway in the Church of England during Elizabeth's whole reign and far into the Stuart period: Strype, the ecclesiastical annalist, gives ample evidence of this, and among the more curious examples is the surmise that the comet of 1572 was a token of Divine wrath provoked by the St. Bartholomew massacre.

[11] For Bodin, see *Theatr.,* lib. ii, cited by Pingré, vol. i, p. 45; also a vague citation in Baudrillart, *Bodin et son Temps,* p. 360. For Polydore Virgil, see *English History,* p. 97 (in *Camden Society Publications*). For Cranmer, see *Remains,* vol. ii, p. 535 (in *Parker Society Publications*). For Latimer, see *Sermons,* second Sunday in Advent, 1552.

As to the Stuart period, Archbishop Spottiswoode seems to have been active in carrying the superstition from the sixteenth century to the seventeenth, and Archbishop Bramhall cites Scripture in support of it. Rather curiously, while the diary of Archbishop Laud shows so much superstition regarding dreams as portents, it shows little or none regarding comets; but Bishop Jeremy Taylor, strong as he was, evidently favoured the usual view. John Howe, the eminent Nonconformist divine in the latter part of the century, seems to have regarded the comet superstition as almost a fundamental article of belief; he laments the total neglect of comets and portents generally, declaring that this neglect betokens want of reverence for the Ruler of the world; he expresses contempt for scientific inquiry regarding comets, insists that they may be natural bodies and yet supernatural portents, and ends by saying, "I conceive it very safe to suppose that some very considerable thing, either in the way of judgment or mercy, may ensue, according as the cry of persevering wickedness or of penitential prayer is more or less loud at that time."[12]

The Reformed Church of Scotland supported the superstition just as strongly. John Knox saw in comets tokens of the wrath of Heaven; other authorities considered them "a warning to the king to extirpate the Papists"; and as late as 1680, after Halley had won his victory, comets were announced on high authority in the Scottish Church to be "prodigies of great judgment on these lands for our sins, for never was the Lord more provoked by a people."

While such was the view of the clergy during the sixteenth and seventeenth centuries, the laity generally accepted it as a matter of course. Among the great leaders in literature there was at least general acquiescence in it. Both Shakespeare and Milton recognise it, whether they fully accept it or not. Shakespeare makes the Duke of Bedford, lamenting at the bier of Henry V, say:

[12] For *Liturgical Services of the Reign of Queen Elizabeth*, see *Parker Society Publications*, pp. 569, 570. For Strype, see his *Ecclesiastical Memorials*, vol. iii, art i, p. 472; also his *Annals of the Reformation*, vol. ii, part ii, p. 151; and his *Life of Sir Thomas Smith*, pp. 161, 162. For Spottiswoode, see *History of the Church of Scotland* (Edinburgh reprint, 1851), vol. i, pp. 185, 186. For Bramhall, see his *Works*, Oxford, 1844, vol. iv, pp. 60, 307, etc. For Jeremy Taylor, see his *Sermons on the Life of Christ*. For John Howe, see his *Works*, London, 1862, vol. iv, pp. 140, 141.

"Comets, importing change of time and states,
Brandish your crystal tresses in the sky;
And with them scourge the bad revolting stars,
That have consented unto Henry's death."

Milton, speaking of Satan preparing for combat, says:

"On the other side,
Incensed with indignation, Satan stood
Unterrified, and like a comet burned,
That fires the length of Ophiuchus huge
In the arctic sky, and from its horrid hair
Shakes pestilence and war."

We do indeed find that in some minds the discoveries of Tycho Brahe and Kepler begin to take effect, for, in 1621, Burton in his *Anatomy of Melancholy* alludes to them as changing public opinion somewhat regarding comets; and, just before the middle of the century, Sir Thomas Browne expresses a doubt whether comets produce such terrible effects, "since it is found that many of them are above the moon."[13] Yet even as late as the last years of the seventeenth century we have English authors of much power battling for this supposed scriptural view; and among the natural and typical results we find, in 1682, Ralph Thoresby, a Fellow of the Royal Society, terrified at the comet of that year, and writing in his diary the following passage: "Lord, fit us for whatever changes it may portend; for, though I am not ignorant that such meteors proceed from natural causes, yet are they frequently also the presages of imminent calamities." Interesting is it to note here that this was Halley's comet, and that Halley was at this very moment making those scientific studies upon it which were to free the civilized world forever from such terrors as distressed Thoresby.

The belief in comets as warnings against sin was especially one of those held "always, everywhere, and by all," and by Eastern Christians as well as by Western. One of the most striking scenes in the history of the Eastern Church is that which took place at the condemnation of Nikon, the great Patriarch of Moscow. Turning toward his judges, he pointed

[13] For John Knox, see his *Historie of the Reformation of Religion within the Realm of Scotland* (Edinburgh, 1732), lib. iv; also Chambers, *Domestic Annals of Scotland*, vol. ii, pp. 410-412. For Burton, see his *Anatomy of Melancholy*, part ii, sect. 2. For Browne, see the *Vulgar and Common Errors*, book vi, chap. xiv.

to a comet then blazing in the sky, and said, "God's besom shall sweep you all away!"

Of all countries in western Europe, it was in Germany and German Switzerland that this superstition took strongest hold.

That same depth of religious feeling which produced in those countries the most terrible growth of witchcraft persecution, brought superstition to its highest development regarding comets. No country suffered more from it in the Middle Ages. At the Reformation Luther declared strongly in favour of it. In one of his Advent sermons he said, "The heathen write that the comet may arise from natural causes, but God creates not one that does not foretoken a sure calamity." Again he said, "Whatever moves in the heaven in an unusual way is certainly a sign of God's wrath." And sometimes, yielding to another phase of his belief, he declared them works of the devil, and declaimed against them as "harlot stars."[14]

Melanchthon, too, in various letters refers to comets as heralds of Heaven's wrath, classing them, with evil conjunctions of the planets and abortive births, among the "signs" referred to in Scripture. Zwingli, boldest of the greater Reformers in shaking off traditional beliefs, could not shake off this, and insisted that the comet of 1531 betokened calamity. Arietus, a leading Protestant theologian, declared, "The heavens are given us not merely for our pleasure, but also as a warning of the wrath of God for the correction of our lives." Lavater insisted that comets are signs of death or calamity, and cited proofs from Scripture.

Catholic and Protestant strove together for the glory of this doctrine. It was maintained with especial vigour by Fromundus, the eminent professor and Doctor of Theology at the Catholic University of Louvain, who so strongly opposed the Copernican system; at the beginning of the seventeenth century, even so gifted an astronomer as Kepler yielded somewhat to the belief; and near the end of that century

[14] For Thoresby, see his *Diary* (London, 1830), vol. i, p. 132. Halley's great service is described further on in this chapter. For Nikon's speech, see Dean Stanley's *History of the Eastern Church*, p. 485. For very striking examples of this mediæval terror in Germany, see Von Raumer, *Geschichte der Hohenstaufen*, vol. vi, p. 538. For the Reformation period, see Wolf, *Gesch. d. Astronomie*; also Prætorius, *Ueber d. Cometstern* (Erfurt, 1580), in which the above sentences of Luther are printed on the title-page as epigraphs. For "Huren-Sternen," see the sermon of Celichius, described later.

Voigt declared that the comet of 1618 clearly presaged the downfall of the Turkish Empire, and he stigmatized as "atheists and Epicureans" all who did not believe comets to be God's warnings.[15]

[2. Theological Efforts to Crush the Scientific View]

3. The Invasion of Scepticism

* * *

In the seventeenth century able arguments against the superstition,[16] on general grounds, began to be multiplied. In Holland, Balthasar Bekker opposed this, as he opposed the witchcraft delusion, on general philosophic grounds; and Lubienitzky wrote in a compromising spirit to prove that comets were often followed by good as by evil events. In France, Pierre Petit, formerly geographer of Louis XIII, and an intimate friend of Descartes, addressed to the young Louis XIV a vehement protest against the superstition, basing his arguments not on astronomy, but on common sense. A very effective part of the little treatise was devoted to answering the authority of the fathers of the early Church. To do this, he simply reminded his readers that St. Augustine and St. John Damascenus had also opposed the doctrine of the antipodes. The book did good service in France, and was translated in Germany a few years later.[17]

All these were denounced as infidels and heretics, yet none the less did they set men at thinking, and prepare the way for a far greater genius; for toward the end of the same century the philosophic attack was taken up by Pierre Bayle, and in the whole series of philosophic champions he is chief.

[15] For Melanchthon, see Wolf, *ubi supra.* For Zwingli, see Wolf, p. 235. For Arietus, see Mädler, *Geschichte der Himmelskunde,* vol. ii. For Kepler's superstition, see Wolf, p. 281. For Voigt, see *Himmels-Magnaten Reichstage,* Hamburg, 1676. For both Fromundus and Voigt, see also Mädler, vol. ii, p. 399, and Lecky, *Rationalism in Europe,* vol. i, p. 28.

[16] [I.e., the superstition that comets are "signs" of impending wrath. or causes of evils.—Ed.]

[17] Bekker's views may be found in his *Onderzoek van de Betekening der Cometen,* Leeuwarden, 1683. For Lubienitzky's, see his *Theatrum Cometicum,* Amsterdam, 1667, in part ii: *Historia Cometarum,* preface "to the reader." For Petit, see his *Dissertation sur la Nature des Comètes,* Paris, 1665 (German translation, Dresden and Zittau, 1681).

While professor at the University of Sedan he had observed the alarm caused by the comet of 1680, and he now brought all his reasoning powers to bear upon it. Thoughts deep and witty he poured out in volume after volume. Catholics and Protestants were alike scandalized. Catholic France spurned him, and Jurieu, the great Reformed divine, called his cometary views "atheism," and tried hard to have Protestant Holland condemn him. Though Bayle did not touch immediately the mass of mankind, he wrought with power upon men who gave themselves the trouble of thinking. It was indeed unfortunate for the Church that theologians, instead of taking the initiative in this matter, left it to Bayle; for, in tearing down the pretended scriptural doctrine of comets, he tore down much else: of all men in his time, no one so thoroughly prepared the way for Voltaire.

Bayle's whole argument is rooted in the prophecy of Seneca. He declares: "Comets are bodies subject to the ordinary law of Nature, and not prodigies amenable to no law." He shows historically that there is no reason to regard comets as portents of earthly evils. As to the fact that such evils occur after the passage of comets across the sky, he compares the person believing that comets cause these evils to a woman looking out of a window into a Paris street and believing that the carriages pass because she looks out. As to the accomplishment of some predictions, he cites the shrewd saying of Henry IV, to the effect that "the public will remember one prediction that comes true better than all the rest that have proved false." Finally, he sums up by saying: "The more we study man, the more does it appear that pride is his ruling passion, and that he affects grandeur even in his misery. Mean and perishable creature that he is, he has been able to persuade men that he can not die without disturbing the whole course of Nature and obliging the heavens to put themselves to fresh expense in order to light his funeral pomp. Foolish and ridiculous vanity! If we had a just idea of the universe, we should soon comprehend that the death or birth of a prince is too insignificant a matter to stir the heavens."[18]

[18] Regarding Bayle, see Mädler, *Himmelskunde,* vol. i, p. 327. For special points of interest in Bayle's argument, see his *Pensées Diverses sur les Comètes,* Amsterdam, 1749, pp. 79, 102, 134, 206. For the response to Jurieu, see the *Continuation des Pensées,* Rotterdam, 1705; also Champion, p. 164, Lecky, *ubi supra,* and Guillemin, pp. 29, 30.

This great philosophic champion of right reason was followed by a literary champion hardly less famous; for Fontenelle now gave to the French theatre his play of *The Comet*, and a point of capital importance in France was made by rendering the army of ignorance ridiculous.[19]

Such was the line of philosophic and literary attack, as developed from Scaliger to Fontenelle. But beneath and in the midst of all of it, from first to last, giving firmness, strength, and new sources of vitality to it, was the steady development of scientific effort; and to the series of great men who patiently wrought and thought out the truth by scientific methods through all these centuries belong the honours of the victory.

For generations men in various parts of the world had been making careful observations on these strange bodies. As far back as the time when Luther and Melanchthon and Zwingli were plunged into alarm by various comets from 1531 to 1539, Peter Apian kept his head sufficiently cool to make scientific notes of their paths through the heavens. A little later, when the great comet of 1556 scared popes, emperors, and reformers alike, such men as Fabricius at Vienna and Heller at Nuremberg quietly observed its path. In vain did men like Dieterich and Heerbrand and Celich from various parts of Germany denounce such observations and investigations as impious; they were steadily continued, and in 1577 came the first which led to the distinct foundation of the modern doctrine. In that year appeared a comet which again plunged Europe into alarm. In every European country this alarm was strong, but in Germany strongest of all. The churches were filled with terror-stricken multitudes. Celich preaching at Magdeburg was echoed by Heerbrand preaching at Tübingen, and both these from thousands of other pulpits, Catholic and Protestant, throughout Europe. In the midst of all this din and outcry a few men quietly but steadily observed the monster; and Tycho Brahe announced, as the result, that its path lay farther from the earth than the orbit of the moon. Another great astronomical genius, Kepler, confirmed this. This distinct beginning of the new doctrine was bitterly opposed by theologians; they denounced it as one of the evil results of that scientific meddling with the designs of Providence against which they had so long declaimed in pulpits and professors' chairs; they even brought forward some astrono-

[19] See Fontenelle, cited by Champion, p. 167.

mers ambitious or wrong-headed enough to testify that Tycho and Kepler were in error.[20]

Nothing could be more natural than such opposition; for this simple announcement by Tycho Brahe began a new era. It shook the very foundation of cometary superstition. The Aristotelian view, developed by the theologians, was that what lies within the moon's orbit appertains to the earth and is essentially transitory and evil, while what lies beyond it belongs to the heavens and is permanent, regular, and pure. Tycho Brahe and Kepler, therefore, having by means of scientific observation and thought taken comets out of the category of meteors and appearances in the neighbourhood of the earth, and placed them among the heavenly bodies, dealt a blow at the very foundations of the theological argument, and gave a great impulse to the idea that comets are themselves heavenly bodies moving regularly and in obedience to law.

4. Theological Efforts at Compromise—the Final Victory of Science

Attempts were now made to compromise. It was declared that, while some comets were doubtless supralunar, some must be sublunar. But this admission was no less fatal on another account. During many centuries the theory favoured by the Church had been, as we have seen, that the earth was surrounded by hollow spheres, concentric and transparent, forming a number of glassy strata incasing one another "like the different coatings of an onion," and that each of these in its movement about the earth carries one or more of the heavenly bodies. Some maintained that these spheres were crystal; but Lactantius, and with him various fathers of the Church, spoke of the heavenly vault as made of ice. Now, the admission that comets could move beyond the moon was fatal to this theory, for it sent them crashing through these spheres of ice or crystal, and therefore through the whole sacred fabric of the Ptolemaic theory.[21]

[20] See Mädler, *Himmelskunde,* vol. i, pp. 181, 197; also Wolf, *Gesch. d. Astronomie,* and Janssen, *Gesch. d. deutschen Volkes,* vol. v, p. 350. Heerbrand's sermon, cited above, is a good specimen of the theologic attitude. See Pingré, vol. ii, p. 81

[21] For these features in cometary theory, see Pingré, vol. i, p. 89; also Humboldt, *Cosmos* (English translation, London, 1868), vol. iii, p. 169.

Here we may pause for a moment to note one of the chief differences between scientific and theological reasoning considered in themselves. Kepler's main reasoning as to the existence of a law for cometary movement was right; but his secondary reasoning, that comets move nearly in straight lines, was wrong. His right reasoning was developed by Gassendi in France, by Borelli in Italy, by Hevel and Doerfel in Germany, by Eysat and Bernouilli in Switzerland, by Percy and— most important of all, as regards mathematical demonstrations —by Newton in England. The general theory, which was true, they accepted and developed; the secondary theory, which was found untrue, they rejected; and, as a result, both of what they thus accepted and of what they rejected, was evolved the basis of the whole modern cometary theory.

Very different was this from the theological method. As a rule, when there arises a thinker as great in theology as Kepler in science, the whole mass of his conclusions ripens into a dogma. His disciples labour not to test it, but to establish it; and while, in the Catholic Church, it becomes a dogma to be believed or disbelieved under the penalty of damnation, it becomes in the Protestant Church the basis for one more sect.

Various astronomers laboured to develop the truth discovered by Tycho and strengthened by Kepler. Cassini seemed likely to win for Italy the glory of completing the great structure; but he was sadly fettered by Church influences, and was obliged to leave most of the work to others. Early among these was Hevel. He gave reasons for believing that comets move in parabolic curves toward the sun. Then came a man who developed this truth further—Samuel Doerfel; and it is a pleasure to note that he was a clergyman. The comet of 1680, which set Erni in Switzerland, Mather in New England, and so many others in all parts of the world at declaiming, set Doerfel at thinking. Undismayed by the authority of Origen and St. John Chrysostom, the arguments of Luther, Melanchthon, and Zwingli, the outcries of Celich, Heerbrand, and Dieterich, he pondered over the problem in his little Saxon parsonage, until in 1681 he set forth his proofs that comets are heavenly bodies moving in parabolas of which the sun is the focus. Bernouilli arrived at the same conclusion; and, finally, this great series of men and works was closed by the greatest of all, when Newton, in 1686, having taken the data furnished by the comet of 1680, demonstrated that comets are guided in their movements by the same principle that controls the planets in their orbits. Thus was completed the evolution of this new truth in science.

Yet we are not to suppose that these two great series of philosophical and scientific victories cleared the field of all opponents. Declamation and pretended demonstration of the old theologic view were still heard; but the day of complete victory dawned when Halley, after most thorough observation and calculation, recognised the comet of 1682 as one which had already appeared at stated periods, and foretold its return in about seventy-five years; and the battle was fully won when Clairaut, seconded by Lalande and Mme. Lepaute, predicted distinctly the time when the comet would arrive at its perihelion, and this prediction was verified.[22] Then it was that a Roman heathen philosopher was proved more infallible and more directly under Divine inspiration than a Roman Christian pontiff; for the very comet which the traveller finds to-day depicted on the Bayeux tapestry as portending destruction to Harold and the Saxons at the Norman invasion of England, and which was regarded by Pope Calixtus as portending evil to Christendom, was found six centuries later to be, as Seneca had prophesied, a heavenly body obeying the great laws of the universe, and coming at regular periods. Thenceforth the whole ponderous enginery of this superstition, with its proof-texts regarding "signs in the heavens," its theological reasoning to show the moral necessity of cometary warnings, and its ecclesiastical fulminations against the "atheism, godlessness, and infidelity" of scientific investigation, was seen by all thinking men to be as weak against the scientific method as Indian arrows against needle guns. Copernicus, Galileo, Cassini, Doerfel, Newton, Halley, and Clairaut had gained the victory.[23]

* * *

[22] See Pingré, vol. i, p. 53; Grant, *History of Physical Astronomy*, p. 305, etc., etc. For a curious partial anticipation by Hooke, in 1664, of the great truth announced by Halley in 1682, see *Pepys's Diary* for March 1, 1664. For excellent summaries of the whole work of Halley and Clairaut and their forerunners and associates, see Pingré, Mädler, Wolf, Arago, *et al.*

[23] In accordance with Halley's prophecy, the comet of 1682 has returned in 1759 and 1835. See Mädler, Guillemin, Watson, Grant, Delambre, Proctor, article *Astronomy* in *Encycl. Brit.*, and especially, for details, Wolf, pp. 407-412 and 701-722. For clear statement regarding Doerfel, see Wolf, p. 411.

The victory was indeed complete. Happily, none of the fears expressed by [various opponents] were realized. No catastrophe has ensued either to religion or to morals. In the realm of religion the Psalms of David remain no less beautiful, the great utterances of the Hebrew prophets no less powerful; the Sermon on the Mount, "the first commandment, and the second, which is like unto it," the definition of "pure religion and undefiled" by St. James, appeal no less to the deepest things in the human heart. In the realm of morals, too, serviceable as the idea of firebrands thrown by the right hand of an avenging God to scare a naughty world might seem, any competent historian must find that the destruction of the old theological cometary theory was followed by moral improvement rather than by deterioration. We have but to compare the general moral tone of society to-day, wretchedly imperfect as it is, with that existing in the time when this superstition had its strongest hold. We have only to compare the court of Henry VIII with the court of Victoria, the reign of the later Valois and earlier Bourbon princes with the present French Republic, the period of the Medici and Sforzas and Borgias with the period of Leo XIII and Humbert, the monstrous wickedness of the Thirty Years' War with the ennobling patriotism of the Franco-Prussian struggle, and the despotism of the miserable German princelings of the sixteenth and seventeenth centuries with the reign of the Emperor William.

The gain is not simply that mankind has arrived at a clearer conception of law in the universe; not merely that thinking men see more clearly that we are part of a system not requiring constant patching and arbitrary interference; but perhaps best of all is the fact that science has cleared away one more series of those dogmas which tend to debase rather than to develop man's whole moral and religious nature. In this emancipation from terror and fanaticism, as in so many other results of scientific thinking, we have a proof of the inspiration of those great words, "THE TRUTH SHALL MAKE YOU FREE."

Chapter 5

From Genesis to Geology

[1. Growth of Theological Explanations]

2. Efforts to Suppress the Scientific View

*   *   *

STRANGE AS IT MAY AT FIRST SEEM, the theological war against a scientific method in geology was waged more fiercely in Protestant countries than in Catholic. The older Church had learned by her costly mistakes, especially in the cases of Copernicus and Galileo, what dangers to her claim of infallibility lay in meddling with a growing science. In Italy, therefore, comparatively little opposition was made, while England furnished the most bitter opponents to geology so long as the controversy could be maintained, and the most active negotiators in patching up a truce on the basis of a sham science afterward. The Church of England did, indeed, produce some noble men, like Bishop Clayton and John Mitchell, who stood firmly by the scientific method; but these appear generally to have been overwhelmed by a chorus of churchmen and dissenters, whose mixtures of theology and science, sometimes tragic in their results and sometimes comic, are among the most instructive things in modern history.[1]

We have already noted that there are generally three pe-

[1] For a comparison between the conduct of Italian and English ecclesiastics as regards geology, see Lyell, *Principles of Geology,* tenth English edition, vol. i, p. 33. For a philosophical statement of reasons why the struggle was more bitter and the attempt at deceptive compromises more absurd in England than elsewhere, see Maury, *L'Ancienne Académie des Sciences,* second edition, p. 152. For very frank confessions of the reasons why the Roman Catholic Church has become more careful in her dealings with science, see Roberts, *The Pontifical Decrees against the Earth's Movement,* London, 1885, especially pp. 94 and 132, 133, and St. George Mivart's article in the *Nineteenth Century* for July, 1885. The first of these gentlemen, it must not be forgotten, is a Roman Catholic clergyman, and the second an eminent layman of the same Church, and both admit that it was the Pope, speaking *ex cathedra,* who erred in the Galileo case; but their explanation is that God allowed

riods or phases in a theological attack upon any science. The first of these is marked by the general use of scriptural texts and statements against the new scientific doctrine; the third by attempts at compromise by means of far-fetched reconciliations of textual statements with ascertained fact; but the second or intermediate period between these two is frequently marked by the pitting against science of some great doctrine in theology. We saw this in astronomy, when Bellarmin and his followers insisted that the scientific doctrine of the earth revolving about the sun is contrary to the theological doctrine of the incarnation. So now against geology it was urged that the scientific doctrine that fossils represent animals which died before Adam contradicts the theological doctrine of Adam's fall and the statement that "death entered the world by sin."

In this second stage of the theological struggle with geology, England was especially fruitful in champions of orthodoxy, first among whom may be named Thomas Burnet. In the last quarter of the seventeenth century, just at the time when Newton's great discovery was given to the world, Burnet issued his *Sacred Theory of the Earth*. His position was commanding; he was a royal chaplain and a cabinet officer. Planting himself upon the famous text in the second epistle of Peter,[2] he declares that the flood had destroyed the old and created a new world. The Newtonian theory he refuses to accept. In his theory of the deluge he lays less stress upon the "opening of the windows of heaven" than upon the "breaking up of the fountains of the great deep." On this latter point he comes forth with great strength. His theory is that the earth is hollow, and filled with fluid like an egg. Mixing together sundry texts from Genesis and from the second epistle of Peter, the theological doctrine of the "Fall," an astronomical theory regarding the ecliptic, and various notions adapted from Descartes, he insisted that, before sin brought on the Deluge, the earth was of perfect mathematical form, smooth and beautiful, "like an egg," with neither seas nor islands nor valleys nor rocks, "with not a wrinkle, scar, or fracture," and that all creation was equally perfect.

In the second book of his great work Burnet went still

---

the Pope and Church to fall into this grievous error, which has cost so dear, in order to show once and for all that the Church has no right to decide questions in science.

[2] See II Peter iii, 6.

further. As in his first book he had mixed his texts of Genesis and St. Peter with Descartes, he now mixed the account of the Garden of Eden in Genesis with heathen legends of the golden age, and concluded that before the flood there was over the whole earth perpetual spring, disturbed by no rain more severe than the falling of the dew.

In addition to his other grounds for denying the earlier existence of the sea, he assigned the reason that, if there had been a sea before the Deluge, sinners would have learned to build ships, and so, when the Deluge set in, could have saved themselves.

The work was written with much power, and attracted universal attention. It was translated into various languages, and called forth a multitude of supporters and opponents in all parts of Europe. Strong men rose against it, especially in England, and among them a few dignitaries of the Church; but the Church generally hailed the work with joy. Addison praised it in a Latin ode, and for nearly a century it exercised a strong influence upon European feeling, and aided to plant more deeply than ever the theological opinion that the earth as now existing is merely a ruin; whereas, before sin brought on the Flood, it was beautiful in its "egg-shaped form," and free from every imperfection.

A few years later came another writer of the highest standing—William Whiston, professor at Cambridge, who in 1696 published his *New Theory of the Earth*. Unlike Burnet, he endeavoured to avail himself of the Newtonian idea, and brought in, to aid the geological catastrophe caused by human sin, a comet, which broke open "the fountains of the great deep."

But, far more important than either of these champions, there arose in the eighteenth century, to aid in the subjection of science to theology, three men of extraordinary power— John Wesley, Adam Clarke, and Richard Watson. All three were men of striking intellectual gifts, lofty character, and noble purpose, and the first-named one of the greatest men in English history; yet we find them in geology hopelessly fettered by the mere letter of Scripture, and by a temporary phase in theology. As in regard to witchcraft and the doctrine of comets, so in regard to geology, this theological view drew Wesley into enormous error.[3] The great doctrine which

[3] For his statement that "the giving up of witchcraft is in effect the giving up of the Bible," see Wesley's *Journal*, 1766-68.

Wesley, Watson, Clarke, and their compeers, following St. Augustine, Bede, Peter Lombard, and a long line of the greatest minds in the universal Church, thought it especially necessary to uphold against geologists was, that death entered the world by sin—by the first transgression of Adam and Eve. The extent to which the supposed necessity of upholding this doctrine carried Wesley seems now almost beyond belief. Basing his theology on the declaration that the Almighty after creation found the earth and all created things "very good," he declares, in his sermon on the *Cause and Cure of Earthquakes,* that no one who believes the Scriptures can deny that "sin is the moral cause of earthquakes, whatever their natural cause may be." Again, he declares that earthquakes are the "effect of that curse which was brought upon the earth by the original transgression." Bringing into connection with Genesis the declaration of St. Paul that "the whole creation groaneth and travaileth together in pain until now," he finds additional scriptural proof that the earthquakes were the result of Adam's fall. He declares, in his sermon on *God's Approbation of His Works,* that "before the sin of Adam there were no agitations within the bowels of the earth, no violent convulsions, no concussions of the earth, no earthquakes, but all was unmoved as the pillars of heaven. There were then no such things as eruptions of fires; no volcanoes or burning mountains." Of course, a science which showed that earthquakes had been in operation for ages before the appearance of man on the planet, and which showed, also, that those very earthquakes which he considered as curses resultant upon the Fall were really blessings, producing the fissures in which we find to-day those mineral veins so essential to modern civilization, was entirely beyond his comprehension. He insists that earthquakes are "God's strange works of judgment, the proper effect and punishment of sin."

So, too, as to death and pain. In his sermon on the *Fall of Man* he took the ground that death and pain entered the world by Adam's transgression, insisting that the carnage now going on among animals is the result of Adam's sin. Speaking of the birds, beasts, and insects, he says that, before sin entered the world by Adam's fall, "none of these attempted to devour or in any way hurt one another"; that "the spider was then as harmless as the fly and did not then lie in wait for blood." Here, again, Wesley arrayed his early followers against geology, which reveals, in the fossil remains of carnivorous animals, pain and death countless ages before the appearance of man. The half-digested fragments of weaker animals within the fossilized bodies of the stronger have destroyed all Wesley's arguments in behalf of his great theory.[4]

Dr. Adam Clarke held similar views. He insisted that thorns and thistles were given as a curse to human labour, on account of Adam's sin, and appeared upon the earth for the first time after Adam's fall. So, too, Richard Watson, the most prolific writer of the great evangelical reform period, and the author of the *Institutes*, the standard theological treatise on the evangelical side, says, in a chapter treating of the Fall, and especially of the serpent which tempted Eve: "We have no reason at all to believe that the animal had a serpentine form in any mode or degree until his transformation. That he was then degraded to a reptile, to go upon his belly, imports, on the contrary, an entire alteration and loss of the original form." All that admirable adjustment of the serpent to its environment which delights naturalists was to the Wesleyan divine simply an evil result of the sin of Adam and Eve. Yet here again geology was obliged to confront theology in revealing the *python* in the Eocene, ages before man appeared.[5]

The immediate results of such teaching by such men was to throw many who would otherwise have resorted to observation and investigation back upon scholastic methods. Again reappears the old system of solving the riddle by phrases. In 1733, Dr. Theodore Arnold urged the theory of "models," and insisted that fossils result from "infinitesimal particles brought together in the creation to form the outline of all the creatures and objects upon and within the earth"; and Arnold's work gained wide acceptance.[6]

Such was the influence of this succession of great men that toward the close of the last century the English opponents of geology on biblical grounds seemed likely to sweep

[4] See Wesley's sermon on *God's Approbation of His Works*, parts xi and xii.

[5] See *Westminster Review*, October, 1870, article on *John Wesley's Cosmogony*, with citations from Wesley's *Sermons*, Watson's *Institutes of Theology*, Adam Clarke's *Commentary on the Holy Scriptures*, etc.

[6] See citation in Mr. Ward's article, as above, p. 390.

all before them.[7] Cramping our whole inheritance of sacred literature within the rules of a historical compend, they showed the terrible dangers arising from the revelations of geology, which make the earth older than the six thousand years required by Archbishop Usher's interpretation of the Old Testament. Nor was this feeling confined to ecclesiastics. Williams, a thoughtful layman, declared that such researches led to infidelity and atheism, and are "nothing less than to depose the Almighty Creator of the universe from his office." The poet Cowper, one of the mildest of men, was also aroused by these dangers, and in his most elaborate poem wrote:

> "Some drill and bore
> The solid earth, and from the strata there
> Extract a register, by which we learn
> That He who made it, and revealed its date
> To Moses, was mistaken in its age!"

John Howard summoned England to oppose "those scientific systems which are calculated to tear up in the public mind every remaining attachment to Christianity."

With this special attack upon geological science by means of the dogma of Adam's fall, the more general attack by the literal interpretation of the text was continued. The legendary husks and rinds of our sacred books were insisted upon as equally precious and nutritious with the great moral and religious truths which they envelop. Especially precious were the six days—each "the evening and the morning"—and the exact statements as to the time when each part of creation came into being. To save these, the struggle became more and more desperate.

Difficult as it is to realize it now, within the memory of many now living the battle was still raging most fiercely in England, and both kinds of artillery usually brought against a new science were in full play, and filling the civilized world with their roar.

*   *   *

[7] [For a modern treatment, see the excellent work by Charles Coulston Gillispie, *Genesis and Geology* (Harper Torchbooks, 1959). This work, incidentally, suggests certain qualifications to White's general thesis concerning the warfare of science with theology.— Ed.]

The favourite weapon of the orthodox party was the charge that the geologists were "attacking the truth of God." They declared geology "not a subject of lawful inquiry," denouncing it as "a dark art," as "dangerous and disreputable," as "a forbidden province," as "infernal artillery," and as "an awful evasion of the testimony of revelation."[8]

* * *

But it is a duty and a pleasure to state here that one great Christian scholar did honour to religion and to himself by quietly accepting the claims of science and making the best of them, despite all these clamours. This man was Nicholas Wiseman, better known afterward as Cardinal Wiseman. The conduct of this pillar of the Roman Catholic Church contrasts admirably with that of timid Protestants, who were filling England with shrieks and denunciations.[9]

And here let it be noted that one of the most interesting skirmishes in this war occurred in New England. Prof. Stuart, of Andover, justly honoured as a Hebrew scholar, declared that to speak of six periods of time for the creation was flying in the face of Scripture; that Genesis expressly speaks of six days, each made up of "the evening and the morning," and not six periods of time.

To him replied a professor in Yale College, James Kingsley. In an article admirable for keen wit and kindly temper, he showed that Genesis speaks just as clearly of a solid firmament as of six ordinary days, and that, if Prof. Stuart had surmounted one difficulty and accepted the Copernican theory, he might as well get over another and accept the revelations of geology. The encounter was quick and decisive, and the victory was with science and the broader scholarship of Yale.[10]

* * *

3. The First Great Effort at Compromise, Based on the Flood of Noah

Long before the end of the struggle already described, even

[8] See Pye Smith, D.D., *Geology and Scripture,* pp. 156, 157, 168, 169.

[9] Wiseman, *Twelve Lectures on the Connection between Science and Revealed Religion,* first American edition, New York, 1837. As to the comparative severity of the struggle regarding astronomy, geology, etc., in Catholic and Protestant countries, see Lecky, *England in the Eighteenth Century,* chap. ix, p. 525.

[10] See *Silliman's Journal,* vol. xxx, p. 114.

at a very early period, the futility of the usual scholastic weapons had been seen by the more keen-sighted champions of orthodoxy; and, as the difficulties of the ordinary attack upon science became more and more evident, many of these champions endeavoured to patch up a truce. So began the third stage in the war—the period of attempts at compromise.

The position which the compromise party took was that the fossils were produced by the Deluge of Noah.

This position was strong, for it was apparently based upon Scripture. Moreover, it had high ecclesiastical sanction, some of the fathers having held that fossil remains, even on the highest mountains, represented animals destroyed at the Deluge. Tertullian was especially firm on this point, and St. Augustine thought that a fossil tooth discovered in North Africa must have belonged to one of the giants mentioned in Scripture.[11]

In the sixteenth century especially, weight began to be attached to this idea by those who felt the worthlessness of various scholastic explanations. Strong men in both the Catholic and the Protestant camps accepted it; but the man who did most to give it an impulse into modern theology was Martin Luther. He easily saw that scholastic phrase-making could not meet the difficulties raised by fossils, and he naturally urged the doctrine of their origin at Noah's Flood.[12]

With such support, it soon became the dominant theory in Christendom: nothing seemed able to stand against it; but before the end of the same sixteenth century it met some serious obstacles. Bernard Palissy, one of the most keen-sighted of scientific thinkers in France, as well as one of the most devoted of Christians, showed that it was utterly untenable. Conscientious investigators in other parts of Europe, and especially in Italy, showed the same thing; all in vain.[13] In vain did good men protest against the injury sure to be brought upon religion by tying it to a scientific theory sure to be exploded; the doctrine that fossils are the remains of animals drowned at the

[11] For Tertullian, see his *De Pallio*, c. ii (Migne, *Patr. Lat.*, vol. ii, p. 1033). For Augustine's view, see Cuvier, *Recherches sur les Ossements fossiles,* fourth edition, vol. ii, p. 143.
[12] For Luther's cpinion, see his *Commentary on Genesis.*
[13] For a very full statement of the honourable record of Italy in this respect, and for the enlightened views of some Italian churchmen, see Stoppani, *Il Dogma e le Scienze Positive,* Milan, 1886, pp. 203 *et seq.*

Flood continued to be upheld by the great majority of theological leaders for nearly three centuries as "sound doctrine," and as a blessed means of reconciling science with Scripture. To sustain this scriptural view, efforts energetic and persistent were put forth both by Catholics and Protestants.

In France, the learned Benedictine, Calmet, in his great works on the Bible, accepted it as late as the beginning of the eighteenth century, believing the mastodon's bones exhibited by Mazurier to be those of King Teutobocus, and holding them valuable testimony to the existence of the giants mentioned in Scripture and of the early inhabitants of the earth overwhelmed by the Flood.[14]

But the greatest champion appeared in England. We have already seen how, near the close of the seventeenth century, Thomas Burnet prepared the way in his *Sacred Theory of the Earth* by rejecting the discoveries of Newton, and showing how sin led to the breaking up of the "foundations of the great deep"; and we have also seen how Whiston, in his *New Theory of the Earth,* while yielding a little and accepting the discoveries of Newton, brought in a comet to aid in producing the Deluge; but far more important than these in permanent influence was John Woodward, professor at Gresham College, a leader in scientific thought at the University of Cambridge, and, as a patient collector of fossils and an earnest investigator of their meaning, deserving of the highest respect. In 1695 he published his *Natural History of the Earth,* and rendered one great service to science, for he yielded another point, and thus destroyed the foundations for the old theory of fossils. He showed that they were not "sports of Nature," or "models inserted by the Creator in the strata for some inscrutable purpose," but that they were really remains of living beings, as Xenophanes had asserted two thousand years before him. So far, he rendered a great service both to science and religion; but, this done, the text of the Old Testament narrative and the famous passage in St. Peter's Epistle were too strong for him, and he, too, insisted that the fossils were produced by the Deluge. Aided by his great authority, the assault on the true scientific position was vigorous: Mazurier exhibited certain fossil remains of a mammoth discovered in France as bones

[14] For the steady adherence to this sacred theory, see Audiat, *Vie de Palissy,* p. 412, and Cantu, *Histoire Universelle,* vol. xv, p. 492. For Calmet, see his *Dissertation sur les Géants,* cited in Berger de Xivrey, *Traditions Tératologiques,* p. 191.

of the giants mentioned in Scripture; Father Torrubia did the same thing in Spain; Increase Mather sent to England similar remains discovered in America, with a like statement.

For the edification of the faithful, such "bones of the giants mentioned in Scripture" were hung up in public places. Jurieu saw some of them thus suspended in one of the churches of Valence; and Henrion, apparently under the stimulus thus given, drew up tables showing the size of our antediluvian ancestors, giving the height of Adam as 123 feet 9 inches and that of Eve as 118 feet 9 inches and 9 lines.[15]

But the most brilliant service rendered to the theological theory came from another quarter; for, in 1726, Scheuchzer, having discovered a large fossil lizard, exhibited it to the world as the "human witness of the Deluge":[16] this great discovery was hailed everywhere with joy, for it seemed to prove not only that human beings were drowned at the Deluge, but that "there were giants in those days." Cheered by the applause thus gained, he determined to make the theological position impregnable. Mixing together various texts of Scripture with notions derived from the philosophy of Descartes and the speculations of Whiston, he developed the theory that "the fountains of the great deep" were broken up by the direct physical action of the hand of God, which, being literally applied to the axis of the earth, suddenly stopped the earth's rotation, broke up "the fountains of the great deep," spilled the water therein contained, and produced the Deluge. But his service to sacred science did not end here, for he prepared an edition of the Bible, in which magnificent engravings in great number illustrated his view and enforced it upon all readers. Of these engravings no less than thirty-four were devoted to the Deluge alone.[17]

[15] See Cuvier, *Recherches sur les Ossements fossiles,* fourth edition, vol. ii, p. 56; also Geoffroy St.-Hilaire, cited by Berger de Xivrey, *Traditions Tératologiques,* p. 190.
[16] *Homo diluvii testis.*
[17] See Zoeckler, vol. ii, p. 172; also Scheuchzer, *Physica Sacra,* Augustæ Vindel et Ulmæ, 1732. For the ancient belief regarding giants, see Leopardi, *Saggio.* For accounts of the views of Mazurier and Scheuchzer, see Cuvier; also Büchner, *Man in Past, Present, and Future,* English translation, pp. 235, 236. For Increase Mather's views, see *Philosophical Transactions,* vol. xxiv, p. 85. As to similar fossils sent from New York to the Royal Society as remains of giants, see Weld, *History of the Royal Society,* vol. i, p. 421. For Father Torrubia and his *Gigantologia Española,* see D'Archiac,

In the midst all this came an episode very comical but very instructive; for it shows that the attempt to shape the deductions of science to meet the exigencies of dogma may mislead heterodoxy as absurdly as orthodoxy.

About the year 1760 news of the discovery of marine fossils in various elevated districts of Europe reached Voltaire. He, too, had a theologic system to support, though his system was opposed to that of the sacred books of the Hebrews; and, fearing that these new discoveries might be used to support the Mosaic accounts of the Deluge, all his wisdom and wit were compacted into arguments to prove that the fossil fishes were remains of fishes intended for food, but spoiled and thrown away by travellers; that the fossil shells were accidentally dropped by crusaders and pilgrims returning from the Holy Land; and that the fossil bones found between Paris and Étampes were parts of a skeleton belonging to the cabinet of some ancient philosopher. Through chapter after chapter, Voltaire, obeying the supposed necessities of his theology, fought desperately the growing results of the geologic investigations of his time.[18]

But far more prejudicial to Christianity was the continued effort on the other side to show that the fossils were caused by the Deluge of Noah.

No supposition was too violent to support this theory, which was considered vital to the Bible. By taking the mere husks and rinds of biblical truth for truth itself, by taking sacred poetry as prose, and by giving a literal interpretation of it, the followers of Burnet, Whiston, and Woodward built up systems which bear to real geology much the same relation that the *Christian Topography* of Cosmas bears to real geography. In vain were exhibited the absolute geological, zoölogical, astronomical proofs that no universal deluge, or deluge covering

---

Introduction à l'Étude de la Paléontologie Stratigraphique, Paris, 1864, p. 201. For admirable summaries, see Lyell, *Principles of Geology,* London, 1867; D'Archiac, *Géologie et Paléontologie,* Paris, 1866; Pictet, *Traité de Paléontologie,* Paris, 1853; Vezian, *Prodrome de la Géologie,* Paris, 1863; Haeckel, *History of Creation,* English translation, New York, 1876, chap. iii; and for recent progress, Prof. O. S. Marsh's *Address on the History and Methods of Paleontology.*

18 See Voltaire, *Dissertation sur les Changements arrivés dans notre Globe;* also Voltaire, *Les Singularités de la Nature,* chap. xii; also Jevons, *Principles of Science,* vol. ii, p. 328.

any large part of the earth, had taken place within the last six thousand or sixty thousand years; in vain did so enlightened a churchman as Bishop Clayton declare that the Deluge could not have extended beyond that district where Noah lived before the Flood; in vain did others, like Bishop Croft and Bishop Stillingfleet, and the nonconformist Matthew Poole, show that the Deluge might not have been and probably was not universal; in vain was it shown that, even if there had been a universal deluge, the fossils were not produced by it: the only answers were the citation of the text, "And all the high mountains which were under the whole heaven were covered," and, to clinch the matter, Worthington and men like him insisted that any argument to show that fossils were not remains of animals drowned at the Deluge of Noah was "infidelity." In England, France, and Germany, belief that the fossils were produced by the Deluge of Noah was widely insisted upon as part of that faith essential to salvation.[19]

But the steady work of science went on: not all the force of the Church—not even the splendid engravings in Scheuchzer's Bible—could stop it, and the foundations of this theological theory began to crumble away. The process was, indeed, slow; it required a hundred and twenty years for the searchers of God's truth, as revealed in Nature—such men as Hooke, Linnæus, Whitehurst, Daubenton, Cuvier, and William Smith—to push their works under this fabric of error, and, by statements which could not be resisted, to undermine it. As we arrive at the beginning of the nineteenth century, science is becoming irresistible in this field. Blumenbach, Von Buch, and Schlotheim led the way, but most important on the Continent was the work of Cuvier. In the early years of the present century his researches among fossils began to throw new light into the whole subject of geology. He was, indeed, very conservative, and even more wary and diplomatic; seem-

[19] For a candid summary of the proofs from geology, astronomy, and zoölogy, that the Noachian Deluge was not universally or widely extended, see McClintock and Strong, *Cyclopædia of Biblical Theology and Ecclesiastical Literature*, article *Deluge*. For general history, see Lyell, D'Archiac, and Vezian. For special cases showing the bitterness of the conflict, see the Rev. Mr. Davis's *Life of Rev. Dr. Pye Smith, passim*. For a late account, see Prof. Huxley on *The Lights of the Church and the Light of Science*, in the *Nineteenth Century* for July, 1890.

ing, like Voltaire, to feel that "among wolves one must howl a little." It was a time of reaction. Napoleon had made peace with the Church, and to disturb that peace was akin to treason. By large but vague concessions Cuvier kept the theologians satisfied, while he undermined their strongest fortress. The danger was instinctively felt by some of the champions of the Church, and typical among these was Chateaubriand, who in his best-known work, once so great, now so little—the *Genius of Christianity*—grappled with the questions of creation by insisting upon a sort of general deception "in the beginning," under which everything was created by a sudden fiat, but with appearances of pre-existence. His words are as follows: "It was part of the perfection and harmony of the nature which was displayed before men's eyes that the deserted nests of last year's birds should be seen on the trees, and that the seashore should be covered with shells which had been the abode of fish, and yet the world was quite new, and nests and shells had never been inhabited."[20] But the real victory was with Brongniart, who, about 1820, gave forth his work on fossil plants, and thus built a barrier against which the enemies of science raged in vain.[21]

*   *   *

One of the first evidences of the completeness of this sur-render has been so well related by the eminent physiologist, Dr. W. B. Carpenter, that it may best be given in his own words: "You are familiar with a book of considerable value, Dr. W. Smith's *Dictionary of the Bible*. I happened to know the influences under which that dictionary was framed. The idea of the publisher and of the editor was to give as much scholarship and such results of modern criticism as should be compatible with a very judicious conservatism. There was to be no objection to geology, but the universality of the Deluge was to be strictly maintained. The editor committed the article *Deluge* to a man of very considerable ability, but when the article came to him he found that it was so excessively heretical that he could not venture to put it in. There was not time for a second article under that head, and if you look in

[20] *Génie du Christianisme,* chap. v, pp. 1-14, cited by Reusch, vol. i, p. 250.
[21] For admirable sketches of Brongniart and other paleobotanists, see Ward, as above.

that dictionary you will find under the word *Deluge* a reference to *Flood.* Before *Flood* came, a second article had been commissioned from a source that was believed safely conservative; but when the article came in it was found to be worse than the first. A third article was then commissioned, and care was taken to secure its 'safety.' If you look for the word *Flood* in the dictionary, you will find a reference to *Noah.* Under that name you will find an article written by a distinguished professor of Cambridge, of which I remember that Bishop Colenso said to me at the time, 'In a very guarded way the writer concedes the whole thing.' You will see by this under what trammels scientific thought has laboured in this department of inquiry."[22]

*   *   *

The time when the struggle was relinquished by enlightened theologians of the Roman Catholic Church may be fixed at about 1862, when Reusch, Professor of Theology at Bonn, in his work on *The Bible and Nature,* cast off the old diluvial theory and all its supporters, accepting the conclusions of science.[23]

But, though the sacred theory with the Deluge of Noah as a universal solvent for geological difficulties was evidently dying, there still remained in various quarters a touching fidelity to it. In Roman Catholic countries the old theory was widely though quietly cherished, and taught from the religious press, the pulpit, and the theological professor's chair. Pope Pius IX was doubtless in sympathy with this feeling when, about 1850, he forbade the scientific congress of Italy to meet at Bologna.[24]

*   *   *

In the Lutheran branch of the Protestant Church we also find echoes of the old belief. Keil, eminent in scriptural interpretation at the University of Dorpat, gave forth in 1860 a treatise insisting that geology is rendered futile and its explanations vain by two great facts: the Curse which drove

[22] See *Official Report of the National Conference of Unitarian and other Christian Churches held at Saratoga, 1882,* p. 97.
[23] See Reusch, *Bibel und Natur,* chap. xxi.
[24] See Whiteside, *Italy in the Nineteenth Century,* vol. iii, chap. xiv.

Adam and Eve out of Eden, and the Flood that destroyed all living things save Noah, his family, and the animals in the ark. In 1867, Phillippi, and in 1869, Dieterich, both theologians of eminence, took virtually the same ground in Germany, the latter attempting to beat back the scientific hosts with a phrase apparently pithy, but really hollow—the declaration that "modern geology observes what is, but has no right to judge concerning the beginning of things." As late as 1876, Zugler took a similar view, and a multitude of lesser lights, through pulpit and press, brought these anti-scientific doctrines to bear upon the people at large—the only effect being to arouse grave doubts regarding Christianity among thoughtful men, and especially among young men, who naturally distrusted a cause using such weapons.

For just at this time the traditional view of the Deluge received its death-blow, and in a manner entirely unexpected. By the investigations of George Smith among the Assyrian tablets of the British Museum, in 1872, and by his discoveries just afterward in Assyria, it was put beyond a reasonable doubt that a great mass of accounts in Genesis are simply adaptations of earlier and especially of Chaldean myths and legends. While this proved to be the fact as regards the accounts of Creation and the fall of man, it was seen to be most strikingly so as regards the Deluge. The eleventh of the twelve tablets, on which the most important of these inscriptions was found, was almost wholly preserved, and it revealed in this legend, dating from a time far earlier than that of Moses, such features peculiar to the childhood of the world as the building of the great ship or ark to escape the flood, the careful caulking of its seams, the saving of a man beloved of Heaven, his selecting and taking with him into the vessel animals of all sorts in couples, the impressive final closing of the door, the sending forth different birds as the flood abated, the offering of sacrifices when the flood had subsided, the joy of the Divine Being who had caused the flood as the odour of the sacrifice reached his nostrils; while throughout all was shown that partiality for the Chaldean sacred number seven which appears so constantly in the Genesis legends and throughout the Hebrew sacred books.

Other devoted scholars followed in the paths thus opened —Sayce in England, Lenormant in France, Schrader in Germany—with the result that the Hebrew account of the Deluge, to which for ages theologians had obliged all geological research to conform, was quietly relegated, even by most eminent Christian scholars, to the realm of myth and legend.[25]

Sundry feeble attempts to break the force of this discovery, and an evidently widespread fear to have it known, have certainly impaired not a little the legitimate influence of the Christian clergy.

And yet this adoption of Chaldean myths into the Hebrew Scriptures furnishes one of the strongest arguments for the value of our Bible as a record of the upward growth of man; for, while the Chaldean legend primarily ascribes the Deluge to the mere arbitrary caprice of one among many gods (Bel), the Hebrew development of the legend ascribes it to the justice, the righteousness, of the Supreme God; thus showing the evolution of a higher and nobler sentiment which demanded a moral cause adequate to justify such a catastrophe.

Unfortunately, thus far, save in a few of the broader and nobler minds among the clergy, the policy of ignoring such new revelations has prevailed, and the results of this policy, both in Roman Catholic and in Protestant countries, are not far to seek. What the condition of thought is among the middle classes of France and Italy needs not to be stated here. In Germany, as a typical fact, it may be mentioned that there was in the year 1881 church accommodation in the city of Berlin for but two per cent of the population, and that even this accommodation was more than was needed. This fact is not due to the want of a deep religious spirit among the North Germans: no one who has lived among them can doubt the existence of such a spirit; but it is due mainly to the fact that, while the simple results of scientific investigation have filtered down among the people at large, the dominant party in the Lutheran Church has steadily refused to recognise this fact, and has persisted in imposing on Scripture the fetters of literal and dogmatic interpretation which Germany has largely outgrown. A similar danger threatens every other country in which the clergy pursue a similar policy. No thinking man, whatever may be his religious views, can fail to regret this.

[25] For George Smith, see his *Chaldean Account of Genesis,* New York, 1876, especially pp. 36, 263, 286; also his special work on the subject. See also Lencrmant, *Les Origines de l'Histoire,* Paris, 1880, chap. viii. For Schrader, see his *The Cuneiform Inscriptions and the Old Testament,* Whitehouse's translation, London, 1885, vol. i, pp. 47-49 and 58-60, and elsewhere.

A thoughtful, reverent, enlightened clergy is a great blessing to any country; and anything which undermines their legitimate work of leading men out of the worship of material things to the consideration of that which is highest is a vast misfortune.[26]

4. Final Efforts at Compromise—the Victory of Science Complete

Before concluding, it may be instructive to note a few especially desperate attempts at truces or compromises, such as always appear when the victory of any science has become absolutely sure. Typical among the earliest of these may be mentioned the effort of Carl von Raumer in 1819. With much pretension to scientific knowledge, but with aspirations bounded by the limits of Prussian orthodoxy, he made a laboured attempt to produce a statement which, by its vagueness, haziness, and "depth," should obscure the real questions at issue. This statement appeared in the shape of an argument, used by Bertrand and others in the previous century, to prove that fossil remains of plants in the coal measures had never existed as living plants, but had been simply a "result of the development of imperfect plant embryos"; and the same misty theory was suggested to explain the existence of fossil animals without supposing the epochs and changes required by geological science.

* * *

But the most noted among efforts to keep geology well within the letter of Scripture is of still more recent date. In the year 1885 Mr. Gladstone found time, amid all his labours and cares as the greatest parliamentary leader in England, to take the field in the struggle for the letter of Genesis against geology.

On the face of it his effort seemed Quixotic, for he confessed at the outset that in science he was "utterly destitute of that kind of knowledge which carries authority," and his argument soon showed that this confession was entirely true.

But he had some other qualities of which much might be expected: great skill in phrase-making, great shrewdness in adapt-

[26] For the foregoing statements regarding Germany the writer relies on his personal observation as a student at the University of Berlin in 1856, as a traveller at various periods afterward, and as Minister of the United States in 1879, 1880, and 1881.

ing the meanings of single words to conflicting necessities in discussion, wonderful power in erecting showy structures of argument upon the smallest basis of fact, and a facility almost preternatural in "explaining away" troublesome realities. So striking was his power in this last respect, that a humorous London chronicler once advised a bigamist, as his only hope, to induce Mr. Gladstone to explain away one of his wives.

At the basis of this theologico-geological structure Mr. Gladstone placed what he found in the text of Genesis: "A grand fourfold division" of animated Nature "set forth in an orderly succession of times." And he arranged this order and succession of creation as follows: "First, the water population; secondly, the air population; thirdly, the land population of animals; fourthly, the land population consummated in man."

His next step was to slide in upon this basis the apparently harmless proposition that this division and sequence "is understood to have been so affirmed in our time by natural science that it may be taken as a demonstrated conclusion and established fact."

Finally, upon these foundations he proceeded to build an argument out of the coincidences thus secured between the record in the Hebrew sacred books and the truths revealed by science as regards this order and sequence, and he easily arrived at the desired conclusion with which he crowned the whole structure, namely, as regards the writer of Genesis, that "his knowledge was divine."[27]

Such was the skeleton of the structure; it was abundantly decorated with the rhetoric in which Mr. Gladstone is so skilful an artificer, and it towered above "the average man" as a structure beautiful and invincible—like some Chinese fortress in the nineteenth century, faced with porcelain and defended with crossbows.

Its strength was soon seen to be unreal. In an essay admirable in its temper, overwhelming in its facts, and absolutely convincing in its argument, Prof. Huxley, late President of the Royal Society, and doubtless the most eminent contemporary authority on the scientific questions concerned, took up the matter.

Mr. Gladstone's first proposition, that the sacred writings give us a great "fourfold division" created "in an orderly succession of times," Prof. Huxley did not presume to gainsay.

[27] See Mr. Gladstone's *Dawn of Creation and Worship,* a reply to Dr. Réville, in the *Nineteenth Century* for November, 1885.

As to Mr. Gladstone's second proposition, that "this great fourfold division . . . created in an orderly succession of times . . . has been so affirmed in our own time by natural science that it may be taken as a demonstrated conclusion and established fact," Prof. Huxley showed that, as a matter of fact, no such "fourfold division" and "orderly succession" exist; that, so far from establishing Mr. Gladstone's assumption that the population of water, air, and land followed each other in the order given, "all the evidence we possess goes to prove that they did not"; that the distribution of fossils through the various strata proves that some land animals originated before sea animals; that there has been a mixing of sea, land, and air "population" utterly destructive to the "great fourfold division" and to the creation "in an orderly succession of times"; that, so far is the view presented in the sacred text, as stated by Mr. Gladstone, from having been "so affirmed in our own time by natural science, that it may be taken as a demonstrated conclusion and established fact" that Mr. Gladstone's assertion is "directly contradictory to facts known to every one who is acquainted with the elements of natural science"; that Mr. Gladstone's only geological authority, Cuvier, had died more than fifty years before, when geological science was in its infancy [and he might have added, when it was necessary to make every possible concession to the Church]; and, finally, he challenged Mr. Gladstone to produce any contemporary authority in geological science who would support his so-called scriptural view. And when, in a rejoinder, Mr. Gladstone attempted to support his view on the authority of Prof. Dana, Prof. Huxley had no difficulty in showing from Prof. Dana's works that Mr. Gladstone's inference was utterly unfounded.

But, while the fabric reared by Mr. Gladstone had been thus undermined by Huxley on the scientific side, another opponent began an attack from the biblical side. The Rev. Canon Driver, professor at Mr. Gladstone's own University of Oxford, took up the question in the light of scriptural interpretation. In regard to the comparative table drawn up by Sir J. W. Dawson, showing the supposed correspondence between the scriptural and the geological order of creation, Canon Driver said: "The two series are evidently at variance. The geological record contains no evidence of clearly defined periods corresponding to the 'days' of Genesis. In Genesis, vegetation is complete two days before animal life appears. Geology shows that they appear simultaneously—even if animal life does not appear first. In Genesis, birds appear together with aquatic creatures, and precede all land animals; according to the evidence of geology, birds are unknown till a period much later than that at which aquatic creatures (including fishes and amphibia) abound, and they are preceded by numerous species of land animals—in particular, by insects and other 'creeping things.' " Of the Mosaic account of the existence of vegetation before the creation of the sun, Canon Driver said, "No reconciliation of this representation with the data of science has yet been found"; and again: "From all that has been said, however reluctant we may be to make the admission, only one conclusion seems possible. Read without prejudice or bias, the narrative of Genesis i. creates an impression at variance with the facts revealed by science." The eminent professor ends by saying that the efforts at reconciliation are "different modes of obliterating the characteristic features of Genesis, and of reading into it a view which it does not express."

Thus fell Mr. Gladstone's fabric of coincidences between the "great fourfold division" in Genesis and the facts ascertained by geology. Prof. Huxley had shattered the scientific parts of the structure, Prof. Driver had removed its biblical foundations, and the last great fortress of the opponents of unfettered scientific investigation was in ruins.

In opposition to all such attempts we may put a noble utterance by a clergyman who has probably done more to save what is essential in Christianity among English-speaking people than any other ecclesiastic of his time. The late Dean of Westminster, Dr. Arthur Stanley, was widely known and beloved on both continents. In his memorial sermon after the funeral of Sir Charles Lyell he said: "It is now clear to diligent students of the Bible that the first and second chapters of Genesis contain two narratives of the creation side by side, differing from each other in almost every particular of time and place and order. It is well known that, when the science of geology first arose, it was involved in endless schemes of attempted reconciliation with the letter of Scripture. There were, there are perhaps still, two modes of reconciliation of Scripture and science, which have been each in their day attempted, *and each has totally and deservedly failed.* One is the endeavour to wrest the words of the Bible from their natural meaning and *force it to speak the language of science.*" And again, speaking of the earliest known example, which was the interpolation of the word "not" in Leviticus xi, 6, he continues: "This is the earliest instance of *the falsification of Scripture to meet the demands of science;* and it has been followed in later times by the various efforts which have been made to twist the earlier chapters of the book of Genesis into *apparent* agreement with the last results of geology—representing days not to be days, morning and evening not to be morning and evening, the Deluge not to be the Deluge, and the ark not to be the ark."

After a statement like this we may fitly ask, Which is the more likely to strengthen Christianity for its work in the twentieth century which we are now about to enter—a large, manly, honest, fearless utterance like this of Arthur Stanley, or hair-splitting sophistries, bearing in their every line the germs of failure, like those attempted by Mr. Gladstone?

The world is finding that the scientific revelation of creation is ever more and more in accordance with worthy conceptions of that great Power working in and through the universe. More and more it is seen that inspiration has never ceased, and that its prophets and priests are not those who work to fit the letter of its older literature to the needs of dogmas and sects, but those, above all others, who patiently, fearlessly, and reverently devote themselves to the search for truth as truth, in the faith that there is a Power in the universe wise enough to make truth-seeking safe and good enough to make truth-telling useful.[28]

Chapter 6

The Antiquity of Man, Egyptology, and Assyriology

1. The Sacred Chronology

IN THE GREAT RANGES of investigation which bear most directly upon the origin of man, there are two in which Science within the last few years has gained final victories. The significance of these in changing, and ultimately in reversing, one

[28] For the Huxley-Gladstone controversy, see *The Nineteenth Century* for 1885-'86. For Canon Driver, see his article, *The Cosmogony of Genesis,* in *The Expositor* for January, 1886.

of the greatest currents of theological thought, can hardly be overestimated; not even the tide set in motion by Cusa, Copernicus, and Galileo was more powerful to bring in a new epoch of belief.

The first of these conquests relates to the antiquity of man on the earth.

The fathers of the early Christian Church, receiving all parts of our sacred books as equally inspired, laid little, if any, less stress on the myths, legends, genealogies, and tribal, family, and personal traditions contained in the Old and the New Testaments, than upon the most powerful appeals, the most instructive apologues, and the most lofty poems of prophets, psalmists, and apostles. As to the age of our planet and the life of man upon it, they found in the Bible a carefully recorded series of periods, extending from Adam to the building of the Temple at Jerusalem, the length of each period being explicitly given.

Thus they had a biblical chronology—full, consecutive, and definite—extending from the first man created to an event of known date well within ascertained profane history; as a result, the early Christian commentators arrived at conclusions varying somewhat, but in the main agreeing. Some, like Origen, Eusebius, Lactantius, Clement of Alexandria, and the great fathers generally of the first three centuries, dwelling especially upon the Septuagint version of the Scriptures, thought that man's creation took place about six thousand years before the Christian era. Strong confirmation of this view was found in a simple piece of purely theological reasoning: for, just as the seven candlesticks of the Apocalypse were long held to prove the existence of seven heavenly bodies revolving about the earth, so it was felt that the six days of creation prefigured six thousand years during which the earth in its first form was to endure; and that, as the first Adam came on the sixth day, Christ, the second Adam, had come at the sixth millennial period. Theophilus, Bishop of Antioch, in the second century clinched this argument with the text, "One day is with the Lord as a thousand years."

On the other hand, Eusebius and St. Jerome, dwelling more especially upon the Hebrew text, which we are brought up to revere, thought that man's origin took place at a somewhat shorter period before the Christian era; and St. Jerome's overwhelming authority made this the dominant view throughout western Europe during fifteen centuries.

The simplicity of these great fathers as regards chronology is especially reflected from the tables of Eusebius. In these, Moses, Joshua, and Bacchus,—Deborah, Orpheus, and the Amazons,—Abimelech, the Sphinx, and Œdipus, appear together as personages equally real, and their positions in chronology equally ascertained.

At times great bitterness was aroused between those holding the longer and those holding the shorter chronology, but after all the difference between them, as we now see, was trivial; and it may be broadly stated that in the early Church, "always, everywhere, and by all," it was held as certain, upon the absolute warrant of Scripture, that man was created from four to six thousand years before the Christian era.

To doubt this, and even much less than this, was to risk damnation. St. Augustine insisted that belief in the antipodes and in the longer duration of the earth than six thousand years were deadly heresies, equally hostile to Scripture. Philastrius, the friend of St. Ambrose and St. Augustine, whose fearful catalogue of heresies served as a guide to intolerance throughout the Middle Ages, condemned with the same holy horror those who expressed doubt as to the orthodox number of years since the beginning of the world, and those who doubted an earthquake to be the literal voice of an angry God, or who questioned the plurality of the heavens, or who gainsaid the statement that God brings out the stars from his treasures and hangs them up in the solid firmament above the earth every night.

About the beginning of the seventh century Isidore of Seville, the great theologian of his time, took up the subject. He accepted the dominant view not only of Hebrew but of all other chronologies, without anything like real criticism. The childlike faith of his system may be imagined from his summaries which follow. He tells us:

"Joseph lived one hundred and five years. Greece began to cultivate grain."

"The Jews were in slavery in Egypt one hundred and forty-four years. Atlas discovered astrology."

"Joshua ruled for twenty-seven years. Ericthonius yoked horses together."

"Othniel, forty years. Cadmus introduced letters into Greece."

"Deborah, forty years. Apollo discovered the art of medicine and invented the cithara."

"Gideon, forty years. Mercury invented the lyre and gave it to Orpheus."

Reasoning in this general way, Isidore kept well under the longer date; and, the great theological authority of southern Europe having thus spoken, the question was virtually at rest throughout Christendom for nearly a hundred years.

Early in the eighth century the Venerable Bede took up the problem. Dwelling especially upon the received Hebrew text of the Old Testament, he soon entangled himself in very serious difficulties; but, in spite of the great fathers of the first three centuries, he reduced the antiquity of man on the earth by nearly a thousand years, and, in spite of mutterings against him as coming dangerously near a limit which made the theological argument from the six days of creation to the six ages of the world look doubtful, his authority had great weight, and did much to fix western Europe in its allegiance to the general system laid down by Eusebius and Jerome.

In the twelfth century this belief was re-enforced by a tide of thought from a very different quarter. Rabbi Moses Maimonides and other Jewish scholars, by careful study of the Hebrew text, arrived at conclusions diminishing the antiquity of man still further, and thus gave strength throughout the Middle Ages to the shorter chronology: it was incorporated into the sacred science of Christianity; and Vincent of Beauvais, in his great *Speculum Historiale,* forming part of that still more enormous work intended to sum up all the knowledge possessed by the ages of faith, placed the creation of man at about four thousand years before our era.[1]

[1] For a table summing up the periods, from Adam to the building of the Temple, explicitly given in the Scriptures, see the admirable paper on *The Pope and the Bible,* in *The Contemporary Review* for April, 1893. For the date of man's creation as given by leading chronologists in various branches of the Church, see *L'Art de Vérifier les Dates,* Paris, 1819, vol. i, pp. 27 *et seq.* In this edition there are sundry typographical errors; compare with Wallace, *True Age of the World,* London, 1844. As to preference for the longer computation by the fathers of the Church, see Clinton, *Fasti Hellenici,* vol. ii, p. 291. For the sacred significance of the six days of creation in ascertaining the antiquity of man, see especially Eicken, *Geschichte der mittelalterlichen Weltanschauung;* also Wallace, *True Age of the World,* pp. 2, 3. For the views of St. Augustine, see Topinard, *Anthropologie,* citing the *De Civ. Dei.,* lib. xvi, c. viii, lib. xii, c. x. For the views of Philastrius, see the *De Hæresibus,* c. 102, 112, *et passim,* in Migne, tome xii. For

At the Reformation this view was not disturbed. The same manner of accepting the sacred text which led Luther, Melanchthon, and the great Protestant leaders generally, to oppose the Copernican theory, fixed them firmly in this biblical chronology; the keynote was sounded for them by Luther when he said, "We know, on the authority of Moses, that longer ago than six thousand years the world did not exist." Melanchthon, more exact, fixed the creation of man at 3963 B.C.

But the great Christian scholars continued the old endeavour to make the time of man's origin more precise: there seems to have been a sort of fascination in the subject which developed a long array of chronologists, all weighing the minutest indications in our sacred books, until the Protestant divine De Vignolles, who had given forty years to the study of biblical chronology, declared in 1738 that he had gathered no less than two hundred computations based upon Scripture, and no two alike.

As to the Roman Church, about 1580 there was published, by authority of Pope Gregory XIII, the Roman Martyrology, and this, both as originally published and as revised in 1640 under Pope Urban VIII, declared that the creation of man took place 5199 years before Christ.

But of all who gave themselves up to these chronological studies, the man who exerted the most powerful influence upon the dominant nations of Christendom was Archbishop Usher. In 1650 he published his *Annals of the Ancient and New Testaments,* and it at once became the greatest authority for all English-speaking peoples. Usher was a man of deep and wide theological learning, powerful in controversy; and his careful conclusion, after years of the most profound study of the Hebrew Scriptures, was that man was created 4004 years before the Christian era. His verdict was widely received as final; his dates were inserted in the margins of the authorized version of the English Bible, and were soon practically regarded as equally inspired with the sacred text itself: to question them seriously was to risk preferment in the Church and reputation in the world at large.

The same adhesion to the Hebrew Scriptures which had

Eusebius's simple credulity, see the tables in Palmer's *Egyptian Chronicles,* vol. ii, pp. 828, 829. For Bede, see Usher's *Chronologia Sacra,* cited in Wallace, *True Age of the World,* p. 35. For Isidore of Seville, see the *Etymologia,* lib. v, C. 39; also lib. iii, in Migne, tome lxxxii.

influenced Usher brought leading men of the older Church to the same view: men who would have burned each other at the stake for their differences on other points, agreed on this: Melanchthon and Tostatus, Lightfoot and Jansen, Salmeron and Scaliger, Petavius and Kepler, inquisitors and reformers, Jesuits and Jansenists, priests and rabbis, stood together in the belief that the creation of man was proved by Scripture to have taken place between 3900 and 4004 years before Christ.

In spite of the severe pressure of this line of authorities, extending from St. Jerome and Eusebius to Usher and Petavius, in favour of this scriptural chronology, even devoted Christian scholars had sometimes felt obliged to revolt. The first great source of difficulty was increased knowledge regarding the Egyptian monuments. As far back as the last years of the sixteenth century Joseph Scaliger had done what he could to lay the foundations of a more scientific treatment of chronology, insisting especially that the historical indications in Persia, in Babylon, and above all in Egypt, should be brought to bear on the question. More than that, he had the boldness to urge that the chronological indications of the Hebrew Scriptures should be fully and critically discussed in the light of Egyptian and other records, without any undue bias from theological considerations. His idea may well be called inspired; yet it had little effect as regards a true view of the antiquity of man, even upon himself, for the theological bias prevailed above all his reasonings, even in his own mind. Well does a brilliant modern writer declare that, "among the multitude of strong men in modern times abdicating their reason at the command of their prejudices, Joseph Scaliger is perhaps the most striking example."

Early in the following century Sir Walter Raleigh, in his *History of the World* (1603–1616), pointed out the danger of adhering to the old system. He, too, foresaw one of the results of modern investigation, stating it in these words, which have the ring of prophetic inspiration: "For in Abraham's time all the then known parts of the world were developed. . . . Egypt had many magnificent cities, . . . and these not built with sticks, but of hewn stone, . . . which magnificence needed a parent of more antiquity than these other men have supposed." In view of these considerations Raleigh followed the chronology of the Septuagint version, which enabled him to give to the human race a few more years than were usually allowed.

About the middle of the seventeenth century Isaac Vossius, one of the most eminent scholars of Christendom, attempted to bring the prevailing belief into closer accordance with ascertained facts, but, save by a chosen few, his efforts were rejected. In some parts of Europe a man holding new views on chronology was by no means safe from bodily harm. As an example of the extreme pressure exerted by the old theological system at times upon honest scholars, we may take the case of La Peyrère, who about the middle of the seventeenth century put forth his book on the Pre-Adamites—an attempt to reconcile sundry well-known difficulties in Scripture by claiming that man existed on earth before the time of Adam. He was taken in hand at once; great theologians rushed forward to attack him from all parts of Europe; within fifty years thirty-six different refutations of his arguments had appeared; the Parliament of Paris burned the book, and the Grand Vicar of the archdiocese of Mechlin threw him into prison and kept him there until he was forced, not only to retract his statements, but to abjure his Protestantism.

In England, opposition to the growing truth was hardly less earnest. Especially strong was Pearson, afterward Master of Trinity and Bishop of Chester. In his treatise on the Creed, published in 1659, which has remained a theologic classic, he condemned those who held the earth to be more than fifty-six hundred years old, insisted that the first man was created just six days later, declared that the Egyptian records were forged, and called all Christians to turn from them to "the infallible annals of the Spirit of God."

But, in spite of warnings like these, we see the new idea cropping out in various parts of Europe. In 1672, Sir John Marsham published a work in which he showed himself bold and honest. After describing the heathen sources of Oriental history, he turns to the Christian writers, and, having used the history of Egypt to show that the great Church authorities were not exact, he ends one important argument with the following words: "Thus the most interesting antiquities of Egypt have been involved in the deepest obscurity by the very interpreters of her chronology, who have jumbled everything up (*qui omnia susque deque permiscuerunt*), so as to make them match with their own reckonings of Hebrew chronology.

Truly a very bad example, and quite unworthy of religious writers."

This sturdy protest of Sir John against the dominant system and against the "jumbling" by which Eusebius had endeavoured to cut down ancient chronology within safe and sound orthodox limits, had little effect. Though eminent chronologists of the eighteenth century, like Jackson, Hales, and Drummond, gave forth multitudes of ponderous volumes pleading for a period somewhat longer than that generally allowed, and insisting that the received Hebrew text was grossly vitiated as regards chronology, even this poor favour was refused them; the mass of believers found it more comfortable to hold fast the faith committed to them by Usher, and it remained settled that man was created about four thousand years before our era.

To those who wished even greater precision, Dr. John Lightfoot, Vice-Chancellor of the University of Cambridge, the great rabbinical scholar of his time, gave his famous demonstration from our sacred books that "heaven and earth, centre and circumference, were created together, in the same instant, and clouds full of water," and that "this work took place and man was created by the Trinity on the twenty-third of October, 4004 B.C., at nine o'clock in the morning."

This tide of theological reasoning rolled on through the eighteenth century, swollen by the biblical researches of leading commentators, Catholic and Protestant, until it came in much majesty and force into our own nineteenth century. At the very beginning of the century it gained new strength from various great men in the Church, among whom may be especially named Dr. Adam Clarke, who declared that, "to preclude the possibility of a mistake, the unerring Spirit of God directed Moses in the selection of his facts and the ascertaining of his dates."

All opposition to the received view seemed broken down, and as late as 1835—indeed, as late as 1850—came an announcement in the work of one of the most eminent Egyptologists, Sir J. G. Wilkinson, to the effect that he had modified the results he had obtained from Egyptian monuments, in order that his chronology might not interfere with the received date of the Deluge of Noah.[2]

[2] For Lightfoot, see his *Prolegomena* relating to the age of the world at the birth of Christ; see also in the edition of his works, London, 1822, vol. iv. pp. 64, 112. For Scaliger, see the *De Emen-*

2. The New Chronology

But all investigators were not so docile as Wilkinson, and there soon came a new train of scientific thought which rapidly undermined all this theological chronology. Not to speak of other noted men, we have early in the present century Young, Champollion, and Rosellini, beginning a new epoch in the study of the Egyptian monuments. Nothing could be more cautious than their procedure, but the evidence was soon overwhelming in favour of a vastly longer existence of man in the Nile Valley than could be made to agree with even the longest duration then allowed by theologians.

For, in spite of all the suppleness of men like Wilkinson, it became evident that, whatever system of scriptural chronology was adopted, Egypt was the seat of a flourishing civilization at a period before the "Flood of Noah," and that no such flood had ever interrupted it. This was bad, but worse remained behind: it was soon clear that the civilization of Egypt began earlier than the time assigned for the creation of man, even according to the most liberal of the sacred chronologists.

As time went on, this became more and more evident. The long duration assigned to human civilization in the fragments of Manetho, the Egyptian scribe at Thebes in the third century B.C., was discovered to be more accordant with truth than the chronologies of the great theologians; and, as the

datione Temporu, 1583; also Mark Pattison, *Essays*, Oxford, 1889, vol. i, pp. 162 *et seq.* For Raleigh's misgivings, see his *History of the World*, London, 1614, p. 227, book ii of part i, section 7 of chapter i; also Clinton's *Fasti Hellenici*, vol. ii, p. 293. For Usher, see his *Annales Vet. et Nov. Test.*, London, 1650. For Pearson, see his *Exposition of the Creed*, sixth edition, London, 1692, pp. 59 *et seq.* For Marsham, see his *Chronicus Canon Ægypticus, Ebraicus, Græcus, et Disquisitiones*, London, 1672. For La Peyrère, see especially Quatrefages, in *Revue des Deux Mondes* for 1861; also other chapters in this work. For Jackson, Hales, and others, see Wallace's *True Age of the World*. For Wilkinson, see various editions of his work on Egypt. For Vignolles, see Leblois, vol. iii, p. 617. As to the declarations in favour of the recent origin of man, sanctioned by Popes Gregory XIII and Urban VIII, see Strauchius, cited in Wallace, p. 97. For the general agreement of Church authorities, as stated, see *L'Art de Vérifier les Dates*, as above. As to difficulties of scriptural chronology, see Ewald, *History of Israel*, English translation, London, 1883, pp. 204 *et seq.*

present century has gone on, scientific results have been reached absolutely fatal to the chronological view based by the universal Church upon Scripture for nearly two thousand years.

As is well known, the first of the Egyptian kings of whom mention is made upon the monuments of the Nile Valley is Mena, or Menes. Manetho had given a statement, according to which Mena must have lived nearly six thousand years before the Christian era. This was looked upon for a long time as utterly inadmissible, as it was so clearly at variance with the chronology of our own sacred books; but, as time went on, large fragments of the original work of Manetho were more carefully studied and distinguished from corrupt transcriptions, the lists of kings at Karnak, Sacquarah, and the two temples at Abydos were brought to light, and the lists of court architects were discovered. Among all these monuments the scholar who visits Egypt is most impressed by the sculptured tablets giving the lists of kings. Each shows the monarch of the period doing homage to the long line of his ancestors. Each of these sculptured monarchs has near him a tablet bearing his name. That great care was always taken to keep these imposing records correct is certain; the loyalty of subjects, the devotion of priests, and the family pride of kings were all combined in this; and how effective this care was, is seen in the fact that kings now known to be usurpers are carefully omitted. The lists of court architects, extending over the period from Seti to Darius, throw a flood of light over the other records.

Comparing, then, all these sources, and applying an average from the lengths of the long series of well-known reigns to the reigns preceding, the most careful and cautious scholars have satisfied themselves that the original fragments of Manetho represent the work of a man honest and well informed, and, after making all allowances for discrepancies and the overlapping of reigns, it has become clear that the period known as the reign of Mena must be fixed at more than three thousand years B.C. In this the great Egyptologists of our time concur. Mariette, the eminent French authority, puts the date at 5004 B.C.; Brugsch, the leading Germany authority, puts it at about 4500 B.C.; and Meyer, the latest and most cautious of the historians of antiquity, declares 3180 B.C. the latest possible date that can be assigned it. With these dates the foremost English authorities, Sayce and Flinders Petrie, substantially agree. This view is also confirmed on astronomical grounds by Mr. Lockyer, the Astronomer Royal. We have it, then, as the result of a century of work by the most acute and trained Egyptologists, and with the inscriptions upon the temples and papyri before them, both of which are now read with as much facility as many mediæval manuscripts, that the reign of Mena must be placed more than five thousand years ago.

But the significance of this conclusion can not be fully understood until we bring into connection with it some other facts revealed by the Egyptian monuments.

The first of these is that which struck Sir Walter Raleigh, that, even in the time of the first dynasties in the Nile Valley, a high civilization had already been developed. Take, first, man himself: we find sculptured upon the early monuments types of the various races—Egyptians, Israelites, negroes, and Libyans—as clearly distinguishable in these paintings and sculptures of from four to six thousand years ago as the same types are at the present day. No one can look at these sculptures upon the Egyptian monuments, or even the drawings of them, as given by Lepsius or Prisse d'Avennes, without being convinced that they indicate, even at that remote period, a difference of races so marked that long previous ages must have been required to produce it.

The social condition of Egypt revealed in these early monuments of art forces us to the same conclusion. Those earliest monuments show that a very complex society had even then been developed. We not only have a separation between the priestly and military orders, but agriculturists, manufacturers, and traders, with a whole series of subdivisions in each of these classes. The early tombs show us sculptured and painted representations of a daily life which even then had been developed into a vast wealth and variety of grades, forms, and usages.

Take, next, the political and military condition. One fact out of many reveals a policy which must have been the result of long experience. Just as now, at the end of the nineteenth century, the British Government, having found that they can not rely upon the native Egyptians for the protection of the country, are drilling the negroes from the interior of Africa as soldiers, so the celebrated inscription of Prince Una, as far back as the sixth dynasty, speaks of the Maksi or negroes levied and drilled by tens of thousands for the Egyptian army.

Take, next, engineering. Here we find very early operations in the way of canals, dikes, and great public edifices, so bold in conception and thorough in execution as to fill our greatest engineers of these days with astonishment. The quarrying, conveyance, cutting, jointing, and polishing of the enormous blocks in the interior of the Great Pyramid alone are the marvel of the foremost stone-workers of our century.

As regards architecture, we find not only the pyramids, which date from the very earliest period of Egyptian history, and which are to this hour the wonder of the world for size, for boldness, for exactness, and for skilful contrivance, but also the temples, with long ranges of colossal columns wrought in polished granite, with wonderful beauty of ornamentation, with architraves and roofs vast in size and exquisite in adjustment, which by their proportions tax the imagination, and lead the beholder to ask whether all this can be real.

As to sculpture, we have not only the great Sphinx of Gizeh, so marvellous in its boldness and dignity, dating from the very first period of Egyptian history, but we have ranges of sphinxes, heroic statues, and bas-reliefs, showing that even in the early ages this branch of art had reached an amazing development.

As regards the perfection of these, Lübke, the most eminent German authority on plastic art, referring to the early works in the tombs about Memphis, declares that, "as monuments of the period of the fourth dynasty, they are an evidence of the high perfection to which the sculpture of the Egyptians had attained." Brugsch declares that "every artistic production of those early days, whether picture, writing, or sculpture, bears the stamp of the highest perfection in art." Maspero, the most eminent French authority in this field, while expressing his belief that the Sphinx was sculptured even before the time of Mena, declares that "the art which conceived and carved this prodigious statue was a finished art—an art which had attained self-mastery and was sure of its effects"; while, among the more eminent English authorities, Sayce tells us that "art is at its best in the age of the pyramid-builders," and Sir James Fergusson declares, "We are startled to find Egyptian art nearly as perfect in the oldest periods as in any of the later."

The evidence as to the high development of Egyptian sculpture in the earlier dynasties becomes every day more overwhelming. What exquisite genius the early Egyptian sculptors showed in their lesser statues is known to all who have seen those most precious specimens in the museum at Cairo, which were wrought before the conventional type was adopted in obedience to religious considerations.

In decorative and especially in ceramic art, as early as the fourth and fifth dynasties, we have vases, cups, and other vessels showing exquisite beauty of outline and a general sense of form almost if not quite equal to Etruscan and Grecian work of the best periods.

Take, next, astronomy. Going back to the very earliest period of Egyptian civilization, we find that the four sides of the Great Pyramid are adjusted to the cardinal points with the utmost precision. "The day of the equinox can be taken by observing the sun set across the face of the pyramid, and the neighboring Arabs adjust their astronomical dates by its shadow." Yet this is but one out of many facts which prove that the Egyptians, at the earliest period of which their monuments exist, had arrived at knowledge and skill only acquired by long ages of observation and thought. Mr. Lockyer, Astronomer Royal of Great Britain, has recently convinced himself, after careful examination of various ruined temples at Thebes and elsewhere, that they were placed with reference to observations of stars. To state his conclusion in his own words: "There seems a very high probability that three thousand, and possibly four thousand, years before Christ the Egyptians had among them men with some knowledge of astronomy, and that six thousand years ago the course of the sun through the year was practically very well known, and methods had been invented by means of which in time it might be better known; and that, not very long after that, they not only considered questions relating to the sun, but began to take up other questions relating to the position and movement of the stars."

The same view of the antiquity of man in the Nile Valley is confirmed by philologists. To use the words of Max Duncker: "The oldest monuments of Egypt—and they are the oldest monuments in the world—exhibit the Egyptian in possession of the art of writing." It is found also, by the inscriptions of the early dynasties, that the Egyptian language had even at that early time been developed in all essential particulars to the highest point it ever attained. What long periods it must have required for such a development every scholar in philology can imagine.

As regards medical science, we have the Berlin papyrus, which, although of a later period, refers with careful specification to a medical literature of the first dynasty.

As regards archæology, the earliest known inscriptions point to still earlier events and buildings, indicating a long sequence in previous history.

As to all that pertains to the history of civilization, no man of fair and open mind can go into the museums of Cairo or the Louvre or the British Museum and look at the monuments of those earlier dynasties without seeing in them the results of a development in art, science, laws, customs, and language, which must have required a vast period before the time of Mena. And this conclusion is forced upon us all the more invincibly when we consider the slow growth of ideas in the earlier stages of civilization as compared with the later—a slowness of growth which has kept the natives of many parts of the world in that earliest civilization to this hour. To this we must add the fact that Egyptian civilization was especially immobile: its development into castes is but one among many evidences that it was the very opposite of a civilization developed rapidly.

As to the length of the period before the time of Mena, there is, of course, nothing exact. Manetho gives lists of great personages before that first dynasty, and these extend over twenty-four thousand years. Bunsen, one of the most learned of Christian scholars, declares that not less than ten thousand years were necessary for the development of civilization up to the point where we find it in Mena's time. No one can claim precision for either of these statements, but they are valuable as showing the impression of vast antiquity made upon the most competent judges by the careful study of those remains: no unbiased judge can doubt that an immensely long period of years must have been required for the development of civilization up to the state in which we there find it.

The investigations in the bed of the Nile confirm these views. That some unwarranted conclusions have at times been announced is true; but the fact remains that again and again rude pottery and other evidences of early stages of civilization have been found in borings at places so distant from each other, and at depths so great, that for such a range of concurring facts, considered in connection with the rate of earthy deposit by the Nile, there is no adequate explanation save the existence of man in that valley thousands on thousands of years before the longest time admitted by our sacred chronologists.

Nor have these investigations been of a careless character. Between the years 1851 and 1854, Mr. Horner, an extremely cautious English geologist, sank ninety-six shafts in four rows at intervals of eight English miles, at right angles to the Nile, in the neighborhood of Memphis. In these pottery was brought up from various depths, and beneath the statue of Rameses II at Memphis from a depth of thirty-nine feet. At the rate of the Nile deposit a careful estimate has declared this to indicate a period of over eleven thousand years. So eminent a German authority in geography as Peschel characterizes objections to such deductions as groundless. However this may be, the general results of these investigations, taken in connection with the other results of research, are convincing.

And, finally, as if to make assurance doubly sure, a series of archæologists of the highest standing, French, German, English, and American, have within the past twenty years discovered relics of a savage period, of vastly earlier date than the time of Mena, prevailing throughout Egypt. These relics have been discovered in various parts of the country, from Cairo to Luxor, in great numbers. They are the same sort of prehistoric implements which prove to us the early existence of man in so many other parts of the world at a geological period so remote that the figures given by our sacred chronologists are but trivial. The last and most convincing of these discoveries, that of flint implements in the drift, far down below the tombs of early kings at Thebes, and upon high terraces far above the present bed of the Nile, will be referred to later.

But it is not in Egypt alone that proofs are found of the utter inadequacy of the entire chronological system derived from our sacred books. These results of research in Egypt are strikingly confirmed by research in Assyria and Babylonia. Prof. Sayce exhibits various proofs of this. To use his own words regarding one of these proofs: "On the shelves of the British Museum you may see huge sun-dried bricks, on which are stamped the names and titles of kings who erected or repaired the temples where they have been found. . . . They must . . . have reigned before the time when, according to the margins of our Bibles, the Flood of Noah was covering the earth and reducing such bricks as these to their primeval slime."

This conclusion was soon placed beyond a doubt. The lists of kings and collateral inscriptions recovered from the temples of the great valley between the Tigris and Euphrates, and the records of astronomical observations in that region, showed that there, too, a powerful civilization had grown up at a period far earlier than could be made consistent with our sacred chronology. The science of Assyriology was thus combined with Egyptology to furnish one more convincing proof that, precious as are the moral and religious truths in our sacred books and the historical indications which they give us, these truths and indications are necessarily inclosed in a setting of myth and legend.[3]

[3] As to Manetho, see, for a very full account of his relations to other chronologists, Palmer, *Egyptian Chronicles,* vol. i, chap. ii. For a more recent and readable account, see Brugsch, *Egypt under the Pharaohs,* English edition, London, 1879, chap. iv. For lists of kings at Abydos and elsewhere, also the lists of architects, see Brugsch, Palmer, Mariette, and others; also illustrations in Lepsius. For proofs that the dynasties given were consecutive and not contemporaneous, as was once so fondly argued by those who tried to save Archbishop Usher's chronology, see Mariette; also Sayce's *Herodotus,* appendix, p. 316. For the various race types given on early monuments, see the coloured engravings in Lepsius, *Denkmäler;* also Prisse d'Avennes, and the frontispiece in the English edition of Brugsch; see also statement regarding the same subject in Tylor, *Anthropology,* chap. i. For the fulness of development in Egyptian civilization in the earliest dynasties, see Rawlinson's *Egypt,* London, 1881, chap. xiii; also Brugsch and other works cited. For the perfection of Egyptian engineering, I rely not merely upon my own observation, but on what is far more important, the testimony of my friend the Hon. J. G. Batterson, probably the largest and most experienced worker in granite in the United States, who acknowledges, from personal observation, that the early Egyptian work is, in boldness and perfection, far beyond anything known since, and a source of perpetual wonder to him. As to the perfection of Egyptian architecture, see very striking statements in Fergusson, *History of Architecture,* book i, chap. i. As to the pyramids, showing a very high grade of culture already reached under the earliest dynasties, see Lübke, *Gesch. der Arch.,* book i. For Sayce's views, see his *Herodotus,* appendix, p. 348. As

to sculpture, see for representations photographs published by the Boulak Museum, and such works as the *Description de l'Égypte*, Lepsius's *Denkmäler*, and Prisse d'Avennes; see also a most valuable small work, easy of access, Maspero, *Archæology*, translated by Miss A. B. Edwards, New York and London, 1887, chaps. i. and ii. See especially in Prisse, vol. ii, the statue of Chafré the Scribe, and the group of "Tea" and his wife. As to the artistic value of the Sphinx, see Maspero, as above, pp. 202, 203. See also similar ideas in Lübke's *History of Sculpture*, vol. i, p. 24. As to astronomical knowledge evidenced by the Great Pyramid, see Tylor, as above, p. 21; also Lockyer, *On Some Points in the Early History of Astronomy*, in *Nature* for 1891, and especially in the issues of June 4th and July 2d; also his *Dawn of Astronomy, passim*. For a recent and conservative statement as to the date of Mena, see Flinders Petrie, *History of Egypt*, London, 1894, chap. ii. For delineations of vases, etc., showing Grecian proportion and beauty of form under the fourth and fifth dynasties, see Prisse, vol. ii, *Art Industriel*. As to the philological question, and the development of language in Egypt, with the hieroglyphic system of writing, see Rawlinson's *Egypt*, London, 1881, chap. xiii; also Lenormant; also Max Düncker, *Geschichte des Alterthums*, Abbott's translation, 1877. As to the medical papyrus of Berlin, see Brugsch, vol. i, p. 58, but especially the *Papyrus Ebers*. As to the corruption of later copies of Manetho and fidelity of originals as attested by the monuments, see Brugsch, chap. iv. On the accuracy of the present Egyptian chronology as regards long periods, see ibid., vol. i, p. 32. As to the pottery found deep in the Nile and the value of Horner's discovery, see Peschel, *Races of Man*, New York, 1876, pp. 42-44. For succinct statement, see also Laing, *Problems of the Future*, p. 94. For confirmatory proofs from Assyriology, see Sayce, *Lectures on the Religion of the Babylonians* (Hibbert Lectures for 1887), London, 1887, introductory chapter, and especially pp. 21-25. See also Laing, *Human Origins*, chap. ii, for an excellent summary. For an account of flint implements recently found in gravel terraces fifteen hundred feet above the present level of the Nile, and showing evidences of an age vastly greater even than those dug out of the gravel at Thebes, see article by Flinders Petrie in *London Times* of April 18th, 1895.

210 / History of the Warfare of Science with Theology

Chapter 7

The Antiquity of Man and Prehistoric Archæology

1. The Thunder-stones

WHILE THE VIEW of chronology based upon the literal acceptance of Scripture texts was thus shaken by researches in Egypt, another line of observation and thought was slowly developed, even more fatal to the theological view.

From a very early period there had been dug from the earth, in various parts of the world, strangely shaped masses of stone, some rudely chipped, some polished: in ancient times the larger of these were very often considered as thunderbolts, the smaller as arrows, and all of them as weapons which had been hurled by the gods and other supernatural personages. Hence a sort of sacredness attached to them. In Chaldea, they were built into the wall of temples; in Egypt, they were strung about the necks of the dead; in India, fine specimens are to this day seen upon altars, receiving prayers and sacrifices.

Naturally these beliefs were brought into the Christian mythology and adapted to it. During the Middle Ages many of these well-wrought stones were venerated as weapons, which during the "war in heaven" had been used in driving forth Satan and his hosts; hence in the eleventh century an Emperor of the East sent to the Emperor of the West a "heaven axe"; and in the twelfth century a Bishop of Rennes asserted the value of thunder-stones as a divinely-appointed means of securing success in battle, safety on the sea, security against thunder, and immunity from unpleasant dreams. Even as late as the seventeenth century a French ambassador brought a stone hatchet, which still exists in the museum at Nancy, as a present to the Prince-Bishop of Verdun, and claimed for it health-giving virtues.

In the last years of the sixteenth century Michael Mercati tried to prove that the "thunder-stones" were weapons or implements of early races of men; but from some cause his book was not published until the following century, when other thinkers had begun to take up the same idea, and then it had to contend with a theory far more accordant with theologic modes of reasoning in science. This was the theory of the learned Tollius, who in 1649 told the world that these chipped or smoothed stones were "generated in the sky by a fulgurous exhalation conglobed in a cloud by the circumposed humour."

But about the beginning of the eighteenth century a fact of great importance was quietly established. In the year 1715 a large pointed weapon of black flint was found in contact with the bones of an elephant, in a gravel bed near Gray's Inn Lane, in London. The world in general paid no heed to this: if the attention of theologians was called to it, they dismissed it summarily with a reference to the Deluge of Noah; but the specimen was labelled, the circumstances regarding it were recorded, and both specimen and record carefully preserved.

In 1723 Jussieu addressed the French Academy on *The Origin and Uses of Thunder-stones.* He showed that recent travellers from various parts of the world had brought a number of weapons and other implements of stone to France, and that they were essentially similar to what in Europe had been known as "thunder-stones." A year later this fact was clinched into the scientific mind of France by the Jesuit Lafitau, who published a work showing the similarity between the customs of aborigines then existing in other lands and those of the early inhabitants of Europe. So began, in these works of Jussieu and Lafitau, the science of Comparative Ethnography.

But it was at their own risk and peril that thinkers drew from these discoveries any conclusions as to the antiquity of man. Montesquieu, having ventured to hint, in an early edition of his *Persian Letters,* that the world might be much older than had been generally supposed, was soon made to feel danger both to his book and to himself, so that in succeeding editions he suppressed the passage.

In 1730 Mahudel presented a paper to the French Academy of Inscriptions on the so-called "thunder-stones," and also presented a series of plates which showed that these were stone implements, which must have been used at an early period in human history.

In 1778 Buffon, in his *Époques de la Nature,* intimated his belief that "thunder-stones" were made by early races of men; but he did not press this view, and the reason for his reserve was obvious enough: he had already one quarrel with the theologians on his hands, which had cost him dear —public retraction and humiliation. His declaration, therefore, attracted little notice.

In the year 1800 another fact came into the minds of thinking men in England. In that year John Frere presented to the London Society of Antiquaries sundry flint implements found in the clay beds near Hoxne; that they were of human make was certain, and, in view of the undisturbed depths in which they were found, the theory was suggested that the men who made them must have lived at a very ancient geological epoch; yet even this discovery and theory passed like a troublesome dream, and soon seemed to be forgotten.

About twenty years later Dr. Buckland published a discussion of the subject, in the light of various discoveries in the drift and in caves. It received wide attention, but theology was soothed by his temporary concession that these striking relics of human handiwork, associated with the remains of various extinct animals, were proofs of the Deluge of Noah.

In 1823 Boué, of the Vienna Academy of Sciences, showed to Cuvier sundry human bones found deep in the alluvial deposits of the upper Rhine, and suggested that they were of an early geological period; this Cuvier virtually, if not explicitly, denied. Great as he was in his own field, he was not a great geologist; he, in fact, led geology astray for many years. Moreover, he lived in a time of reaction; it was the period of the restored Bourbons, of the Voltairean King Louis XVIII, governing to please orthodoxy. Boué's discovery was, therefore, at first opposed, then enveloped in studied silence.

Cuvier evidently thought, as Voltaire had felt under similar circumstances, that "among wolves one must howl a little"; and his leading disciple, Élie de Beaumont, who succeeded him in the sway over geological science in France, was even more opposed to the new view than his great master had been. Boué's discoveries were, therefore, apparently laid to rest forever.[1]

[1] For the general history of early views regarding stone implements, see the first chapters in Cartailhac, *La France Préhistorique;* also Joly, *L'Homme avant les Métaux;* also Lyell, Lubbock, and Evans. For lightning-stones in China and elsewhere, see citation from a Chinese encyclopædia of 1662, in Tylor, *Early History of Mankind,* p. 209. On the universality of this belief, on

In 1825 Kent's Cavern, near Torquay, was explored by the Rev. Mr. McEnery, a Roman Catholic clergyman, who seems to have been completely overawed by orthodox opinion in England and elsewhere; for, though he found human bones and implements mingled with remains of extinct animals, he kept his notes in manuscript, and they were only brought to light more than thirty years later by Mr. Vivian.

The coming of Charles X, the last of the French Bourbons, to the throne, made the orthodox pressure even greater. It was the culmination of the reactionary period—the time in France when a clerical committee, sitting at the Tuileries, took such measures as were necessary to hold in check all science that was not perfectly "safe"; the time in Austria when Kaiser Franz made his famous declaration to sundry professors, that what he wanted of them was simply to train obedient subjects, and that those who did not make this their purpose would be dismissed; the time in Germany when Nicholas of Russia and the princelings and ministers under his control, from the King of Prussia downward, put forth all their might in behalf of "scriptural science"; the time in Italy when a scientific investigator, arriving at any conclusion distrusted by the Church, was sure of losing his place and in danger of losing his liberty; the time in England when what little science was taught was held in due submission to Archdeacon Paley; the time in the United States when the first thing essential in science was, that it be adjusted to the ideas of revival exhorters.

Yet men devoted to scientific truth laboured on; and in 1828 Tournal, of Narbonne, discovered in the cavern of Bize specimens of human industry, with a fragment of a human skeleton, among bones of extinct animals. In the following year Christol published accounts of his excavations in the caverns of Gard; he had found in position, and under conditions which forbade the idea of after-disturbance, human remains mixed with bones of the extinct hyena of the early Quaternary period. Little general notice was taken of this,

---

the surviving use of stone implements even into civilized times, and on their manufacture to-day, see ibid., chapter viii. For the treatment of Boué's discovery, see especially Mortillet, Le Préhistorique, Paris, 1885, p. 11. For the suppression of the passage in Montesquieu's Persian Letters, see Letter 113, cited in Schlosser's History of the Eighteenth Century (English translation), vol. i, p. 135.

for the reactionary orthodox atmosphere involved such discoveries in darkness.

But in the French Revolution of 1830 the old politico-theological system collapsed: Charles X and his advisers fled for their lives; the other continental monarchs got glimpses of new light; the priesthood in charge of education were put on their good behaviour for a time, and a better era began.

Under the constitutional monarchy of the house of Orleans in France and Belgium less attention was therefore paid by Government to the saving of souls; and we have in rapid succession new discoveries of remains of human industry, and even of human skeletons so mingled with bones of extinct animals as to give additional proofs that the origin of man was at a period vastly earlier than any which theologians had dreamed of.

A few years later the reactionary clerical influence against science in this field rallied again. Schmerling in 1833 had explored a multitude of caverns in Belgium, especially at Engis and Engihoul, and had found human skulls and bones closely associated with bones of extinct animals, such as the cave bear, hyena, elephant, and rhinoceros, while mingled with these were evidences of human workmanship in the shape of chipped flint implements; discoveries of a similar sort had been made by De Serres in France and by Lund in Brazil; but, at least as far as continental Europe was concerned, these discoveries were received with much coolness both by Catholic leaders of opinion in France and Belgium and by Protestant leaders in England and Holland. Schmerling himself appears to have been overawed, and gave forth a sort of apologetic theory, half scientific, half theologic, vainly hoping to satisfy the clerical side.

Nor was it much better in England. Sir Charles Lyell, so devoted a servant of prehistoric research thirty years later, was still holding out against it on the scientific side; and, as to the theological side, it was the period when that great churchman, Dean Cockburn, was insulting geologists from the pulpit of York Minster, and the Rev. Mellor Brown denouncing geology as "a black art," "a forbidden province"; and when, in America, Prof. Moses Stuart and others like him were belittling the work of Benjamin Silliman and Edward Hitchcock.

In 1840 Godwin Austin presented to the Royal Geological

Society an account of his discoveries in Kent's Cavern, near Torquay, and especially of human bones and implements mingled with bones of the elephant, rhinoceros, cave bear, hyena, and other extinct animals; yet this memoir, like that of McEnery fifteen years before, found an atmosphere so unfavourable that it was not published.

2. The Flint Weapons and Implements

At the middle of the nineteenth century came the beginning of a new epoch in science—an epoch when all these earlier discoveries were to be interpreted by means of investigations in a different field: for, in 1847, a man previously unknown to the world at large, Boucher de Perthes, published at Paris the first volume of his work on *Celtic and Antediluvian Antiquities,* and in this he showed engravings of typical flint implements and weapons, of which he had discovered thousands upon thousands in the high drift beds near Abbeville, in northern France.

The significance of this discovery was great indeed—far greater than Boucher himself at first supposed. The very title of his book showed that he at first regarded these implements and weapons as having belonged to men overwhelmed at the Deluge of Noah; but it was soon seen that they were something very different from proofs of the literal exactness of Genesis: for they were found in terraces at great heights above the river Somme, and, under any possible theory having regard to fact, must have been deposited there at a time when the river system of northern France was vastly different from anything known within the historic period. The whole discovery indicated a series of great geological changes since the time when these implements were made, requiring cycles of time compared to which the space allowed by the orthodox chronologists was as nothing.

His work was the result of over ten years of research and thought. Year after year a force of men under his direction had dug into these high-terraced gravel deposits of the river Somme, and in his book he now gave, in the first full form, the results of his labour. So far as France was concerned, he was met at first by what he calls "a conspiracy of silence," and then by a contemptuous opposition among orthodox scientists, at the head of whom stood Élie de Beaumont.

This heavy, sluggish opposition seemed immovable: nothing that Boucher could do or say appeared to lighten the pressure of the orthodox theological opinion behind it; not even his belief that these fossils were remains of men drowned at the Deluge of Noah, and that they were proofs of the literal exactness of Genesis seemed to help the matter. His opponents felt instinctively that such discoveries boded danger to the accepted view, and they were right: Boucher himself soon saw the folly of trying to account for them by the orthodox theory.

And it must be confessed that not a little force was added to the opposition by certain characteristics of Boucher de Perthes himself. Gifted, far-sighted, and vigorous as he was, he was his own worst enemy. Carried away by his own discoveries, he jumped to the most astounding conclusions. The engravings in the later volume of his great work, showing what he thought to be human features and inscriptions upon some of the flint implements, are worthy of a comic almanac; and at the National Museum of Archæology at St. Germain, beneath the shelves bearing the remains which he discovered, which mark the beginning of a new epoch in science, are drawers containing specimens hardly worthy of a penny museum, but from which he drew the most unwarranted inferences as to the language, religion, and usages of prehistoric man.

Boucher triumphed none the less. Among his bitter opponents at first was Dr. Rigollot, who in 1855, searching earnestly for materials to refute the innovator, dug into the deposits of St. Acheul—and was converted: for he found implements similar to those of Abbeville, making still more certain the existence of man during the Drift period. So, too, Gaudry a year later made similar discoveries.

But most important was the evidence of the truth which now came from other parts of France and from other countries. The French leaders in geological science had been held back not only by awe of Cuvier but by recollections of Scheuchzer. Ridicule has always been a serious weapon in France, and the ridicule which finally overtook the supporters of the attempt of Scheuchzer, Mazurier, and others, to square geology with Genesis, was still remembered. From the great body of French geologists, therefore, Boucher secured at first no aid. His support came from the other side of the Channel. The most eminent English geologists, such as Falconer, Prestwich, and Lyell, visited the beds at Abbeville and

St. Acheul, convinced themselves that the discoveries of Boucher, Rigollot, and their colleagues were real, and then quietly but firmly told England the truth.

And now there appeared a most effective ally in France. The arguments used against Boucher de Perthes and some of the other early investigators of bone caves had been that the implements found might have been washed about and turned over by great floods, and therefore that they might be of a recent period; but in 1861 Edward Lartet published an account of his own excavations at the Grotto of Aurignac, and the proof that man had existed in the time of the Quaternary animals was complete. This grotto had been carefully sealed in prehistoric times by a stone at its entrance; no interference from disturbing currents of water had been possible; and Lartet found, in place, bones of eight out of nine of the main species of animals which characterize the Quaternary period in Europe; and upon them marks of cutting implements, and in the midst of them coals and ashes.

Close upon these came the excavations at Eyzies by Lartet and his English colleague, Christy. In both these men there was a carefulness in making researches and a sobriety in stating results which converted many of those who had been repelled by the enthusiasm of Boucher de Perthes. The two colleagues found in the stony deposits made by the water dropping from the roof of the cave at Eyzies the bones of numerous animals extinct or departed to arctic regions—one of these a vertebra of a reindeer with a flint lance-head still fast in it, and with these were found evidences of fire.

Discoveries like these were thoroughly convincing; yet there still remained here and there gainsayers in the supposed interest of Scripture, and these, in spite of the convincing array of facts, insisted that in some way, by some combination of circumstances, these bones of extinct animals of vastly remote periods might have been brought into connection with all these human bones and implements of human make in all these different places, refusing to admit that these ancient relics of men and animals were of the same period. Such gainsayers virtually adopted the reasoning of quaint old Persons, who, having maintained that God created the world "about five thousand sixe hundred and odde yeares agoe," added, "And if they aske what God was doing before this short number of yeares, we answere with St. Augustine replying to such curious questioners, that He was framing

Hell for them." But a new class of discoveries came to silence this opposition. At La Madeleine in France, at the Kessler cave in Switzerland, and at various other places, were found rude but striking carvings and engravings on bone and stone representing sundry specimens of those long-vanished species; and these specimens, or casts of them, were soon to be seen in all the principal museums. They showed the hairy mammoth, the cave bear, and various other animals of the Quaternary period, carved rudely but vigorously by contemporary men; and, to complete the significance of these discoveries, travellers returning from the icy regions of North America brought similar carvings of animals now existing in those regions, made by the Eskimos during their long arctic winters to-day.[2]

As a result of these discoveries and others like them, showing that man was not only contemporary with long-extinct animals of past geological epochs, but that he had already developed into a stage of culture above pure savagery, the

[2] For the explorations in Belgium, see Dupont, *Le Temps Préhistorique en Belgique*. For the discoveries by McEnery and Godwin Austin, see Lubbock, *Prehistoric Times*, London, 1869, chap. x; also Cartailhac, Joly, and others above cited. For Boucher de Perthes, see his *Antiquités Celtiques et Antédiluviennes*, Paris, 1847–'64, vol. iii, pp. 526 *et seq.* For sundry extravagances of Boucher de Perthes, see Reinach, *Description raisonnée du Musée de St.-Germain-en-Laye*, Paris, 1889, vol. i, pp. 16 *et seq.* For the mixture of sound and absurd results in Boucher's work, see Cartailhac as above, p. 19. Boucher had published in 1838 a work entitled *De la Création*, but it seems to have dropped dead from the press. For the attempts of Scheuchzer to reconcile geology and Genesis by means of the *Homo diluvii testis*, and similar "diluvian fossils," see the chapter on *Geology* in this series. The original specimens of those prehistoric engravings upon bone and stone may be best seen at the Archæological Museum of St.-Germain and the British Museum. For engravings of some of the most recent, see especially Dawkins's *Early Man in Britain*, chap. vii, and the *Description du Musée de St.-Germain*. As to the Kessler etchings and their antiquity, see D. G. Brinton, in *Science*, August 12, 1892. For comparison of this prehistoric work with that produced to-day by the Eskimos and others, see Lubbock, *Prehistoric Times*, chapters x and xiv. For very striking exhibitions of this same artistic gift in a higher field to-day by descendants of the barbarian tribes of northern America, see the very remarkable illustrations in Rink, *Danish Greenland*, London, 1877, especially those in chap. xiv.

tide of thought began to turn. Especially was this seen in 1863, when Lyell published the first edition of his *Geological Evidence of the Antiquity of Man;* and the fact that he had so long opposed the new ideas gave force to the clear and conclusive argument which led him to renounce his early scientific beliefs.

Research among the evidences of man's existence in the early Quaternary, and possibly in the Tertiary period, was now pressed forward along the whole line. In 1864 Gabriel Mortillet founded his review devoted to this subject; and in 1865 the first of a series of scientific congresses. devoted to such researches was held in Italy. These investigations went on vigorously in all parts of France and spread rapidly to other countries. The explorations which Dupont began in 1864, in the caves of Belgium, gave to the museum at Brussels eighty thousand flint implements, forty thousand bones of animals of the Quaternary period, and a number of human skulls and bones found mingled with these remains. From Germany, Italy, Spain, America, India, and Egypt similar results were reported.

Especially noteworthy were the further explorations of the caves and drift throughout the British Islands. The discovery by Colonel Wood, in 1861, of flint tools in the same strata with bones of the earlier forms of the rhinoceros was but typical of many. A thorough examination of the caverns of Brixham and Torquay, by Pengelly and others, made it still more evident that man had existed in the early Quaternary period. The existence of a period before the Glacial epoch or between different glacial epochs in England, when the Englishman was a savage, using rude stone tools, was then fully ascertained, and, what was more significant, there were clearly shown a gradation and evolution even in the history of that period. It was found that this ancient Stone epoch showed progress and development. In the upper layers of the caves, with remains of the reindeer, who, although he has migrated from these regions, still exists in more northern climates, were found stone implements revealing some little advance in civilization; next below these, sealed up in the stalagmite, came, as a rule, another layer, in which the remains of reindeer were rare and those of the mammoth more frequent, the implements found in this stratum being less skilfully made than those in the upper and more recent layers; and, finally, in the lowest levels, near the floors of

220 / History of the Warfare of Science with Theology

these ancient caverns, with remains of the cave bear and others of the most ancient extinct animals, were found stone implements evidently of a yet ruder and earlier stage of human progress. No fairly unprejudiced man can visit the cave and museum at Torquay without being convinced that there were a gradation and an evolution in these beginnings of human civilization. The evidence is complete; the masses of breccia taken from the cave, with the various soils, implements, and bones carefully kept in place, put this progress beyond a doubt.

All this indicated a great antiquity for the human race, but in it lay the germs of still another great truth, even more important and more serious in its consequences to the older theologic view, which will be discussed in the following chapter.[3]

*   *   *

Chapter 8

The "Fall of Man" and Anthropology

IN THE PREVIOUS CHAPTERS we have seen how science, especially within the eighteenth and nineteenth centuries, has thoroughly changed the intelligent thought of the world in regard to the antiquity of man upon our planet; and how the fabric built upon the chronological indications in our sacred books—first, by the early fathers of the Church, afterward by the mediæval doctors, and finally by the reformers and modern orthodox chronologists—has virtually disappeared before an entirely different view forced upon us, especially by Egyptian and Assyrian studies, as well as by geology and archæology.

[3] [For more recent evidence and speculation on the antiquity of man and his pre-historic evolution, see the September, 1960, issue of Scientific American (Vol. 203, No. 3), especially Sherwood L. Washburn, "Tools and Human Evolution," and William W. Howells, "The Distribution of Man." The entire magazine, however, devoted to the subject "The Human Species," makes fascinating reading. Suggestions for further reading are included with each article.—Ed.]

In this chapter I purpose to present some outlines of the work of Anthropology, especially as assisted by Ethnology, in showing what the evolution of human civilization has been.

Here, too, the change from the old theological view based upon the letter of our sacred books to the modern scientific view based upon evidence absolutely irrefragable is complete. Here, too, we are at the beginning of a vast change in the basis and modes of thought upon man—a change even more striking than that accomplished by Copernicus and Galileo, when they substituted for a universe in which sun and planets revolved about the earth a universe in which the earth is but the merest grain or atom revolving with other worlds, larger and smaller, about the sun; and all these forming but one among innumerable systems.

Ever since the beginning of man's effective thinking upon the great problems around him, two antagonistic views have existed regarding the life of the human race upon earth. The first of these is the belief that man was created "in the beginning" a perfect being, endowed with the highest moral and intellectual powers, but that there came a "Fall," and, as its result, the entrance into the world of evil, toil, sorrow, and death.

Nothing could be more natural than such an explanation of the existence of evil, in times when men saw everywhere miracle and nowhere law. It is, under such circumstances, by far the most easy of explanations, for it is in accordance with the appearances of things: men adopted it just as naturally as they adopted the theory that the Almighty hangs up the stars as lights in the solid firmament above the earth, or hides the sun behind a mountain at night, or wheels the planets around the earth, or flings comets as "signs and wonders" to scare a wicked world, or allows evil spirits to control thunder, lightning, and storm, and to cause diseases of body and mind, or opens the "windows of heaven" to let down "the waters that be above the heavens," and thus to give rain upon the earth.

A belief, then, in a primeval period of innocence and perfection—moral, intellectual, and physical—from which men for some fault fell, is perfectly in accordance with what we should expect.

Among the earliest known records of our race we find this view taking shape in the Chaldean legends of war between the gods, and of a fall of man; both of which seemed necessary to explain the existence of evil.

In Greek mythology perhaps the best-known statement was made by Hesiod: to him it was revealed, regarding the men of the most ancient times, that they were at first "a golden race," that "as gods they were wont to live, with a life void of care, without labour and trouble; nor was wretched old age at all impending; but ever did they delight themselves out of the reach of all ills, and they died as if overcome by sleep; all blessings were theirs: of its own will the fruitful field would bear them fruit, much and ample, and they gladly used to reap the labours of their hands in quietness along with many good things, being rich in flocks and true to the blessed gods." But there came a "fall," caused by human curiosity. Pandora, the first woman created, received a vase which, by divine command, was to remain closed; but she was tempted to open it, and troubles, sorrow, and disease escaped into the world, hope alone remaining.

So, too, in Roman mythological poetry the well-known picture by Ovid is but one among the many exhibitions of this same belief in a primeval golden age—a Saturnian cycle; one of the constantly recurring attempts, so universal and so natural in the early history of man, to account for the existence of evil, care, and toil on earth by explanatory myths and legends.

This view, growing out of the myths, legends, and theologies of earlier peoples, we also find embodied in the sacred tradition of the Jews, and especially in one of the documents which form the impressive poem beginning the books attributed to Moses. As to the Christian Church, no word of its Blessed Founder indicates that it was committed by him to this theory, or that he even thought it worthy of his attention. How, like so many other dogmas never dreamed of by Jesus of Nazareth and those who knew him best, it was developed, it does not lie within the province of this chapter to point out; nor is it worth our while to dwell upon its evolution in the early Church, in the Middle Ages, at the Reformation, and in various branches of the Protestant Church; suffice it that, though among English-speaking nations by far the most important influence in its favour has come from Milton's inspiration rather than from that of older sacred books, no doctrine has been more universally accepted, "always, everywhere, and by all," from the earliest fathers of the Church down to the present hour.

On the other hand appeared at an early period the opposite view—that mankind, instead of having fallen from a high intellectual, moral, and religious condition, has slowly risen from low and brutal beginnings. In Greece, among the philosophers contemporary with Socrates, we find Critias depicting a rise of man, from a time when he was beastlike and lawless, through a period when laws were developed, to a time when morality received enforcement from religion; but among all the statements of this theory the most noteworthy is that given by Lucretius in his great poem on *The Nature of Things*. Despite its errors, it remains among the most remarkable examples of prophetic insight in the history of our race. The inspiration of Lucretius gave him almost miraculous glimpses of truth; his view of the development of civilization from the rudest beginnings to the height of its achievements is a wonderful growth, rooted in observation and thought, branching forth into a multitude of striking facts and fancies; and among these is the statement regarding the sequence of inventions:

"Man's earliest arms were fingers, teeth, and nails,
And stones and fragments from the branching woods;
Then copper next; and last, as latest traced,
The tyrant, iron."

Thus did the poet prophesy one of the most fruitful achievements of modern science: the discovery of that series of epochs which has been so carefully studied in our century.

Very striking, also, is the statement of Horace, though his idea is evidently derived from Lucretius. He dwells upon man's first condition on earth as low and bestial, and pictures him lurking in caves, progressing from the use of his fists and nails, first to clubs, then to arms which he had learned to forge, and, finally, to the invention of the names of things, to literature, and to laws.[1]

[1] For the passage in Hesiod, as given, see the *Works and Days,* lines 109-120, in Banks's translation. As to Horace, see the *Satires,* i, 3, 99. As to the relation of the poetic account of the Fall in Genesis to Chaldean myths, see Smith, *Chaldean Account of Genesis,* pp. 13, 17. For a very instructive separation of the Jehovistic

During the mediæval ages of faith this view was almost entirely obscured, and at the Reformation it seemed likely to remain so. Typical of the simplicity of belief in "the Fall" cherished among the Reformers is Luther's declaration regarding Adam and Eve. He tells us, "they entered into the garden about noon, and having a desire to eat, she took the apple; then came the fall—according to our account at about two o'clock." But in the revival of learning the old eclipsed truth reappeared, and in the first part of the seventeenth century we find that, among the crimes for which Vanini was sentenced at Toulouse to have his tongue torn out and to be burned alive, was his belief that there is a gradation extending upward from the lowest to the highest form of created beings.

Yet, in the same century, the writings of Bodin, Bacon, Descartes, and Pascal were evidently undermining the old idea of "the Fall." Bodin especially, brilliant as were his services to orthodoxy, argued lucidly against the doctrine of general human deterioration.

Early in the eighteenth century Vico presented the philosophy of history as an upward movement of man out of animalism and barbarism. This idea took firm hold upon human thought, and in the following centuries such men as Lessing and Turgot gave new force to it.

The investigations of the last forty years have shown that

---

and Elohistic parts of Genesis, with the account of the "Fall" as given in the former, see Lenormant, *La Génèse*, Paris, 1883, pp. 166-168; also Bacon, *Genesis of Genesis*. Of the lines of Lucretius—

> "Arma antiqua, manus, ungues, dentesque fuerunt,
> Et lapides, et item sylvarum fragmina rami,
> Posterius ferri vis est, aerisque reperta,
> Sed prior aeris erat, quam ferri cognitus usus"—

the translation given is that of Good. For a more exact prose translation, see Munro's Lucretius, fourth edition, which is much more careful, at least in the proof-reading, than the first edition. As regards Lucretius's prophetic insight into some of the greatest conclusions of modern science, see Munro's translation and notes, fourth edition, book v, notes ii, p. 335. On the relation of several passages in Horace to the ideas of Lucretius, see Munro as above. For the passage from Luther, see the *Table Talk*, Hazlitt's translation, p. 242.

Lucretius and Horace were inspired prophets: what they saw by the exercise of reason illumined by poetic genius, has been now thoroughly based upon facts carefully ascertained and arranged—until Thomsen and Nilsson, the northern archæologists, have brought these prophecies to evident fulfilment, by presenting a scientific classification dividing the age of prehistoric man in various parts of the world between an old stone period, a new stone period, a period of beaten copper, a period of bronze, and a period of iron, and arraying vast masses of facts from all parts of the world, fitting thoroughly into each other, strengthening each other, and showing beyond a doubt that, instead of a *fall*, there has been a *rise* of man, from the earliest indications in the Quaternary, or even, possibly, in the Tertiary period.[2]

The first blow at the fully developed doctrine of "the Fall" came, as we have seen, from geology. According to that doctrine, as held quite generally from its beginnings among the fathers and doctors of the primitive Church down to its culmination in the minds of great Protestants like John Wesley, the statement in our sacred books that "death entered the world by sin" was taken as a historic fact, necessitating the conclusion that, before the serpent persuaded Eve to eat of the forbidden fruit, death on our planet was unknown. Naturally, when geology revealed, in the strata of a period long before the coming of man on earth, a vast multitude of carnivorous tribes fitted to destroy their fellow-creatures on land and sea, and within the fossilized skeletons of many of these the partially digested remains of animals, this doctrine was too heavy to be carried, and it was quietly dropped.

[2] For Vanini, see Topinard, *Éléments d'Anthropologie*, p. 52. For a brief and careful summary of the agency of Eccard in Germany, Goguet in France, Hoare in England, and others in various parts of Europe, as regards this development of the scientific view during the eighteenth century, see Mortillet, *Le Préhistorique*, Paris, 1885, chap. i. For the agency of Bodin, Bacon, Descartes, and Pascal, see Flint, *Philosophy of History,* introduction, pp. 28 *et seq.* For a shorter summary, see Lubbock, *Prehistoric Man.* For the statements by the northern archæologists, see Nilsson, Worsaae, and the other main works cited in this article. For a generous statement regarding the great services of the Danish archæologists in this field, see Quatrefages, introduction to Cartailhac, *Les Âges Préhistoriques de l'Espagne et du Portugal.*

But about the middle of the nineteenth century the doctrine of the rise of man as opposed to the doctrine of his "fall" received a great accession of strength from a source most unexpected. As we saw in the last chapter, the facts proving the great antiquity of man foreshadowed a new and even more remarkable idea regarding him. We saw, it is true, that the opponents of Boucher de Perthes, while they could not deny his discovery of human implements in the drift, were successful in securing a verdict of "Not proven" as regarded his discovery of human bones; but their triumph was short-lived. Many previous discoveries, little thought of up to that time, began to be studied, and others were added which resulted not merely in confirming the truth regarding the antiquity of man, but in establishing another doctrine which the opponents of science regarded with vastly greater dislike—the doctrine that man has not fallen from an original high estate in which he was created about six thousand years ago, but that, from a period vastly earlier than any warranted by the sacred chronologists, he has been, in spite of lapses and deteriorations, rising.

A brief review of this new growth of truth may be useful. As early as 1835 Prof. Jaeger had brought out from a quantity of Quaternary remains dug up long before at Cannstadt, near Stuttgart, a portion of a human skull, apparently of very low type. A battle raged about it for a time, but this finally subsided, owing to uncertainties arising from the circumstances of the discovery.

In 1856, in the Neanderthal, near Düsseldorf, among Quaternary remains gathered on the floor of a grotto, another skull was found bearing the same evidence of a low human type. As in the case of the Cannstadt skull, this again was fiercely debated, and finally the questions regarding it were allowed to remain in suspense. But new discoveries were made: at Eguisheim, at Brux, at Spy, and elsewhere, human skulls were found of a similarly low type; and, while each of the earlier discoveries was open to debate, and either, had no other been discovered, might have been considered an abnormal specimen, the combination of all these showed conclusively that not only had a race of men existed at that remote period, but that it was of a type as low as the lowest, perhaps below the lowest, now known.

Research was now redoubled, and, as a result, human skulls and complete skeletons of various types began to be discovered in the ancient deposits of many other parts of the world, and especially in France, Belgium, Germany, the Caucasus, Africa, and North and South America.

But soon began to emerge from all these discoveries a fact of enormous importance. The skulls and bones found at Cro Magnon, Solutré, Furfooz, Grenelle, and elsewhere, were compared, and it was thus made certain that various races had already appeared and lived in various grades of civilization, even in those exceedingly remote epochs; that even then there were various strata of humanity ranging from races of a very low to those of a very high type; and that upon any theory—certainly upon the theory of the origin of mankind from a single pair—two things were evident: first, that long, slow processes during vast periods of time must have been required for the differentiation of these races, and for the evolution of man up to the point where the better specimens show him, certainly in the early Quaternary and perhaps in the Tertiary period; and, secondly, that there had been from the first appearance of man, of which we have any traces, an *upward* tendency.[3]

This second conclusion, the upward tendency of man from low beginnings, was made more and more clear by bringing into relations with these remains of human bodies and of extinct animals the remains of human handiwork. As stated in the last chapter, the river drift and bone caves in Great Britain, France, and other parts of the world, revealed a

[3] For Wesley's statement of the amazing consequences of the entrance of death into the world by sin, see citations from his sermon on *The Fall of Man* in the chapter on Geology. For Boucher de Perthes, see his *Life* by Ledieu, especially chapters v and xix; also letters in the appendix; also *Les Antiquités Celtiques et Antédiluviennes,* as cited in previous chapters of this work. For an account of the Neanderthal man and other remains mentioned, see Quatrefages, *Human Species,* chap. xxvi; also Mortillet, *Le Préhistorique,* Paris, 1885, pp. 232 *et seq.;* also other writers cited in this chapter. For the other discoveries mentioned, see the same sources. For an engraving of the skull and the restored human face of the Neanderthal man, see Reinach, *Antiquités Nationales,* etc., vol. i, 138. For the vast regions over which that early race spread, see Quatrefages as above, p. 307. See also the same author, *Histoire Générale des Races Humaines,* in the *Bibliothéque Ethnologique,* Paris, 1887, p. 4. In the vast mass of literature bearing on this subject, see Quatrefages, Dupont, Reinach, Joly, Mortillet, Tylor, and Lubbock, in works cited through these chapters.

progression, even in the various divisions of the earliest Stone period; for, beginning at the very lowest strata of these remains, on the floors of the caverns, associated mainly with the bones of extinct animals, such as the cave bear, the hairy elephant, and the like, were the rudest implements; then, in strata above these, sealed in the stalagmite of the cavern floors, lying with the bones of animals extinct but more recent, stone implements were found, still rude, but, as a rule, of an improved type; and, finally, in a still higher stratum, associated with bones of animals like the reindeer and bison, which, though not extinct, have departed to other climates, were rude stone implements, on the whole of a still better workmanship. Such was the foreshadowing, even at that early rude Stone period, of the proofs that the tendency of man has been from his earliest epoch and in all parts of the world, as a rule, upward.

But this rule was to be much further exemplified. About 1850, while the French and English geologists were working more especially among the relics of the drift and cave periods, noted archæologists of the North—Forchammer, Steenstrup, and Worsaae—were devoting themselves to the investigation of certain remains upon the Danish Peninsula. These remains were of two kinds: first, there were vast shell-heaps or accumulations of shells and other refuse cast aside by rude tribes which at some unknown age in the past lived on the shores of the Baltic, principally on shellfish. That these shell-heaps were very ancient was evident: the shells of oysters and the like found in them were far larger than any now found on those coasts; their size, so far from being like that of the corresponding varieties which now exist in the brackish waters of the Baltic, was in every case like that of those varieties which only thrive in the waters of the open salt sea. Here was a clear indication that at the time when man formed these shell-heaps those coasts were in far more direct communication with the salt sea than at present, and that sufficient time must have elapsed since that period to have wrought enormous changes in sea and land throughout those regions.

Scattered through these heaps were found indications of a grade of civilization when man still used implements of stone, but implements and weapons which, though still rude, showed a progress from those of the drift and early cave period, some of them being of polished stone.

With these were other evidences that civilization had progressed. With implements rude enough to have survived from early periods, other implements never known in the drift and bone caves began to appear, and, though there were few if any bones of other domestic animals, the remains of dogs were found; everything showed that there had been a progress in civilization between the former Stone epoch and this.

The second series of discoveries in Scandinavia was made in the peat-beds: these were generally formed in hollows or bowls varying in depth from ten to thirty feet, and a section of them, like a section of the deposits in the bone caverns, showed a gradual evolution of human culture. The lower strata in these great bowls were found to be made up chiefly of mosses and various plants matted together with the trunks of fallen trees, sometimes of very large diameter; and the botanical examination of the lowest layer of these trees and plants in the various bowls revealed a most important fact: for this layer, the first in point of time, was always of the Scotch fir—which now grows nowhere in the Danish islands, and can not be made to grow anywhere in them—and of plants which are now extinct in these regions, but have retreated within the arctic circle. Coming up from the bottom of these great bowls there was found above the first layer a second, in which were matted together masses of oak trees of different varieties; these, too, were relics of a bygone epoch, since the oak has almost entirely disappeared from Denmark. Above these came a third stratum made up of fallen beech trees; and the beech is now, and has been since the beginning of recorded history, the most common tree of the Danish Peninsula.

Now came a second fact of the utmost importance as connected with the first. Scattered, as a rule, through the lower of these deposits, that of the extinct fir trees and plants, were found implements and weapons of smooth stone; in the layer of oak trees were found implements of bronze; and among the layer of beeches were found implements and weapons of iron.

The general result of these investigations in these two sources, the shell-mounds and the peat deposits, was the same: the first civilization evidenced in them was marked by the use of stone implements more or less smooth, showing a progress from the earlier rude Stone period made known by the bone caves; then came a later progress to a higher civilization, marked by the use of bronze implements; and, finally, a still higher development when iron began to be used.

The labours of the Danish archæologists have resulted in the formation of a great museum at Copenhagen, and on the specimens they have found, coupled with those of the drift and bone caves, is based the classification between the main periods or divisions in the evolution of the human race above referred to.

It was not merely in Scandinavian lands that these results were reached; substantially the same discoveries were made in Ireland and France, in Sardinia and Portugal, in Japan and in Brazil, in Cuba and in the United States; in fact, as a rule, in nearly every part of the world which was thoroughly examined.[4]

But from another quarter came a yet more striking indication of this same evolution. As far back as the year 1829 there were discovered, in the Lake of Zurich, piles and other antiquities indicating a former existence of human dwellings, standing in the water at some distance from the shore; but the usual mixture of thoughtlessness and dread of new ideas seems to have prevailed, and nothing was done until about

[4] For the general subject, see Mortillet, Le Préhistorique, p. 498, et passim. For examples of the rude stone implements, improving as we go from earlier to later layers in the bone caves, see Boyd Dawkins, Early Man in Britain, chap. vii, p. 186; also Quatrefages, Human Species, New York, 1879, pp. 305 et seq. An interesting gleam of light is thrown on the subject in De Baye, Grottes Préhistoriques de la Marne, pp. 31 et seq.; also Evans, as cited in the previous chapter. For the more recent investigations in the Danish shell-heaps, see Boyd Dawkins, Early Man in Britain, pp. 303, 304. For these evidences of advanced civilization in the shell-heaps, see Mortillet, p. 498. He, like Nilsson, says that only the bones of the dog were found; but compare Dawkins, p. 305. For the very full list of these discoveries, with their bearing on each other, see Mortillet, p. 499. As to those in Scandinavian countries, see Nilsson, The Primitive Inhabitants of Scandinavia, third edition, with Introduction by Lubbock, London, 1868; also the Pre-History of the North, by Worsaae, English translation, London, 1886. For shell-mounds and their contents in the Spanish Peninsula, see Cartailhac's greater work already cited. For summary of such discoveries throughout the world, see Mortillet, Le Préhistorique, pp. 497 et seq.

1853, when new discoveries of the same kind were followed up vigorously, and Rütimeyer, Keller, Troyon, and others showed not only in the Lake of Zurich, but in many other lakes in Switzerland, remains of former habitations, and, in the midst of these, great numbers of relics, exhibiting the grade of civilization which those lake-dwellers had attained.

Here, too, were accumulated proofs of the upward tendency of the human race. Implements of polished stone, bone, leather, pottery of various grades, woven cloth, bones of several kinds of domestic animals, various sorts of grain, bread which had been preserved by charring, and a multitude of evidences of progress never found among the earlier, ruder relics of civilization, showed yet more strongly that man had arrived here at a still higher stage than his predecessor of the drift, cave, and shell-heap periods, and had gone on from better to better.

Very striking evidences of this upward tendency were found in each class of implements. As by comparing the chipped flint implements of the lower and earlier strata in the cave period with those of the later and upper strata we saw progress, so, in each of the periods of polished stone, bronze, and iron, we see, by similar comparisons, a steady progress from rude to perfected implements; and especially is this true in the remains of the various lake-dwellings, for among these can be traced out constant increase in the variety of animals domesticated, and gradual improvements in means of subsistence and in ways of living.

Incidentally, too, a fact, at first sight of small account, but on reflection exceedingly important, was revealed. The earlier bronze implements were frequently found to imitate in various minor respects implements of stone; in other words, forms were at first given to bronze implements natural in working stone, but not natural in working bronze. This showed the *direction* of the development—that it was upward from stone to bronze, not downward from bronze to stone; that it was progress rather than decline.

These investigations were supplemented by similar researches elsewhere. In many other parts of the world it was found that lake-dwellers had existed in different grades of civilization, but all within a certain range, intermediate between the cave-dwellers and the historic period. To explain this epoch of the lake-dwellers History came in with the account given by Herodotus of the lake-dwellings on

Lake Prasias, which gave protection from the armies of Persia. Still more important, Comparative Ethnography showed that to-day, in various parts of the world, especially in New Guinea and West Africa, races of men are living in lake-dwellings built upon piles, and with a range of implements and weapons strikingly like many of those discovered in these ancient lake deposits of Switzerland.

In Great Britain, France, Germany, Italy, Ireland, Scotland, and other countries, remains of a different sort were also found, throwing light on this progress. The cromlechs, cranogs, mounds, and the like, though some of them indicate the work of weaker tribes pressed upon by stronger, show, as a rule, the same upward tendency.

At a very early period in the history of these discoveries, various attempts were made—nominally in the interest of religion, but really in the interest of sundry creeds and catechisms framed when men knew little or nothing of natural laws—to break the force of such evidences of the progress and development of the human race from lower to higher. Out of all the earlier efforts two may be taken as fairly typical, for they exhibit the opposition to science as developed under two different schools of theology, each working in its own way. The first of these shows great ingenuity and learning, and is presented by Mr. Southall in his book, published in 1875, entitled *The Recent Origin of the World.* In this he grapples first of all with the difficulties presented by the early date of Egyptian civilization, and the keynote of his argument is the statement made by an eminent Egyptologist, at a period before modern archæological discoveries were well understood, that "Egypt laughs the idea of a rude Stone age, a polished Stone age, a Bronze age, an Iron age, to scorn."

Mr. Southall's method was substantially that of the late excellent Mr. Gosse in geology. Mr. Gosse, as the readers of this work may remember, felt obliged, in the supposed interest of Genesis, to urge that safety to men's souls might be found in believing that, six thousand years ago, the Almighty, for some inscrutable purpose, suddenly set Niagara pouring very near the spot where it is pouring now; laid the various strata, and sprinkled the fossils through them like plums through a pudding; scratched the glacial grooves upon the rocks, and did a vast multitude of things, subtle and cunning, little and great, in all parts of the world, required to delude geologists of modern times into the conviction that all these things were the result of a steady progress through long epochs. On a similar plan, Mr. Southall proposed, at the very beginning of his book, as a final solution of the problem, the declaration that Egypt, with its high civilization in the time of Mena, with its races, classes, institutions, arrangements, language, monuments—all indicating an evolution through a vast previous history—was a sudden creation which came fully made from the hands of the Creator. To use his own words, "The Egyptians had no Stone age, and were born civilized."

There is an old story that once on a time a certain jovial King of France, making a progress through his kingdom, was received at the gates of a provincial town by the mayor's deputy, who began his speech on this wise: "May it please your Majesty, there are just thirteen reasons why His Honour the Mayor can not be present to welcome you this morning. The first of these reasons is that he is dead." On this the king graciously declared that this first reason was sufficient, and that he would not trouble the mayor's deputy for the twelve others.

So with Mr. Southall's argument: one simple result of scientific research out of many is all that it is needful to state, and this is, that in these later years we have a new and convincing evidence of the existence of prehistoric man in Egypt in his earliest, rudest beginnings; the very same evidence which we find in all other parts of the world which have been carefully examined. This evidence consists of stone implements and weapons which have been found in Egypt in such forms, at such points, and in such positions that when studied in connection with those found in all other parts of the world, from New Jersey to California, from France to India, and from England to the Andaman Islands, they force upon us the conviction that civilization in Egypt, as in all other parts of the world, was developed by the same slow process of evolution from the rudest beginnings.

It is true that men learned in Egyptology had discouraged the idea of an earlier Stone age in Egypt, and that among these were Lepsius and Brugsch; but these men were not trained in prehistoric archæology; their devotion to the study of the monuments of Egyptian civilization had evidently drawn them away from sympathy, and indeed from acquaintance, with the work of men like Boucher de Perthes, Lartet,

Nilsson, Troyon, and Dawkins. But a new era was beginning. In 1867 Worsaae called attention to the prehistoric implements found on the borders of Egypt; two years later Arcelin discussed such stone implements found beneath the soil of Sakkara and Gizeh, the very focus of the earliest Egyptian civilization; in the same year Hamy and Lenormant found such implements washed out from the depths higher up the Nile at Thebes, near the tombs of the kings; and in the following year they exhibited more flint implements found at various other places. Coupled with these discoveries was the fact that Horner and Linant found a copper knife at twenty-four feet, and pottery at sixty feet, below the surface. In 1872 Dr. Reil, director of the baths at Helouan, near Cairo, discovered implements of chipped flint; and in 1877 Dr. Jukes Brown made similar discoveries in that region. In 1878 Oscar Fraas, summing up the question, showed that the stone implements were mainly such as are found in the prehistoric deposits of other countries, and that, Zittel having found them in the Libyan Desert, far from the oases, there was reason to suppose that these implements were used before the region became a desert and before Egypt was civilized. Two years later Dr. Mook, of Würzburg, published a work giving the results of his investigations, with careful drawings of the rude stone implements discovered by him in the upper Nile Valley, and it was evident that, while some of these implements differed slightly from those before known, the great mass of them were of the character so common in the prehistoric deposits of other parts of the world.

A yet more important contribution to this mass of facts was made by Prof. Henry Haynes, of Boston, who in the winter of 1877 and 1878 began a very thorough investigation of the subject, and discovered, a few miles east of Cairo, many flint implements. The significance of Haynes's discoveries was twofold: First, there were, among these, stone axes like those found in the French drift beds of St. Acheul, showing that the men who made or taught men how to make these in Egypt were passing through the same phase of savagery as that of Quaternary France; secondly, he found a workshop for making these implements, proving that these flint implements were not brought into Egypt by invaders, but were made to meet the necessities of the country. From this first field Prof. Haynes went to Helouan, north of Cairo, and there found, as Dr. Reil had done, various worked flints, some of them like those discovered by M. Rivière in the caves of southern France; thence he went up the Nile to Luxor, the site of ancient Thebes, began a thorough search in the Tertiary limestone hills, and found multitudes of chipped stone implements, some of them, indeed, of original forms, but most of forms common in other parts of the world under similar circumstances, some of the chipped stone axes corresponding closely to those found in the drift beds of northern France.

All this seemed to show conclusively that, long ages before the earliest period of Egyptian civilization of which the monuments of the first dynasties give us any trace, mankind in the Nile Valley was going through the same slow progress from the period when, standing just above the brutes, he defended himself with implements of rudely chipped stone.

But in 1881 came discoveries which settled the question entirely. In that year General Pitt-Rivers, a Fellow of the Royal Society and President of the Anthropological Institute, and J. F. Campbell, Fellow of the Royal Geographical Society of England, found implements not only in alluvial deposits, associated with the bones of the zebra, hyena, and other animals which have since retreated farther south, but, at Djebel Assas, near Thebes, they found implements of chipped flint in the hard, stratified gravel, from six and a half to ten feet below the surface; relics evidently, as Mr. Campbell says, "beyond calculation older than the oldest Egyptian temples and tombs." They certainly proved that Egyptian civilization had not issued in its completeness, and all at once, from the hand of the Creator in the time of Mena. Nor was this all. Investigators of the highest character and ability—men like Hull and Flinders Petrie—revealed geological changes in Egypt requiring enormous periods of time, and traces of man's handiwork dating from a period when the waters in the Nile Valley extended hundreds of feet above the present level. Thus was ended the contention of Mr. Southall.

Still another attack upon the new scientific conclusions came from France, when in 1883 the Abbé Hamard, Priest of the Oratory, published his *Age of Stone and Primitive Man*. He had been especially vexed at the arrangement of prehistoric implements by periods at the Paris Exposition of 1878; he bitterly complains of this as having an anti-Christian tendency, and rails at science as "the idol of the day." He attacks Mortillet, one of the leaders in French archæology, with a great display of contempt; speaks of the "venom" in books on prehistoric man generally; complains that the Church is too mild and gentle with such monstrous doctrines; bewails the concessions made to science by some eminent preachers; and foretells his own martyrdom at the hands of men of science.

Efforts like this accomplished little, and a more legitimate attempt was made to resist the conclusions of archæology by showing that knives of stone were used in obedience to a sacred ritual in Egypt for embalming, and in Judea for circumcision, and that these flint knives might have had this later origin. But the argument against the conclusions drawn from this view was triple: First, as we have seen, not only stone knives, but axes and other implements of stone similar to those of a prehistoric period in western Europe were discovered; secondly, these implements were discovered in the hard gravel drift of a period evidently far earlier than that of Mena; and, thirdly, the use of stone implements in Egyptian and Jewish sacred functions within the historic period, so far from weakening the force of the arguments for the long and slow development of Egyptian civilization from the men who used rude flint implements to the men who built and adorned the great temples of the early dynasties, is really an argument in favour of that long evolution. A study of comparative ethnology has made it clear that the sacred stone knives and implements of the Egyptian and Jewish priestly ritual were natural survivals of that previous period. For sacrificial or ritual purposes, the knife of stone was considered more sacred than the knife of bronze or iron, simply because it was ancient; just as to-day, in India, Brahman priests kindle the sacred fire not with matches or flint and steel, but by a process found in the earliest, lowest stages of human culture—by violently boring a pointed stick into another piece of wood until a spark comes; and just as to-day, in Europe and America, the architecture of the Middle Ages survives as a special religious form in the erection of our most recent churches, and to such an extent that thousands on thousands of us feel that we can not worship fitly unless in the midst of windows, decorations, vessels, implements, vestments, and ornaments, no longer used for other purposes, but which have survived in sundry branches of the Christian Church, and derived a special sanctity from the fact that they are of ancient origin.

Taking, then, the whole mass of testimony together, even though a plausible or very strong argument against single

evidences may be made here and there, the force of its combined mass remains, and leaves both the vast antiquity of
man and the evolution of civilization from its lowest to its
highest forms, as proved by the prehistoric remains of Egypt
and so many other countries in all parts of the world, beyond
a reasonable doubt. Most important of all, the recent discoveries in Assyria have thrown a new light upon the evolution
of the dogma of "the fall of man." Reverent scholars like
George Smith, Sayce, Delitzsch, Jensen, Schrader, and their
compeers have found in the Ninevite records the undoubted
source of that form of the fall legend which was adopted by
the Hebrews and by them transmitted to Christianity.[5]

[5] For Mr. Southall's views, see his *Recent Origin of Man,* p. 20,
and elsewhere. For Mr. Gosse's views, see his *Omphalos* as cited
in the chapter on Geology in this work. For a summary of the
work of Arcelin, Hamy, Lenormant, Richard, Lubbock, Mook,
and Haynes, see Mortillet, *Le Préhistorique, passim.* As to Zittel's
discovery, see Oscar Fraas's *Aus dem Orient,* Stuttgart, 1878. As to
the striking similarities of the stone implements found in Egypt
with those found in the drift and bone caves, see Mook's monograph, Würzburg, 1880, cited in the next chapter, especially Plates
IX, XI, XII. For even more striking reproductions of photographs
showing this remarkable similarity between Egyptian and European chipped stone remains, see H. W. Haynes, *Palæolithic Implements in Upper Egypt,* Boston, 1881. See also Evans, *Ancient
Stone Implements,* chap. i, pp. 8, 9, 44, 102, 316, 329. As to stone
implements used by priests of Jehovah, priests of Baal, priests of
Moloch, priests of Odin, and Egyptian priests, as religious survivals, see Cartailhac, as above, 6 and 7; also Lartet, in De Luynes,
Expedition to the Dead Sea; also Nilsson, *Primitive Inhabitants
of Scandinavia,* pp. 96, 97; also Sayce, *Herodotus,* p. 171, note.
For the discoveries by Pitt-Rivers, see the *Journal of the Anthropological Institute of Great Britain and Ireland* for 1882, vol. xi,
pp. 382 *et seq.;* and for Campbell's decision regarding them, see
ibid., pp. 396, 397. For facts summed up in the words, "It is most
probable that Egypt at a remote period passed like many other
countries through its stone period," see Hilton Price, F. S. A.,
F. G. S., paper in the *Journal of the Archæological Institute of
Great Britain and Ireland* for 1884, p. 56. Specimens of palæolithic
implements from Egypt—knives, arrowheads, spearheads, flakes,
and the like, both of peculiar and ordinary forms—may be seen
in various museums, but especially in that of Prof. Haynes, of
Boston. Some interesting light is also thrown into the subject by
the specimens obtained by General Wilson and deposited in the
Smithsonian Institution at Washington. For the Abbé Hamard's
attack, see his *L'Age de la Pierre et l'Homme Primitif,* Paris, 1883

238 / History of the Warfare of Science with Theology

Chapter 9

The "Fall of Man" and Ethnology

WE HAVE SEEN that, closely connected with the main lines
of investigation in archæology and anthropology, there were
other researches throwing much light on the entire subject.
In a previous chapter we saw especially that Lafitau and
Jussieu were among the first to collect and compare facts bearing on the natural history of man, gathered by travellers in
various parts of the earth, thus laying foundations for the
science of comparative ethnology. It was soon seen that ethnology had most important bearings upon the question of
the material, intellectual, moral, and religious evolution of the
human race; in every civilized nation, therefore, appeared
scholars who began to study the characteristics of various
groups of men as ascertained from travellers, and to compare
the results thus gained with each other and with those obtained by archæology.

Thus, more and more clear became the evidences that the
tendency of the race has been upward from low beginnings.
It was found that groups of men still existed possessing characteristics of those in the early periods of development to
whom the drift and caves and shell-heaps and pile-dwellings
bear witness; groups of men using many of the same implements and weapons, building their houses in the same way,
seeking their food by the same means, enjoying the same
amusements, and going through the same general stages of
culture; some being in a condition corresponding to the earlier,
some to the later, of those early periods.

From all sides thus came evidence that we have still upon
the earth examples of all the main stages in the development
of human civilization; that from the period when man appears
little above the brutes, and with little if any religion in any
accepted sense of the word, these examples can be arranged
in an ascending series leading to the highest planes which

—especially his preface. For the stone weapon found in the high
drift behind Esneh, see Flinders Petrie, *History of Egypt,* chap. i.
Of these discoveries by Pitt-Rivers and others Maspero appears to
know nothing.

humanity has reached; that philosophic observers may among these examples study existing beliefs, usages, and institutions back through earlier and earlier forms, until, as a rule, the whole evolution can be easily divined if not fully seen. Moreover, the basis of the whole structure became more and more clear: the fact that "the lines of intelligence have always been what they are, and have always operated as they do now; that man has progressed from the simple to the complex, from the particular to the general."

As this evidence from ethnology became more and more strong, its significance to theology aroused attention, and naturally most determined efforts were made to break its force. On the Continent the two great champions of the Church in this field were De Maistre and De Bonald; but the two attempts which may be especially recalled as the most influential among English-speaking peoples were those of Whately, Archbishop of Dublin, and the Duke of Argyll.

First in the combat against these new deductions of science was Whately. He was a strong man, whose breadth of thought and liberality in practice deserve all honour; but these very qualities drew upon him the distrust of his orthodox brethren; and, while his writings were powerful in the first half of the present century to break down many bulwarks of unreason, he seems to have been constantly in fear of losing touch with the Church, and therefore to have promptly attacked some scientific reasonings, which, had he been a layman, not holding a brief for the Church, he would probably have studied with more care and less prejudice. He was not slow to see the deeper significance of archæology and ethnology in their relations to the theological conception of "the Fall," and he set the battle in array against them.

His contention was, to use his own words, that "no community ever did or ever can emerge unassisted by external helps from a state of utter barbarism into anything that can be called civilization"; and that, in short, all imperfectly civilized, barbarous, and savage races are but fallen descendants of races more fully civilized. This view was urged with his usual ingenuity and vigour, but the facts proved too strong for him: they made it clear, first, that many races were without simple possessions, instruments, and arts which never, probably, could have been lost if once acquired—as, for example, pottery, the bow for shooting, various domesticated animals, spinning, the simplest principles of agriculture, household economy, and the like; and, secondly, it was shown as a simple matter of fact that various savage and barbarous tribes *had* raised themselves by a development of means which no one from outside could have taught them; as in the cultivation and improvement of various indigenous plants, such as the potato and Indian corn among the Indians of North America; in the domestication of various animals peculiar to their own regions, such as the llama among the Indians of South America; in the making of sundry fabrics out of materials and by processes not found among other nations, such as the bark cloth of the Polynesians; and in the development of weapons peculiar to sundry localities, but known in no others, such as the boomerang in Australia.

Most effective in bringing out the truth were such works as those of Sir John Lubbock and Tylor; and so conclusive were they that the arguments of Whately were given up as untenable by the other of the two great champions above referred to, and an attempt was made by him to form the diminishing number of thinking men supporting the old theological view on a new line of defence.

This second champion, the Duke of Argyll, was a man of wide knowledge and strong powers in debate, whose high moral sense was amply shown in his adhesion to the side of the American Union in the struggle against disunion and slavery, despite the overwhelming majority against him in the high aristocracy to which he belonged. As an honest man and close thinker, the duke was obliged to give up completely the theological view of the antiquity of man. The whole biblical chronology as held by the universal Church, "always, everywhere, and by all," he sacrificed, and gave all his powers in this field to support the theory of "the Fall." *Noblesse oblige*: the duke and his ancestors had been for centuries the chief pillars of the Church of Scotland, and it was too much to expect that he could break away from a tenet which forms really its "chief cornerstone."

Acknowledging the insufficiency of Archbishop Whately's argument, the duke took the ground that the lower, barbarous, savage, brutal races were the remains of civilized races which, in the struggle for existence, had been pushed and driven off to remote and inclement parts of the earth, where the conditions necessary to a continuance in their early civilization were absent; that, therefore, the descendants of primeval, civilized men degenerated and sank in the scale of culture. To use his own words, the weaker races were "driven by the stronger to the woods and rocks," so that they became "mere outcasts of the human race."

In answer to this, while it was conceded, first, that there have been examples of weaker tribes sinking in the scale of culture after escaping from the stronger into regions unfavourable to civilization, and, secondly, that many powerful nations have declined and decayed, it was shown that the men in the most remote and unfavourable regions have not always been the lowest in the scale; that men have been frequently found "among the woods and rocks" in a higher state of civilization than on the fertile plains, such examples being cited as Mexico, Peru, and even Scotland; and that, while there were many examples of special and local decline, overwhelming masses of facts point to progress as a rule.

The improbability, not to say impossibility, of many of the conclusions arrived at by the duke appeared more and more strongly as more became known of the lower tribes of mankind. It was necessary on his theory to suppose many things which our knowledge of the human race absolutely forbids us to believe: for example, it was necessary to suppose that the Australians or New Zealanders, having once possessed so simple and convenient an art as that of the potter, had lost every trace of it; and that the same tribes, having once had so simple a means of saving labour as the spindle or small stick weighted at one end for spinning, had given it up and gone back to twisting threads with the hand. In fact, it was necessary to suppose that one of the main occupations of man from "the beginning" had been the forgetting of simple methods, processes, and implements which all experience in the actual world teaches us are never entirely forgotten by peoples who have once acquired them.

Some leading arguments of the duke were overthrown by simple statements of fact. Thus, his instance of the Eskimo as pushed to the verge of habitable America, and therefore living in the lowest depths of savagery, which, even if it were true, by no means proved a general rule, was deprived of its force by the simple fact that the Eskimos are by no means the lowest race on the American continent, and that various tribes far more centrally and advantageously placed, as, for instance, those in Brazil, are really inferior to them in the scale of culture. Again, his statement that "in Africa there appear to be no traces of any time when the natives were not acquainted with the use of iron," is met by the fact that from the Nile Valley to the Cape of Good Hope we find, wherever examination has been made, the same early stone implements which in all other parts of the world precede the use of iron, some of which would not have been made had their makers possessed iron. The duke also tried to show that there were no distinctive epochs of stone, bronze, and iron, by adducing the fact that some stone implements are found even in some high civilizations. This is indeed a fact. We find some few European peasants to-day using stone mallet-heads; but this proves simply that the old stone mallet-heads have survived as implements cheap and effective.

The argument from Comparative Ethnology in support of the view that the tendency of mankind is upward has received strength from many sources. Comparative Philology shows that in the less civilized, barbarous, and savage races childish forms of speech prevail—frequent reduplications and the like—of which we have survivals in the later and even in the most highly developed languages. In various languages, too, we find relics of ancient modes of thought in the simplest words and expressions used for arithmetical calculations. Words and phrases for this purpose are frequently found to be derived from the words for hands, feet, fingers, and toes, just as clearly as in our own language some of our simplest measures of length are shown by their names to have been measures of parts of the human body, as the cubit, the foot, and the like, and therefore to date from a time when exactness was not required. To add another out of many examples, it is found to-day that various rude nations go through the simplest arithmetical processes by means of pebbles. Into our own language, through the Latin, has come a word showing that our distant progenitors reckoned in this way: the word *calculate* gives us an absolute proof of this. According to the theory of the Duke of Argyll, men ages ago used pebbles (*calculi*) in performing the simplest arithmetical calculations because we to-day "*calculate*." No reduction to absurdity could be more thorough. The simple fact must be that we "calculate" because our remote ancestors used pebbles in their arithmetic.

Comparative Literature and Folklore also show among peoples of a low culture to-day childish modes of viewing nature, and childish ways of expressing the relations of man to nature, such as clearly survive from a remote ancestry;

noteworthy among these are the beliefs in witches and fairies, and multitudes of popular and poetic expressions in the most civilized nations.

So, too, Comparative Ethnography, the basis of Ethnology, shows in contemporary barbarians and savages a childish love of playthings and games, of which we have many survivals.

All these facts, which were at first unobserved or observed as matters of no significance, have been brought into connection with a fact in biology acknowledged alike by all important schools; by Agassiz on one hand and by Darwin on the other—namely, as stated by Agassiz, that "the young states of each species and group resemble older forms of the same group," or, as stated by Darwin, that "in two or more groups of animals, however much they may at first differ from each other in structure and habits, if they pass through closely similar embryonic stages, we may feel almost assured that they have descended from the same parent form, and are therefore closely related."[1]

[1] For the stone forms given to early bronze axes, etc., see Nilsson, *Primitive Inhabitants of Scandinavia,* London, 1868, Lubbock's *Introduction,* p. 31; and for plates, see Lubbock's *Prehistoric Man,* chap. ii; also Cartailhac, *Les Ages Préhistoriques de l'Espagne et du Portugal,* p. 227; also Keller, *Lake Dwellings;* also Troyon, *Habitations Lacustres;* also Boyd Dawkins, *Early Man in Great Britain,* p. 292; also Lubbock, p. 6; also Lyell, *Antiquity of Man,* chap. ii. For the cranogs, etc., in the north of Europe, see Munro, *Ancient Scottish Lake Dwellings,* Edinburgh, 1882. For mounds and greater stone constructions in the extreme south of Europe, see Cartailhac's work on Spain and Portugal above cited, part iii, chap. iii. For the source of Mr. Southall's contention, see Brugsch, *Egypt of the Pharaohs.* For the two sides of the question whether in the lowest grades of savagery there is really any recognition of a superior power, or anything which can be called, in any accepted sense, religion, compare Quatrefages with Lubbock, in works already cited. For a striking but rather *ad captandum* effort to show that there is a moral and religious sense in the very lowest Australian tribes, see one of the discourses of Archbishop Vaughan on *Science and Religion,* Baltimore, 1879. For one out of multitudes of striking and instructive resemblances in ancient stone implements and those now in use among sundry savage tribes, see comparison between old Scandinavian arrowheads and those recently brought from Tierra del Fuego, in Nilsson as above, especially in Plate V. For a brief and admirable statement of the arguments on both sides, see Sir J. Lubbock's Dundee paper, given in the appen-

[Chapter 10

The "Fall of Man" and History]

Chapter 11

From "The Prince of the Power of the Air" to Meteorology

1. Growth of a Theological Theory

THE POPULAR BELIEFS of classic antiquity regarding storms, thunder, and lightning, took shape in myths representing Vulcan as forging thunderbolts, Jupiter as flinging them at his enemies, Æolus as intrusting the winds in a bag to Æneas, and the like. An attempt at their further theological development is seen in the Pythagorean statement that lightnings are intended to terrify the damned in Tartarus.

But at a very early period we see the beginning of a scientific view. In Greece, the Ionic philosophers held that such phenomena are obedient to law. Plato, Aristotle, and many lesser lights, attempted to account for them on natural grounds; and their explanations, though crude, were based upon observation and thought. In Rome, Lucretius, Seneca, Pliny, and others, inadequate as their statements were, implanted at least the germs of a science. But, as the Christian

---

dix to the American edition of his *Origin of Civilization*, etc. For the general argument referred to between Whately and the Duke of Argyll on one side and Lubbock on the other, see Lubbock's Dundee paper as above cited; Tylor, *Early History of Mankind*, especially p. 193; and the Duke of Argyll, *Primeval Man*, part iv. For difficulties of savages in arithmetic, see Lubbock, as above, pp. 459 *et seq.* For a very temperate and judicial view of the whole question, see Tylor as above, chaps. vii and xiii. For a brief summary of the scientific position regarding the stagnation and deterioration of races, resulting in the statement that such deterioration "in no way contradicts the theory that civilization itself is developed from low to high stages," see Tylor, *Anthropology*, chap. i. For striking examples of the testimony of language to upward progress, see Tylor, chap. xii.

Church rose to power, this evolution was checked; the new leaders of thought found, in the Scriptures recognized by them as sacred, the basis for a new view, or rather for a modification of the old view.

This ending of a scientific evolution based upon observation and reason, and this beginning of a sacred science based upon the letter of Scripture and on theology, are seen in the utterances of various fathers in the early Church. As to the general features of this new development, Tertullian held that sundry passages of Scripture prove lightning identical with hell-fire; and this idea was transmitted from generation to generation of later churchmen, who found an especial support of Tertullian's view in the sulphurous smell experienced during thunderstorms. St. Hilary thought the firmament very much lower than the heavens, and that it was created not only for the support of the upper waters, but also for the tempering of our atmosphere.[1] St. Ambrose held that thunder is caused by the winds breaking through the solid firmament, and cited from the prophet Amos the sublime passage regarding "Him that establisheth the thunders."[2] He shows, indeed, some conception of the true source of rain; but his whole reasoning is limited by various scriptural texts. He lays great stress upon the firmament as a solid outer shell of the universe: the heavens he holds to be not far outside this outer shell, and argues regarding their character from St. Paul's Epistle to the Corinthians and from the one hundred and forty-eighth Psalm. As to "the waters which are above the firmament," he takes up the objection of those who hold that, this outside of the universe being spherical, the waters must slide off it, especially if the firmament revolves; and he points out that it is by no means certain that the *outside* of the firmament *is* spherical, and insists that, if it does revolve, the water is just what is needed to lubricate and cool its axis.

St. Jerome held that God at the Creation, having spread out the firmament between heaven and earth, and having separated the upper waters from the lower, caused the upper waters to be frozen into ice, in order to keep all in place. A

[1] For Tertullian, see the *Apol. contra gentes,* c. 47; also Augustin de Angelis, *Lectiones Meteorologicæ,* p. 64. For Hilary, see *In Psalm. CXXXV* (Migne, *Patr. Lat.,* vol. ix, p. 773).

[2] "Firmans tonitrua" (Amos iv, 13); the phrase does not appear in our version.

proof of this view Jerome found in the words of Ezekiel regarding "the crystal stretched above the cherubim."[3]

The germinal principle in accordance with which all these theories were evolved was most clearly proclaimed to the world by St. Augustine in his famous utterance: "Nothing is to be accepted save on the authority of Scripture, since greater is that authority than all the powers of the human mind."[4] No treatise was safe thereafter which did not breathe the spirit and conform to the letter of this maxim. Unfortunately, what was generally understood by the "authority of Scripture" was the tyranny of sacred books imperfectly transcribed, viewed through distorting superstitions, and frequently interpreted by party spirit.

Following this precept of St. Augustine there were developed, in every field, theological views of science which have never led to a single truth—which, without exception, have forced mankind away from the truth, and have caused Christendom to stumble for centuries into abysses of error and sorrow. In meteorology, as in every other science with which he dealt, Augustine based everything upon the letter of the sacred text; and it is characteristic of the result that this man, so great when untrammelled, thought it his duty to guard especially the whole theory of the "waters above the heavens."

In the sixth century this theological reasoning was still further developed, as we have seen, by Cosmas Indicopleustes. Finding a sanction for the old Egyptian theory of the universe in the ninth chapter of Hebrews, he insisted that the earth is a flat parallelogram, and that from its outer edges rise immense walls supporting the firmament; then, throwing together the reference to the firmament in Genesis and the outburst of

[3] For Ambrose, see the *Hexæmeron*, lib. ii, cap. 3, 4; lib. iii, cap 5 (Migne, *Patr. Lat.*, vol. xiv, pp. 148-150, 153, 165). The passage as to lubrication of the heavenly axis is as follows: "Deinde cum ipsi dicant volvi orbem cœli stellis ardentibus refulgentem, nonne divina providentia necessario prospexit, ut intra orbem cœli, et supra orbem redundaret aqua, quæ illa ferventis axis incendia temperaret?" For Jerome, see his *Epistola,* lxix, cap. 6 (Migne, *Patr. Lat.*, vol. xxii, p. 659).

[4] "Major est quippe Scripturæ hujus auctoritas, quam omnis humani ingenii capacitas."—Augustine, *De Genesi ad Lit.*, lib. ii, cap. 5 (Migne, *Patr. Lat.*, vol. xxxiv, pp. 266, 267). Or, as he is cited by Vincent of Beauvais (*Spec. Nat.*, lib. iv, 98): "Non est aliquid temere diffiniendum, sed quantum Scriptura dicit accipiendum, cujus major est auctoritas quam omnis humani ingenii capacitas."

poetry in the Psalms regarding the "waters that be above the heavens," he insisted that over the terrestrial universe are solid arches bearing a vault supporting a vast cistern "containing the waters"; finally, taking from Genesis the expression regarding the "windows of heaven," he insisted that these windows are opened and closed by the angels whenever the Almighty wishes to send rain upon the earth or to withhold it.

This was accepted by the universal Church as a vast contribution to thought; for several centuries it was the orthodox doctrine, and various leaders in theology devoted themselves to developing and supplementing it.

About the beginning of the seventh century, Isidore, Bishop of Seville, was the ablest prelate in Christendom, and was showing those great qualities which led to his enrolment among the saints of the Church. His theological view of science marks an epoch. As to the "waters above the firmament," Isidore contends that they must be lower than the uppermost heaven, though higher than the lower heaven, because in the one hundred and forty-eighth Psalm they are mentioned *after* the heavenly bodies and the "heaven of heavens," but *before* the terrestrial elements. As to their purpose, he hesitates between those who held that they were stored up there by the prescience of God for the destruction of the world at the Flood, as the words of Scripture that "the windows of heaven were opened" seemed to indicate, and those who held that they were kept there to moderate the heat of the heavenly bodies. As to the firmament, he is in doubt whether it envelops the earth "like an eggshell," or is merely spread over it "like a curtain"; for he holds that the passage in the one hundred and fourth Psalm may be used to support either view.

Having laid these scriptural foundations, Isidore shows considerable power of thought; indeed, at times, when he discusses the rainbow, rain, hail, snow, and frost, his theories are rational, and give evidence that, if he could have broken away from his adhesion to the letter of Scripture, he might have given a strong impulse to the evolution of a true science.[5]

[5] For Cosmas, see his *Topographia Christiana* (in Montfaucon, *Collectio nova patrum,* vol. ii), and the more complete account of his theory given in the chapter on *Geography* in this work. For Isidore, see the *Etymologiæ,* lib. xiii, cap. 7-9, *De ordine creaturarum,* cap. 3, 4, and *De natura rerum,* cap. 29, 30 (Migne, *Patr. Lat.,* vol. lxxxii, pp. 476, 477, vol. lxxxiii, pp. 920-922, 1001-1003).

About a century later appeared, at the other extremity of Europe, the second in the trio of theological men of science in the early Middle Ages—Bede the Venerable. The nucleus of his theory also is to be found in the accepted view of the "firmament" and of the "waters above the heavens," derived from Genesis. The firmament he holds to be spherical, and of a nature subtile and fiery; the upper heavens, he says, which contain the angels, God has tempered with ice, lest they inflame the lower elements. As to the waters placed above the firmament, lower than the spiritual heavens, but higher than all corporeal creatures, he says, "Some declare that they were stored there for the Deluge, but others, more correctly, that they are intended to temper the fire of the stars." He goes on with long discussions as to various elements and forces in Nature, and dwells at length upon the air, of which he says that the upper, serene air is over the heavens; while the lower, which is coarse, with humid exhalations, is sent off from the earth, and that in this are lightning, hail, snow, ice, and tempests, finding proof of this in the one hundred and forty-eighth Psalm, where these are commanded to "praise the Lord from the earth."[6]

So great was Bede's authority, that nearly all the anonymous speculations of the next following centuries upon these subjects were eventually ascribed to him. In one of these spurious treatises an attempt is made to get new light upon the sources of the waters above the heavens, the main reliance being the sheet containing the animals let down from heaven, in the vision of St. Peter. Another of these treatises is still more curious, for it endeavours to account for earthquakes and tides by means of the leviathan mentioned in Scripture. This characteristic passage runs as follows: "Some say that the earth contains the animal leviathan, and that he holds his tail after a fashion of his own, so that it is sometimes scorched by the sun, whereupon he strives to get hold of the sun, and so the earth is shaken by the motion of his indignation; he drinks in also, at times, such huge masses of the waves that when he belches them forth all the seas feel their effect." And this theological theory of the tides, as caused by the alternate suction and belching of leviathan, went far and wide.[7]

In the writings thus covered with the name of Bede there

[6] See Bede, De natura rerum (Migne, Patr. Lat., vol. xc).
[7] See the treatise De mundi constitutione, in Bede's Opera (Migne, Patr. Lat., vol. xc, p. 884).

is much showing a scientific spirit, which might have come to something of permanent value had it not been hampered by the supposed necessity of conforming to the letter of Scripture. It is as startling as it is refreshing to hear one of these mediæval theorists burst out as follows against those who are content to explain everything by the power of God: "What is more pitiable than to say that a thing *is,* because God is able to do it, and not to show any reason why it is so, nor any purpose for which it is so; just as if God did everything that he is able to do! You talk like one who says that God is able to make a calf out of a log. But *did* he ever do it? Either, then, show a reason why a thing is so, or a purpose wherefore it is so, or else cease to declare it so."[8]

The most permanent contribution of Bede to scientific thought in this field was his revival of the view that the firmament is made of ice; and he supported this from the words in the twenty-sixth chapter of Job, "He bindeth up the waters in his thick cloud, and the cloud is not rent under them."

About the beginning of the ninth century appeared the third in that triumvirate of churchmen who were the oracles of sacred science throughout the early Middle Ages—Rabanus Maurus, Abbot of Fulda and Archbishop of Mayence. Starting, like all his predecessors, from the first chapter of Genesis, borrowing here and there from the ancient philosophers, and excluding everything that could conflict with the letter of Scripture, he follows, in his work upon the universe, his two predecessors, Isidore and Bede, developing especially St. Jerome's theory, drawn from Ezekiel, that the firmament is strong enough to hold up the "waters above the heavens," because it is made of ice.

For centuries the authority of these three great teachers was unquestioned, and in countless manuals and catechisms their doctrine was translated and diluted for the common mind. But about the second quarter of the twelfth century a priest, Honorius of Autun, produced several treatises which show that thought on this subject had made some little progress. He explained the rain rationally, and mainly in the mod-

---

[8] For this remonstrance, see the *Elementa philosophiæ,* in Bede's *Opera* (Migne, *Patr. Lat.,* vol. xc, p. 1139). This treatise, which has also been printed, under the title of *De philosophia mundi,* among the works of Honorius of Autun, is believed by modern scholars (Hauréau, Werner, Poole) to be the production of William of Conches.

ern manner; with the thunder he is less successful, but insists that the thunderbolt "is not stone, as some assert." His thinking is vigorous and independent. Had theorists such as he been many, a new science could have been rapidly evolved, but the theological current was too strong.[9]

The strength of this current which overwhelmed the thought of Honorius is seen again in the work of the Dominican monk, John of San Geminiano, who in the thirteenth century gave forth his *Summa de Exemplis* for the use of preachers in his order. Of its thousand pages, over two hundred are devoted to illustrations drawn from the heavens and the elements. A characteristic specimen is his explanation of the Psalmist's phrase, "The arrows of the thunder." These, he tells us, are forged out of a dry vapour rising from the earth and kindled by the heat of the upper air, which then, coming into contact with a cloud just turning into rain, "is conglutinated like flour into dough," but, being too hot to be extinguished, its particles become merely sharpened at the lower end, and so blazing arrows, cleaving and burning everything they touch.[10]

But far more important, in the thirteenth century, was the fact that the most eminent scientific authority of that age, Albert the Great, Bishop of Ratisbon, attempted to reconcile the speculations of Aristotle with theological views derived from the fathers. In one very important respect he improved upon the meteorological views of his great master. The thunderbolt, he says, is no mere fire, but the product of black clouds containing much mud, which, when it is baked by the intense heat, forms a fiery black or red stone that falls from the sky, tearing beams and crushing walls in its course: such he has seen with his own eyes.[11]

The monkish encyclopædists of the later Middle Ages added

[9] For Rabanus Maurus, see the *Comment. in Genesim* and *De Universo* (Migne, *Patr. Lat.*, vol. cvii, cxi). For a charmingly naïve example of the primers referred to, see the little Anglo-Saxon manual of astronomy, sometimes attributed to Ælfric; it is in the vernacular, but is translated in Wright's *Popular Treatises on Science during the Middle Ages*. Bede is, of course, its chief source. For Honorius, see the *De imagine mundi* and *Hexæmeron* (Migne, *Patr. Lat.*, vol. clxxii). The *De philosophia mundi*, the most rational of all, is, however, believed by modern scholars to be unjustly ascribed to him. See note above.

[10] See Joannes à S. Geminiano, *Summa*, c. 75.

[11] See Albertus Magnus, *II Sent., Op.*, vol. xv, p. 137, a. (cited by Heller, *Gesch. d. Physik*, vol. i, p. 184) and his *Liber Methaur-*

little to these theories. As we glance over the pages of Vincent of Beauvais, the monk Bartholomew, and William of Conches, we note only a growing deference to the authority of Aristotle as supplementing that of Isidore and Bede and explaining sacred Scripture. Aristotle is treated like a Church father, but extreme care is taken not to go beyond the great maxim of St. Augustine; then, little by little, Bede and Isidore fall into the background, Aristotle fills the whole horizon, and his utterances are second in sacredness only to the text of Holy Writ.

A curious illustration of the difficulties these mediæval scholars had to meet in reconciling the scientific theories of Aristotle with the letter of the Bible is seen in the case of the rainbow. It is to the honour of Aristotle that his conclusions regarding the rainbow, though slightly erroneous, were based upon careful observation and evolved by reasoning alone; but his Christian commentators, while anxious to follow him, had to bear in mind the scriptural statement that God had created the rainbow as a sign to Noah that there should never again be a Flood on the earth. Even so bold a thinker as Cardinal d'Ailly, whose speculations as to the geography of the earth did so much afterward in stimulating Columbus, faltered before this statement, acknowledging that God alone could explain it; but suggested that possibly never before the Deluge had a cloud been suffered to take such a position toward the sun as to cause a rainbow.

The learned cardinal was also constrained to believe that certain stars and constellations have something to do in causing the rain, since these would best explain Noah's foreknowledge of the Deluge. In connection with this scriptural doctrine of winds came a scriptural doctrine of earthquakes: they were believed to be caused by winds issuing from the earth, and this view was based upon the passage in the one hundred and thirty-fifth Psalm, "He bringeth the wind out of his treasuries."[12]

Such were the main typical attempts during nearly fourteen centuries to build up under theological guidance and within

---

orum, III, iv, 18 (of which I have used the edition of Venice, 1488).

[12] For D'Ailly, see his Concordia astronomicæ veritatis cum theologia (Paris, 1483—in the Imago mundi—and Venice, 1490); also Eck's commentary on Aristotle's Meteorologica (Augsburg, 1519), lib. ii, nota 2; also Reisch, Margarita philosophica, lib. ix, c. 18.

scriptural limitations a sacred science of meteorology. But these theories were mainly evolved in the effort to establish a basis and general theory of phenomena: it still remained to account for special manifestations, and here came a twofold development of theological thought.

On one hand, these phenomena were attributed to the Almighty, and, on the other, to Satan. As to the first of these theories, we constantly find the Divine wrath mentioned by the earlier fathers as the cause of lightning, hailstorms, hurricanes, and the like.

In the early days of Christianity we see a curious struggle between pagan and Christian belief upon this point. Near the close of the second century the Emperor Marcus Aurelius, in his effort to save the empire, fought a hotly contested battle with the Quadi, in what is now Hungary. While the issue of this great battle was yet doubtful there came suddenly a blinding storm beating into the faces of the Quadi, and this gave the Roman troops the advantage, enabling Marcus Aurelius to win a decisive victory. Votaries of each of the great religions claimed that this storm was caused by the object of their own adoration. The pagans insisted that Jupiter had sent the storm in obedience to their prayers, and on the Antonine Column at Rome we may still see the figure of Olympian Jove casting his thunderbolts and pouring a storm of rain from the open heavens against the Quadi. On the other hand, the Christians insisted that the storm had been sent by Jehovah in obedience to *their* prayers; and Tertullian, Eusebius, St. Gregory of Nyssa, and St. Jerome were among those who insisted upon this meteorological miracle; the first two, indeed, in the fervour of their arguments for its reality, allowing themselves to be carried considerably beyond exact historical truth.[13]

As time went on, the fathers developed this view more and more from various texts in the Jewish and Christian sacred books, substituting for Jupiter flinging his thunderbolts the Almighty wrapped in thunder and sending forth his lightnings. Through the Middle Ages this was fostered until it came to be accepted as a mere truism, entering into all mediæval thinking, and was still further developed by an attempt

[13] For the authorities, pagan and Christian, see the note of Merivale, in his *History of the Romans under the Empire,* chap. lxviii. He refers for still fuller citations to Fynes Clinton's *Fasti Rom.,* p. 24.

to specify the particular sins which were thus punished. Thus even the rational Florentine historian Villani ascribed floods and fires to the "too great pride of the city of Florence and the ingratitude of the citizens toward God," which, "of course," says a recent historian, "meant their insufficient attention to the ceremonies of religion."[14]

In the thirteenth century the Cistercian monk, Cæsarius of Heisterbach, popularized the doctrine in central Europe. His rich collection of anecdotes for the illustration of religious truths was the favourite recreative reading in the convents for three centuries, and exercised great influence over the thought of the later Middle Ages. In this work he relates several instances of the Divine use of lightning, both for rescue and for punishment. Thus he tells us how the steward (*cellerarius*) of his own monastery was saved from the clutch of a robber by a clap of thunder which, in answer to his prayer, burst suddenly from the sky and frightened the bandit from his purpose; how, in a Saxon theatre, twenty men were struck down, while a priest escaped, not because he was not a greater sinner than the rest, but because the thunderbolt had respect for his profession! It is Cæsarius, too, who tells us the story of the priest of Treves, struck by lightning in his own church, whither he had gone to ring the bell against the storm, and whose sins were revealed by the course of the lightning, for it tore his clothes from him and consumed certain parts of his body, showing that the sins for which he was punished were vanity and unchastity.[15]

This mode of explaining the Divine interference more minutely is developed century after century, and we find both Catholics and Protestants assigning as causes of unpleasant meteorological phenomena whatever appears to them wicked or even unorthodox. Among the English Reformers, Tyndale quotes in this kind of argument the thirteenth chapter of I. Samuel, showing that, when God gave Israel a king, it thundered and rained. Archbishop Whitgift, Bishop Bale, and Bishop Pilkington insisted on the same view. In Protestant Germany, about the same period, Plieninger took a dislike to the new Gregorian calendar and published a volume of *Brief Reflections,* in which he insisted that the elements had given utterance to God's anger against it, calling attention to the

[14] See Trollope, *History of Florence,* vol. i, p. 64.
[15] See Cæsarius Heisterbacensis, *Dialogus miraculorum,* lib. x, c. 28-30.

fact that violent storms raged over almost all Germany during the very ten days which the Pope had taken out for the correction of the year, and that great floods began with the first days of the corrected year.[16]

Early in the seventeenth century, Majoli, Bishop of Voltoraria, in southern Italy, produced his huge work *Dies Canicularii,* or *Dog Days,* which remained a favourite encyclopædia in Catholic lands for over a hundred years. Treating of thunder and lightning, he compares them to bombs against the wicked, and says that the thunderbolt is "an exhalation condensed and cooked into stone," and that "it is not to be doubted that, of all instruments of God's vengeance, the thunderbolt is the chief"; that by means of it Sennacherib and his army were consumed; that Luther was struck by lightning in his youth as a caution against departing from the Catholic faith; that blasphemy and Sabbath-breaking are the sins to which this punishment is especially assigned, and he cites the case of Dathan and Abiram. Fifty years later the Jesuit Stengel developed this line of thought still further in four thick quarto volumes on the judgments of God, adding an elaborate schedule for the use of preachers in the sermons of an entire year. Three chapters were devoted to thunder, lightning, and storms. That the author teaches the agency in these of diabolical powers goes without saying; but this can only act, he declares, by Divine permission, and the thunderbolt is always the finger of God, which rarely strikes a man save for his sins, and the nature of the special sin thus punished may be inferred from the bodily organs smitten. A few years later, in Protestant Swabia, Pastor Georg Nuber issued a volume of "weather-sermons," in which he discusses nearly every sort of elemental disturbances—storms, floods, droughts, lightning, and hail. These, he says, come direct from God for human sins, yet no doubt with discrimination, for there are five sins which God especially punishes with lightning and hail—namely, impenitence, incredulity, neglect of the repair of churches, fraud in the payment of tithes to the clergy, and

[16] For Tyndale, see his *Doctrinal Treatises,* p. 194, and for Whitgift, see his *Works,* vol. ii, pp. 477-483; Bale, *Works,* pp. 244, 245; and Pilkington, *Works,* pp. 177, 536 (all in *Parker Society Publications*). Bishop Bale cites especially Job xxxviii, Ecclesiasticus xiii, and Revelation viii, as supporting the theory. For Plieninger's words, see Janssen, *Geschichte des deutschen Volkes,* vol. v, p. 350.

oppression of subordinates, each of which points he supports with a mass of scriptural texts.[17]

This doctrine having become especially precious both to Catholics and to Protestants, there were issued handbooks of prayers against bad weather: among these was the *Spiritual Thunder and Storm Booklet,* produced in 1731 by a Protestant scholar, Stöltzlin, whose three or four hundred pages of prayer and song, "sighs for use when it lightens fearfully," and "cries of anguish when the hailstorm is drawing on," show a wonderful adaptability to all possible meteorological emergencies. The preface of this volume is contributed by Prof. Dilherr, pastor of the great church of St. Sebald at Nuremberg, who, in discussing the Divine purposes of storms, adds to the three usually assigned—namely, God's wish to manifest his power, to display his anger, and to drive sinners to repentance—a fourth, which, he says, is that God may show us "with what sort of a storm-bell he will one day ring in the last judgment."

About the end of the first quarter of the eighteenth century we find, in Switzerland, even the eminent and rational Professor of Mathematics, Scheuchzer, publishing his *Physica Sacra,* with the Bible as a basis, and forced to admit that the elements, in the most literal sense, utter the voice of God. The same pressure was felt in New England. Typical are the sermons of Increase Mather on *The Voice of God in Stormy Winds.* He especially lays stress on the voice of God speaking to Job out of the whirlwind, and upon the text, "Stormy wind fulfilling his word." He declares, "When there are great tempests, the angels oftentimes have a hand therein, . . . yea, and sometimes evil angels." He gives several cases of blasphemers struck by lightning, and says, "Nothing can be more dangerous for mortals than to contemn dreadful providences, and, in particular, dreadful tempests."

His distinguished son, Cotton Mather, disentangled himself somewhat from the old view, as he had done in the interpretation of comets. In his *Christian Philosopher,* his *Thoughts for the Day of Rain,* and his *Sermon preached at the Time of the Late Storm* (in 1723), he is evidently tending toward the modern view. Yet, from time to time, the older

---

[17] For Majoli, see *Dies Can.,* I, i; for Stengel, see the *De judiciis divinis,* vol. ii, pp. 15-61, and especially the example of the *impurus et saltator sacerdos, fulmine castratus,* pp. 26, 27. For Nuber, see his *Conciones meteoricæ,* Ulm, 1661.

view has reasserted itself, and in France, as recently as the year 1870, we find the Bishop of Verdun ascribing the drought afflicting his diocese to the sin of Sabbath-breaking.[18]

This theory, which attributed injurious meteorological phenomena mainly to the purposes of God, was a natural development, and comparatively harmless; but at a very early period there was evolved another theory, which, having been ripened into a doctrine, cost the earth dear indeed. Never, perhaps, in the modern world has there been a dogma more prolific of physical, mental, and moral agony throughout whole nations and during whole centuries. This theory, its development by theology, its fearful results to mankind, and its destruction by scientific observation and thought, will next be considered.

2. Diabolic Agency in Storms

While the fathers and schoolmen were labouring to deduce a science of meteorology from our sacred books, there oozed up in European society a mass of traditions and observances which had been lurking since the days of paganism; and, although here and there appeared a churchman to oppose them, the theologians and ecclesiastics ere long began to adopt them and to clothe them with the authority of religion.

Both among the pagans of the Roman Empire and among the barbarians of the North the Christian missionaries had found it easier to prove the new God supreme than to prove the old gods powerless. Faith in the miracles of the new religion seemed to increase rather than to diminish faith in the miracles of the old; and the Church at last began admitting the latter as facts, but ascribing them to the devil. Jupiter and Odin sank into the category of ministers of Satan, and transferred to that master all their former powers. A renewed study of Scripture by theologians elicited overwhelming proofs of the truth of this doctrine. Stress was especially laid on the declaration of Scripture, "The gods of the heathen are

[18] For Stöltzlin, see his *Geistliches Donner- und Wetter-Büchlein* (Zürich, 1731). For Increase Mather, see his *The Voice of God,* etc. (Boston, 1704). This rare volume is in the rich collection of the American Antiquarian Society at Worcester. For Cotton Mather's view, see the chapter *From Signs and Wonders to Law,* in this work. For the Bishop of Verdun, see the *Semaine relig. de Lorraine,* 1870, p. 445 (cited by "Paul Parfait," in his *Dossier des Pèlerinages,* pp. 141-143).

devils."[19] Supported by this and other texts, it soon became a dogma. So strong was the hold it took, under the influence of the Church, that not until late in the seventeenth century did its substantial truth begin to be questioned.

With no field of action had the sway of the ancient deities been more identified than with that of atmospheric phenomena. The Roman heard Jupiter, and the Teuton heard Thor, in the thunder. Could it be doubted that these powerful beings would now take occasion, unless hindered by the command of the Almighty, to vent their spite against those who had deserted their altars? Might not the Almighty himself be willing to employ the malice of these powers of the air against those who had offended him?

It was, indeed, no great step, for those whose simple faith accepted rain or sunshine as an answer to their prayers, to suspect that the untimely storms or droughts, which baffled their most earnest petitions, were the work of the arch-enemy, "the prince of the power of the air."

The great fathers of the Church had easily found warrant for this doctrine in Scripture. St. Jerome declared the air to be full of devils, basing this belief upon various statements in the prophecies of Isaiah and in the Epistle to the Ephesians. St. Augustine held the same view as beyond controversy.[20]

During the Middle Ages this doctrine of the diabolical origin of storms went on gathering strength. Bede had full faith in it, and narrates various anecdotes in support of it. St. Thomas Aquinas gave it his sanction, saying in his all-authoritative *Summa*, "Rains and winds, and whatsoever occurs by local impulse alone, can be caused by demons." "It

[19] For so the Vulgate and all the early versions rendered Ps. xcvi, 5.

[20] For St. Jerome, see his *Com. in Ep. ad Ephesios* (lib. iii, cap. 6); commenting on the text, "Our battle is not with flesh and blood," he explains this as meaning the devils in the air, and adds: "Nam et in alio loco de dæmonibus quod in aere isto vagentur, Apostolus ait: *In quibus ambulastis aliquando juxta sæculum mundi istius, secundum principem potestatis aeris spiritus, qui nunc operatur in filios diffidentiæ* (Eph. ii, 2). Hæc autem omnium doctorum opinio est, quod aer iste qui cœlum et terram medius dividens, inane appellatur, plenus sit contrariis fortitudinibus." See also his *Com. in Isaiam*, lib. xiii, cap. 50 (Migne, *Patr. Lat.*, vol. xxiv, p. 477). For Augustine, see the *De Civitate Dei, passim*.

is," he says, "a dogma of faith that the demons can produce wind, storms, and rain of fire from heaven."

Albert the Great taught the same doctrine, and showed how a certain salve thrown into a spring produced whirlwinds. The great Franciscan—the "seraphic doctor"—St. Bonaventura, whose services to theology earned him one of the highest places in the Church, and to whom Dante gave special honour in paradise, set upon this belief his high authority. The lives of the saints, and the chronicles of the Middle Ages, were filled with it. Poetry and painting accepted the idea and developed it. Dante wedded it to verse, and at Venice this thought may still be seen embodied in one of the grand pictures of Bordone: a shipload of demons is seen approaching Venice in a storm, threatening destruction to the city, but St. Mark, St. George, and St. Nicholas attack the vessel, and disperse the hellish crew.[21]

The popes again and again sanctioned this doctrine, and it was amalgamated with various local superstitions, pious imaginations, and interesting arguments, to strike the fancy of the people at large. A strong argument in favour of a diabolical origin of the thunderbolt was afforded by the eccentricities of its operation. These attracted especial attention in the Middle Ages, and the popular love of marvel generalized isolated phenomena into rules. Thus it was said that the lightning strikes the sword in the sheath, gold in the purse, the foot in the shoe, leaving the sheath and purse and shoe unharmed; that it consumes a human being internally without injuring the skin; that it destroys nets in the water, but not on the land; that it kills one man, and leaves untouched another standing beside him; that it can tear through a house and enter the earth without moving a stone from its place; that it injures the heart of a tree, but not the bark; that wine is poisoned by it, while poisons struck by it lose their venom;

[21] For Bede, see the *Hist. Eccles.*, vol. i, p. 17; *Vita Cuthberti*, c. 17 (Migne, tome xliv). For Thomas Aquinas, see the *Summa*, pars I, qu. lxxx, art. 2. The second citation I owe to Rydberg, *Magic of the Middle Ages*, p. 73, where the whole interesting passage is given at length. For Albertus Magnus, see the *De Potentia Dæmonum* (cited by Maury, *Légendes Pieuses*). For Bonaventura, see the *Comp. Theol. Veritat.*, ii, 26. For Dante, see *Purgatorio*, c. 5. On Bordone's picture, see Maury, *Légendes Pieuses*, p. 18, note.

that a man's hair may be consumed by it and the man be un-hurt.[22]

These peculiar phenomena, made much of by the alle-gorizing sermonizers of the day, were used in moral lessons from every pulpit. Thus the Carmelite, Matthias Farinator, of Vienna, who at the Pope's own instance compiled early in the fifteenth century that curious handbook of illustrative examples for preachers, the *Lumen Animæ*, finds a spiritual analogue for each of these anomalies.[23]

This doctrine grew, robust and noxious, until, in the fif-teenth, sixteenth, and seventeenth centuries, we find its bloom in a multitude of treatises by the most learned of the Catholic and Protestant divines, and its fruitage in the torture chambers and on the scaffolds throughout Christendom. At the Refor-mation period, and for nearly two hundred years afterward, Catholics and Protestants vied with each other in promoting this growth. John Eck, the great opponent of Luther, gave to the world an annotated edition of Aristotle's *Physics,* which was long authoritative in the German universities; and, though the text is free from this doctrine, the woodcut illustrating the earth's atmosphere shows most vividly, among the clouds of mid-air, the devils who there reign supreme.[24]

Luther, in the other religious camp, supported the super-stition even more zealously, asserting at times his belief that the winds themselves are only good or evil spirits, and declar-ing that a stone thrown into a certain pond in his native region would cause a dreadful storm because of the devils kept prisoners there.[25]

Just at the close of the same century, Catholics and Prot-estants welcomed alike the great work of Delrio. In this, the power of devils over the elements is proved first from the Holy Scriptures, since, he declares, "they show that Satan brought fire down from heaven to consume the servants and flocks of Job, and that he stirred up a violent wind, which overwhelmed in ruin the sons and daughters of Job at their feasting." Next, Delrio insists on the agreement of all the orthodox fathers, that it was the devil himself who did this,

[22] See, for lists of such *admiranda,* any of the early writers—e.g., Vincent of Beauvais, Reisch's *Margarita,* or Eck's *Aristotle.*
[23] See the *Lumen Animæ,* Eichstadt, 1479.
[24] See Eck, *Aristotelis Meteorologica,* Augsburg, 1519.
[25] For Luther, see the *Table Talk;* also Michelet, *Life of Luther* (translated by Hazlitt, p. 321).

and attention is called to the fact that the hail with which the Egyptians were punished is expressly declared in Holy Scripture to have been brought by the evil angels. Citing from the Apocalypse, he points to the four angels standing at the four corners of the earth, holding back the winds and preventing their doing great damage to mortals; and he dwells especially upon the fact that the devil is called by the apostle a "prince of the power of the air." He then goes on to cite the great fathers of the Church—Clement, Jerome, Augustine, and Thomas Aquinas.[26]

This doctrine was spread not only in ponderous treatises, but in light literature and by popular illustrations. In the *Compendium Maleficarum* of the Italian monk Guacci, perhaps the most amusing book in the whole literature of witchcraft, we may see the witch, *in propria persona,* riding the diabolic goat through the clouds while the storm rages around and beneath her; and we may read a rich collection of anecdotes, largely contemporary, which establish the required doctrine beyond question.

The first and most natural means taken against this work of Satan in the air was prayer; and various petitions are to be found scattered through the Christian liturgies—some very beautiful and touching. This means of escape has been relied upon, with greater or less faith, from those days to these. Various mediæval saints and reformers, and devoted men in all centuries, from St. Giles to John Wesley, have used it with results claimed to be miraculous. Whatever theory any thinking man may hold in the matter, he will certainly not venture a reproachful word: such prayers have been in all ages a natural outcome of the mind of man in trouble.[27]

[26] For Delrio, see his *Disquisitiones Magicæ,* first printed at Liége in 1599-1600, but reprinted again and again throughout the seventeenth century. His interpretation of Psalm lxxviii, 47-49, was apparently shared by the translators of our own authorized version. For citations by him, see Revelation vii, 1; Ephesians ii, 2. Even according to modern commentators (e.g., Alford), the word here translated "power" denotes not *might,* but *government, court, hierarchy;* and in this sense it was always used by the ecclesiastical writers, whose conception is best rendered by our plural— "powers." See Delrio, *Disquisitiones Magicæ,* lib. ii, c. 11.

[27] For Guacci, see his *Compendium Maleficarum* (Milan, 1608). For the cases of St. Giles, John Wesley, and others stilling the tempests, see Brewer, *Dictionary of Miracles, s. v. Prayer.*

But against the "power of the air" were used other means of a very different character and tendency, and foremost among these was exorcism. In an exorcism widely used and ascribed to Pope Gregory XIII, the formula is given: "I, a priest of Christ, . . . do command ye, most foul spirits, who do stir up these clouds, . . . that ye depart from them, and disperse yourselves into wild and untilled places, that ye may be no longer able to harm men or animals or fruits or herbs, or whatsoever is designed for human use." But this is mild, indeed, compared to some later exorcisms, as when the ritual runs: "All the people shall rise, and the priest, turning toward the clouds, shall pronounce these words: 'I exorcise ye, accursed demons, who have dared to use, for the accomplishment of your iniquity, those powers of Nature by which God in divers ways worketh good to mortals; who stir up winds, gather vapours, form clouds, and condense them into hail. . . . I exorcise ye, . . . that ye relinquish the work ye have begun, dissolve the hail, scatter the clouds, disperse the vapours, and restrain the winds.' " The rubric goes on to order that then there shall be a great fire kindled in an open place, and that over it the sign of the cross shall be made, and the one hundred and fourteenth Psalm chanted, while malodorous substances, among them sulphur and asafœtida, shall be cast into the flames. The purpose seems to have been literally to "smoke out" Satan.[28]

Manuals of exorcisms became important—some bulky quartos, others handbooks. Noteworthy among the latter is one by the Italian priest Locatelli, entitled *Exorcisms most Powerful and Efficacious for the Dispelling of Aërial Tempests, whether raised by Demons at their own Instance or at the Beck of some Servant of the Devil.*[29]

The Jesuit Gretser, in his famous book on *Benedictions and Maledictions,* devotes a chapter to this subject, dismissing summarily the scepticism that questions the power of

[28] See Polidorus Valerius, *Practica exorcistarum;* also the *Thesaurus exorcismorum* (Cologne, 1626), pp. 158-162.
[29] That is, *Exorcismi,* etc. A "corrected" second edition was printed at Laybach, 1680, in 24mo, to which is appended another manual of *Preces et conjurationes contra aëreas tempestates, omnibus sacerdotibus utiles et necessaria,* printed at the monastery of Kempten (in Bavaria) in 1667. The latter bears as epigraph the passage from the gospels describing Christ's stilling of the winds.

devils over the elements, and adducing the story of Job as conclusive.[30]

Nor was this theory of exorcism by any means confined to the elder Church. Luther vehemently upheld it, and prescribed especially the first chapter of St. John's gospel as of unfailing efficacy against thunder and lightning, declaring that he had often found the mere sign of the cross, with the text, "The word was made flesh," sufficient to put storms to flight.[31]

From the beginning of the Middle Ages until long after the Reformation the chronicles give ample illustration of the successful use of such exorcisms. So strong was the belief in them that it forced itself into minds comparatively rational, and found utterance in treatises of much importance.

But, since exorcisms were found at times ineffectual, other means were sought, and especially fetiches of various sorts. One of the earliest of these appeared when Pope Alexander I, according to tradition, ordained that holy water should be kept in churches and bedchambers to drive away devils.[32] Another safeguard was found in relics, and of similar efficacy were the so-called "conception billets" sold by the Carmelite monks. They contained a formula upon consecrated paper, at which the devil might well turn pale. Buried in the corner of a field, one of these was thought to give protection against bad weather and destructive insects.[33]

But highest in repute during centuries was the *Agnus Dei* —a piece of wax blessed by the Pope's own hand, and stamped with the well-known device representing the "Lamb of God." Its powers were so marvellous that Pope Urban V thought three of these cakes a fitting gift from himself to the Greek Emperor. In the Latin doggerel recounting their virtues, their meteorological efficacy stands first, for especial stress is laid on their power of dispelling the thunder. The stress thus laid by Pope Urban, as the infallible guide of Christendom, on the efficacy of this fetich, gave it great value throughout Europe,

[30] See Gretser, *De benedictionibus et maledictionibus,* lib. ii, c. 48.
[31] So, at least, says Gretser (in his *De ben. et mal.,* as above).
[32] "Instituit ut aqua quam sanctam appellamus sale admixta interpositis sacris orationibus et in templis et in cubiculis ad fugandos dæmones retineretur."—Platina, *Vitæ Pontif.* But the story is from the False Decretals.
[33] See Rydberg, *The Magic of the Middle Ages,* translated by Edgren, pp. 63-66.

and the doggerel verses reciting its virtues sank deep into the popular mind. It was considered a most potent means of dispelling hail, pestilence, storms, conflagrations, and enchantments; and this feeling was deepened by the rules and rites for its consecration. So solemn was the matter, that the manufacture and sale of this particular fetich was, by a papal bull of 1471, reserved for the Pope himself, and he only performed the required ceremony in the first and seventh years of his pontificate. Standing unmitred, he prayed: "O God, . . . we humbly beseech thee that thou wilt bless these waxen forms, figured with the image of an innocent lamb, . . . that, at the touch and sight of them, the faithful may break forth into praises, and that the crash of hailstorms, the blast of hurricanes, the violence of tempests, the fury of winds, and the malice of thunderbolts may be tempered, and evil spirits flee and tremble before the standard of thy holy cross, which is graven upon them."[34]

[34] These pious charms are still in use in the Church, and may be found described in any ecclesiastical cyclopædia. The doggerel verses run as follows:

"Tonitrua magna terret,	Inimicos nostros domat,
Et peccata nostra delet;	Prægnantem cum partu salvat,
Ab incendio præservat,	Dona dignis multa confert,
A submersione servat,	Utque malis mala defert.
A morte cita liberat,	Portio, quamvis parva sit,
Et Cacodæmones fugat,	Ut magna tamen proficit."

See these verses cited in full faith, so late as 1743, in Father Vincent of Berg's *Enchiridium,* pp. 23, 24, where is an ample statement of the virtues of the *Agnus Dei,* and instructions for its use. A full account of the rites used in consecrating this fetich, with the prayers and benedictions which gave colour to this theory of the powers of the *Agnus Dei,* may be found in the ritual of the Church. I have used the edition entitled *Sacrarum ceremoniarum sive rituum Sanctæ Romanæ Ecclesiæ libri tres,* Rome, 1560, in folio. The form of the papal prayer is as follows: "Deus, . . . te suppliciter deprecamur, ut . . . has cereas formas, innocentissimi agni imagine figuratas, benedicere . . . digneris, ut per ejus tactum et visum fideles invitentur ad laudes, fragor grandinum, procella turbinum, impetus tempestatum, ventorum rabies, infesta tonitrua temperentur, fugiant atque tremiscant maligni spiritus ante Sanctæ Crucis vexillum, quod in illis exsculptum est. . . ." (*Sacr. Cer. Rom. Eccl.,* as above). If any are curious as to the extent to which this consecrated wax was a specific for all spiritual and most temporal ills during the sixteenth and seventeenth centuries, let them consult the Jesuit *Litteræ annuæ, passim.*

Another favourite means with the clergy of the older Church for bringing to naught the "power of the air," was found in great processions bearing statues, relics, and holy emblems through the streets. Yet even these were not always immediately effective. One at Liége, in the thirteenth century, thrice proved unsuccessful in bringing rain, when at last it was found that the image of the Virgin had been forgotten! A new procession was at once formed, the *Salve Regina* sung, and the rain came down in such torrents as to drive the devotees to shelter.[35]

In Catholic lands this custom remains to this day, and very important features in these processions are the statues and the reliquaries of patron saints. Some of these excel in bringing sunshine, others in bringing rain. The Cathedral of Chartres is so fortunate as to possess sundry relics of St. Taurin, especially potent against dry weather, and some of St. Piat, very nearly as infallible against wet weather. In certain regions a single saint gives protection alternately against wet and dry weather—as, for example, St. Godeberte at Noyon. Against storms St. Barbara is very generally considered the most powerful protectress; but, in the French diocese of Limoges, Notre Dame de Crocq has proved a most powerful rival, for when, a few years since, all the neighbouring parishes were ravaged by storms, not a hailstone fell in the canton which she protected. In the diocese of Tarbes, St. Exupère is especially invoked against hail, peasants flocking from all the surrounding country to his shrine.[36]

But the means of baffling the powers of the air which came to be most widely used was the ringing of consecrated church bells.

This usage had begun in the time of Charlemagne, and there is extant a prohibition of his against the custom of baptizing bells and of hanging certain tags[37] on their tongues as a protection against hailstorms; but even Charlemagne

[35] John of Winterthur describes many such processions in Switzerland in the thirteenth century, and all the monkish chronicles speak of them. See also Rydberg, *Magic of the Middle Ages*, p. 74.
[36] As to protection by special saints as stated, see the *Guide du touriste et du pèlerin à Chartres*, 1867 (cited by "Paul Parfait," in his *Dossier des Pèlerinages*); also pp. 139-145 of the *Dossier*.
[37] *Perticæ*. See Montanus, *Hist. Nachricht von den Glocken* (Chemnitz, 1726), p. 121; and Meyer, *Der Aberglaube des Mittelalters*, p. 186.

was powerless against this current of mediæval superstition. The theological reasons were soon poured into it, and in the year 968 Pope John XIII gave it the highest ecclesiastical sanction by himself baptizing the great bell of his cathedral church, the Lateran, and christening it with his own name.[38]

This idea was rapidly developed, and we soon find it supported in ponderous treatises, spread widely in sermons, and popularized in multitudes of inscriptions cast upon the bells themselves. This branch of theological literature may still be studied in multitudes of church towers throughout Europe. A bell at Basle bears the inscription, "Ad fugandos demones." Another, in Lugano, declares "The sound of this bell vanquishes tempests, repels demons, and summons men." Another, at the Cathedral of Erfurt, declares that it can "ward off lightning and malignant demons." A peal in the Jesuit church at the university town of Pont-à-Mousson bore the words, "They praise God, put to flight the clouds, affright the demons, and call the people." This is dated 1634. Another bell in that part of France declares, "It is I who dissipate the thunders" (*Ego sum qui dissipo tonitrua*).[39]

Another, in one of the forest cantons of Switzerland, bears a doggerel couplet, which may be thus translated:

"On the devil my spite I'll vent,
    And, God helping, bad weather prevent."[40]

Very common were inscriptions embodying this doctrine in sonorous Latin.

Naturally, then, there grew up a ritual for the consecration of bells.

* * *

[38] For statements regarding Pope John and bell superstitions, see Higgins's *Anacalypsis,* vol. ii, p. 70. See also Platina, *Vitæ Pontif.,* s. v. John XIII, and Baronius, *Annales Ecclesiastici,* sub anno 968. The conjecture of Baronius that the bell was named after St. John the Baptist, is even more startling than the accepted tradition of the Pope's sponsorship.

[39] For these illustrations, with others equally striking, see Meyer, *Der Aberglaube des Mittelalters,* pp. 185, 186. For the later examples, see Germain, *Anciennes cloches lorraines* (Nancy, 1885), pp. 23, 27.

[40] "An dem Tüfel will ich mich rächen,
    Mit der hilf gotz alle bösen wetter zerbrechen."
                    (See Meyer, as above.)

These bell baptisms became matters of great importance. Popes, kings, and prelates were proud to stand as sponsors. Four of the bells at the Cathedral of Versailles having been destroyed during the French Revolution, four new ones were baptized, on the 6th of January, 1824, the Voltairean King, Louis XVIII, and the pious Duchess d'Angoulême standing as sponsors.

In some of these ceremonies zeal appears to have outrun knowledge, and one of Luther's stories, at the expense of the older Church, was that certain authorities thus christened a bell "Hosanna," supposing that to be the name of a woman.

To add to the efficacy of such baptisms, water was sometimes brought from the river Jordan.[41]

The prayers used at bell baptisms fully recognise this doctrine. The ritual of Paris embraces the petition that, "whensoever this bell shall sound, it shall drive away the malign influences of the assailing spirits, the horror of their apparitions, the rush of whirlwinds, the stroke of lightning, the harm of thunder, the disasters of storms, and all the spirits of the tempest." Another prayer begs that "the sound of this bell may put to flight the fiery darts of the enemy of men"; and others vary the form but not the substance of this petition. The great Jesuit theologian, Bellarmin, did indeed try to deny the reality of this baptism; but this can only be regarded as a piece of casuistry suited to Protestant hardness of heart, or as strategy in the warfare against heretics.[42]

Forms of baptism were laid down in various manuals sanctioned directly by papal authority, and sacramental efficacy was everywhere taken for granted.[43] The development of this idea in the older Church was too strong to be resisted;[44] but,

[41] See Montanus, as above, who cites Beck, *Lutherthum vor Luthero*, p. 294, for the statement that many bells were carried to the Jordan by pilgrims for this purpose.

[42] For prayers at bell baptisms, see Arago, *Œuvres*, Paris, 1854, vol. iv, p. 322.

[43] As has often been pointed out, the ceremony was in all its details—even to the sponsors, the wrapping a garment about the baptized, the baptismal fee, the feast—precisely the same as when a child was baptized. Magius, who is no sceptic, relates from his own experience an instance of this sort, where a certain bishop stood sponsor for two bells, giving them both his own name—William. (See his *De Tintinnabulis*, vol. xiv.)

[44] And no wonder, when the oracle of the Church, Thomas Aquinas, expressly pronounced church bells, "provided they have

as a rule, the Protestant theologians of the Reformation, while admitting that storms were caused by Satan and his legions, opposed the baptism of bells, and denied the theory of their influence in dispersing storms. Luther, while never doubting that troublesome meteorological phenomena were caused by devils, regarded with contempt the idea that the demons were so childish as to be scared by the clang of bells; his theory made them altogether too powerful to be affected by means so trivial. The great English Reformers, while also accepting very generally the theory of diabolic interference in storms, reproved strongly the baptizing of bells, as the perversion of a sacrament and involving blasphemy. Bishop Hooper declared reliance upon bells to drive away tempests, futile. Bishop Pilkington, while arguing that tempests are direct instruments of God's wrath, is very severe against using "unlawful means," and among these he names "the hallowed bell"; and these opinions were very generally shared by the leading English clergy.[45]

Toward the end of the sixteenth century the Elector of

been duly consecrated and baptized," the foremost means of "frustrating the atmospheric mischiefs of the devil," and likened steeples in which bells are ringing to a hen brooding her chickens, "for the tones of the consecrated metal repel the demons and avert storm and lightning"; when pre-Reformation preachers of such universal currency as Joannes Herolt declared, "Bells, as all agree, are baptized with the result that they are secure from the power of Satan, terrify the demons, compel the powers"; when Geiler of Kaisersberg especially commended bell-ringing as a means of beating off the devil in storms; and when a canonist like Durandus explained the purpose of the rite to be, that "the demons hearing the trumpets of the Eternal King, to wit, the bells, may flee in terror, and may cease from the stirring up of tempests." See Herolt, *Sermones Discipuli*, vol. xvii, and Durandus, *De ritibus ecclesiæ*, vol. ii, p. 12. I owe the first of these citations to Rydberg, and the others to Montanus. For Geiler, see Dacheux, *Geiler de Kaisersberg*, pp. 280, 281.

[45] The baptism of bells was, indeed, one of the express complaints of the German Protestant princes at the Reformation. See their *Gravam. Cent. German. Grav.*, p. 51. For Hooper, see his *Early Writings*, p. 197 (in *Parker Society Publications*). For Pilkington, see his *Works*, p. 177 (in same). Among others sharing these opinions were Tyndale, Bishop Ridley, Archbishop Sandys, Becon, Calfhill, and Rogers. It is to be noted that all these speak of the rite as "baptism."

Saxony strictly forbade the ringing of bells against storms, urging penance and prayer instead; but the custom was not so easily driven out of the Protestant Church, and in some quarters was developed a Protestant theory of a rationalistic sort, ascribing the good effects of bell-ringing in storms to the calling together of the devout for prayer or to the suggestion of prayers during storms at night. As late as the end of the seventeenth century we find the bells of Protestant churches in northern Germany rung for the dispelling of tempests. In Catholic Austria this bell-ringing seems to have become a nuisance in the last century, for the Emperor Joseph II found it necessary to issue an edict against it; but this doctrine had gained too large headway to be arrested by argument or edict, and the bells may be heard ringing during storms to this day in various remote districts in Europe.[46] For this was no mere superficial view. It was really part of a deep theological current steadily developed through the Middle Ages, the fundamental idea of the whole being the direct influence of the bells upon the "Power of the Air"; and it is perhaps worth our while to go back a little and glance over the coming of this current into the modern world. Having grown steadily through the Middle Ages, it appeared in full strength at the Reformation period; and in the sixteenth century Olaus Magnus, Archbishop of Upsala and Primate of Sweden, in his great work on the northern nations, declares it a well-established fact that cities and harvests may be saved from lightning by the ringing of bells and the burning of consecrated incense, accompanied by prayers; and he cautions his readers that the workings of the thunderbolt are rather to be marvelled at than inquired into. Even as late as 1673 the Franciscan professor Lealus, in Italy, in a schoolbook which was received with great applause in his region, taught unhesitatingly the agency of demons in storms, and the power of bells over them, as well as the portentousness of comets and the movement of the heavens by angels. He dwells especially, too, upon the perfect

---

[46] For Elector of Saxony, see Peuchen, *Disp. circa tempestates,* Jena, 1697. For the Protestant theory of bells, see, e.g., the *Conciones Selectæ* of Superintendent Conrad Dieterich (cited by Peuchen, *Disp. circa tempestates*). For Protestant ringing of bells to dispel tempests, see Schwimmer, *Physicalische Luftfragen,* 1692 (cited by Peuchen, as above). He pictures the whole population of a Thuringian district flocking to the churches on the approach of a storm.

protection afforded by the waxen *Agnus Dei*. How strong this current was, and how difficult even for philosophical minds to oppose, is shown by the fact that both Descartes and Francis Bacon speak of it with respect, admitting the fact, and suggesting very mildly that the bells may accomplish this purpose by the concussion of the air.[47]

But no such moderate doctrine sufficed, and the renowned Bishop Binsfeld, of Treves, in his noted treatise on the credibility of the confessions of witches, gave an entire chapter to the effect of bells in calming atmospheric disturbances. Basing his general doctrine upon the first chapter of Job and the second chapter of Ephesians, he insisted on the reality of diabolic agency in storms; and then, by theological reasoning, corroborated by the statements extorted in the torture chamber, he showed the efficacy of bells in putting the hellish legions to flight.[48] This continued, therefore, an accepted tenet, developed in every nation, and coming to its climax near the end of the seventeenth century. At that period—the period of Isaac Newton—Father Augustin de Angelis, rector of the Clementine College at Rome, published under the highest Church authority his lectures upon meteorology. Coming from the centre of Catholic Christendom, at so late a period, they are very important as indicating what had been developed under the influence of theology during nearly seventeen hundred years. This learned head of a great college at the heart of Christendom taught that "the surest remedy against thunder is that which our Holy Mother the Church practises, namely, the ringing of bells when a thunderbolt impends: thence follows a twofold effect, physical and moral—a physical, because the sound variously disturbs and agitates the air, and by agitation disperses the hot exhalations and dispels the thunder; but the moral effect is the more certain, because by the sound the faithful are stirred to pour forth their prayers, by which they win from God the turning away of the thunderbolt." Here we see in this branch of thought, as in so many others, at the close of the seventeenth century, the dawn of rational-

[47] For Olaus Magnus, see the *De gentibus septentrionalibus* (Rome, 1555), lib. i, c. 12, 13. For Descartes, see his *De meteor.*, c. 7. For Bacon, see his *Natural History*, cent. 2, 127. In his *Historia Ventorum* he again alludes to the belief, and without comment.

[48] See Binsfeld, *De Confessionibus Malef.*, pp. 308-314, edition of 1623.

ism. Father De Angelis now keeps demoniacal influence in the background. Little, indeed, is said of the efficiency of bells in putting to flight the legions of Satan: the wise professor is evidently preparing for that inevitable compromise which we see in the history of every science when it is clear that it can no longer be suppressed by ecclesiastical fulminations.[49]

3. The Agency of Witches

But, while this comparatively harmless doctrine of thwarting the powers of the air by fetiches and bell-ringing was developed, there were evolved another theory and a series of practices sanctioned by the Church, which must forever be considered as among the most fearful calamities in human history. Indeed, few errors have ever cost so much shedding of innocent blood over such wide territory and during so many generations. Out of the old doctrine—pagan and Christian—of evil agency in atmospheric phenomena was evolved the belief that certain men, women, and children may secure infernal aid to produce whirlwinds, hail, frosts, floods, and the like.

As early as the ninth century one great churchman, Agobard, Archbishop of Lyons, struck a heavy blow at this superstition. His work, *Against the Absurd Opinion of the Vulgar touching Hail and Thunder,* shows him to have been one of the most devoted apostles of right reason whom human history has known. By argument and ridicule, and at times by a lofty eloquence, he attempted to breast this tide. One passage is of historical significance. He declares: "The wretched world lies now under the tyranny of foolishness; things are believed by Christians of such absurdity as no one ever could aforetime induce the heathen to believe."[50]

All in vain; the tide of superstition continued to roll on; great theologians developed it and ecclesiastics favoured it; until as we near the end of the mediæval period the infallible voice of Rome is heard accepting it, and clinching this belief into the mind of Christianity. For, in 1437, Pope Eugene IV, by virtue of the teaching power conferred on him by the Al-

[49] For De Angelis, see his *Lectiones Meteorol.*, p. 75.
[50] For a very interesting statement of Agobard's position and work, with citations from his *Liber contra insulsam vulgi opinionem de grandine et tonitruis,* see Poole, *Illustrations of the History of Mediæval Thought,* pp. 40 *et seq.* The works of Agobard are in vol. civ of Migne's *Patrol. Lat.*

mighty, and under the divine guarantee against any possible error in the exercise of it, issued a bull exhorting the inquisitors of heresy and witchcraft to use greater diligence against the human agents of the Prince of Darkness, and especially against those who have the power to produce bad weather. In 1445 Pope Eugene returned again to the charge, and again issued instructions and commands infallibly committing the Church to the doctrine. But a greater than Eugene followed, and stamped the idea yet more deeply into the mind of the Church. On the 7th of December, 1484, Pope Innocent VIII sent forth his bull *Summis Desiderantes*. Of all documents ever issued from Rome, imperial or papal, this has doubtless, first and last, cost the greatest shedding of innocent blood. Yet no document was ever more clearly dictated by conscience. Inspired by the scriptural command, "Thou shalt not suffer a witch to live," Pope Innocent exhorted the clergy of Germany to leave no means untried to detect sorcerers, and especially those who by evil weather destroy vineyards, gardens, meadows, and growing crops. These precepts were based upon various texts of Scripture, especially upon the famous statement in the book of Job; and, to carry them out, witch-finding inquisitors were authorized by the Pope to scour Europe, especially Germany, and a manual was prepared for their use—the Witch-Hammer, *Malleus Maleficarum*. In this manual, which was revered for centuries, both in Catholic and Protestant countries, as almost divinely inspired, the doctrine of Satanic agency in atmospheric phenomena was further developed, and various means of detecting and punishing it were dwelt upon.[51]

With the application of torture to thousands of women, in accordance with the precepts laid down in the *Malleus,* it was not difficult to extract masses of proof for this sacred

[51] For the bull of Pope Eugene, see Raynaldus, *Annales Eccl.,* pp. 1437, 1445. The Latin text of the bull *Summis Desiderantes* may be found in the *Malleus Maleficarum*, in Binsfeld's *De Confessionibus* cited below, or in Roskoff's *Geschichte des Teufels* (Leipsic, 1869), vol. i, pp. 222-225. There is, so far as I know, no good analysis, in any English book, of the contents of the *Witch-Hammer*; but such may be found in Roskoff's *Geschichte des Teufels*, or in Soldan's *Geschichte der Hexenprozesse.* Its first dated edition is that of 1489; but Prof. Burr has shown that it was printed as early as 1486. It was, happily, never translated into any modern tongue.

theory of meteorology. The poor creatures, writhing on the rack, held in horror by those who had been nearest and dearest to them, anxious only for death to relieve their sufferings, confessed to anything and everything that would satisfy the inquisitors and judges. All that was needed was that the inquisitors should ask leading questions[52] and suggest satisfactory answers: the prisoners, to shorten the torture, were sure sooner or later to give the answer required, even though they knew that this would send them to the stake or scaffold. Under the doctrine of "excepted cases," there was no limit to torture for persons accused of heresy or witchcraft; even the safeguards which the old pagan world had imposed upon torture were thus thrown down, and the prisoner *must* confess.

The theological literature of the Middle Ages was thus enriched with numberless statements regarding modes of Satanic influence on the weather. Pathetic, indeed, are the records; and none more so than the confessions of these poor creatures, chiefly women and children, during hundreds of years, as to their manner of raising hailstorms and tempests. Such confessions, by tens of thousands, are still to be found in the judicial records of Germany, and indeed of all Europe. Typical among these is one on which great stress was laid during ages, and for which the world was first indebted to one of these poor women. Crazed by the agony of torture, she declared that, returning with a demon through the air from the witches' sabbath, she was dropped upon the earth in the confusion which resulted among the hellish legions when they heard the bells sounding the *Ave Maria*. It is sad to note that, after a contribution so valuable to sacred science, the poor woman was condemned to the flames. This revelation speedily ripened the belief that, whatever might be going on at the witches' sabbath—no matter how triumphant Satan might be —at the moment of sounding the consecrated bells the Satanic power was paralyzed. This theory once started, proofs came in to support it, during a hundred years, from the torture chambers in all parts of Europe.

[52] For still extant lists of such questions, see the *Zeitschrift für deutsche Culturgeschichte* for 1858, pp. 522-528, or Diefenbach, *Der Hexenwahn in Deutschland,* pp. 15-17. Father Vincent of Berg (in his *Enchiridium*) gives a similar list for use by priests in the confession of the accused. Manuscript lists of this sort which have actually done service in the courts of Baden and Bavaria may be seen in the library of Cornell University.

Throughout the later Middle Ages the Dominicans had been the main agents in extorting and promulgating these revelations, but in the centuries following the Reformation the Jesuits devoted themselves with even more keenness and vigour to the same task. Some curious questions incidentally arose. It was mooted among the orthodox authorities whether the damage done by storms should or should not be assessed upon the property of convicted witches. The theologians inclined decidedly to the affirmative; the jurists, on the whole, to the negative.[53]

In spite of these tortures, lightning and tempests continued, and great men arose in the Church throughout Europe in every generation to point out new cruelties for the discovery of "weather-makers," and new methods for bringing their machinations to naught.

But here and there, as early as the sixteenth century, we begin to see thinkers endeavouring to modify or oppose these methods. At that time Paracelsus called attention to the reverberation of cannon as explaining the rolling of thunder, but he was confronted by one of his greatest contemporaries. Jean Bodin, as superstitious in natural as he was rational in political science, made sport of the scientific theory, and declared thunder to be "a flaming exhalation set in motion by evil spirits, and hurled downward with a great crash and a horrible smell of sulphur." In support of this view, he dwelt upon the confessions of tortured witches, upon the acknowledged agency of demons in the Will-o'-the-wisp, and specially upon the passage in the one hundred and fourth Psalm, "Who maketh his angels spirits, his ministers a flaming fire."

To resist such powerful arguments by such powerful men was dangerous indeed. In 1513, Pomponatius, professor at Padua, published a volume of *Doubts as to the Fourth Book of Aristotle's Meteorologica,* and also dared to question this power of devils; but he soon found it advisable to explain that, while as a *philosopher* he might doubt, yet as a *Christian* he of course believed everything taught by Mother Church—devils and all—and so escaped the fate of several others who dared to question the agency of witches in atmospheric and other disturbances.

A few years later Agrippa of Nettesheim made a some-

[53] For proofs of the vigour of the Jesuits in this persecution, see not only the histories of witchcraft, but also the *Annuæ litteræ* of the Jesuits themselves, *passim.*

what similar effort to breast this theological tide in northern Europe. He had won a great reputation in various fields, but especially in natural science, as science was then understood. Seeing the folly and cruelty of the prevailing theory, he attempted to modify it, and in 1518, as Syndic of Metz, endeavoured to save a poor woman on trial for witchcraft. But the chief inquisitor, backed by the sacred Scriptures, the papal bulls, the theological faculties, and the monks, was too strong for him; he was not only forced to give up his office, but for this and other offences of a similar sort was imprisoned, driven from city to city and from country to country, and after his death his clerical enemies, especially the Dominicans, pursued his memory with calumny, and placed over his grave probably the most malignant epitaph ever written.

As to argument, these efforts were met especially by Jean Bodin in his famous book, the *Démonomanie des Sorciers,* published in 1580. It was a work of great power by a man justly considered the leading thinker in France, and perhaps in Europe. All the learning of the time, divine and human, he marshalled in support of the prevailing theory. With inexorable logic he showed that both the veracity of sacred Scripture and the infallibility of a long line of popes and councils of the Church were pledged to it, and in an eloquent passage this great publicist warned rulers and judges against any mercy to witches—citing the example of King Ahab condemned by the prophet to die for having pardoned a man worthy of death, and pointing significantly to King Charles IX of France, who, having pardoned a sorcerer, died soon afterward.[54]

In the last years of the sixteenth century the persecutions

[54] To the argument cited above, Bodin adds: "Id certissimam dæmonis præsentiam significat: nam ubicunque dæmones cum hominibus nefaria societatis fide copulantur, fœdissimum semper relinquunt sulphuris odorem, quod sortilegi sæpissime experiuntur et confitentur." See Bodin's *Universæ Naturæ Theatrum,* Frankfort, 1597, pp. 208-211. The first edition of the book by Pomponatius, which was the earliest of his writings, is excessively rare, but it was reprinted at Venice just a half-century later. It is in his *De incantationibus,* however, that he speaks especially of devils. As to Pomponatius, see, besides these, Creighton's *History of the Papacy during the Reformation,* and an excellent essay in Franck's *Moralistes et Philosophes.* For Agrippa, see his biography by Prof. Henry Morley, London, 1856. For Bodin, see a statement of his general line of argument in Lecky, *Rationalism in Europe,* vol. i, chap. i.

for witchcraft and magic were therefore especially cruel; and in the western districts of Germany the main instrument in them was Binsfeld, Suffragan Bishop of Treves.

At that time Cornelius Loos was a professor at the university of that city. He was a devoted churchman, and one of the most brilliant opponents of Protestantism, but he finally saw through the prevailing belief regarding occult powers, and in an evil hour for himself embodied his idea in a book entitled *True and False Magic*. The book, though earnest, was temperate, but this helped him and his cause not at all. The texts of Scripture clearly sanctioning belief in sorcery and magic stood against him, and these had been confirmed by the infallible teachings of the Church and the popes from time immemorial; the book was stopped in the press, the manuscript confiscated, and Loos thrown into a dungeon.

The inquisitors having wrought their will upon him, in the spring of 1593 he was brought out of prison, forced to recant on his knees before the assembled dignitaries of the Church, and thenceforward kept constantly under surveillance and at times in prison. Even this was considered too light a punishment, and his arch-enemy, the Jesuit Delrio, declared that, but for his death by the plague, he would have been finally sent to the stake.[55]

That this threat was not unmeaning had been seen a few years earlier in a case even more noted, and in the same city. During the last decades of the sixteenth century, Dietrich Flade, an eminent jurist, was rector of the University of Treves, and chief judge of the Electoral Court, and in the latter capacity he had to pass judgment upon persons tried on the capital charge of magic and witchcraft. For a time he yielded to the long line of authorities, ecclesiastical and judicial, supporting the reality of this crime; but he at last seems to have realized that it was unreal, and that the confessions in

[55] What remains of the manuscript of Loos, which until recently was supposed to be lost, was found, hidden away on the shelves of the old Jesuit library at Treves, by Mr. George Lincoln Burr, now a professor at Cornell University; and Prof. Burr's copy of the manuscript is now in the library of that institution. For a full account of the discovery and its significance, see the *New York Nation* for November 11, 1886. The facts regarding the after-life of Loos were discovered by Prof. Burr in manuscript records at Brussels.

his torture chamber, of compacts with Satan, riding on broomsticks to the witch-sabbath, raising tempests, producing diseases, and the like, were either the results of madness or of willingness to confess anything and everything, and even to die, in order to shorten the fearful tortures to which the accused were in all cases subjected until a satisfactory confession was obtained.

On this conviction of the unreality of many at least of the charges Flade seems to have acted, and he at once received his reward. He was arrested by the authority of the archbishop and charged with having sold himself to Satan—the fact of his hesitation in the persecution being perhaps what suggested his guilt. He was now, in his turn, brought into the torture chamber over which he had once presided, was racked until he confessed everything which his torturers suggested, and finally, in 1589, was strangled and burnt.

Of that trial a record exists in the library of Cornell University in the shape of the original minutes of the case, and among them the depositions of Flade when under torture, taken down from his own lips in the torture chamber. In these depositions this revered and venerable scholar and jurist acknowledged the truth of every absurd charge brought against him—anything, everything, which would end the fearful torture: compared with that, death was nothing.[56]

Nor was even a priest secure who ventured to reveal the unreality of magic. When Friedrich Spee, the Jesuit poet of western Germany, found, in taking the confessions of those about to be executed for magic, that without exception, just when about to enter eternity and utterly beyond hope of pardon, they all retracted their confessions made under torture, his sympathies as a man rose above his loyalty to his order, and he published his *Cautio Criminalis* as a warning, stating with entire moderation the facts he had observed and the necessity of care. But he did not dare publish it under his own name, nor did he even dare publish it in a Catholic town; he gave it to the world anonymously, and, in order to prevent any tracing of the work to him through the confessional, he secretly caused it to be published in the Protestant town of Rinteln.

Nor was this all. Nothing shows so thoroughly the hold

[56] For the case of Flade, see the careful study by Prof. Burr, *The Fate of Dietrich Flade,* in the *Papers of the American Historical Association,* 1891.

that this belief in magic had obtained as the conduct of Spee's powerful friend and contemporary, John Philip von Schönborn, later the Elector and Prince Archbishop of Mayence.

As a youth, Schönborn had loved and admired Spee, and had especially noted his persistent melancholy and his hair whitened even in his young manhood. On Schönborn's pressing him for the cause, Spee at last confessed that his sadness, whitened hair, and premature old age were due to his recollections of the scores of men and women and children whom he had been obliged to see tortured and sent to the scaffold and stake for magic and witchcraft, when he as their father confessor positively knew them to be innocent. The result was that, when Schönborn became Elector and Archbishop of Mayence, he stopped the witch persecutions in that province, and prevented them as long as he lived. But here was shown the strength of theological and ecclesiastical traditions and precedents. Even a man so strong by family connections, and enjoying such great temporal and spiritual power as Schönborn, dared not openly give his reasons for this change of policy. So far as is known, he never uttered a word publicly against the reality of magic, and under his successor in the electorate witch trials were resumed.

The great upholders of the orthodox view retained full possession of the field. The victorious Bishop Binsfeld, of Treves, wrote a book to prove that everything confessed by the witches under torture, especially the raising of storms and the general controlling of the weather, was worthy of belief; and this book became throughout Europe a standard authority, both among Catholics and Protestants. Even more inflexible was Remigius, criminal judge in Lorraine. On the title-page of his manual he boasts that within fifteen years he had sent nine hundred persons to death for this imaginary crime.[57]

Protestantism fell into the superstition as fully as Cathol-

[57] For Spee and Schönborn, see Soldan and other German authorities. There are copies of the first editions of the *Cautio Criminalis* in the library of Cornell University. Binsfeld's book bore the title of *Tractatus de confessionibus maleficorum et sagarum*. First published at Treves in 1589, it appeared subsequently four times in the original Latin, as well as in two distinct German translations, and in a French one. Remigius's manual was entitled *Dæmonolatreia*, and was first printed at Lyons in 1595.

278 / History of the Warfare of Science with Theology

icism. In the same century John Wier, a disciple of Agrippa, tried to frame a pious theory which, while satisfying orthodoxy, should do something to check the frightful cruelties around him. In his book *De Præstigiis Dæmonum,* published in 1563, he proclaimed his belief in witchcraft, but suggested that the compacts with Satan, journeys through the air on broomsticks, bearing children to Satan, raising storms and producing diseases—to which so many women and children confessed under torture—were delusions suggested and propagated by Satan himself, and that the persons charged with witchcraft were therefore to be considered "as possessed"— that is, rather as sinned against than sinning.[58]

But neither Catholics nor Protestants would listen for a moment to any such suggestion. Wier was bitterly denounced and persecuted. Nor did Bekker, a Protestant divine in Holland, fare any better in the following century. For his *World Bewitched,* in which he ventured not only to question the devil's power over the weather, but to deny his bodily existence altogether, he was solemnly tried by the synod of his Church and expelled from his pulpit, while his views were condemned as heresy, and overwhelmed with a flood of refutations whose mere catalogue would fill pages; and these cases were typical of many.

The Reformation had, indeed, at first deepened the superstition; the new Church being anxious to show itself equally orthodox and zealous with the old. During the century following the first great movement, the eminent Lutheran jurist and theologian Benedict Carpzov, whose boast was that he had read the Bible fifty-three times, especially distinguished himself by his skill in demonstrating the reality of witchcraft, and by his cruelty in detecting and punishing it. The torture chambers were set at work more vigorously than ever, and a long line of theological jurists followed to maintain the system and to extend it.

To argue against it, or even doubt it, was exceedingly dangerous. Even as late as the beginning of the eighteenth century, when Christian Thomasius, the greatest and bravest German between Luther and Lessing, began the efforts which put an end to it in Protestant Germany, he did not dare at first, bold as he was, to attack it in his own name, but pre-

[58] For Wier, or Weyer, see, beside his own works, the excellent biography by Prof. Binz, of Bonn.

sented his views as the university thesis of an irresponsible student.[59]

The same stubborn resistance to the gradual encroachment of the scientific spirit upon the orthodox doctrine of witch-craft was seen in Great Britain. Typical as to the attitude both of Scotch and English Protestants were the theory and prac-tice of King James I, himself the author of a book on *Demon-ology,* and nothing if not a theologian. As to theory, his treatise on *Demonology* supported the worst features of the superstition; as to practice, he ordered the learned and acute work of Reginald Scot, *The Discoverie of Witchcraft,* one of the best treatises ever written on the subject, to be burned by the hangman, and he applied his own knowledge to inves-tigating the causes of the tempests which beset his bride on her voyage from Denmark. Skilful use of unlimited torture soon brought these causes to light. A Dr. Fian, while his legs were crushed in the "boots" and wedges were driven under his finger nails, confessed that several hundred witches had gone to sea in a sieve from the port of Leith, and had raised storms and tempests to drive back the princess.

With the coming in of the Puritans the persecution was even more largely, systematically, and cruelly developed. The great witch-finder, Matthew Hopkins, having gone through the county of Suffolk and tested multitudes of poor old women by piercing them with pins and needles, declared that county to be infested with witches. Thereupon Parliament issued a commission, and sent two eminent Presbyterian divines to ac-company it, with the result that in that county alone sixty persons were hanged for witchcraft in a single year. In Scot-land matters were even worse. The *auto da fé* of Spain was celebrated in Scotland under another name, and with Presby-terian ministers instead of Roman Catholic priests as the main attendants. At Leith, in 1664, nine women were burned to-gether. Condemnations and punishments of women in batches were not uncommon. Torture was used far more freely than in England, both in detecting witches and in punishing them. The natural argument developed in hundreds of pulpits was this: If the All-wise God punishes his creatures with tortures

[59] For Thomasius, see his various biographies by Luden and others; also the treatises on witchcraft of Soldan and others. Manuscript notes of his lectures, and copies of his earliest books on witchcraft as well as on other forms of folly, are to be found in the library of Cornell University.

infinite in cruelty and duration, why should not his ministers. as far as they can, imitate him?

The strongest minds in both branches of the Protestant Church in Great Britain devoted themselves to maintaining the superstition. The newer scientific modes of thought, and especially the new ideas regarding the heavens, revealed first by Copernicus and Galileo and later by Newton, Huygens, and Halley, were gradually dissipating the whole domain of the Prince of the Power of the Air; but from first to last a long line of eminent divines, Anglican and Calvinistic, strove to resist the new thought. On the Anglican side, in the seventeenth century, Meric Casauban, Doctor of Divinity and a high dignitary of Canterbury,—Henry More, in many respects the most eminent scholar in the Church,—Cudworth, by far the most eminent philosopher, and Dr. Joseph Glanvil, the most cogent of all writers in favour of witchcraft, supported the orthodox superstition in treatises of great power; and Sir Matthew Hale, the greatest jurist of the period, condemning two women to be burned for witchcraft, declared that he based his judgment on the direct testimony of Holy Scripture. On the Calvinistic side were the great names of Richard Baxter, who applauded some of the worst cruelties in England, and of Increase and Cotton Mather, who stimulated the worst in America; and these marshalled in behalf of this cruel superstition a long line of eminent divines, the most earnest of all, perhaps, being John Wesley.

Nor was the Lutheran Church in Sweden and the other Scandinavian countries behind its sister churches, either in persecuting witchcraft or in repressing doubts regarding the doctrine which supported it.

But in spite of all these great authorities in every land, in spite of such summary punishments as those of Flade, Loos, and Bekker, and in spite of the virtual exclusion from church preferment of all who doubted the old doctrine, the new scientific view of the heavens was developed more and more; the physical sciences were more and more cultivated; the new scientific atmosphere in general more and more prevailed; and at the end of the seventeenth century this vast growth of superstition began to wither and droop. Montaigne, Bayle, and Voltaire in France, Thomasius in Germany, Calef in New England, and Beccaria in Italy, did much also to create an intellectual and moral atmosphere fatal to it.

And here it should be stated, to the honour of the Church

of England, that several of her divines showed great courage in opposing the dominant doctrine. Such men as Harsnet, Archbishop of York, and Morton, Bishop of Lichfield, who threw all their influence against witch-finding cruelties even early in the seventeenth century, deserve lasting gratitude. But especially should honour be paid to the younger men in the Church, who wrote at length against the whole system: such men as Wagstaffe and Webster and Hutchinson, who in the humbler ranks of the clergy stood manfully for truth, with the certainty that by so doing they were making their own promotion impossible.

By the beginning of the eighteenth century the doctrine was evidently dying out. Where torture had been abolished, or even made milder, "weather-makers" no longer confessed, and the fundamental proofs in which the system was rooted were evidently slipping away. Even the great theologian Fromundus, at the University of Louvain, the oracle of his age, who had demonstrated the futility of the Copernican theory, had foreseen this and made the inevitable attempt at compromise, declaring that devils, though *often*, are not *always* or even for the most part the causes of thunder. The learned Jesuit Caspar Schott, whose *Physica Curiosa* was one of the most popular books of the seventeenth century, also ventured to make the same mild statement. But even such concessions by such great champions of orthodoxy did not prevent frantic efforts in various quarters to bring the world back under the old dogma: as late as 1743 there was published in Catholic Germany a manual by Father Vincent of Berg, in which the superstition was taught to its fullest extent, with the declaration that it was issued for the use of priests under the express sanction of the theological professors of the University of Cologne; and twenty-five years later, in 1768, we find in Protestant England John Wesley standing firmly for witchcraft, and uttering his famous declaration, "The giving up of witchcraft is in effect the giving up of the Bible." The latest notable demonstration in Scotland was made as late as 1773, when "the divines of the Associated Presbytery" passed a resolution declaring their belief in witchcraft, and deploring the general scepticism regarding it.[60]

[60] For Carpzov and his successors, see authorities already given. The best account of James's share in the extortion of confessions may be found in the collection of *Curious Tracts* published at

4. Franklin's Lightning-rod

But in the midst of these efforts by Catholics like Father Vincent and by Protestants like John Wesley to save the old sacred theory, it received its death-blow. In 1752 Franklin made his experiments with the kite on the banks of the Schuylkill; and, at the moment when he drew the electric spark from the cloud, the whole tremendous fabric of the-

Edinburgh in 1820. See also King James's own *Demonologie*, and Pitcairn's *Criminal Trials of Scotland*, vol. i, part ii, pp. 213-223. For Casaubon, see his *Credulity and Incredulity in Things Natural*, pp. 66, 67. For Glanvil, More, Casaubon, Baxter, Wesley, and others named, see Lecky, as above. As to Increase Mather, in his sermons, already cited, on *The Voice of God in Stormy Winds*, Boston, 1704, he says: "When there are great tempests, the Angels oftentimes have a Hand therein. . . . Yea, and sometimes, by Divine Permission, Evil Angels have a Hand in such Storms and Tempests as are very hurtful to Men on the Earth." Yet "for the most part, such Storms are sent by the Providence of God as a Sign of His Displeasure for the Sins of Men," and sometimes "as Prognosticks and terrible Warnings of Great Judgments not far off." From the height of his erudition Mather thus rebukes the timid voice of scientific scepticism: "There are some who would be esteemed the Wits of the World, that ridicule those as Superstitious and Weak Persons, which look upon Dreadful Tempests as Prodromous of other Judgements. Nevertheless, the most Learned and Judicious Writers, not only of the Gentiles, but amongst Christians, have Embraced such a Persuasion; their Sentiments therein being Confirmed by the Experience of many Ages." For another curious turn given to this theory, with reference to sanitary science, see Deodat Lawson's famous sermon at Salem, in 1692, on *Christ's Fidelity a Shield against Satan's Malignity*, p. 21 of the second edition. For Cotton Mather, see his biography by Barrett Wendell, pp. 91, 92; also the chapter on *Diabolism and Hysteria* in this work. For Fromundus, see his *Meteorologica* (London, 1656), lib. iii, c. 9, and lib. ii, c. 3. For Schott, see his *Physica Curiosa* (edition of Würzburg, 1667), p. 1249. For Father Vincent of Berg, see his *Enchiridium quadripartitum* (Cologne, 1743). Besides benedictions and exorcisms for all emergencies, it contains full directions for the manufacture of the *Agnus Dei*, and of another sacred panacea called "*Heiligthum*," not less effective against evil powers,—gives formulæ to be worn for protection against the devil,—suggests a list of signs by which diabolical possession may be recognised, and prescribes the questions to be asked by priests in the examination of witches. For Wesley, see his *Journal* for 1768. The whole citation is given in Lecky.

ological meteorology reared by the fathers, the popes, the mediæval doctors, and the long line of great theologians, Catholic and Protestant, collapsed; the "Prince of the Power of the Air" tumbled from his seat; the great doctrine which had so long afflicted the earth was prostrated forever.

The experiment of Franklin was repeated in various parts of Europe, but, at first, the Church seemed careful to take no notice of it. The old church formulas against the Prince of the Power of the Air were still used, but the theological theory, especially in the Protestant Church, began to grow milder. Four years after Franklin's discovery Pastor Karl Koken, member of the Consistory and official preacher to the City Council of Hildesheim, was moved by a great hailstorm to preach and publish a sermon on *The Revelation of God in Weather*. Of "the Prince of the Power of the Air" he says nothing; the theory of diabolical agency he throws overboard altogether; his whole attempt is to save the older and more harmless theory, that the storm is the voice of God. He insists that, since Christ told Nicodemus that men "know not whence the wind cometh," it can not be of mere natural origin, but is sent directly by God himself, as David intimates in the Psalm, "out of His secret places." As to the hailstorms, he lays great stress upon the plague of hail sent by the Almighty upon Egypt, and clinches all by insisting that God showed at Mount Sinai his purpose to startle the body before impressing the conscience.

While the theory of diabolical agency in storms was thus drooping and dying, very shrewd efforts were made at compromise. The first of these attempts we have already noted, in the effort to explain the efficacy of bells in storms by their simple use in stirring the faithful to prayer, and in the concession made by sundry theologians, and even by the great Lord Bacon himself, that church bells might, under the sanction of Providence, disperse storms by agitating the air. This gained ground somewhat, though it was resisted by one eminent Church authority, who answered shrewdly that, in that case, cannon would be even more pious instruments. Still another argument used in trying to save this part of the theological theory was that the bells were consecrated instruments for this purpose, "like the horns at whose blowing the walls of Jericho fell."[61]

But these compromises were of little avail. In 1766 Father

[61] For Koken, see his *Offenbarung Gottes in Wetter*, Hildesheim,

Sterzinger attacked the very groundwork of the whole diabolic theory. He was, of course, bitterly assailed, insulted, and hated; but the Church thought it best not to condemn him. More and more the "Prince of the Power of the Air" retreated before the lightning-rod of Franklin. The older Church, while clinging to the old theory, was finally obliged to confess the supremacy of Franklin's theory practically; for his lightning-rod did what exorcisms, and holy water, and processions, and the *Agnus Dei,* and the ringing of church bells, and the rack, and the burning of witches, had failed to do. This was clearly seen, even by the poorest peasants in eastern France, when they observed that the grand spire of Strasburg Cathedral, which neither the sacredness of the place, nor the bells within it, nor the holy water and relics beneath it, could protect from frequent injuries by lightning, was once and for all protected by Franklin's rod. Then came into the minds of multitudes the answer to the question which had so long exercised the leading theologians of Europe and America, namely, "Why should the Almighty strike his own consecrated temples, or suffer Satan to strike them?"

Yet even this practical solution of the question was not received without opposition.

In America the earthquake of 1755 was widely ascribed, especially in Massachusetts, to Franklin's rod. The Rev. Thomas Prince, pastor of the Old South Church, published a sermon on the subject, and in the appendix expressed the opinion that the frequency of earthquakes may be due to the erection of "iron points invented by the sagacious Mr. Franklin." He goes on to argue that "in Boston are more erected than anywhere else in New England, and Boston seems to be more dreadfully shaken. Oh! there is no getting out of the mighty hand of God."

Three years later, John Adams, speaking of a conversation with Arbuthnot, a Boston physician, says: "He began to prate upon the presumption of philosophy in erecting iron rods to draw the lightning from the clouds. He railed and foamed against the points and the presumption that erected them. He talked of presuming upon God, as Peter attempted to walk upon the water, and of attempting to control the artillery of heaven."

° 1756; and for the answer to Bacon, see Gretser's *De benedictionibus,* lib. ii, cap. 46.

As late as 1770 religious scruples regarding lightning-rods were still felt, the theory being that, as thunder and lightning were tokens of the Divine displeasure, it was impiety to prevent their doing their full work. Fortunately, Prof. John Winthrop, of Harvard, showed himself wise in this, as in so many other things: in a lecture on earthquakes he opposed the dominant theology; and as to arguments against Franklin's rods, he declared, "It is as much our duty to secure ourselves against the effects of lightning as against those of rain, snow, and wind by the means God has put into our hands."

Still, for some years theological sentiment had to be regarded carefully. In Philadelphia, a popular lecturer on science for some time after Franklin's discovery thought it best in advertising his lectures to explain that "the erection of lightning-rods is not chargeable with presumption nor inconsistent with any of the principles either of natural or revealed religion."[62]

In England, the first lightning conductor upon a church was not put up until 1762, ten years after Franklin's discovery. The spire of St. Bride's Church in London was greatly injured by lightning in 1750, and in 1764 a storm so wrecked its masonry that it had to be mainly rebuilt; yet for years after this the authorities refused to attach a lightning-rod. The Protestant Cathedral of St. Paul's, in London, was not protected until sixteen years after Franklin's discovery, and the tower of the great Protestant church at Hamburg not until a year later still. As late as 1783 it was declared in Germany, on excellent authority, that within a space of thirty-three years nearly four hundred towers had been damaged and one hundred and twenty bell-ringers killed.

In Roman Catholic countries a similar prejudice was shown, and its cost at times was heavy. In Austria, the church of Rosenberg, in the mountains of Carinthia, was struck so frequently and with such loss of life that the peasants feared at last to attend service. Three times was the spire rebuilt, and it was not until 1778—twenty-six years after Franklin's discovery—that the authorities permitted a rod to be attached. Then all trouble ceased.

[62] Regarding opposition to Franklin's rods in America, see Prince's *Sermon*, especially p. 23; also Quincy, *History of Harvard University,* vol. ii, p. 219; also *Works of John Adams,* vol. ii, pp. 51, 52; also Parton's *Life of Franklin,* vol. i, p. 294.

A typical case in Italy was that of the tower of St. Mark's, at Venice. In spite of the angel at its summit and the bells consecrated to ward off the powers of the air, and the relics in the cathedral hard by, and the processions in the adjacent square, the tower was frequently injured and even ruined by lightning. In 1388 it was badly shattered; in 1417, and again in 1489, the wooden spire surmounting it was utterly consumed; it was again greatly injured in 1548, 1565, 1653, and in 1745 was struck so powerfully that the whole tower, which had been rebuilt of stone and brick, was shattered in thirty-seven places. Although the invention of Franklin had been introduced into Italy by the physicist Beccaria, the tower of St. Mark's still went unprotected, and was again badly struck in 1761 and 1762; and not until 1766—fourteen years after Franklin's discovery—was a lightning-rod placed upon it; and it has never been struck since.[63]

So, too, though the beautiful tower of the Cathedral of Siena, protected by all possible theological means, had been struck again and again, much opposition was shown to placing upon it what was generally known as "the heretical rod"; but the tower was at last protected by Franklin's invention, and in 1777, though a very heavy bolt passed down the rod, the church received not the slightest injury. This served to reconcile theology and science, so far as that city was concerned; but the case which did most to convert the Italian theologians to the scientific view was that of the church of San Nazaro, at Brescia. The Republic of Venice had stored in the vaults of this church over two hundred thousand pounds of powder. In 1767, seventeen years after Franklin's discovery, no rod having been placed upon it, it was struck by lightning, the powder in the vaults was exploded, one sixth of the entire city destroyed, and over three thousand lives were lost.[64]

Such examples as these, in all parts of Europe, had their effect. The formulas for conjuring off storms, for consecrating bells to ward off lightning and tempests, and for putting to flight the powers of the air, were still allowed to stand in the liturgies; but the lightning-rod, the barometer, and the

[63] For reluctance in England to protect churches with Franklin's rods, see Priestley, *History of Electricity*, London, 1775, vol. i, pp. 407, 465 *et seq.*

[64] See article on *Lightning* in the *Edinburgh Review* for October, 1844.

thermometer, carried the day. A vigorous line of investigators succeeding Franklin completed his victory. The traveller in remote districts of Europe still hears the church bells
ringing during tempests; the Polish or Italian peasant is still
persuaded to pay fees for sounding bells to keep off hailstorms; but the universal tendency favours more and more the
use of the lightning-rod, and of the insurance offices where
men can be relieved of the ruinous results of meteorological
disturbances in accordance with the scientific laws of average, based upon the ascertained recurrence of storms. So,
too, though many a poor seaman trusts to his charm that
has been bathed in holy water, or that has touched some
relic, the tendency among mariners is to value more and
more those warnings which are sent far and wide each day
over the earth and under the sea by the electric wires in
accordance with laws ascertained by observation.

Yet, even in our own time, attempts to revive the old
theological doctrine of meteorology have not been wanting.
Two of these, one in a Roman Catholic and another in a
Protestant country, will serve as types of many, to show how
completely scientific truth has saturated and permeated minds
supposed to be entirely surrendered to the theological view.

The Island of St. Honorat, just off the southern coast of
France, is deservedly one of the places most venerated in
Christendom. The monastery of Lérins, founded there in the
fourth century, became a mother of similar institutions in
western Europe, and a centre of religious teaching for the
Christian world. In its atmosphere, legends and myths grew
in beauty and luxuriance. Here, as the chroniclers tell us,
at the touch of St. Honorat, burst forth a stream of living
water, which a recent historian of the monastery declares
a greater miracle than that of Moses; here he destroyed, with
a touch of his staff, the reptiles which infested the island,
and then forced the sea to wash away their foul remains.
Here, to please his sister, Sainte-Marguerite, a cherry tree
burst into full bloom every month; here he threw his cloak
upon the waters and it became a raft, which bore him safely
to visit the neighbouring island; here St. Patrick received from
St. Just the staff with which he imitated St. Honorat by driving
all reptiles from Ireland.

Pillaged by Saracens and pirates, the island was made all
the more precious by the blood of Christian martyrs. Popes
and kings made pilgrimages to it; saints, confessors, and

bishops went forth from it into all Europe; in one of its cells St. Vincent of Lérins wrote that famous definition of pure religion which, for nearly fifteen hundred years, has virtually superseded that of St. James. Naturally, the monastery became most illustrious, and its seat "the Mediterranean Isle of Saints."

But toward the close of the last century, its inmates having become slothful and corrupt, it was dismantled, all save a small portion torn down, and the island became the property first of impiety, embodied in a French actress, and finally of heresy, embodied in an English clergyman.

Bought back for the Church by the Bishop of Fréjus in 1859, there was little revival of life for twelve years. Then came the reaction, religious and political, after the humiliation of France and the Vatican by Germany; and of this reaction the monastery of St. Honorat was made one of the most striking outward and visible signs. Pius IX interested himself directly in it, called into it a body of Cistercian monks, and it became the chief seat of their order in France. To restore its sacredness the strict system of La Trappe was established—labour, silence, meditation on death. The word thus given from Rome was seconded in France by cardinals, archbishops, and all churchmen especially anxious for promotion in this world or salvation in the next. Worn-out dukes and duchesses of the Faubourg Saint-Germain united in this enterprise of pious reaction with the frivolous youngsters, the *petits crevés,* who haunt the purlieus of Notre Dame de Lorette. The great church of the monastery was handsomely rebuilt and a multitude of altars erected; and beautiful frescoes and stained windows came from the leaders of the reaction. The whole effect was, perhaps, somewhat theatrical and thin, but it showed none the less earnestness in making the old "Isle of Saints" a protest against the hated modern world.

As if to bid defiance still further to modern liberalism, great store of relics was sent in; among these, pieces of the true cross, of the white and purple robes, of the crown of thorns, sponge, lance, and winding-sheet of Christ,—the hair, robe, veil, and girdle of the Blessed Virgin; relics of St. John the Baptist, St. Joseph, St. Mary Magdalene, St. Paul, St. Barnabas, the four evangelists, and a multitude of other saints: so many that the bare mention of these treasures requires twenty-four distinct heads in the official catalogue recently published at the monastery. Besides all this—what was considered even more powerful in warding off harm from the revived monastery—the bones of Christian martyrs were brought from the Roman catacombs and laid beneath the altars.[65]

All was thus conformed to the mediæval view; nothing was to be left which could remind one of the nineteenth century; the "ages of faith" were to be restored in their simplicity. Pope Leo XIII commended to the brethren the writings of St. Thomas Aquinas as their one great object of study, and works published at the monastery dwelt upon the miracles of St. Honorat as the most precious refutation of modern science.

High in the cupola, above the altars and relics, were placed the bells. Sent by pious donors, they were solemnly baptized and consecrated in 1871, four bishops officiating, a multitude of the faithful being present from all parts of Europe, and the sponsors of the great tenor bell being the Bourbon claimant to the ducal throne of Parma and his duchess. The good bishop who baptized the bells consecrated them with a formula announcing their efficacy in driving away the "Prince of the Power of the Air," and the lightning and tempests he provokes.

And then, above all, at the summit of the central spire, high above relics, altars, and bells, was placed—*a lightning-rod*.[66]

The account of the monastery, published under the direction of the present worthy abbot, more than hints at the saving, by its bells, of a ship which was wrecked a few years since on that coast; and yet, to protect the bells and church and monks and relics from the very foe whom, in the mediæ-val faith, all these were thought most powerful to drive

[65] See the *Guide des Visiteurs à Lérins*, published at the monastery in 1880, p. 204; also the *Histoire de Lérins*, mentioned below.

[66] See *Guide*, as above, p. 84. *Les Isles de Lérins*, by the Abbé Alliez (Paris, 1860), and the *Histoire de Lérins*, by the same author, are the authorities for the general history of the abbey, and are especially strong in presenting the miracles of St. Honorat, etc. The *Cartulaire* of the monastery, recently published, is also valuable. But these do not cover the recent revival, for an account of which recourse must be had to the very interesting and naïve *Guide* already cited.

away, recourse was had to the scientific discovery of that "arch-infidel," Benjamin Franklin!

Perhaps the most striking recent example in Protestant lands of this change from the old to the new occurred not long since in one of the great Pacific dependencies of the British crown. At a time of severe drought an appeal was made to the bishop, Dr. Moorhouse, to order public prayers for rain. The bishop refused, advising the petitioners for the future to take better care of their water supply, virtually telling them, "Heaven helps those who help themselves." But most noteworthy in this matter was it that the English Government, not long after, scanning the horizon to find some man to take up the good work laid down by the lamented Bishop Fraser, of Manchester, chose Dr. Moorhouse; and his utterance upon meteorology, which a few generations since would have been regarded by the whole Church as blasphemy, was universally alluded to as an example of strong good sense, proving him especially fit for one of the most important bishoprics in England.

Throughout Christendom, the prevalence of the conviction that meteorology is obedient to laws is more and more evident. In cities especially, where men are accustomed each day to see posted in public places charts which show the storms moving over various parts of the country, and to read in the morning papers scientific prophecies as to the weather, the old view can hardly be very influential.

Significant of this was the feeling of the American people during the fearful droughts a few years since in the States west of the Missouri. No days were appointed for fasting and prayer to bring rain; there was no attribution of the calamity to the wrath of God or the malice of Satan; but much was said regarding the folly of our people in allowing the upper regions of their vast rivers to be denuded of forests, thus subjecting the States below to alternations of drought and deluge. Partly as a result of this, a beginning has been made of teaching forest culture in many schools, tree-planting societies have been formed, and "Arbor Day" is recognised in several of the States. A true and noble theology can hardly fail to recognise, in the love of Nature and care for our fellow-men thus promoted, something far better, both from a religious and a moral point of view, than any efforts to win the Divine favour by flattery, or to avert Satanic malice by fetichism.

[Chapter 12

From Magic to Chemistry and Physics]

[1. The Supremacy of Magic]

Chapter 13

From Miracles to Medicine

1. The Early and Sacred Theories of Disease

NOTHING IN THE EVOLUTION of human thought appears more inevitable than the idea of supernatural intervention in producing and curing disease. The causes of disease are so intricate that they are reached only after ages of scientific labour. In those periods when man sees everywhere miracle and nowhere law,—when he attributes all things which he can not understand to a will like his own,—he naturally ascribes his diseases either to the wrath of a good being or to the malice of an evil being.

This idea underlies the connection of the priestly class with the healing art: a connection of which we have survivals among rude tribes in all parts of the world, and which is seen in nearly every ancient civilization—especially in the powers over disease claimed in Egypt by the priests of Osiris and Isis, in Assyria by the priests of Gibil, in Greece by the priests of Æsculapius, and in Judea by the priests and prophets of Jahveh.

In Egypt there is evidence, reaching back to a very early period, that the sick were often regarded as afflicted or possessed by demons; the same belief comes constantly before us in the great religions of India and China; and, as regards Chaldea, the Assyrian tablets recovered in recent years, while revealing the source of so many myths and legends transmitted to the modern world through the book of Genesis, show especially this idea of the healing of diseases by the casting out of devils. A similar theory was elaborated in Persia. Naturally, then, the Old Testament, so precious in showing the evolution of religious and moral truth among men, attributes such diseases as the leprosy of Miriam and Uzziah, the boils of Job, the dysentery of Jehoram, the withered hand of Jeroboam, the fatal illness of Asa, and many other ills, to the wrath of God or the malice of Satan; while, in the New Testament, such examples as the woman "bound by Satan," the rebuke of the fever, the casting out of the devil which was dumb, the healing of the person whom "the devil ofttimes casteth into the fire"—of which case one of the greatest modern physicians remarks that never was there a truer description of epilepsy—and various other episodes, show this same inevitable mode of thought as a refracting medium through which the teachings and doings of the Great Physician were revealed to future generations.

In Greece, though this idea of an occult evil agency in producing bodily ills appeared at an early period, there also came the first beginnings, so far as we know, of a really scientific theory of medicine. Five hundred years before Christ, in the bloom period of thought—the period of Æschylus, Phidias, Pericles, Socrates, and Plato—appeared Hippocrates, one of the greatest names in history. Quietly but thoroughly he broke away from the old tradition, developed scientific thought, and laid the foundations of medical science upon experience, observation, and reason so deeply and broadly that his teaching remains to this hour among the most precious possessions of our race.

His thought was passed on to the School of Alexandria, and there medical science was developed yet further, especially by such men as Herophilus and Erasistratus. Under their lead studies in human anatomy began by dissection; the old prejudice which had weighed so long upon science, preventing that method of anatomical investigation without which there can be no real results, was cast aside apparently forever.[1]

[1] For extended statements regarding medicine in Egypt, Judea, and Eastern nations generally, see Sprengel, *Histoire de la Médecine,* and Haeser; and for more succinct accounts, Baas, *Geschichte der Medicin,* pp. 15-29; also Isensee; also Frédault, *Histoire de la Médecine,* chap. i. For the effort in Egyptian medicine to deal with demons and witches, see Heinrich Brugsch, *Die Aegyptologie,* Leipsic, 1891, p. 77; and for references to the *Papyrus Ebers,* etc., pp. 155, 407, and following. For fear of dissection and prejudices against it in Egypt, like those in mediæval Europe, see Maspero

But with the coming in of Christianity a great new chain of events was set in motion which modified this development most profoundly. The influence of Christianity on the healing art was twofold: there was first a blessed impulse—the thought, aspiration, example, ideals, and spirit of Jesus of Nazareth. This spirit, then poured into the world, flowed down through the ages, promoting self-sacrifice for the sick and wretched. Through all those succeeding centuries, even through the rudest, hospitals and infirmaries sprang up along this blessed stream. Of these were the Eastern establishments for the cure of the sick at the earliest Christian periods, the Infirmary of Monte Cassino and the Hôtel-Dieu at Lyons in the sixth century, the Hôtel-Dieu at Paris in the seventh, and the myriad refuges for the sick and suffering which sprang up in every part of Europe during the following centuries. Vitalized by this stream, all mediæval growths of mercy bloomed luxuriantly. To say nothing of those at an earlier period, we have in the time of the Crusades great charitable organizations like the Order of St. John of Jerusalem, and thenceforward every means of bringing the spirit of Jesus to

---

and Sayce, *Dawn of Civilization,* p. 216. For the derivation of priestly medicine in Egypt, see Baas, pp. 16, 22. For the fame of Egyptian medicine at Rome, see Sharpe, *History of Egypt,* vol. ii, pp. 151, 184. For Assyria, see especially George Smith in Delitzsch's German translation, p. 34, and F. Delitzsch's appendix, p. 27. On the cheapness and commonness of miracles of healing in antiquity, see Sharpe, quoting St. Jerome, vol. ii, pp. 276, 277. As to the influence of Chaldean ideas of magic and disease on neighbouring nations, see Maspero and Sayce, as above, pp. 782, 783. As to the freedom of ancient Greece from the idea of demoniacal intervention in disease, see Lecky, *History of European Morals,* vol. i, p. 404 and note. But, on the other hand, see reference in Homer to diseases caused by a "demon." For the evolution of medicine before and after Hippocrates, see Sprengel. For a good summing up of the work of Hippocrates, see Baas, p. 201. For the necessary passage of medicine in its early stages under priestly control, see Cabanis, *The Revolution of Medical Science,* London, 1806, chap. ii. On Jewish ideas regarding demons, and their relation to sickness, see Toy, *Judaism and Christianity,* Boston, 1891, pp. 168 *et seq.* For avoidance of dissections of human subjects even by Galen and his disciples, see Maurice Albert, *Les Médecins Grecs à Rome,* Paris, 1894, chap. xi. For Herophilus, Erasistratus, and the School of Alexandria, see Sprengel, vol. i, pp. 433, 434 *et seq.*

help afflicted humanity. So, too, through all those ages we have a succession of men and women devoting themselves to works of mercy, culminating during modern times in saints like Vincent de Paul, Francke, Howard, Elizabeth Fry, Florence Nightingale, and Muhlenberg.

But while this vast influence, poured forth from the heart of the Founder of Christianity, streamed through century after century, inspiring every development of mercy, there came from those who organized the Church which bears his name, and from those who afterward developed and directed it, another stream of influence—a theology drawn partly from prehistoric conceptions of unseen powers, partly from ideas developed in the earliest historic nations, but especially from the letter of the Hebrew and Christian sacred books.

The theology developed out of our sacred literature in relation to the cure of disease was mainly twofold: first, there was a new and strong evolution of the old idea that physical disease is produced by the wrath of God or the malice of Satan, or by a combination of both, which theology was especially called in to explain; secondly, there were evolved theories of miraculous methods of cure, based upon modes of appeasing the Divine anger, or of thwarting Satanic malice.

Along both these streams of influence, one arising in the life of Jesus, and the other in the reasonings of theologians, legends of miracles grew luxuriantly. It would be utterly unphilosophical to attribute these as a whole to conscious fraud. Whatever part priestcraft may have taken afterward in sundry discreditable developments of them, the mass of miraculous legends, century after century, grew up mainly in good faith, and as naturally as elms along water-courses or flowers upon the prairie.

2. Growth of Legends of Healing—The Life of Xavier as a Typical Example

Legends of miracles have thus grown about the lives of all great benefactors of humanity in early ages, and about saints and devotees. Throughout human history the lives of such personages, almost without exception, have been accompanied or followed by a literature in which legends of miraculous powers form a very important part—a part constantly increasing until a different mode of looking at nature and of weighing testimony causes miracles to disappear. While modern thought holds the testimony to the vast mass of such legends in all ages as worthless, it is very widely acknowledged that great and gifted beings who endow the earth with higher religious ideas, gaining the deepest hold upon the hearts and minds of multitudes, may at times exercise such influence upon those about them that the sick in mind or body are helped or healed.

We have within the modern period very many examples which enable us to study the evolution of legendary miracles. Out of these I will select but one, which is chosen because it is the life of one of the most noble and devoted men in the history of humanity, one whose biography is before the world with its most minute details—in his own letters, in the letters of his associates, in contemporary histories, and in a multitude of biographies: this man is St. Francis Xavier. From these sources I draw the facts now to be given, but none of them are of Protestant origin; every source from which I shall draw is Catholic and Roman, and published under the sanction of the Church.

Born a Spanish noble, Xavier at an early age cast aside all ordinary aims, devoted himself to study, was rapidly advanced to a professorship at Paris, and in this position was rapidly winning a commanding influence, when he came under the sway of another Spaniard even greater, though less brilliantly endowed, than himself—Ignatius Loyola, founder of the Society of Jesus. The result was that the young professor sacrificed the brilliant career on which he had entered at the French capital, went to the far East as a simple missionary, and there devoted his remaining years to redeeming the lowest and most wretched of our race.

Among the various tribes, first in lower India and afterward in Japan, he wrought untiringly—toiling through village after village, collecting the natives by the sound of a hand-bell, trying to teach them the simplest Christian formulas; and thus he brought myriads of them to a nominal confession of the Christian faith. After twelve years of such efforts, seeking new conquests for religion, he sacrificed his life on the desert island of San Chan.

During his career as a missionary he wrote great numbers of letters, which were preserved and have since been published; and these, with the letters of his contemporaries, exhibit clearly all the features of his life. His own writings are very minute, and enable us to follow him fully. No account of a miracle wrought by him appears either in his own letters or in any contemporary document.[2] At the outside, but two or three things occurred in his whole life, as exhibited so fully by himself and his contemporaries, for which the most earnest devotee could claim anything like Divine interposition; and these are such as may be read in the letters of very many fervent missionaries, Protestant as well as Catholic. For example, in the beginning of his career, during a journey in Europe with an ambassador, one of the servants in fording a stream got into deep water and was in danger of drowning. Xavier tells us that the ambassador prayed very earnestly, and that the man finally struggled out of the stream. But within sixty years after his death, at his canonization, and by various biographers, this had been magnified into a miracle, and appears in the various histories dressed out in glowing colours. Xavier tells us that the ambassador prayed for the safety of the young man; but his biographers tell us that it was Xavier who prayed, and finally, by the later writers, Xavier is represented as lifting horse and rider out of the stream by a clearly supernatural act.

Still another claim to miracle is based upon his arriving at Lisbon and finding his great colleague, Simon Rodriguez, ill of fever. Xavier informs us in a very simple way that Rodriguez was so overjoyed to see him that the fever did not return. This is entirely similar to the cure which Martin Luther wrought upon Melanchthon. Melanchthon had broken down and was supposed to be dying, when his joy at the long-delayed visit of Luther brought him to his feet again, after which he lived for many years.

Again, it is related that Xavier, finding a poor native woman very ill, baptized her, saying over her the prayers of the Church, and she recovered.

Two or three occurrences like these form the whole basis for the miraculous account, so far as Xavier's own writings are concerned.

Of miracles in the ordinary sense of the word there is in

[2] This statement was denied with much explosive emphasis by a writer in the *Catholic World* for September and October, 1891, but he brought no *fact* to support this denial. I may perhaps be allowed to remind the reverend writer that since the days of Pascal, whose eminence in the Church he will hardly dispute, the bare assertion even of a Jesuit father against established facts needs some support other than mere scurrility.

these letters of his no mention. Though he writes of his doings with especial detail, taking evident pains to note everything which he thought a sign of Divine encouragement, he says nothing of his performing miracles, and evidently knows nothing of them. This is clearly not due to his unwillingness to make known any token of Divine favour. As we have seen, he is very prompt to report anything which may be considered an answer to prayer or an evidence of the power of religious means to improve the bodily or spiritual health of those to whom he was sent.

Nor do the letters of his associates show knowledge of any miracles wrought by him. His brother missionaries, who were in constant and loyal fellowship with him, make no allusions to them in their communications with each other or with their brethren in Europe.

Of this fact we have many striking evidences. Various collections of letters from the Jesuit missionaries in India and the East generally, during the years of Xavier's activity, were published, and in not one of these letters written during Xavier's lifetime appears any account of a miracle wrought by him. As typical of these collections we may take perhaps the most noted of all, that which was published about twenty years after Xavier's death by a Jesuit father, Emanuel Acosta.

The letters given in it were written by Xavier and his associates not only from Goa, which was the focus of all missionary effort and the centre of all knowledge regarding their work in the East, but from all other important points in the great field. The first of them were written during the saint's lifetime, but, though filled with every sort of detail regarding missionary life and work, they say nothing regarding any miracles by Xavier.

The same is true of various other similar collections published during the sixteenth and seventeenth centuries. In not one of them does any mention of a miracle by Xavier appear in a letter from India or the East contemporary with him.

This silence regarding his miracles was clearly not due to any "evil heart of unbelief." On the contrary, these good missionary fathers were prompt to record the slightest occurrence which they thought evidence of the Divine favour: it is indeed touching to see how eagerly they grasp at the most trivial things which could be thus construed.

Their ample faith was fully shown. One of them, in

Acosta's collection, sends a report that an illuminated cross had been recently seen in the heavens; another, that devils had been cast out of the natives by the use of holy water; another, that various cases of disease had been helped and even healed by baptism; and sundry others sent reports that the blind and dumb had been restored, and that even lepers had been cleansed by the proper use of the rites of the Church; but to Xavier no miracles are imputed by his associates during his life or during several years after his death.

On the contrary, we find his own statements as to his personal limitations, and the difficulties arising from them, fully confirmed by his brother workers. It is interesting, for example, in view of the claim afterward made that the saint was divinely endowed for his mission with the "gift of tongues," to note in these letters confirmation of Xavier's own statement utterly disproving the existence of any such divine gift, and detailing the difficulties which he encountered from his want of knowing various languages, and the hard labour which he underwent in learning the elements of the Japanese tongue.

Until about ten years after Xavier's death, then, as Emanuel Acosta's publication shows, the letters of the missionaries continued without any indication of miracles performed by the saint. Though, as we shall see presently, abundant legends had already begun to grow elsewhere, not one word regarding these miracles came as yet from the country which, according to later accounts accepted and sanctioned by the Church, was at this very period filled with miracles; not the slightest indication of them from the men who were supposed to be in the very thick of these miraculous manifestations.

But this negative evidence is by no means all. There is also positive evidence—direct testimony from the Jesuit order itself—that Xavier wrought no miracles.

For not only did neither Xavier nor his co-workers know anything of the mighty works afterward attributed to him, but the highest contemporary authority on the whole subject, a man in the closest correspondence with those who knew most about the saint, a member of the Society of Jesus in the highest standing and one of its accepted historians, not only expressly tells us that Xavier wrought no miracles, but gives the reasons why he wrought none.

This man was Joseph Acosta, a provincial of the Jesuit

order, its visitor in Aragon, superior at Valladolid, and finally rector of the University of Salamanca. In 1571, nineteen years after Xavier's death, Acosta devoted himself to writing a work mainly concerning the conversion of the Indies, and in this he refers especially and with the greatest reverence to Xavier, holding him up as an ideal and his work as an example.

But on the same page with this tribute to the great missionary Acosta goes on to discuss the reasons why progress in the world's conversion is not so rapid as in the early apostolic times, and says that an especial cause why apostolic preaching could no longer produce apostolic results "lies in the missionaries themselves, because there is now no power of working miracles."

He then asks, "Why should our age be so completely destitute of them?" This question he answers at great length, and one of his main contentions is that in early apostolic times illiterate men had to convert the learned of the world, whereas in modern times the case is reversed, learned men being sent to convert the illiterate; and hence that "in the early times miracles were necessary, but in our time they are not."

This statement and argument refer, as we have seen, directly to Xavier by name, and to the period covered by his activity and that of the other great missionaries of his time. That the Jesuit order and the Church at large thought this work of Acosta trustworthy is proved by the fact that it was published at Salamanca a few years after it was written, and republished afterward with ecclesiastical sanction in France.[3]

[3] The work of Joseph Acosta is in the Cornell University Library, its title being as follows: *De Natura Novi Orbis libri duo et De Promulgatione Evangelii apud Barbaros, sive De Procuranda Indorum Salute, libri, sex, autore Josepho Acosta, presbytero Societatis Jesu. I. H. S. Salmanticæ, apud Guillelmum Foquel, MDLXXXIX.* For the passages cited directly contradicting the working of miracles by Xavier and his associates, see lib. ii, cap. ix, of which the title runs, *Cur Miracula in Conversione gentium non fiant nunc, ut olim, a Christi prædicatoribus,* especially pp. 242-245; also lib. ii, cap. viii, pp. 237 *et seq.* For a passage which shows that Xavier was not then at all credited with "the miraculous gift of tongues," see lib. i, cap. vii, p. 173. Since writing the above, my attention has been called to the alleged miraculous preservation of Xavier's body claimed in sundry letters contemporary with its dis-

interment at San Chan and reinterment at Goa. There is no reason why this preservation need in itself be doubted, and no reason why it should be counted miraculous. Such exceptional preservation of bodies has been common enough in all ages, and, alas for the claims of the Church, quite as common of pagans or Protestants as of good Catholics. One of the most famous cases is that of the fair Roman maiden, Julia, daughter of Claudius, over whose exhumation at Rome, in 1485, such ado was made by the sceptical scholars of the Renaissance. Contemporary observers tell us enthusiastically that she was very beautiful, perfectly preserved, "the bloom of youth still upon her cheeks," and exhaling a "sweet odour"; but this enthusiasm was so little to the taste of Pope Innocent VIII that he had her reburied secretly by night. Only the other day, in June of the year 1895, there was unearthed at Stade, in Hanover, the "perfectly preserved" body of a soldier of the eighth century. So, too, I might mention the bodies preserved at the church of St. Thomas at Strasburg, beneath the Cathedral of Bremen, and elsewhere during hundreds of years past; also the cases of "adipoceration" in various American cemeteries, which never grow less wonderful by repetition from mouth to mouth and in the public prints. But, while such preservation is not incredible nor even strange, there is much reason why precisely in the case of a saint like St. Francis Xavier the evidence for it should be received with especial caution. What the touching fidelity of disciples may lead them to believe and proclaim regarding an adored leader in a time when faith is thought more meritorious than careful statement, and miracle more probable than the natural course of things, is seen, for example, in similar pious accounts regarding the bodies of many other saints, especially that of St. Carlo Borromeo, so justly venerated by the Church for his beautiful and charitable life. And yet any one looking at the relics of various saints, especially those of St. Carlo, preserved with such tender care in the crypt of Milan Cathedral, will see that they have shared the common fate, being either mummified or reduced to skeletons; and this is true in all cases, so far as my observation has extended. What even a great theologian can be induced to believe and testify in a somewhat similar matter, is seen in St. Augustine's declaration that the flesh of the peacock, which in antiquity and in the early Church was considered a bird somewhat supernaturally endowed, is incorruptible. The saint declares that he tested it and found it so (see the *De Civitate Dei*, xxi, c. 4, under the passage beginning *Quis enim Deus*). With this we may compare the testimony of the pious author of Sir John Mandeville's *Travels*, that iron floats upon the Dead Sea while feathers sink in it, and that he would not have believed this had he not seen it. So, too, testimony to the "sweet odour" diffused by the exhumed remains of the saint seems to indicate feeling rather than fact—the highly wrought feeling of disci-

Nothing shows better than the sequel how completely the evolution of miraculous accounts depends upon the intellectual atmosphere of any land and time, and how independent it is of fact.

For, shortly after Xavier's heroic and beautiful death in 1552, stories of miracles wrought by him began to appear. At first they were few and feeble; and two years later Melchior Nunez, Provincial of the Jesuits in the Portuguese dominions, with all the means at his command, and a correspondence extending throughout Eastern Asia, had been able to hear of but three. These were entirely from hear-

---

ples standing by—the same feeling which led those who visited St. Simon Stylites on his heap of ordure, and other hermits unwashed and living in filth, to dwell upon the delicious "odour of sanctity" pervading the air. In point, perhaps, is Louis Veuillot's idealization of the "*parfum de Rome*," in face of the fact, to which the present writer and thousands of others can testify, that under papal rule Rome was materially one of the most filthy cities in Christendom. For the case of Julia, see the contemporary letter printed by Janitschek, *Gesellschaft der Renaissance in Italien*, p. 120, note 167; also Infessura, *Diarium Rom. Urbis*, in Muratori, tom. iii, pt. 2, col. 1192, 1193, and elsewhere; also Symonds, *Renaissance in Italy: Age of the Despots*, p. 22. For the case at Stade, see press dispatch from Berlin in newspapers of June 24, 25, 1895. The copy of Emanuel Acosta I have mainly used is that in the Royal Library at Munich, *De Japonicis rebus epistolarum libri iiii, item recogniti; et in Latinum ex Hispanico sermone conversi*, Dilingæ, MDLXXI. I have since obtained and used the work now in the library of Cornell University, being the letters and commentary published by Emanuel Acosta and attached to Maffei's book on the *History of the Indies*, published at Antwerp in 1685. For the first beginnings of miracles wrought by Xavier, as given in the letters of the missionaries, see that of Almeida, lib. ii, p. 183. Of other collections, or selections from collections, of letters which fail to give any indication of miracles wrought by Xavier during his life, see Wytfliet and Magin, *Histoire Universelle des Indes Occidentales et Orientales, et de la Conversion des Indiens*, Douay, 1611. Though several letters of Xavier and his fellow-missionaries are given, dated at the very period of his alleged miracles, not a trace of miracles appears in these. Also *Epistolæ Japonicæ de multorum in variis Insulis Gentilium ad Christi fidem Conversione*, Lovanii, 1570. These letters were written by Xavier and his companions from the East Indies and Japan, and cover the years from 1549 to 1564. Though these refer frequently to Xavier, there is no mention of a miracle wrought by him in any of them written during his lifetime.

say. First, John Deyro said he knew that Xavier had the gift of prophecy; but, unfortunately, Xavier himself had reprimanded and cast off Deyro for untruthfulness and cheatery. Secondly, it was reported vaguely that at Cape Comorin many persons affirmed that Xavier had raised a man from the dead. Thirdly, Father Pablo de Santa Fé had heard that in Japan Xavier had restored sight to a blind man. This seems a feeble beginning, but little by little the stories grew, and in 1555 De Quadros, Provincial of the Jesuits in Ethiopia, had heard of nine miracles, and asserted that Xavier had healed the sick and cast out devils. The next year, being four years after Xavier's death, King John III of Portugal, a very devout man, directed his viceroy Barreto to draw up and transmit to him an authentic account of Xavier's miracles, urging him especially to do the work "with zeal and speedily." We can well imagine what treasures of grace an obsequious viceroy, only too anxious to please a devout king, could bring together by means of the hearsay of ignorant, compliant natives through all the little towns of Portuguese India.

But the letters of the missionaries who had been co-workers or immediate successors of Xavier in his Eastern field were still silent as regards any miracles by him, and they remained silent for nearly ten years. In the collection of letters published by Emanuel Acosta and others no hint at any miracles by him is given, until at last, in 1562, fully ten years after Xavier's death, the first faint beginnings of these legends appear in them.

At that time the Jesuit Almeida, writing at great length to the brethren, stated that he had found a pious woman who believed that a book left behind by Xavier had healed sick folk when it was laid upon them, and that he had met an old man who preserved a whip left by the saint which, when properly applied to the sick, had been found good both for their bodies and their souls. From these and other small beginnings grew, always luxuriant and sometimes beautiful, the vast mass of legends which we shall see hereafter.

This growth was affectionately garnered by the more zealous and less critical brethren in Europe until it had become enormous; but it appears to have been thought of little value by those best able to judge.

For when, in 1562, Julius Gabriel Eugubinus delivered a solemn oration on the condition and glory of the Church, before the papal legates and other fathers assembled at the Council of Trent, while he alluded to a multitude of things showing the Divine favour, there was not the remotest allusion to the vast multitude of miracles which, according to the legends, had been so profusely lavished on the faithful during many years, and which, if they had actually occurred, formed an argument of prodigious value in behalf of the special claims of the Church.

The same complete absence of knowledge of any such favours vouchsafed to the Church, or at least of any belief in them, appears in that great Council of Trent among the fathers themselves. Certainly there, if anywhere, one might on the Roman theory expect Divine illumination in a matter of this kind. The presence of the Holy Spirit in the midst of it was especially claimed, and yet its members, with all their spiritual as well as material advantages for knowing what had been going on in the Church during the previous thirty years, and with Xavier's own friend and colleague, Laynez, present to inform them, show not the slightest sign of any suspicion of Xavier's miracles. We have the letters of Julius Gabriel to the foremost of these fathers assembled at Trent, from 1557 onward for a considerable time, and we have also a multitude of letters written from the Council by bishops, cardinals, and even by the Pope himself, discussing all sorts of Church affairs, and in not one of these is there evidence of the remotest suspicion that any of these reports which they must have heard, regarding Xavier's miracles, were worthy of mention.

*　　*　　*

So, too, when in 1588, thirty-six years after Xavier's death, the Jesuit father Maffei, who had been especially conversant with Xavier's career in the East, published his *History of India,* though he gave a biography of Xavier which shows fervent admiration for his subject, he dwelt very lightly on the alleged miracles. But the evolution of miraculous legends still went on. Six years later, in 1594, Father Tursellinus published his *Life of Xavier,* and in this appears to have made the first large use of the information collected by the Portuguese viceroy and the more zealous brethren. This work shows a vast increase in the number of miracles over those given by all sources together up to that time. Xavier is represented as not only curing the sick, but casting out devils, stilling the tempest, raising the dead, and performing miracles of every sort.

In 1622 came the canonization proceedings at Rome. Among the speeches made in the presence of Pope Gregory XV, supporting the claims of Xavier to saintship, the most important was by Cardinal Monte. In this the orator selects out ten great miracles from those performed by Xavier during his lifetime and describes them minutely. He insists that on a certain occasion Xavier, by the sign of the cross, made sea-water fresh, so that his fellow-passengers and the crew could drink it; that he healed the sick and raised the dead in various places; brought back a lost boat to his ship; was on one occasion lifted from the earth bodily and transfigured before the bystanders; and that, to punish a blaspheming town, he caused an earthquake and buried the offenders in cinders from a volcano: this was afterward still more highly developed, and the saint was represented in engravings as calling down fire from heaven and thus destroying the town.

The most curious miracle of all is the eighth on the cardinal's list. Regarding this he states that, Xavier having during one of his voyages lost overboard a crucifix, it was restored to him after he had reached the shore by a crab.

The cardinal also dwelt on miracles performed by Xavier's relics after his death, the most original being that sundry lamps placed before the image of the saint and filled with holy water burned as if filled with oil.

This latter account appears to have deeply impressed the Pope, for in the Bull of Canonization issued by virtue of his power of teaching the universal Church infallibly in all matters pertaining to faith and morals, His Holiness dwells especially upon the miracle of the lamp filled with holy water and burning before Xavier's image.

Xavier having been made a saint, many other *Lives* of him appeared, and, as a rule, each surpassed its predecessor in the multitude of miracles. In 1622 appeared that compiled and published under the sanction of Father Vitelleschi, and in it not only are new miracles increased, but some old ones are greatly improved. One example will suffice to show the process. In his edition of 1596, Tursellinus had told how, Xavier one day needing money, and having asked Vellio, one of his friends, to let him have some, Vellio gave him the key of a safe containing thirty thousand gold pieces. Xavier took three hundred and returned the key to Vellio; whereupon Vellio, finding only three hundred pieces gone, reproached Xavier for not taking more, saying that he had expected to give him half of all that the strong box contained. Xavier, touched by this generosity, told Vellio that the time of his death should be made known to him, that he might have opportunity to repent of his sins and prepare for eternity. But twenty-six years later the *Life of Xavier* published under the sanction of Vitelleschi, giving the story, says that Vellio on opening the safe found that *all* his money remained as he had left it, and that *none at all* had disappeared; in fact, that there had been a miraculous restitution. On his blaming Xavier for not taking the money, Xavier declares to Vellio that not only shall he be apprised of the moment of his death, but that the box shall always be full of money. Still later biographers improved the account further, declaring that Xavier promised Vellio that the strong box should *always* contain money sufficient for all his needs. In that warm and uncritical atmosphere this and other legends grew rapidly, obedient to much the same laws which govern the evolution of fairy tales.[4]

In 1682, one hundred and thirty years after Xavier's death, appeared his biography by Father Bouhours; and this became a classic. In it the old miracles of all kinds were enormously multiplied, and many new ones given. Miracles

[4] The writer in the *Catholic World,* already mentioned, rather rashly asserts that there is no such *Life of Xavier* as that I have above quoted. The reverend Jesuit father has evidently glanced over the bibliographies of Carayon and De Backer, and, not finding it there under the name of Vitelleschi, has spared himself further trouble. It is sufficient to say that the book may be seen by him in the library of Cornell University. Its full title is as follows: *Compendio della Vita del S. P. Francesco Xaverio della Compagnia di Giesù, Canonizato con S. Ignatio Fondatore dell' istessa Religione dalla Santità di N. S. Gregorio XV. Composto, e dato in luce per ordine del Reverendiss. P. Mutio Vitelleschi Preposito Generale della Comp. di Giesù. In Venetia, MDCXXII, Appresso Antonio Pinelli. Con Licenza de' Superiori.* My critic hazards a guess that the book may be a later edition of Torsellino (Tursellinus), but here again he is wrong. It is entirely a different book, giving in its preface a list of sources comprising eleven authorities besides Torsellino.

few and small in Tursellinus became many and great in Bouhours. In Tursellinus, Xavier during his life saves one person
from drowning, in Bouhours he saves during his life three;
in Tursellinus, Xavier during his life raises four persons from
the dead, in Bouhours fourteen; in Tursellinus there is one
miraculous supply of water, in Bouhours three; in Tursellinus
there is no miraculous draught of fishes, in Bouhours there
is one; in Tursellinus, Xavier is transfigured twice, in Bouhours five times: and so through a long series of miracles
which, in the earlier lives appearing either not at all or in very
moderate form, are greatly increased and enlarged by Tursellinus, and finally enormously amplified and multiplied by
Father Bouhours.

And here it must be borne in mind that Bouhours, writing
ninety years after Tursellinus, could not have had access to
any new sources. Xavier had been dead one hundred and
thirty years, and of course all the natives upon whom he had
wrought his miracles, and their children and grandchildren,
were gone. It can not then be claimed that Bouhours had the
advantage of any new witnesses, nor could he have had anything new in the way of contemporary writings; for, as we
have seen, the missionaries of Xavier's time wrote nothing
regarding his miracles, and certainly the ignorant natives of
India and Japan did not commit any account of his miracles
to writing. Nevertheless, the miracles of healing given in
Bouhours were more numerous and brilliant than ever. But
there was far more than this. Although during the lifetime of
Xavier there is neither in his own writings nor in any contemporary account any assertion of a resurrection from the
dead wrought by him, we find that shortly after his death
stories of such resurrections began to appear. A simple statement of the growth of these may throw some light on the
evolution of miraculous accounts generally. At first it was
affirmed that some people at Cape Comorin said that he had
raised one person; then it was said that there were two persons; then in various authors—Emanuel Acosta, in his commentaries written as an afterthought nearly twenty years
after Xavier's death, De Quadros, and others—the story
wavers between one and two cases; finally, in the time of
Tursellinus, four cases had been developed. In 1622, at the
canonization proceedings, three were mentioned; but by the
time of Father Bouhours there were fourteen—all raised
from the dead by Xavier himself during his lifetime—and

the name, place, and circumstances are given with much detail in each case.[5]

It seems to have been felt as somewhat strange at first that Xavier had never alluded to any of these wonderful miracles; but ere long a subsidiary legend was developed, to the effect that one of the brethren asked him one day if he had raised the dead, whereat he blushed deeply and cried out against the idea, saying: "And so I am said to have raised the dead! What a misleading man I am! Some men brought a youth to me just as if he were dead, who, when I commanded him to arise in the name of Christ, straightway arose."

Noteworthy is the evolution of other miracles. Tursellinus, writing in 1594, tells us that on the voyage from Goa to Malacca, Xavier having left the ship and gone upon an island, was afterward found by the persons sent in search of him so deeply absorbed in prayer as to be unmindful of all things about him. But in the next century Father Bouhours develops the story as follows: "The servants found the man of God raised from the ground into the air, his eyes fixed upon heaven, and rays of light about his countenance."

Instructive, also, is a comparison between the successive accounts of his noted miracle among the Badages at Travancore, in 1544. Xavier in his letters makes no reference to anything extraordinary; and Emanuel Acosta, in 1571, declares simply that "Xavier threw himself into the midst of the Christians, that reverencing him they might spare the rest." The inevitable evolution of the miraculous goes on; and twenty years later Tursellinus tells us that, at the onslaught of the Badages, "they could not endure the majesty of his countenance and the splendour and rays which issued from his eyes, and out of reverence for him they spared the

[5] The writer in the *Catholic World,* already referred to, has based an attack here upon a misconception—I will not call it a deliberate misrepresentation—of his own by stating that these resurrections occurred after Xavier's death, and were due to his intercession or the use of his relics. This statement of the Jesuit father is utterly without foundation, as a simple reference to Bouhours will show. I take the liberty of commending to his attention *The Life of St. Francis Xavier,* by Father Dominic Bouhours, translated by James Dryden, Dublin, 1838. For examples of raising the dead by the saint *during his lifetime,* see pp. 69, 82, 93, 111, 218, 307, 316, 321— fourteen cases in all.

others." The process of incubation still goes on during ninety years more, and then comes Father Bouhour's account. Having given Xavier's prayer on the battlefield, Bouhours goes on to say that the saint, crucifix in hand, rushed at the head of the people toward the plain where the enemy was marching, and "said to them in a threatening voice, 'I forbid you in the name of the living God to advance farther, and on His part command you to return in the way you came.' These few words cast a terror into the minds of those soldiers who were at the head of the army; they remained confounded and without motion. They who marched afterward, seeing that the foremost did not advance, asked the reason of it. The answer was returned from the front ranks that they had before their eyes an unknown person habited in black, of more than human stature, of terrible aspect, and darting fire from his eyes. . . . They were seized with amazement at the sight, and all of them fled in precipitate confusion."

Curious, too, is the after-growth of the miracle of the crab restoring the crucifix. In its first form Xavier lost the crucifix in the sea, and the earlier biographers dwell on the sorrow which he showed in consequence; but the later historians declare that the saint threw the crucifix into the sea in order to still a tempest, and that, after his safe getting to land, a crab brought it to him on the shore. In this form we find it among illustrations of books of devotion in the next century.

But perhaps the best illustration of this evolution of Xavier's miracles is to be found in the growth of another legend; and it is especially instructive because it grew luxuriantly despite the fact that it was utterly contradicted in all parts of Xavier's writings as well as in the letters of his associates and in the work of the Jesuit father, Joseph Acosta.

Throughout his letters, from first to last, Xavier constantly dwells upon his difficulties with the various languages of the different tribes among whom he went. He tells us how he surmounted these difficulties: sometimes by learning just enough of a language to translate into it some of the main Church formulas; sometimes by getting the help of others to patch together some pious teachings to be learned by rote; sometimes by employing interpreters; and sometimes by a mixture of various dialects, and even by signs. On one occasion he tells us that a very serious difficulty arose, and that his voyage to China was delayed because, among other things, the interpreter he had engaged had failed to meet him.

In various *Lives* which appeared between the time of his death and his canonization this difficulty is much dwelt upon; but during the canonization proceedings at Rome, in the speeches then made, and finally in the papal bull, great stress was laid upon the fact that Xavier possessed *the gift of tongues.* It was declared that he spoke to the various tribes with ease in their own languages. This legend of Xavier's miraculous gift of tongues was especially mentioned in the papal bull, and was solemnly given forth by the pontiff as an infallible statement to be believed by the universal Church. Gregory XV having been prevented by death from issuing the *Bull of Canonization,* it was finally issued by Urban VIII; and there is much food for reflection in the fact that the same Pope who punished Galileo, and was determined that the Inquisition should not allow the world to believe that the earth revolves about the sun, thus solemnly ordered the world, under pain of damnation, to believe in Xavier's miracles, including his "gift of tongues," and the return of the crucifix by the pious crab. But the legend was developed still further: Father Bouhours tells us, "The holy man spoke very well the language of those barbarians without having learned it, and had no need of an interpreter when he instructed." And, finally, in our own time, the Rev. Father Coleridge, speaking of the saint among the natives, says, "He could speak the language excellently, though he had never learned it."

In the early biography, Tursellinus writes: "Nothing was a greater impediment to him than his ignorance of the Japanese tongues; for, ever and anon, when some uncouth expression offended their fastidious and delicate ears, the awkward speech of Francis was a cause of laughter." But Father Bouhours, a century later, writing of Xavier at the same period, says, "He preached in the afternoon to the Japanese in their language, but so naturally and with so much ease that he could not be taken for a foreigner."

And finally, in 1872, Father Coleridge, of the Society of Jesus, speaking of Xavier at this time, says, "He spoke freely, flowingly, elegantly, as if he had lived in Japan all his life."

Nor was even this sufficient to make the legend complete, it was finally declared that, when Xavier addressed the natives of various tribes, each heard the sermon in his own language in which he was born.

All this, as we have seen, directly contradicts not only the plain statements of Xavier himself, and various incidental testimonies in the letters of his associates, but the explicit declaration of Father Joseph Acosta. The latter historian dwells especially on the labour which Xavier was obliged to bestow on the study of the Japanese and other languages, and says, "Even if he had been endowed with the apostolic gift of tongues, he could not have spread more widely the glory of Christ."[6]

It is hardly necessary to attribute to the orators and biographers generally a conscious attempt to deceive. The simple fact is, that as a rule they thought, spoke, and wrote in obedience to the natural laws which govern the luxuriant growth of myth and legend in the warm atmosphere of love and devotion which constantly arises about great religious

[6] For the evolution of the miracles of Xavier, see his *Letters*, with *Life,* published by Léon Pagès, Paris, 1855; also Maffei, *Historiarum Indicarum libri xvi,* Venice, 1589; also the lives by Tursellinus, various editions, beginning with that of 1594; Vitelleschi, 1622; Bouhours, 1682; Massei, second edition, 1682 (Rome), and others; Bartoli, Baltimore, 1868; Coleridge, 1872. In addition to these, I have compared, for a more extended discussion of this subject hereafter, a very great number of editions of these and other biographies of the saint, with speeches at the canonization, the bull of Gregory XV, various books of devotion, and a multitude of special writings, some of them in manuscript, upon the glories of the saint, including a large mass of material in the Royal Library at Munich and in the British Museum. I have relied entirely upon Catholic authors, and have not thought it worth while to consult any Protestant author. The illustration of the miracle of the crucifix and crab in its final form is given in *La Dévotion de Dix Vendredis à l'Honneur de St. François Xavier,* Bruxelles, 1699, Fig. 24: the pious crab is represented as presenting the crucifix which by a journey of forty leagues he has brought from the depths of the ocean to Xavier, who walks upon the shore. The book is in the Cornell University Library. For the letter of King John to Barreto, see Léon Pagès's *Lettres de St. François Xavier,* Paris, 1855, vol. ii, p. 465. For the miracle among the Badages, compare Tursellinus, lib. ii, c. x, p. 16, with Bouhours, Dryden's translation, pp. 146, 147. For the miracle of the gift of tongues, in its higher development, see Bouhours, p. 235, and Coleridge, vol. i, pp. 172 and 208; and as to Xavier's own account, see Coleridge, vol. i, pp. 151, 154, and vol. ii, p. 551.

leaders in times when men have little or no knowledge of natural law, when there is little care for scientific evidence, and when he who believes most is thought most meritorious.[7]

[7] Instances can be given of the same evolution of miraculous legend in our own time. To say nothing of the sacred fountain at La Salette, which preserves its healing powers in spite of the fact that the miracle which gave rise to them has twice been pronounced fraudulent by the French courts, and to pass without notice a multitude of others, not only in Catholic but in Protestant countries, the present writer may allude to one which in the year 1893 came under his own observation. On arriving in St. Petersburg to begin an official residence there, his attention was arrested by various portraits of a priest of the Russo-Greek Church; they were displayed in shop windows and held an honoured place in many private dwellings. These portraits ranged from lifelike photographs, which showed a plain, shrewd, kindly face, to those which were idealized until they bore a strong resemblance to the conventional representations of Jesus of Nazareth. On making inquiries, the writer found that these portraits represented Father Ivan, of Cronstadt, a priest noted for his good deeds, and very widely believed to be endowed with the power of working miracles.

One day, in one of the most brilliant reception rooms of the northern capital, the subject of Father Ivan's miracles having been introduced, a gentleman in very high social position and entirely trustworthy spoke as follows: "There is something very surprising about these miracles. I am slow to believe in them, but I know the following to be a fact: The late Metropolitan Archbishop of St. Petersburg loved quiet, and was very averse to anything which could possibly cause scandal. Hearing of Father Ivan's miracles, he summoned him to his presence and solemnly commanded him to abstain from all the things which had given rise to his reported miracles, and with this injunction dismissed him. Hardly had the priest left the room when the archbishop was struck with blindness and remained in this condition until the priest returned and removed his blindness by intercessory prayers." When the present writer asked the person giving this account if he directly knew these facts, he replied that he was, of course, not present when the miracle was wrought, but that he had the facts immediately from persons who knew all the parties concerned and were cognizant directly of the circumstances of the case.

Some time afterward, the present writer being at an afternoon reception at one of the greater embassies, the same subject was touched upon, when an eminent general spoke as follows: "I am not inclined to believe in miracles, in fact am rather sceptical, but the proofs of those wrought by Father Ivan are overwhelming."

These examples will serve to illustrate the process which in thousands of cases has gone on from the earliest days of the Church until a very recent period. Everywhere miraculous cures became the rule rather than the exception throughout Christendom.

[3. The Mediæval Miracles of Healing Check Medical Science]

4. The Attribution of Disease to Satanic Influence—"Pastoral Medicine" Checks Scientific Effort

Especially prejudicial to a true development of medical science among the first Christians was their attribution of

---

He then went on to say that the late Metropolitan Archbishop was a man who loved quiet and disliked scandal; that on this account he had summoned Father Ivan to his palace and ordered him to put an end to the conduct which had caused the reports concerning his miraculous powers, and then, with a wave of the arm, had dismissed him. The priest left the room, and from that moment the archbishop's arm was paralyzed, and it remained so until the penitent prelate summoned the priest again, by whose prayers the arm was restored to its former usefulness. There was present at the time another person besides the writer who had heard the previous statement as to the blindness of the archbishop, and on their both questioning the general if he were sure that the archbishop's arm was paralyzed, as stated, he declared that he could not doubt it, as he had it directly from persons entirely trustworthy, who were cognizant of all the facts.

Some time later, the present writer, having an interview with the most eminent lay authority in the Greek Church, a functionary whose duties had brought him into almost daily contact with the late archbishop, asked him which of these stories was correct. This gentleman answered immediately: "Neither; I saw the archbishop constantly, and no such event occurred: he was never paralyzed and never blind."

The same gentleman then went on to say that, in his belief, Father Ivan had shown remarkable powers in healing the sick, and the greatest charity in relieving the distressed. It was made clearly evident that Father Ivan is a saintlike man, devoted to the needy and distressed and exercising an enormous influence over them— an influence so great that crowds await him whenever he visits the capital. In the atmosphere of Russian devotion myths and legends grow luxuriantly about him, nor is belief in him confined to the peasant class. In the autumn of 1894 he was summoned to the bedside of the Emperor Alexander III. Unfortunately for the peace of Europe, his intercession at that time proved unavailing.

disease to diabolic influence. As we have seen, this idea had come from far, and, having prevailed in Chaldea, Egypt, and Persia, had naturally entered into the sacred books of the Hebrews. Moreover, St. Paul had distinctly declared that the gods of the heathen were devils; and everywhere the early Christians saw in disease the malignant work of these dethroned powers of evil. The Gnostic and Manichæan struggles had ripened the theologic idea that, although at times diseases are punishments by the Almighty, the main agency in them is Satanic. The great fathers and renowned leaders of the early Church accepted and strengthened this idea. Origen said: "It is demons which produce famine, unfruitfulness, corruptions of the air, pestilences; they hover concealed in clouds in the lower atmosphere, and are attracted by the blood and incense which the heathen offer to them as gods." St. Augustine said: "All diseases of Christians are to be ascribed to these demons; chiefly do they torment fresh-baptized Christians, yea, even the guiltless, newborn infants." Tertullian insisted that a malevolent angel is in constant attendance upon every person. Gregory of Nazianzus declared that bodily pains are provoked by demons, and that medicines are useless, but that they are often cured by the laying on of consecrated hands. St. Nilus and St. Gregory of Tours, echoing St. Ambrose, gave examples to show the sinfulness of resorting to medicine instead of trusting to the intercession of saints.

St. Bernard, in a letter to certain monks, warned them that to seek relief from disease in medicine was in harmony neither with their religion nor with the honour and purity of their order. This view even found its way into the canon law, which declared the precepts of medicine contrary to Divine knowledge. As a rule, the leaders of the Church discouraged the theory that diseases are due to natural causes, and most of them deprecated a resort to surgeons and physicians rather than to supernatural means.[8]

[8] For Chaldean, Egyptian, and Persian ideas as to the diabolic origin of disease, see authorities already cited, especially Maspero and Sayce. For Origen, see the *Contra Celsum,* lib. viii, chap. xxxi. For Augustine, see *De Divinatione Dæmonum,* chap. iii (p. 585 of Migne, vol. xl). For Tertullian and Gregory of Nazianzus, see citations in Sprengel and in Fort, p. 6. For St. Nilus, see his life, in the Bollandise *Acta Sanctorum.* For Gregory of Tours, see his *Historia Francorum,* lib. v, cap. 6, and his *De Mirac. S. Martini,* lib. ii, cap. 60. I owe these citations to Mr. Lea (*History of the Inquisition of*

Out of these and similar considerations was developed the vast system of "pastoral medicine," so powerful not only through the Middle Ages, but even in modern times, both among Catholics and Protestants. As to its results, we must bear in mind that, while there is no need to attribute the mass of stories regarding miraculous cures to conscious fraud, there was without doubt, at a later period, no small admixture of belief biased by self-interest, with much pious invention and suppression of facts. Enormous revenues flowed into various monasteries and churches in all parts of Europe from relics noted for their healing powers. Every cathedral, every great abbey, and nearly every parish church claimed possession of healing relics. While, undoubtedly, a childlike faith was at the bottom of this belief, there came out of it unquestionably a great development of the mercantile spirit. The commercial value of sundry relics was often very high. In the year 1056 a French ruler pledged securities to the amount of ten thousand solidi for the production of the relics of St. Just and St. Pastor, pending a legal decision regarding the ownership between him and the Archbishop of Narbonne. The Emperor of Germany on one occasion demanded, as a sufficient pledge for the establishment of a city market, the arm of St. George. The body of St. Sebastian brought enormous wealth to the Abbey of Soissons; Rome, Canterbury, Treves, Marburg, every great city, drew large revenues from similar sources, and the Venetian Republic ventured very considerable sums in the purchase of relics.

Naturally, then, corporations, whether lay or ecclesiastical, which drew large revenue from relics looked with little favour on a science which tended to discredit their investments.

Nowhere, perhaps, in Europe can the philosophy of this development of fetichism be better studied to-day than at Cologne. At the cathedral, preserved in a magnificent shrine since about the twelfth century, are the skulls of the Three

---

the Middle Ages, vol. iii, p. 410, note). For the letter of St. Bernard to the monks of St. Anastasius, see his Epistola in Migne, tom. 182, pp. 550, 551. For the canon law, see under De Consecratione, dist. v, c. xxi, "Contraria sunt divinæ cognitioni præcepta medicinæ: a jejunio revocant, lucubrare non sinunt, ab omni intentione meditationis abducunt." For the turning of the Greek mythology into a demonology as largely due to St. Paul, see I Corinthians x, 20: "The things which the Gentiles sacrifice, they sacrifice to devils, and not to God."

Kings, or Wise Men of the East, who, guided by the star of Bethlehem, brought gifts to the Saviour. These relics were an enormous source of wealth to the cathedral chapter during many centuries. But other ecclesiastical bodies in that city were both pious and shrewd, and so we find that not far off, at the church of St. Gereon, a cemetery has been dug up, and the bones distributed over the walls as the relics of St. Gereon and his Theban band of martyrs! Again, at the neighbouring church of St. Ursula, we have the later spoils of another cemetery, covering the interior walls of the church as the bones of St. Ursula and her eleven thousand virgin martyrs: the fact that many of them, as anatomists now declare, are the bones of *men* does not appear in the Middle Ages to have diminished their power of competing with the relics at the other shrines in healing efficiency.

No error in the choice of these healing means seems to have diminished their efficacy. When Prof. Buckland, the eminent osteologist and geologist, discovered that the relics of St. Rosalia at Palermo, which had for ages cured diseases and warded off epidemics, were the bones of a goat, this fact caused not the slightest diminution in their miraculous power.

Other developments of fetich cure were no less discouraging to the evolution of medical science. Very important among these was the Agnus Dei, or piece of wax from the Paschal candles, stamped with the figure of a lamb and consecrated by the Pope. In 1471 Pope Paul II expatiated to the Church on the efficacy of this fetich in preserving men from fire, shipwreck, tempest, lightning, and hail, as well as in assisting women in childbirth; and he reserved to himself and his successors the manufacture of it. Even as late as 1517 Pope Leo X issued, for a consideration, tickets bearing a cross and the following inscription: "This cross measured forty times makes the height of Christ in his humanity. He who kisses it is preserved for seven days from falling-sickness, apoplexy, and sudden death."

Naturally, the belief thus sanctioned by successive heads of the Church, infallible in all teaching regarding faith and morals, created a demand for amulets and charms of all kinds; and under this influence we find a reversion to old pagan fetiches. Nothing, on the whole, stood more constantly in the way of any proper development of medical science than these fetich cures, whose efficacy was based on theological reasoning and sanctioned by ecclesiastical policy.

It would be expecting too much from human nature to imagine that pontiffs who derived large revenues from the sale of the Agnus Dei, or priests who derived both wealth and honours from cures wrought at shrines under their care, or lay dignitaries who had invested heavily in relics, should favour the development of any science which undermined their interests.[9]

5. Theological Opposition to Anatomical Studies

Yet a more serious stumbling-block, hindering the beginnings of modern medicine and surgery, was a theory regarding the unlawfulness of meddling with the bodies of the dead. This theory, like so many others which the Church cherished as peculiarly its own, had really been inherited from the old pagan civilizations. So strong was it in Egypt that the embalmer was regarded as accursed; traces of it appear in Græco-Roman life, and hence it came into the early Church, where it was greatly strengthened by the addition of perhaps the most noble of mystic ideas—the recognition of the human body as the temple of the Holy Spirit. Hence Tertullian denounced the anatomist Herophilus as a butcher, and St. Augustine spoke of anatomists generally in similar terms.

But this nobler conception was alloyed with a mediæval superstition even more effective, when the formula known as the Apostles' Creed had, in its teachings regarding the resurrection of the body, supplanted the doctrine laid down by St. Paul. Thence came a dread of mutilating the body in such a way that some injury might result to its final resurrection at the Last Day, and additional reasons for hindering dissections in the study of anatomy.

To these arguments against dissection was now added another—one which may well fill us with amazement. It is the remark of the foremost of recent English philosophical historians, that of all organizations in human history the Church

9 See Fort's *Medical Economy during the Middle Ages,* pp. 211-213; also the *Handbooks* of Murray and Baedeker for North Germany, and various histories of medicine *passim*; also Collin de Plancy and scores of others. For the discovery that the relics of St. Rosalia at Palermo are simply the bones of a goat, see Gordon, *Life of Buckland,* pp. 94-96. For an account of the Agnus Dei, see Rydberg, pp. 62, 63; and for "Conception Billets," pp. 64 and 65. For Leo X's tickets, see Häusser (professor at Heidelberg), *Period of the Reformation,* English translation, p. 17.

of Rome has caused the greatest spilling of innocent blood. No one conversant with history, even though he admit all possible extenuating circumstances, and honour the older Church for the great services which can undoubtedly be claimed for her, can deny this statement. Strange is it, then, to note that one of the main objections developed in the Middle Ages against anatomical studies was the maxim that "the Church abhors the shedding of blood."

On this ground, in 1248, the Council of Le Mans forbade surgery to monks. Many other councils did the same, and at the end of the thirteenth century came the most serious blow of all; for then it was that Pope Boniface VIII, without any of that foresight of consequences which might well have been expected in an infallible teacher, issued a decretal forbidding a practice which had come into use during the Crusades, namely, the separation of the flesh from the bones of the dead whose remains it was desired to carry back to their own country.

The idea lying at the bottom of this interdiction was in all probability that which had inspired Tertullian to make his bitter utterance against Herophilus; but, be that as it may, it soon came to be considered as extending to all dissection, and thereby surgery and medicine were crippled for more than two centuries; it was the worst blow they ever received, for it impressed upon the mind of the Church the belief that all dissection is sacrilege, and led to ecclesiastical mandates withdrawing from the healing art the most thoughtful and cultivated men of the Middle Ages and giving up surgery to the lowest class of nomadic charlatans.

So deeply was this idea rooted in the mind of the universal Church that for over a thousand years surgery was considered dishonourable: the greatest monarchs were often unable to secure an ordinary surgical operation; and it was only in 1406 that a better beginning was made, when the Emperor Wenzel of Germany ordered that dishonour should no longer attach to the surgical profession.[10]

[10] As to religious scruples against dissection, and abhorrence of the *Paraschites*, or embalmer, see Maspero and Sayce, *The Dawn of Civilization*, p. 216. For denunciation of surgery by the Church authorities, see Sprengel, vol. ii, pp. 432-435; also Fort, pp. 452 *et seq.*; and for the reasoning which led the Church to forbid surgery to priests, see especially Frédault, *Histoire de la Médecine*, p.

6. New Beginnings of Medical Science

In spite of all these opposing forces, the evolution of medical science continued, though but slowly. In the second century of the Christian era Galen had made himself a great authority at Rome, and from Rome had swayed the medical science of the world: his genius triumphed over the defects of his method; but, though he gave a powerful impulse to medicine, his dogmatism stood in its way long afterward.

The places where medicine, such as it thus became, could be applied, were at first mainly the infirmaries of various monasteries, especially the larger ones of the Benedictine order: these were frequently developed into hospitals. Many monks devoted themselves to such medical studies as were permitted, and sundry churchmen and laymen did much to secure and preserve copies of ancient medical treatises. So, too, in the cathedral schools established by Charlemagne and others, provision was generally made for medical teaching; but all this instruction, whether in convents or schools, was wretchedly poor. It consisted not in developing by individual thought and experiment the gifts of Hippocrates, Aristotle, and Galen, but almost entirely in the parrot-like repetition of their writings.

But, while the inherited ideas of Church leaders were thus unfavourable to any proper development of medical science, there were two bodies of men outside the Church who, though largely fettered by superstition, were far less so than the monks and students of ecclesiastical schools: these were the Jews and Mohammedans. The first of these especially had inherited many useful sanitary and hygienic ideas, which had probably been first evolved by the Egyptians, and from them

---

200. As to the decretal of Boniface VIII, the usual statement is that he forbade all dissections. While it was undoubtedly construed universally to prohibit dissections for anatomical purposes, its declared intent was as stated in the text; that it was constantly construed against anatomical investigations cannot for a moment be denied. This construction is taken for granted in the great *Histoire Littéraire de la France,* founded by the Benedictines, certainly a very high authority as to the main current of opinion in the Church. For the decretal of Boniface VIII, see the *Corpus Juris Canonici.* I have used the edition of Paris, 1618, where it may be found on pp. 866, 867. See also, in spite of the special pleading of Giraldi, the Benedictine *Hist. Lit. de la France,* tome xvi, p. 98.

transmitted to the modern world mainly through the sacred books attributed to Moses.

The Jewish scholars became especially devoted to medical science. To them is largely due the building up of the School of Salerno, which we find flourishing in the tenth century. Judged by our present standards its work was poor indeed, but compared with other medical instruction of the time it was vastly superior: it developed hygienic principles especially, and brought medicine upon a higher plane.

Still more important is the rise of the School of Montpellier; this was due almost entirely to Jewish physicians, and it developed medical studies to a yet higher point, doing much to create a medical profession worthy of the name throughout southern Europe.

As to the Arabians, we find them from the tenth to the fourteenth century, especially in Spain, giving much thought to medicine, and to chemistry as subsidiary to it. About the beginning of the ninth century, when the greater Christian writers were supporting fetich by theology, Almamon, the Moslem, declared, "They are the elect of God, his best and most useful servants, whose lives are devoted to the improvement of their rational faculties." The influence of Avicenna, the translator of the works of Aristotle, extended throughout all Europe during the eleventh century. The Arabians were indeed much fettered by tradition in medical science, but their translations of Hippocrates and Galen preserved to the world the best thus far developed in medicine, and still better were their contributions to pharmacy: these remain of value to the present hour.[11]

Various Christian laymen also rose above the prevailing theologic atmosphere far enough to see the importance of promoting scientific development. First among these we may

[11] For the great services rendered to the development of medicine by the Jews, see Monteil, *Médecine en France,* p. 58; also the historians of medicine generally. For the quotation from Almamon, see Gibbon, vol. x, p. 42. For the services of both Jews and Arabians, see Bédarride, *Histoire des Juifs,* p. 115; also Sismondi, *Histoire des Français,* tome i, p. 191. For the Arabians, especially, see Rosseeuw Saint-Hilaire, *Histoire d'Espagne,* Paris, 1844, vol. iii, pp. 191 *et seq.* For the tendency of the Mosaic books to insist on hygienic rather than therapeutical treatment, and its consequences among Jewish physicians, see Sprengel, but especially Frédault, p. 14.

name the Emperor Charlemagne; he and his great minister, Alcuin, not only promoted medical studies in the schools they founded, but also made provision for the establishment of botanic gardens in which those herbs were especially cultivated which were supposed to have healing virtues. So, too, in the thirteenth century, the Emperor Frederick II, though under the ban of the Pope, brought together in his various journeys, and especially in his crusading expeditions, many Greek and Arabic manuscripts, and took special pains to have those which concerned medicine preserved and studied; he also promoted better ideas of medicine and embodied them in laws.[12]

* * *

From the Church itself, even when the theological atmosphere was most dense, rose here and there men who persisted in something like scientific effort. As early as the ninth century, Bertharius, a monk of Monte Cassino, prepared two manuscript volumes of prescriptions selected from ancient writers; other monks studied them somewhat, and, during succeeding ages, scholars like Hugo, Abbot of St. Denis,—Notker, monk of St. Gall,—Hildegard, Abbess of Rupertsberg,—Milo, Archbishop of Beneventum,—and John of St. Amand, Canon of Tournay, did something for medicine as they understood it. Unfortunately, they generally understood its theory as a mixture of deductions from Scripture with dogmas from Galen, and its practice as a mixture of incantations with fetiches. Even Pope Honorius III did something for the establishment of medical schools; but he did so much more to place ecclesiastical and theological fetters upon teachers and taught, that the value of his gifts may well be doubted. All germs of a higher evolution of medicine were for ages well kept under by the theological spirit. As far back as the sixth century so great a man as Pope Gregory I showed himself hostile to the development of this science. In the beginning of the twelfth century the Council of Rheims interdicted the study of law and physic to monks, and a multi-

---

[12] For the progress of sciences subsidiary to medicine even in the darkest ages, see Fort, pp. 374, 375; also Isensee, *Geschichte der Medicin,* pp. 225 *et seq.*; also Monteil, p. 89; Heller, *Geschichte der Physik,* vol. i, bk. 3; also Kopp, *Geschichte der Chemie.* For Frederick II and his *Medicinal-Gesetz,* see Baas, p. 221, but especially Von Raumer, *Geschichte der Hohenstaufen,* Leipsic, 1872, vol. iii, p. 259.

tude of other councils enforced this decree. About the middle of the same century St. Bernard still complained that monks had too much to do with medicine; and a few years later we have decretals like those of Pope Alexander III forbidding monks to study or practise it. For many generations there appear evidences of a desire among the more broad-minded churchmen to allow the cultivation of medical science among ecclesiastics: Popes like Clement III and Sylvester II seem to have favoured this, and we even hear of an Archbishop of Canterbury skilled in medicine; but in the beginning of the thirteenth century the Fourth Council of the Lateran forbade surgical operations to be practised by priests, deacons, and subdeacons; and some years later Honorius III reiterated this decree and extended it. In 1243 the Dominican order forbade medical treatises to be brought into their monasteries, and finally all participation of ecclesiastics in the science and art of medicine was effectually prevented.[13]

7. Theological Discouragement of Medicine

While various churchmen, building better than they knew, thus did something to lay foundations for medical study, the Church authorities, as a rule, did even more to thwart it among the very men who, had they been allowed liberty, would have cultivated it to the highest advantage.

Then, too, we find cropping out everywhere the feeling that, since supernatural means are so abundant, there is something irreligious in seeking cure by natural means: ever and anon we have appeals to Scripture, and especially to the case of King Asa, who trusted to physicians rather than to the priests of Jahveh, and so died. Hence it was that St. Bernard declared that monks who took medicine were guilty of conduct un-

[13] For statements as to these decrees of the highest Church and monastic authorities against medicine and surgery, see Sprengel, Baas, *Geschichte der Medicin*, p. 204, and elsewhere; also Buckle, *Posthumous Works*, vol. ii, p. 567. For a long list of Church dignitaries who practised a semi-theological medicine in the Middle Ages, see Baas, pp. 204, 205. For Bertharius, Hildegard, and others mentioned, see also Sprengel and other historians of medicine. For clandestine study and practice of medicine by sundry ecclesiastics in spite of the prohibitions by the Church, see Von Raumer, *Hohenstaufen*, vol. vi, p. 438. For some remarks on this subject by an eminent and learned ecclesiastic, see Ricker, O. S. B., professor in the University of Vienna, *Pastoral-Psychiatrie*, Wien, 1894, pp. 12, 13.

becoming to religion. Even the School of Salerno was held in aversion by multitudes of strict churchmen, since it prescribed rules for diet, thereby indicating a belief that diseases arise from natural causes and not from the malice of the devil: moreover, in the medical schools Hippocrates was studied, and he had especially declared that demoniacal possession is "nowise more divine, nowise more infernal, than any other disease." Hence it was, doubtless, that the Lateran Council, about the beginning of the thirteenth century, forbade physicians, under pain of exclusion from the Church, to undertake medical treatment without calling in ecclesiastical advice.

This view was long cherished in the Church, and nearly two hundred and fifty years later Pope Pius V revived it by renewing the command of Pope Innocent and enforcing it with penalties. Not only did Pope Pius order that all physicians before administering treatment should call in "a physician of the soul," on the ground, as he declares, that "bodily infirmity frequently arises from sin," but he ordered that, if at the end of three days the patient had not made confession to a priest, the medical man should cease his treatment, under pain of being deprived of his right to practise, and of expulsion from the faculty if he were a professor, and that every physician and professor of medicine should make oath that he was strictly fulfilling these conditions.

Out of this feeling had grown up another practice, which made the development of medicine still more difficult—the classing of scientific men generally with sorcerers and magic-mongers: from this largely rose the charge of atheism against physicians, which ripened into a proverb, "Where there are three physicians there are two atheists."[14]

* * *

Still another charge against physicians who showed a talent for investigation was that of Mohammedanism and Averroism; and Petrarch stigmatized Averroists as "men who deny Genesis and bark at Christ."[15]

The effect of this widespread ecclesiastical opposition was,

[14] *"Ubi sunt tres medici ibi sunt duo athei."* For the bull of Pius V, see the *Bullarium Romanum,* ed. Gaude, Naples, 1882, tom. vii, pp. 430, 431.

[15] For Averroes, see Renan, *Averroès et l'Averroisme,* Paris, 1861, pp. 327-335. For a perfectly just statement of the only circumstances which can justify a charge of atheism, see Rev. Dr. Deems, in *Popular Science Monthly,* February, 1876.

that for many centuries the study of medicine was relegated mainly to the lowest order of practitioners. There was, indeed, one orthodox line of medical evolution during the later Middle Ages: St. Thomas Aquinas insisted that the forces of the body are independent of its physical organization, and that therefore these forces are to be studied by the scholastic philosophy and the theological method, instead of by researches into the structure of the body; as a result of this, mingled with survivals of various pagan superstitions, we have in anatomy and physiology such doctrines as the increase and decrease of the brain with the phases of the moon, the ebb and flow of human vitality with the tides of the ocean, the use of the lungs to fan the heart, the function of the liver as the seat of love, and that of the spleen as the centre of wit.

Closely connected with these methods of thought was the doctrine of *signatures*. It was reasoned that the Almighty must have set his sign upon the various means of curing disease which he has provided: hence it was held that blood-root, on account of its red juice, is good for the blood; liverwort, having a leaf like the liver, cures diseases of the liver; eye-bright, being marked with a spot like an eye, cures diseases of the eyes; celandine, having a yellow juice, cures jaundice; bugloss, resembling a snake's head, cures snakebite; red flannel, looking like blood, cures blood-taints, and therefore rheumatism; bear's grease, being taken from an animal thickly covered with hair, is recommended to persons fearing baldness.[16]

Still another method evolved by this theological pseudo-science was that of disgusting the demon with the body which he tormented: hence the patient was made to swallow or apply to himself various unspeakable ordures, with such medicines as the livers of toads, the blood of frogs and rats, fibres of the hangman's rope, and ointment made from the body of gibbeted criminals. Many of these were survivals of heathen superstitions, but theologic reasoning wrought into them an orthodox significance. As an example of this mixture of heathen with Christian magic, we may cite the following from a mediæval medical book as a salve against "nocturnal goblin visitors": "Take hop plant, wormwood, bishopwort, lupine,

[16] For a summary of the superstitions which arose under the theological doctrine of signatures, see Dr. Eccles's admirable little tract on the *Evolution of Medical Science,* p. 140; see also Scoffern *Science and Folk Lore,* p. 76.

ash-throat, henbane, harewort, viper's bugloss, heathberry plant, cropleek, garlic, grains of hedgerife, githrife, and fennel. Put these worts into a vessel, set them under the altar, sing over them nine masses, boil them in butter and sheep's grease, add much holy salt, strain through a cloth, throw the worts into running water. If any ill tempting occur to a man, or an elf or goblin night visitors come, smear his body with this salve, and put it on his eyes, and cense him with incense, and sign him frequently with the sign of the cross. His condition will soon be better."[17]

As to surgery, this same amalgamation of theology with survivals of pagan beliefs continued to check the evolution of medical science down to the modern epoch. The nominal hostility of the Church to the shedding of blood withdrew, as we have seen, from surgical practice the great body of her educated men; hence surgery remained down to the fifteenth century a despised profession, its practice continued largely in the hands of charlatans, and down to a very recent period the name "barber-surgeon" was a survival of this. In such surgery, the application of various ordures relieved fractures; the touch of the hangman cured sprains; the breath of a donkey expelled poison; friction with a dead man's tooth cured toothache.[18]

The enormous development of miracle and fetich cures in the Church continued during century after century, and here probably lay the main causes of hostility between the Church on the one hand and the better sort of physicians on the other; namely, in the fact that the Church supposed herself in possession of something far better than scientific methods in

[17] For a list of unmentionable ordures used in Germany near the end of the seventeenth century, see Lammert, *Volksmedizin und medizinischer Aberglaube in Bayern,* Würzburg, 1869, p. 34, note. For the English prescription given, see Cockayne, *Leechdoms, Wortcunning, and Starcraft of Early England,* in the Master of the Rolls' series, London, 1865, vol. ii, pp. 345 and following. Still another of these prescriptions given by Cockayne covers three or four octavo pages. For very full details of this sort of sacred pseudo-science in Germany, with accounts of survivals of it at the present time, see Wuttke, Prof. der Theologie in Halle, *Der Deutsche Volksaberglaube der Gegenwart,* Berlin, 1869, *passim.* For France, see Rambaud, *Histoire de la Civilisation française,* pp. 371 *et seq.*
[18] On the low estate of surgery during the Middle Ages, see the histories of medicine already cited, and especially Kotelmann, *Gesundheitspflege im Mittelalter,* Hamburg, 1890, pp. 216 *et seq.*

medicine. Under the sway of this belief a natural and laudable veneration for the relics of Christian martyrs was developed more and more into pure fetichism.

Thus the water in which a single hair of a saint had been dipped was used as a purgative; water in which St. Remy's ring had been dipped cured fevers; wine in which the bones of a saint had been dipped cured lunacy; oil from a lamp burning before the tomb of St. Gall cured tumours; St. Valentine cured epilepsy; St. Christopher, throat diseases; St. Eutropius, dropsy; St. Ovid, deafness; St. Gervase, rheumatism; St. Apollonia, toothache; St. Vitus, St. Anthony, and a multitude of other saints, the maladies which bear their names. Even as late as 1784 we find certain authorities in Bavaria ordering that any one bitten by a mad dog shall at once put up prayers at the shrine of St. Hubert, and not waste his time in any attempts at medical or surgical cure.[19] In the twelfth century we find a noted cure attempted by causing the invalid to drink water in which St. Bernard had washed his hands. Flowers which had rested on the tomb of a saint, when steeped in water, were supposed to be especially efficacious in various diseases. The pulpit everywhere dwelt with unction on the reality of fetich cures, and among the choice stories collected by Archbishop Jacques de Vitry for the use of preachers was one which, judging from its frequent recurrence in monkish literature, must have sunk deep into the popular mind: "Two lazy beggars, one blind, the other lame, try to avoid the relics of St. Martin, borne about in procession, so that they may not be healed and lose their claim to alms. The blind man takes the lame man on his shoulders to guide him, but they are caught in the crowd and healed against their will."[20]

Very important also throughout the Middle Ages were the medical virtues attributed to saliva. The use of this remedy had early Oriental sanction. It is clearly found in Egypt. Pliny devotes a considerable part of one of his chapters to it; Galen approved it; Vespasian, when he visited Alexandria, is said to have cured a blind man by applying saliva to his eyes; but

[19] See Baas, p. 614; also Biedermann.
[20] For the efficacy of flowers, see the Bollandist *Lives of the Saints,* cited in Fort, p. 279; also pp. 457, 458. For the story of those unwillingly cured, see the *Exempla* of Jacques de Vitry, edited by Prof. T. F. Crane, of Cornell University, London, 1890, pp. 52, 182.

the great example impressed most forcibly upon the mediæval mind was the use of it ascribed in the fourth Gospel to Jesus himself: thence it came not only into Church ceremonial, but largely into medical practice.[21]

As the theological atmosphere thickened, nearly every country had its long list of saints, each with a special power over some one organ or disease. The clergy, having great influence over the medical schools, conscientiously mixed this fetich medicine with the beginnings of science. In the tenth century, even at the School of Salerno, we find that the sick were cured not only by medicine, but by the relics of St. Matthew and others.

Human nature, too, asserted itself, then as now, by making various pious cures fashionable for a time and then allowing them to become unfashionable. Just as we see the relics of St. Cosmo and St. Damian in great vogue during the early Middle Ages, but out of fashion and without efficacy afterward, so we find in the thirteenth century that the bones of St. Louis, having come into fashion, wrought multitudes of cures, while in the fourteenth, having become unfashionable, they ceased to act, and gave place for a time to the relics of St. Roch of Montpellier and St. Catherine of Sienna, which in their turn wrought many cures until they too became out of date and yielded to other saints. Just so in modern times the healing miracles of La Salette have lost prestige in some measure, and those of Lourdes have come into fashion.[22]

Even such serious matters as fractures, calculi, and difficult parturition, in which modern science has achieved some of its greatest triumphs, were then dealt with by relics; and to this hour the *ex votos* hanging at such shrines as those of St.

[21] As to the use of saliva in medicine, see Story, *Castle of St. Angelo, and Other Essays,* London, 1877, pp. 208 and elsewhere. For Pliny, Galen, and others, see the same, p. 211; see also the book of *Tobit,* chap. xi, 2-13. For the case of Vespasian, see Suetonius, *Life of Vespasian*; also Tacitus, *Historiæ,* lib. iv, c. 81. For its use by St. Francis Xavier, see Coleridge, *Life and Letters of St. Francis Xavier,* London, 1872.

[22] For one of these lists of saints curing diseases, see Pettigrew, *On Superstitions connected with Medicine*; for another, see Jacob, *Superstitions Populaires,* pp. 96-100; also Rydberg, p. 69; also Maury, Rambaud, and others. For a comparison of fashions in miracles with fashions in modern healing agents, see Littré, *Médecine et Médecins,* pp. 118, 136, and elsewhere; also Sprengel, vol. ii, p. 143.

Geneviève at Paris, of St. Antony at Padua, of the Druid image at Chartres, of the Virgin at Einsiedeln and Lourdes, of the fountain at La Salette, are survivals of this same conception of disease and its cure.

So, too, with a multitude of sacred pools, streams, and spots of earth. In Ireland, hardly a parish has not had one such sacred centre; in England and Scotland there have been many; and as late as 1805 the eminent Dr. Milner, of the Roman Catholic Church, gave a careful and earnest account of a miraculous cure wrought at a sacred well in Flintshire. In all parts of Europe the pious resort to wells and springs continued long after the close of the Middle Ages, and has not entirely ceased to-day.

It is not at all necessary to suppose intentional deception in the origin and maintenance of all fetich cures. Although two different judicial investigations of the modern miracles at La Salette have shown their origin tainted with fraud, and though the recent restoration of the Cathedral of Trondhjem has revealed the fact that the healing powers of the sacred spring which once brought such great revenues to that shrine were assisted by angelic voices spoken through a tube in the walls, not unlike the pious machinery discovered in the Temple of Isis at Pompeii, there is little doubt that the great majority of fountain and even shrine cures, such as they have been, have resulted from a natural law, and that belief in them was based on honest argument from Scripture. For the theological argument which thus stood in the way of science was simply this: if the Almighty saw fit to raise the dead man who touched the bones of Elisha, why should he not restore to life the patient who touches at Cologne the bones of the Wise Men of the East who followed the star of the Nativity? If Naaman was cured by dipping himself in the waters of the Jordan, and so many others by going down into the Pool of Siloam, why should not men still be cured by bathing in pools which men equally holy with Elisha have consecrated? If one sick man was restored by touching the garments of St. Paul, why should not another sick man be restored by touching the seamless coat of Christ at Treves, or the winding-sheet of Christ at Besançon? And out of all these inquiries came inevitably that question whose logical answer was especially injurious to the development of medical science: Why should men seek to build up scientific medicine and surgery, when relics, pilgrimages, and sacred observances, according to an overwhelming mass of concurrent testimony, have cured and are curing hosts of sick folk in all parts of Europe?[23]

Still another development of the theological spirit, mixed with professional exclusiveness and mob prejudice, wrought untold injury. Even to those who had become so far emancipated from allegiance to fetich cures as to consult physicians, it was forbidden to consult those who, as a rule, were the best. From a very early period of European history the Jews had taken the lead in medicine; their share in founding the great schools of Salerno and Montpellier we have already noted, and in all parts of Europe we find them acknowledged leaders in the healing art. The Church authorities, enforcing the spirit of the time, were especially severe against these benefactors: that men who openly rejected the means of salvation, and whose souls were undeniably lost, should heal the elect seemed an insult to Providence; preaching friars denounced them from the pulpit, and the rulers in state and church, while frequently secretly consulting them, openly proscribed them.

Gregory of Tours tells us of an archdeacon who, having been partially cured of disease of the eyes by St. Martin, sought further aid from a Jewish physician, with the result that neither the saint nor the Jew could help him afterward. Popes Eugene IV, Nicholas V, and Calixtus III especially forbade Christians to employ them. The Trullanean Council

[23] For sacred fountains in modern times, see Pettigrew, as above, p. 42; also Dalyell, *Darker Superstitions of Scotland,* pp. 82 and following; also Montalembert, *Les Moines d'Occident,* tome iii, p. 323, note. For those in Ireland, with many curious details, see S. C. Hall, *Ireland, its Scenery and Character,* London, 1841, vol. i, p. 282, and *passim.* For the case in Flintshire, see *Authentic Documents relative to the Miraculous Cure of Winifred White, of the Town of Wolverhampton, at Holywell, Flintshire, on the 28th of June, 1805,* by John Milner, D. D., Vicar Apostolic, etc., London, 1805. For sacred wells in France, see Chevart, *Histoire de Chartres,* vol. i, pp. 84-89, and French local histories generally. For superstitions attaching to springs in Germany, see Wuttke, *Volksaberglaube,* §§ 12 and 356. For one of the most exquisitely wrought works of modern fiction, showing perfectly the recent evolution of miraculous powers at a fashionable spring in France, see Gustave Droz, *Autour d'une Source.* The reference to the old pious machinery at Trondhjem is based upon personal observation by the present writer in August, 1893.

in the eighth century, the Councils of Béziers and Alby in the thirteenth, the Councils of Avignon and Salamanca in the fourteenth, the Synod of Bamberg and the Bishop of Passau in the fifteenth, the Council of Avignon in the sixteenth, with many others, expressly forbade the faithful to call Jewish physicians or surgeons; such great preachers as John Geiler and John Herolt thundered from the pulpit against them and all who consulted them. As late as the middle of the seventeenth century, when the City Council of Hall, in Würtemberg, gave some privileges to a Jewish physician "on account of his admirable experience and skill," the clergy of the city joined in a protest, declaring that "it were better to die with Christ than to be cured by a Jew doctor aided by the devil." Still, in their extremity, bishops, cardinals, kings, and even popes, insisted on calling in physicians of the hated race.[24]

[24] For the general subject of the influence of theological ideas upon medicine, see Fort, *History of Medical Economy during the Middle Ages,* New York, 1883, chaps. xiii and xviii; also Collin de Plancy, *Dictionnaire des Reliques, passim*; also *Rambaud, Histoire de la Civilisation française,* Paris, 1885, vol. i, chap. xviii; also Sprengel, vol. ii, p. 345, and elsewhere; also Baas and others. For proofs that the School of Salerno was not founded by the monks, Benedictine or other, but by laymen, who left out a faculty of theology from their organization, see Haeser, *Lehrbuch der Geschichte der Medicin,* vol. i, p. 646; also Baas. For a very striking statement that married professors, women, and Jews were admitted to professional chairs, see Baas, pp. 208 *et seq.*; also summary by Dr. Payne, article in the *Encyc. Brit.* Sprengel's old theory that the school was founded by Benedictines seems now entirely given up; see Haeser and Baas on the subject; also Daremberg, *La Médecine,* p. 133. For the citation from Gregory of Tours, see his *Hist. Francorum,* lib. vi. For the eminence of Jewish physicians and proscription of them, see Beugnot, *Les Juifs d'Occident,* Paris, 1824, pp. 76-94; also Bédarride, *Les Juifs en France, en Italie, et en Espagne,* chaps. v, viii, x, and xiii; also Rénouard, *Histoire de la Médecine,* Paris, 1846, tome i, p. 439; also, especially, Lammert, *Volksmedizin, etc., in Bayern,* p. 6, note. For Church decrees against them, see the *Acta Conciliorum,* ed. Hardouin, vol. x, pp. 1634, 1700, 1870, 1973, etc. For denunciations of them by Geiler and others, see Kotelmann, *Gesundheitspflege im Mittelalter,* pp. 194, 195. For a list of kings and popes who persisted in having Jewish physicians and for other curious information of the sort, see Prof. Levi of Vercelli, *Cristiani ed Ebrei nel Medio Evo,* pp. 200-207; and for a very valuable summary, see Lecky, *History of Rationalism in Europe,* vol. ii, pp. 265-271.

8. Fetich Cures Under Protestantism—The Royal Touch

The Reformation made no sudden change in the sacred theory of medicine. Luther, as is well known, again and again ascribed his own diseases to "devils' spells," declaring that "Satan produces all the maladies which afflict mankind, for he is the prince of death," and that "he poisons the air"; but that "no malady comes from God." From that day down to the faith cures of Boston, Old Orchard, and among the sect of "Peculiar People" in our own time, we see the results among Protestants of seeking the cause of disease in Satanic influence and its cure in fetichism.

Yet Luther, with his sturdy common sense, broke away from one belief which has interfered with the evolution of medicine from the dawn of Christianity until now. When that troublesome declaimer, Carlstadt, declared that "whoso falls sick shall use no physic, but commit his case to God, praying that His will be done," Luther asked, "Do you eat when you are hungry?" and the answer being in the affirmative, he continued, "Even so you may use physic, which is God's gift just as meat and drink is, or whatever else we use for the preservation of life." Hence it was, doubtless, that the Protestant cities of Germany were more ready than others to admit anatomical investigation by proper dissections.[25]

Perhaps the best-known development of a theological view in the Protestant Church was that mainly evolved in England out of a French germ of theological thought—a belief in the efficacy of the royal touch in sundry diseases, especially epilepsy and scrofula, the latter being consequently known as the king's evil. This mode of cure began, so far as history throws light upon it, with Edward the Confessor in the eleventh century, and came down from reign to reign, passing from the Catholic saint to Protestant debauchees upon the English throne, with ever-increasing miraculous efficacy.

Testimony to the reality of these cures is overwhelming. As a simple matter of fact, there are no miracles of healing in the history of the human race more thoroughly attested

[25] For Luther's belief and his answer to Carlstadt, see his *Table Talk*, especially in Hazlitt's edition, pp. 250-257; also his letters *passim*. For recent "faith cures," see Dr. Buckley's articles on *Faith Healing and Kindred Phenomena*, in *The Century*, 1886. For the greater readiness of the Protestant cities to facilitate dissections, see Roth, *Andreas Vesalius*, p. 33.

than those wrought by the touch of Henry VIII, Elizabeth, the Stuarts, and especially of that chosen vessel, Charles II. Though Elizabeth could not bring herself fully to believe in the reality of these cures, Dr. Tooker, the Queen's chaplain, afterward Dean of Lichfield, testifies fully of his own knowledge to the cures wrought by her, as also does William Clowes, the Queen's surgeon. Fuller, in his *Church History*, gives an account of a Roman Catholic who was thus cured by the Queen's touch and converted to Protestantism. Similar testimony exists as to cures wrought by James I. Charles I also enjoyed the same power, in spite of the public declaration against its reality by Parliament. In one case the King saw a patient in the crowd, too far off to be touched, and simply said, "God bless thee and grant thee thy desire"; whereupon, it is asserted, the blotches and humours disappeared from the patient's body and appeared in the bottle of medicine which he held in his hand; at least so says Dr. John Nicholas, Warden of Winchester College, who declares this of his own knowledge to be every word of it true.

But the most incontrovertible evidence of this miraculous gift is found in the case of Charles II, the most thoroughly cynical debauchee who ever sat on the English throne before the advent of George IV. He touched nearly one hundred thousand persons, and the outlay for gold medals issued to the afflicted on these occasions rose in some years as high as ten thousand pounds. John Brown, surgeon in ordinary to his Majesty and to St. Thomas's Hospital, and author of many learned works on surgery and anatomy, published accounts of sixty cures due to the touch of this monarch; and Sergeant-Surgeon Wiseman devotes an entire book to proving the reality of these cures, saying, "I myself have been frequent witness to many hundreds of cures performed by his Majesty's touch alone without any assistance of chirurgery, and these many of them had tyred out the endeavours of able chirurgeons before they came thither." Yet it is especially instructive to note that, while in no other reign were so many people touched for scrofula, and in none were so many cures vouched for, in no other reign did so many people die of that disease: the bills of mortality show this clearly, and the reason doubtless is the general substitution of supernatural for scientific means of cure. This is but one out of many examples showing the havoc which a scientific test always makes among miracles if men allow it to be applied.

To James II the same power continued; and if it be said, in the words of Lord Bacon, that "imagination is next of kin to miracle—a working faith," something else seems required to account for the testimony of Dr. Heylin to cures wrought by the royal touch upon babes in their mothers' arms. Myth-making and marvel-mongering were evidently at work here as in so many other places, and so great was the fame of these cures that we find, in the year before James was de-throned, a pauper at Portsmouth, New Hampshire, petitioning the General Assembly to enable him to make the voyage to England in order that he may be healed by the royal touch.

The change in the royal succession does not seem to have interfered with the miracle; for, though William III evidently regarded the whole thing as a superstition, and on one occa-sion is said to have touched a patient, saying to him, "God give you better health and more sense," Whiston assures us that this person was healed, notwithstanding William's in-credulity.

As to Queen Anne, Dr. Daniel Turner, in his *Art of Sur-gery,* relates that several cases of scrofula which had been unsuccessfully treated by himself and Dr. Charles Bernard, sergeant-surgeon to her Majesty, yielded afterward to the efficacy of the Queen's touch. Naturally does Collier, in his *Ecclesiastical History,* say regarding these cases that to dis-pute them "is to come to the extreme of scepticism, to deny our senses and be incredulous even to ridiculousness." Testi-mony to the reality of these cures is indeed overwhelming, and a multitude of most sober scholars, divines, and doctors of medicine declared the evidence absolutely convincing. That the Church of England accepted the doctrine of the royal touch is witnessed by the special service provided in the *Prayer-Book* of that period for occasions when the King exercised this gift. The ceremony was conducted with great solemnity and pomp: during the reading of the service and the laying on of the King's hands, the attendant bishop or priest recited the words, "They shall lay their hands on the sick, and they shall recover"; afterward came special prayers, the Epistle and Gospel, with the blessing, and finally his Majesty washed his royal hands in golden vessels which high noblemen held for him.

In France, too, the royal touch continued, with similar tes-timony to its efficacy. On a certain Easter Sunday, that pious king, Louis XIV, touched about sixteen hundred persons at Versailles.

This curative power was, then, acknowledged far and wide, by Catholics and Protestants alike, upon the Continent, in Great Britain, and in America; and it descended not only in spite of the transition of the English kings from Catholicism to Protestantism, but in spite of the transition from the legitimate sovereignty of the Stuarts to the illegitimate succession of the House of Orange. And yet, within a few years after the whole world held this belief, it was dead; it had shrivelled away in the growing scientific light at the dawn of the eighteenth century.[26]

9. The Scientific Struggle for Anatomy

We may now take up the evolution of medical science out of the mediæval view and its modern survivals. All through the Middle Ages, as we have seen, some few laymen and ecclesiastics here and there, braving the edicts of the Church and popular superstition, persisted in medical study and practice: this was especially seen at the greater universities, which had become somewhat emancipated from ecclesiastical control. In the thirteenth century the University of Paris gave a strong impulse to the teaching of medicine, and in that and the following century we begin to find the first intelligible reports of medical cases since the coming in of Christianity.

In the thirteenth century also the arch-enemy of the papacy, the Emperor Frederick II, showed his free-thinking tendencies by granting, from time to time, permissions to dissect the human subject. In the centuries following, sundry other monarchs timidly followed his example: thus John of Aragon, in

[26] For the royal touch, see Becket, *Free and Impartial Inquiry into the Antiquity and Efficacy of Touching for the King's Evil,* 1772, cited in Pettigrew, p. 128, and elsewhere; also Scoffern, *Science and Folk Lore,* London, 1870, pp. 413 and following; also Adams, *The Healing Art,* London, 1887, vol. i, pp. 53-60; and especially Lecky, *History of European Morals,* vol. i, chapter on *The Conversion of Rome;* also his *History of England in the Eighteenth Century,* vol. i, chap. i. For curious details regarding the mode of conducting the ceremony, see Evelyn's *Diary;* also Lecky, as above. For the royal touch in France, and for a claim to its possession in feudal times by certain noble families, see Rambaud, *Hist. de la Civ. française,* p. 375.

1391, gave to the University of Lerida the privilege of dissecting one dead criminal every three years.[27]

During the fifteenth century and the earlier years of the sixteenth the revival of learning, the invention of printing, and the great voyages of discovery gave a new impulse to thought, and in this medical science shared: the old theological way of thinking was greatly questioned, and gave place in many quarters to a different way of looking at the universe.

In the sixteenth century Paracelsus appears—a great genius, doing much to develop medicine beyond the reach of sacred and scholastic tradition, though still fettered by many superstitions. More and more, in spite of theological dogmas, came a renewal of anatomical studies by dissection of the human subject. The practice of the old Alexandrian School was thus resumed. Mundinus, Professor of Medicine at Bologna early in the fourteenth century, dared use the human subject occasionally in his lectures; but finally came a far greater champion of scientific truth, Andreas Vesalius, founder of the modern science of anatomy. The battle waged by this man is one of the glories of our race.

From the outset Vesalius proved himself a master. In the search for real knowledge he risked the most terrible dangers, and especially the charge of sacrilege, founded upon the teachings of the Church for ages. As we have seen, even such men in the early Church as Tertullian and St. Augustine held anatomy in abhorrence, and the decretal of Pope Boniface VIII was universally construed as forbidding all dissection, and as threatening excommunication against those practising it. Through this sacred conventionalism Vesalius broke without fear; despite ecclesiastical censure, great opposition in his own profession, and popular fury, he studied his science by the only method that could give useful results. No peril daunted him. To secure material for his investigations, he haunted gibbets and charnel-houses, braving the fires of the Inquisition and the virus of the plague. First of all men he began to place the science of human anatomy on its solid modern foundations—on careful examination and observation of the human body: this was his first great sin, and it was soon aggravated by one considered even greater.

Perhaps the most unfortunate thing that has ever been done for Christianity is the tying it to forms of science which are

[27] For the promotion of medical science and practice, especially in the thirteenth century, by the universities, see Baas, pp. 222-224.

doomed and gradually sinking. Just as, in the time of Roger Bacon, excellent men devoted all their energies to binding Christianity to Aristotle; just as, in the time of Reuchlin and Erasmus, they insisted on binding Christianity to Thomas Aquinas; so, in the time of Vesalius, such men made every effort to link Christianity to Galen. The cry has been the same in all ages; it is the same which we hear in this age for curbing scientific studies: the cry for what is called "sound learning." Whether standing for Aristotle against Bacon, or for Aquinas against Erasmus, or for Galen against Vesalius, the cry is always for "sound learning": the idea always has been that the older studies are "safe."

At twenty-eight years of age Vesalius gave to the world his great work on human anatomy. With it ended the old and began the new; its researches, by their thoroughness, were a triumph of science; its illustrations, by their fidelity, were a triumph of art.

To shield himself, as far as possible, in the battle which he foresaw must come, Vesalius dedicated the work to the Emperor Charles V, and in his preface he argues for his method, and against the parrot repetitions of the mediæval textbooks; he also condemns the wretched anatomical preparations and specimens made by physicians who utterly refused to advance beyond the ancient master. The parrot-like repeaters of Galen gave battle at once. After the manner of their time their first missiles were epithets; and, the vast arsenal of these having been exhausted, they began to use sharper weapons—weapons theologic.

In this case there were especial reasons why the theological authorities felt called upon to intervene. First, there was the old idea prevailing in the Church that the dissection of the human body is forbidden to Christians: this was used with great force against Vesalius, but he at first gained a temporary victory; for, a conference of divines having been asked to decide whether dissection of the human body is sacrilege, gave a decision in the negative.

The reason was simple: the great Emperor Charles V had made Vesalius his physican and could not spare him; but, on the accession of Philip II to the throne of Spain and the Netherlands, the whole scene changed. Vesalius now complained that in Spain he could not obtain even a human skull for his anatomical investigations: the medical and theological reactionists had their way, and to all appearance they have, as a rule, had it in Spain ever since. As late as the last years of the eighteenth century an observant English traveller found that there were no dissections before medical classes in the Spanish universities, and that the doctrine of the circulation of the blood was still denied, more than a century and a half after Sarpi and Harvey had proved it.

Another theological idea barred the path of Vesalius. Throughout the Middle Ages it was believed that there exists in man a bone imponderable, incorruptible, incombustible— the necessary nucleus of the resurrection body. Belief in a resurrection of the physical body, despite St. Paul's Epistle to the Corinthians, had been incorporated into the formula evolved during the early Christian centuries and known as the Apostles' Creed, and was held throughout Christendom, "always, everywhere, and by all." This hypothetical bone was therefore held in great veneration, and many anatomists sought to discover it; but Vesalius, revealing so much else, did not find it. He contented himself with saying that he left the question regarding the existence of such a bone to the theologians. He could not lie; he did not wish to fight the Inquisition; and thus he fell under suspicion.

The strength of this theological point may be judged from the fact that no less eminent a surgeon than Riolan consulted the executioner to find out whether, when he burned a criminal, all the parts were consumed; and only then was the answer received which fatally undermined this superstition. Yet, in 1689 we find it still lingering in France, stimulating opposition in the Church to dissection. Even as late as the eighteenth century, Bernouilli having shown that the living human body constantly undergoes a series of changes, so that all its particles are renewed in a given number of years, so much ill feeling was drawn upon him, from theologians, who saw in this statement danger to the doctrine of the resurrection of the body, that for the sake of peace he struck out his argument on this subject from his collected works.[28]

[28] For permissions to dissect the human subject, given here and there during the Middle Ages, see Roth's *Andreas Vesalius,* Berlin, 1892, pp. 3, 13 *et seq.* For religious antipathies as a factor in the persecution of Vesalius, see the biographies by Boerhaave and Albinos, 1725; Burggraeve's *Études,* 1841; also Haeser, Kingsley, and the latest and most thorough of all, Roth, as above. Even Goethals, despite the timidity natural to a city librarian in a town like Brus-

Still other enroachments upon the theological view were made by the new school of anatomists, and especially by Vesalius. During the Middle Ages there had been developed various theological doctrines regarding the human body; these were based upon arguments showing what the body *ought to be,* and naturally, when anatomical science showed what it *is,* these doctrines fell. An example of such popular theological reasoning is seen in a widespread belief of the twelfth century, that, during the year in which the cross of Christ was captured by Saladin, children, instead of having thirty or thirty-two teeth as before, had twenty or twenty-two. So, too, in Vesalius's time another doctrine of this sort was dominant: it had long been held that Eve, having been made by the Almighty from a rib taken out of Adam's side, there must be one rib fewer on one side of every man than on the other. This creation of Eve was a favourite subject with sculptors and painters, from Giotto, who carved it upon his beautiful Campanile at Florence, to the illuminators of missals, and even to those who illustrated Bibles and religious books in the first years after the invention of printing; but Vesalius and the anatomists who followed him put an end among thoughtful men to this belief in the missing rib, and in doing this dealt a blow at much else in the sacred theory. Naturally, all

---

sels, in which clerical power is strong and relentless, feels obliged to confess that there was a certain admixture of religious hatred in the treatment of Vesalius. See his *Notice Biographique sur André Vesale.* For the resurrection bone, see Roth, as above, pp. 154, 155, and notes. For Vesalius, see especially Portal, *Hist. de l'Anatomie et de la Chirurgie,* Paris, 1770, tome i, p. 407. For neglect of dissection and opposition to Harvey's discovery in Spain, see Townsend's *Travels,* edition of 1792, cited in Buckle, *History of Civilization in England,* vol. ii, pp. 74, 75. Also Henry Morley, in his *Clément Marot, and Other Essays.* For Bernouilli and his trouble with the theologians, see Wolf, *Biographien zur Culturgeschichte der Schweiz,* vol. ii, p. 95. How different Mundinus's practice of dissection was from that of Vesalius may be seen by Cuvier's careful statement that the entire number of dissections by the former was three; the usual statement is that there were but two. See Cuvier, *Hist. des Sci. Nat.,* tome ii, p. 7; also Sprengel, Frédault, Hallam, and Littré; also Whewell, *Hist. of the Inductive Sciences,* vol. iii, p. 328; also, for a very full statement regarding the agency of Mundinus in the progress of anatomy, see Portal, vol. i, pp. 209-216.

these considerations brought the forces of ecclesiasticism against the innovators in anatomy.[29]

A new weapon was now forged: Vesalius was charged with dissecting a living man, and, either from direct persecution, as the great majority of authors assert, or from indirect influences, as the recent apologists for Philip II admit, he became a wanderer: on a pilgrimage to the Holy Land, apparently undertaken to atone for his sin, he was shipwrecked, and in the prime of his life and strength he was lost to the world.

And yet not lost. In this century a great painter has again given him to us. By the magic of Hamann's pencil Vesalius again stands on earth, and we look once more into his cell. Its windows and doors, bolted and barred within, betoken the storm of bigotry which rages without; the crucifix, toward which he turns his eyes, symbolizes the spirit in which he labours; the corpse of the plague-stricken beneath his hand ceases to be repulsive; his very soul seems to send forth rays from the canvas, which strengthen us for the good fight in this age.[30]

His death was hastened, if not caused, by men who conscientiously supposed that he was injuring religion: his poor, blind foes aided in destroying one of religion's greatest apostles. What was his influence on religion? He substituted, for the repetition of worn-out theories, a conscientious and reverent search into the works of the great Power giving life to the universe; he substituted, for representations of the human structure pitiful and unreal, representations revealing truths most helpful to the whole human race.

The death of this champion seems to have virtually ended the contest. Licenses to dissect soon began to be given by sundry popes to universities, and were renewed at intervals of from three to four years, until the Reformation set in mo-

[29] As to the supposed change in the number of teeth, see the *Gesta Philippi Augusti Francorum Regis, . . . descripta a magistro Rigordo,* 1219, edited by Father François Duchesne, in *Historiæ Francorum Scriptores,* tom. v, Paris, 1649, p. 24. For representations of Adam created by the Almighty out of a pile of dust, and of Eve created from a rib of Adam, see the earlier illustrations in the *Nuremberg Chronicle.* As to the relation of anatomy to theology as regards Adam's rib, see Roth, pp. 154, 155.

[30] The original painting of Vesalius at work in his cell, by Hamann, is now at Cornell University.

tion trains of thought which did much to release science from this yoke.[31]

10. Theological Opposition to Inoculation, Vaccination, and the Use of Anæsthetics

I hasten now to one of the most singular struggles of medical science during modern times. Early in the last century Boyer presented inoculation as a preventive of small-pox in France, and thoughtful physicians in England, inspired by Lady Montagu and Maitland, followed his example. Ultra-conservatives in medicine took fright at once on both sides of the Channel, and theology was soon finding profound reasons against the new practice. The French theologians of the Sorbonne solemnly condemned it; the English theologians were most loudly represented by the Rev. Edward Massey, who in 1772 preached and published a sermon entitled *The Dangerous and Sinful Practice of Inoculation*. In this he declared that Job's distemper was probably confluent smallpox; that he had been inoculated doubtless by the devil; that diseases are sent by Providence for the punishment of sin; and that the proposed attempt to prevent them is "a diabolical operation." Not less vigorous was the sermon of the Rev. Mr. Delafaye, entitled *Inoculation an Indefensible Practice*. This struggle went on for thirty years. It is a pleasure to note some churchmen—and among them Madox, Bishop of Worcester —giving battle on the side of right reason; but as late as 1753 we have a noted rector at Canterbury denouncing inoculation from his pulpit in the primatial city, and many of his brethren following his example.

The same opposition was vigorous in Protestant Scotland. A large body of ministers joined in denouncing the new practice as "flying in the face of Providence," and "endeavouring to baffle a Divine judgment."

On our own side of the ocean, also, this question had to

[31] For a curious example of weapons drawn from Galen and used against Vesalius, see Lewes, *Life of Goethe*, p. 343, note. For proofs that I have not overestimated Vesalius, see Portal, *ubi supra*. Portal speaks of him as *"le génie le plus droit qu'eut l' Europe"*; and again, *"Vesale me parait un des plus grands hommes qui ait existé."* For the charge that anatomists dissected living men —against men of science before Vesalius's time—see Littré's chapter on *Anatomy*. For the increased liberty given anatomy by the Reformation, see Roth's *Vesalius*, p. 33.

be fought out. About the year 1721 Dr. Zabdiel Boylston, a physician in Boston, made an experiment in inoculation, one of his first subjects being his own son. He at once encountered bitter hostility, so that the selectmen of the city forbade him to repeat the experiment. Foremost among his opponents was Dr. Douglas, a Scotch physician, supported by the medical profession and the newspapers. The violence of the opposing party knew no bounds; they insisted that inoculation was "poisoning," and they urged the authorities to try Dr. Boylston for murder. Having thus settled his case for this world, they proceeded to settle it for the next, insisting that "for a man to infect a family in the morning with smallpox and to pray to God in the evening against the disease is blasphemy"; that the smallpox is "a judgment of God on the sins of the people," and that "to avert it is but to provoke him more"; that inoculation is "an encroachment on the prerogatives of Jehovah, whose right it is to wound and smite." Among the mass of scriptural texts most remote from any possible bearing on the subject one was employed which was equally cogent against any use of healing means in any disease—the words of Hosea: "He hath torn, and he will heal us; he hath smitten, and he will bind us up."

So bitter was this opposition that Dr. Boylston's life was in danger; it was considered unsafe for him to be out of his house in the evening; a lighted grenade was even thrown into the house of Cotton Mather, who had favoured the new practice, and had sheltered another clergyman who had submitted himself to it.

To the honour of the Puritan clergy of New England, it should be said that many of them were Boylston's strongest supporters. Increase and Cotton Mather had been among the first to move in favour of inoculation, the latter having called Boylston's attention to it; and at the very crisis of affairs six of the leading clergymen of Boston threw their influence on Boylston's side and shared the obloquy brought upon him. Although the gainsayers were not slow to fling into the faces of the Mathers their action regarding witchcraft, urging that their credulity in that matter argued credulity in this, they persevered, and among the many services rendered by the clergymen of New England to their country this ought certainly to be remembered; for these men had to withstand, shoulder to shoulder with Boylston and Benjamin Franklin, the same weapons which were hurled at the supporters of inoculation in Europe—charges of "unfaithfulness to the revealed law of God."

The facts were soon very strong against the gainsayers: within a year or two after the first experiment nearly three hundred persons had been inoculated by Boylston in Boston and neighbouring towns, and out of these only six had died; whereas, during the same period, out of nearly six thousand persons who had taken smallpox naturally, and had received only the usual medical treatment, nearly one thousand had died. Yet even here the gainsayers did not despair, and, when obliged to confess the success of inoculation, they simply fell back upon a new argument, and answered: "It was good that Satan should be dispossessed of his habitation which he had taken up in men in our Lord's day, but it was not lawful that the children of the Pharisees should cast him out by the help of Beelzebub. We must always have an eye to the matter of what we do as well as the result, if we intend to keep a good conscience toward God." But the facts were too strong; the new practice made its way in the New World as in the Old, though bitter opposition continued, and in no small degree on vague scriptural grounds, for more than twenty years longer.[32]

[32] For the general subject, see Sprengel, *Histoire de la Médecine,* vol. vi, pp. 39-80. For the opposition of the Paris Faculty of Theology to inoculation, see the *Journal de Barbier,* vol. vi, p. 294; also the *Correspondance de Grimm et de Diderot,* vol. iii, pp. 259 *et seq.* For bitter denunciations of inoculation by the English clergy, and for the noble stand against them by Madox, see Baron, *Life of Jenner,* vol. i, pp. 231, 232, and vol. ii, pp. 39, 40. For the strenuous opposition of the same clergy, see Weld, *History of the Royal Society,* vol. i, p. 464, note; also, for its comical side, see Nichols's *Literary Illustrations,* vol. v, p. 800. For the same matter in Scotland, see Lecky's *History of the Eighteenth Century,* vol. ii, p. 83. For New England, see Green, *History of Medicine in Massachusetts,* Boston, 1881, pp. 58 *et seq.*; also chapter x of the *Memorial History of Boston,* by the same author and O. W. Holmes. For letter of Dr. Franklin, see *Massachusetts Historical Collections,* second series, vol. vii, p. 17. Several most curious publications issued during the heat of the inoculation controversy have been kindly placed in my hands by the librarians of Harvard College and of the Massachusetts Historical Society, among them *A Reply to Increase Mather,* by John Williams, Boston, printed by J. Franklin, 1721, from which the above scriptural arguments are cited. For the terrible virulence of the smallpox in New England up to the introduction of inoculation, see McMaster, *History of the People of the United States,* first edition, vol. i, p. 30.

The steady evolution of scientific medicine brings us next to Jenner's discovery of vaccination. Here, too, sundry vague survivals of theological ideas caused many of the clergy to side with retrograde physicians. Perhaps the most virulent of Jenner's enemies was one of his professional brethren, Dr. Moseley, who placed on the title-page of his book, *Lues Bovilla*, the motto, referring to Jenner and his followers, "Father, forgive them, for they know not what they do": this book of Dr. Moseley was especially indorsed by the Bishop of Dromore. In 1798 an Anti-vaccination Society was formed by physicians and clergymen, who called on the people of Boston to suppress vaccination, as "bidding defiance to Heaven itself, even to the will of God," and declared that "the law of God prohibits the practice." As late as 1803 the Rev. Dr. Ramsden thundered against vaccination in a sermon before the University of Cambridge, mingling texts of Scripture with calumnies against Jenner; but Plumptre and the Rev. Rowland Hill in England, Waterhouse in America, Thouret in France, Sacco in Italy, and a host of other good men and true, pressed forward, and at last science, humanity, and right reason gained the victory. Most striking results quickly followed. The diminution in the number of deaths from the terrible scourge was amazing. In Berlin, during the eight years following 1783, over four thousand children died of the smallpox; while during the eight years following 1814, after vaccination had been largely adopted, out of a larger number of deaths there were but five hundred and thirty-five from this disease. In Würtemberg, during the twenty-four years following 1772, one in thirteen of all the children died of smallpox, while during the eleven years after 1822 there died of it only one in sixteen hundred. In Copenhagen, during twelve years before the introduction of vaccination, fifty-five hundred persons died of smallpox, and during the sixteen years after its introduction only one hundred and fifty-eight persons died of it throughout all Denmark. In Vienna, where the average yearly mortality from this disease had been over eight hundred, it was steadily and rapidly reduced, until in 1803 it had fallen to less than thirty; and in London, formerly so afflicted by this scourge, out of all her inhabitants there died of it in 1890 but one. As to the world at large, the result is summed up by one of the most honoured English physicians of our time, in the declaration that "Jenner has saved, is now saving, and will

continue to save in all coming ages, more lives in one generation than were destroyed in all the wars of Napoleon."

It will have been noticed by those who have read this history
thus far that the record of the Church generally was far more
honourable in this struggle than in many which preceded it:
the reason is not difficult to find; the decline of theology en-
ured to the advantage of religion, and religion gave powerful
aid to science.

Yet there have remained some survivals both in Protestantism and in Catholicism which may be regarded with curiosity. A small body of perversely ingenious minds in the
medical profession in England have found a few ardent allies
among the less intellectual clergy. The Rev. Mr. Rothery and
the Rev. Mr. Allen, of the Primitive Methodists, have for
sundry vague theological reasons especially distinguished
themselves by opposition to compulsory vaccination; but it is
only just to say that the great body of the English clergy have
for a long time taken the better view.

Far more painful has been the recent history of the other
great branch of the Christian Church—a history developed
where it might have been least expected: the recent annals
of the world hardly present a more striking antithesis between Religion and Theology.

On the religious side few things in the history of the Roman
Church have been more beautiful than the conduct of its
clergy in Canada during the great outbreak of ship-fever
among immigrants at Montreal about the middle of the present century. Day and night the Catholic priesthood of that
city ministered fearlessly to those victims of sanitary ignorance; fear of suffering and death could not drive these ministers from their work; they laid down their lives cheerfully
while carrying comfort to the poorest and most ignorant of
our kind: such was the record of their religion. But in 1885
a record was made by their theology. In that year the smallpox broke out with great virulence in Montreal. The Protestant population escaped almost entirely by vaccination; but
multitudes of their Catholic fellow-citizens, under some vague
survival of the old orthodox ideas, refused vaccination and
suffered fearfully. When at last the plague became so serious
that travel and trade fell off greatly and quarantine began to
be established in neighbouring cities, an effort was made to
enforce compulsory vaccination. The result was, that large
numbers of the Catholic working population resisted and even

threatened bloodshed. The clergy at first tolerated and even encouraged this conduct: the Abbé Filiatrault, priest of St. James's Church, declared in a sermon that, "if we are afflicted with smallpox, it is because we had a carnival last winter, feasting the flesh, which has offended the Lord; . . . it is to punish our pride that God has sent us smallpox." The clerical press went further: the *Étendard* exhorted the faithful to take up arms rather than submit to vaccination, and at least one of the secular papers was forced to pander to the same sentiment. The Board of Health struggled against this superstition, and addressed a circular to the Catholic clergy, imploring them to recommend vaccination; but, though two or three complied with this request, the great majority were either silent or openly hostile. The Oblate Fathers, whose church was situated in the very heart of the infected district, continued to denounce vaccination; the faithful were exhorted to rely on devotional exercises of various sorts; under the sanction of the hierarchy a great procession was ordered with a solemn appeal to the Virgin, and the use of the rosary was carefully specified.

Meantime, the disease, which had nearly died out among the Protestants, raged with ever-increasing virulence among the Catholics; and, the truth becoming more and more clear, even to the most devout, proper measures were at last enforced and the plague was stayed, though not until there had been a fearful waste of life among these simple-hearted believers, and germs of scepticism planted in the hearts of their children which will bear fruit for generations to come.[33]

[33] For the opposition of conscientious men to vaccination in England, see Baron, *Life of Jenner,* as above; also vol. ii, p. 43; also Duns's *Life of Simpson,* London, 1873, pp. 248, 249; also *Works of Sir J. Y. Simpson,* vol. ii. For a multitude of statistics showing the diminution of smallpox after the introduction of vaccination, see Russell, p. 380. For the striking record in London for 1890, see an article in the *Edinburgh Review* for January, 1891. The general statement referred to was made in a speech some years since by Sir Spencer Wells. For recent scattered cases of feeble opposition to vaccination by Protestant ministers, see William White, *The Great Delusion,* London, 1885, *passim.* For opposition of the Roman Catholic clergy and peasantry in Canada to vaccination during the smallpox plague of 1885, see the English, Canadian, and American newspapers, but especially the very temperate and accurate correspondence in the *New York Evening Post* during September and October of that year.

Another class of cases in which the theologic spirit has allied itself with the retrograde party in medical science is found in the history of certain remedial agents; and first may be named cocaine. As early as the middle of the sixteenth century the value of coca had been discovered in South America; the natives of Peru prized it highly, and two eminent Jesuits, Joseph Acosta and Antonio Julian, were converted to this view. But the conservative spirit in the Church was too strong; in 1567 the Second Council of Lima, consisting of bishops from all parts of South America, condemned it, and two years later came a royal decree declaring that "the notions entertained by the natives regarding it are an illusion of the devil."

As a pendant to this singular mistake on the part of the older Church came another committed by many Protestants. In the early years of the seventeenth century the Jesuit missionaries in South America learned from the natives the value of the so-called Peruvian bark in the treatment of ague; and in 1638, the Countess of Cinchon, Regent of Peru, having derived great benefit from the new remedy, it was introduced into Europe. Although its alkaloid, quinine, is perhaps the nearest approach to a medical specific, and has diminished the death rate in certain regions to an amazing extent, its introduction was bitterly opposed by many conservative members of the medical profession, and in this opposition large numbers of ultra-Protestants joined, out of hostility to the Roman Church. In the heat of sectarian feeling the new remedy was stigmatized as "an invention of the devil"; and so strong was this opposition that it was not introduced into England until 1653, and even then its use was long held back, owing mainly to anti-Catholic feeling.

What the theological method on the ultra-Protestant side could do to help the world at this very time is seen in the fact that, while this struggle was going on, Hoffmann was attempting to give a scientific theory of the action of the devil in causing Job's boils. This effort at a *quasi*-scientific explanation which should satisfy the theological spirit, comical as it at first seems, is really worthy of serious notice, because it must be considered as the beginning of that inevitable effort at compromise which we see in the history of every science when it begins to appear triumphant.[34]

[34] For the opposition of the South American Church authorities to the introduction of coca, etc., see Martindale, *Coca, Cocaine,*

But I pass to a typical conflict in our days, and in a Protestant country. In 1847, James Young Simpson, a Scotch physician, who afterward rose to the highest eminence in his profession, having advocated the use of anæsthetics in obstetrical cases, was immediately met by a storm of opposition. This hostility flowed from an ancient and time-honoured belief in Scotland. As far back as the year 1591, Eufame Macalyane, a lady of rank, being charged with seeking the aid of Agnes Sampson for the relief of pain at the time of the birth of her two sons, was burned alive on the Castle Hill of Edinburgh; and this old theological view persisted even to the middle of the nineteenth century. From pulpit after pulpit Simpson's use of chloroform was denounced as impious and contrary to Holy Writ; texts were cited abundantly, the ordinary declaration being that to use chloroform was "to avoid one part of the primeval curse on woman." Simpson wrote pamphlet after pamphlet to defend the blessing which he brought into use; but he seemed about to be overcome, when he seized a new weapon, probably the most absurd by which a great cause was ever won: "My opponents forget," he said, "the twenty-first verse of the second chapter of Genesis; it is the record of the first surgical operation ever performed, and that text proves that the Maker of the universe, before he took the rib from Adam's side for the creation of Eve, caused a deep sleep to fall upon Adam." This was a stunning blow, but it did not entirely kill the opposition; they had strength left to maintain that the "deep sleep of Adam took place before the introduction of pain into the world—in a state of innocence." But now a new champion intervened—Thomas Chalmers: with a few pungent arguments from his pulpit he scattered the enemy forever, and the greatest battle of science against suffering was won. This victory was won not less for religion. Wisely did those who raised the monument at Boston to one of the discoverers of anæsthetics inscribe upon its pedestal the words from our

---

and its Salts, London, 1886, p. 7. As to theological and sectarian resistance to quinine, see Russell, pp. 194, 253; also Eccles; also Meryon, *History of Medicine,* London, 1861, vol. i, p. 74, note. For the great decrease in deaths by fever after the use of Peruvian bark began, see statistical tables given in Russell, p. 252; and for Hoffmann's attempt at compromise, ibid., p. 294.

sacred text, "This also cometh forth from the Lord of hosts, which is wonderful in counsel, and excellent in working."[35]

11. Final Breaking Away of the Theological Theory in Medicine

While this development of history was going on, the central idea on which the whole theologic view rested—the idea of diseases as resulting from the wrath of God or malice of Satan—was steadily weakened; and, out of the many things which show this, one may be selected as indicating the drift of thought among theologians themselves.

Toward the end of the eighteenth century the most eminent divines of the American branch of the Anglican Church framed their *Book of Common Prayer*. Abounding as it does in evidences of their wisdom and piety, few things are more noteworthy than a change made in the exhortation to the faithful to present themselves at the communion. While, in the old form laid down in the English *Prayer Book,* the minister was required to warn his flock not "to kindle God's wrath" or "provoke him to plague us with divers diseases and sundry kinds of death," from the American form all this and more of similar import in various services was left out.

Since that day progress in medical science has been rapid indeed, and at no period more so than during the last half of the nineteenth century.

The theological view of disease has steadily faded, and the theological hold upon medical education has been almost entirely relaxed. In three great fields, especially, discoveries have been made which have done much to disperse the atmosphere of miracle. First, there has come knowledge regarding the relation between imagination and medicine, which, though still defective, is of great importance. This relation has been noted during the whole history of the science. When the soldiers of the Prince of Orange, at the siege of Breda in 1625, were dying of scurvy by scores, he sent to the physicians "two or three small vials filled with a decoction of camomile, wormwood, and camphor, gave out that it was a very rare and precious medicine—a medicine of such virtue that two or three drops sufficed to impregnate

[35] For the case of Eufame Macalyane, see Dalyell, *Darker Superstitions of Scotland,* pp. 130, 133. For the contest of Simpson with Scotch ecclesiastical authorities, see Duns, *Life of Sir J. Y. Simpson,* London, 1873, pp. 215-222, and 256-260.

a gallon of water, and that it had been obtained from the East with great difficulty and danger." This statement, made with much solemnity, deeply impressed the soldiers; they took the medicine eagerly, and great numbers recovered rapidly. Again, two centuries later, young Humphry Davy, being employed to apply the bulb of the thermometer to the tongues of certain patients at Bristol after they had inhaled various gases as remedies for disease, and finding that the patients supposed this application of the thermometer-bulb was the cure, finally wrought cures by this application alone, without any use of the gases whatever. Innumerable cases of this sort have thrown a flood of light upon such cures as those wrought by Prince Hohenlohe, by the "metallic tractors," and by a multitude of other agencies temporarily in vogue, but, above all, upon the miraculous cures which in past ages have been so frequent and of which a few survive.

The second department is that of hypnotism. Within the last half-century many scattered indications have been collected and supplemented by thoughtful, patient investigators of genius, and especially by Braid in England and Charcot in France. Here, too, great inroads have been made upon the province hitherto sacred to miracle, and in 1888 the cathedral preacher, Steigenberger, of Augsburg, sounded an alarm. He declared his fears "lest accredited Church miracles lose their hold upon the public," denounced hypnotism as a doctrine of demons, and ended with the singular argument that, inasmuch as hypnotism is avowedly incapable of explaining all the wonders of history, it is idle to consider it at all. But investigations in hypnotism still go on, and may do much in the twentieth century to carry the world yet further from the realm of the miraculous.

In a third field science has won a striking series of victories. Bacteriology, beginning in the researches of Leeuwenhoek in the seventeenth century, continued by O. F. Müller in the eighteenth, and developed or applied with wonderful skill by Ehrenberg, Cohn, Lister, Pasteur, Koch, Billings, Bering, and their compeers in the nineteenth, has explained the origin and proposed the prevention or cure of various diseases widely prevailing, which until recently have been generally held to be "inscrutable providences." Finally, the closer study of psychology, especially in its relations to folklore, has revealed processes involved in the development of myths and legends: the phenomena of "expectant attention," the tendency to marvel-mongering, and the feeling of "joy in believing."

In summing up the history of this long struggle between science and theology, two main facts are to be noted: First, that in proportion as the world approached the "ages of faith" it receded from ascertained truth, and in proportion as the world has receded from the "ages of faith" it has approached ascertained truth; secondly, that, in proportion as the grasp of theology upon education tightened, medicine declined, and in proportion as that grasp has relaxed, medicine has been developed.

The world is hardly beyond the beginning of medical discoveries, yet they have already taken from theology what was formerly its strongest province—sweeping away from this vast field of human effort that belief in miracles which for more than twenty centuries has been the main stumbling-block in the path of medicine; and in doing this they have cleared higher paths not only for science, but for religion.[36]

[36] For the rescue of medical education from the control of theology, especially in France, see Rambaud, *La Civilisation Contemporaine en France*, pp. 682, 683. For miraculous cures wrought by imagination, see Tuke, *Influence of Mind on Body*, vol. ii. For the opposition to scientific study of hypnotism, see *Hypnotismus und Wunder: ein Vortrag, mit Weiterungen*, von Max Steigenberger, Domprediger, Augsburg, 1888, reviewed in *Science*, February 15, 1889, p. 127. For a recent statement regarding the development of studies in hypnotism, see Liégeois, *De la Suggestion et du Somnambulisme dans leurs rapports avec la Jurisprudence*, Paris, 1889, chap. ii. As to joy in believing and exaggerating marvels, see in the London *Graphic* for January 2, 1892, an account of Hindu jugglers by "Professor" Hofmann, himself an expert conjurer. He shows that the Hindu performances have been grossly and persistently exaggerated in the accounts of travellers; that they are easily seen through, and greatly inferior to the jugglers' tricks seen every day in European capitals. The eminent Prof. De Gubernatis, who also had witnessed the Hindu performances, assured the present writer that the current accounts of them were monstrously exaggerated. As to the miraculous in general, the famous *Essay* of Hume holds a most important place in the older literature of the subject; but, for perhaps the most remarkable of all discussions of it, see Conyers Middleton, D. D., *A Free Inquiry into the Miraculous Powers which are supposed to have subsisted in the Christian Church*, London, 1749. For probably the most judicially fair discussion, see Lecky, *History of European Morals*, vol. i, chap. iii; also his *Rationalism in Europe*, vol. i, chaps. i and ii; and for perhaps the

Chapter 14

From Fetich to Hygiene

1. The Theological View of Epidemics and Sanitation

A VERY STRIKING FEATURE in recorded history has been the recurrence of great pestilences. Various indications in ancient times show their frequency, while the famous description of the plague of Athens given by Thucydides, and the discussion of it by Lucretius, exemplify their severity. In the Middle Ages they raged from time to time throughout Europe: such plagues as the Black Death and the sweating sickness swept off vast multitudes, the best authorities estimating that of the former, at the middle of the fourteenth century, more than half the population of England died, and that twenty-five millions of people perished in various parts of Europe. In 1552 sixty-seven thousand patients died of the plague at Paris alone, and in 1580 more than twenty thousand. The great plague in England and other parts of Europe in the seventeenth century was also fearful, and that which swept the south of Europe in the early part of the eighteenth century, as well as the invasions by the cholera at various times during the nineteenth, while less terrible than those of former years, have left a deep impress upon the imaginations of men.

From the earliest records we find such pestilences attributed to the wrath or malice of unseen powers. This had been the prevailing view even in the most cultured ages before the establishment of Christianity: in Greece and Rome especially, plagues of various sorts were attributed to the wrath of the gods; in Judea, the scriptural records of various plagues sent upon the earth by the Divine fiat as a punishment for sin show the continuance of this mode of thought. Among

boldest and most suggestive of recent statements, see Max Müller, *Physical Religion,* being the Gifford Lectures before the University of Glasgow for 1890, London, 1891, lecture xiv. See also, for very cogent statement, and arguments, Matthew Arnold's *Literature and Dogma,* especially chap. v, and, for a recent utterance of great clearness and force, Prof. Osler's *Address before the Johns Hopkins University,* given in *Science* for March 27, 1891.

many examples and intimations of this in our sacred literature, we have the epidemic which carried off fourteen thousand seven hundred of the children of Israel, and which was only stayed by the prayers and offerings of Aaron, the high priest; the destruction of seventy thousand men in the pestilence by which King David was punished for the numbering of Israel, and which was only stopped when the wrath of Jahveh was averted by burnt-offerings; the plague threatened by the prophet Zechariah, and that delineated in the Apocalypse. From these sources this current of ideas was poured into the early Christian Church, and hence it has been that during nearly twenty centuries since the rise of Christianity, and down to a period within living memory, at the appearance of any pestilence the Church authorities, instead of devising sanitary measures, have very generally preached the necessity of immediate atonement for offenses against the Almighty.

This view of the early Church was enriched greatly by a new development of theological thought regarding the powers of Satan and evil angels, the declaration of St. Paul that the gods of antiquity were devils being cited as its sufficient warrant.[1]

Moreover, comets, falling stars, and earthquakes were thought, upon scriptural authority, to be "signs and wonders" —evidences of the Divine wrath, heralds of fearful visitations; and this belief, acting powerfully upon the minds of

[1] For plague during the Peloponnesian war, see Thucydides, vol. ii, pp. 47-55, and vol. iii, p. 87. For a general statement regarding this and other plagues in ancient times, see Lucretius, vol. vi, pp. 1090 et seq.; and for a translation, see vol. i, p. 179, in Munro's edition of 1886. For early views of sanitary science in Greece and Rome, see Forster's *Inquiry*, in *The Pamphleteer*, vol. xxiv, p. 404. For the Greek view of the interference of the gods in disease, especially in pestilence, see Grote's *History of Greece*, vol. i, pp. 251, 485, and vol. vi, p. 213; see also Herodotus, lib. iii, c. xxxiii, and elsewhere. For the Hebrew view of the same interference by the Almighty, see especially Numbers xi, 4-34; also xvi, 49; I Samuel xxiv; also Psalm cvi, 29, also the well-known texts in Zechariah and Revelation. For St. Paul's declaration that the gods of the heathen are devils, see I Cor. x, 20. As to the earlier origin of the plague in Egypt, see Haeser, *Lehrbuch der Geschichte der Medicin und der epidemischen Krankheiten*, Jena, 1875-'82, vol. iii, pp. 15 et seq.

millions, did much to create a panic-terror sure to increase epidemic disease wherever it broke forth.

The main cause of this immense sacrifice of life is now known to have been the want of hygienic precaution, both in the Eastern centres, where various plagues were developed, and in the European towns through which they spread. And here certain theological reasonings came in to resist the evolution of a proper sanitary theory. Out of the Orient had been poured into the thinking of western Europe the theological idea that the abasement of man adds to the glory of God; that indignity to the body may secure salvation to the soul; hence, that cleanliness betokens pride and filthiness humility. Living in filth was regarded by great numbers of holy men, who set an example to the Church and to society, as an evidence of sanctity. St. Jerome and the Breviary of the Roman Church dwell with unction on the fact that St. Hilarion lived his whole life long in utter physical uncleanliness; St. Athanasius glorifies St. Anthony because he had never washed his feet; St. Abraham's most striking evidence of holiness was that for fifty years he washed neither his hands nor his feet; St. Sylvia never washed any part of her body save her fingers; St. Euphraxia belonged to a convent in which the nuns religiously abstained from bathing; St. Mary of Egypt was eminent for filthiness; St. Simon Stylites was in this respect unspeakable—the least that can be said is, that he lived in ordure and stench intolerable to his visitors. The *Lives of the Saints* dwell with complacency on the statement that, when sundry Eastern monks showed a disposition to wash themselves, the Almighty manifested his displeasure by drying up a neighbouring stream until the bath which it had supplied was destroyed.

The religious world was far indeed from the inspired utterance attributed to John Wesley, that "cleanliness is near akin to godliness." For century after century the idea prevailed that filthiness was akin to holiness; and, while we may well believe that the devotion of the clergy to the sick was one cause why, during the greater plagues, they lost so large a proportion of their numbers, we can not escape the conclusion that their want of cleanliness had much to do with it. In France, during the fourteenth century, Guy de Chauliac, the great physician of his time, noted particularly that certain Carmelite monks suffered especially from pestilence, and that they were especially filthy. During the Black Death no less than nine hundred Carthusian monks fell victims in one group of buildings.

Naturally, such an example set by the venerated leaders of thought exercised great influence throughout society, and all the more because it justified the carelessness and sloth to which ordinary humanity is prone. In the principal towns of Europe, as well as in the country at large, down to a recent period, the most ordinary sanitary precautions were neglected, and pestilences continued to be attributed to the wrath of God or the malice of Satan. As to the wrath of God, a new and powerful impulse was given to this belief in the Church toward the end of the sixth century by St. Gregory the Great. In 590, when he was elected Pope, the city of Rome was suffering from a dreadful pestilence: the people were dying by thousands; out of one procession imploring the mercy of Heaven no less than eighty persons died within an hour: what the heathen in an earlier epoch had attributed to Apollo was now attributed to Jehovah, and chroniclers tell us that fiery darts were seen flung from heaven into the devoted city. But finally, in the midst of all this horror, Gregory, at the head of a penitential procession, saw hovering over the mausoleum of Hadrian the figure of the arch-angel Michael, who was just sheathing a flaming sword, while three angels were heard chanting the Regina Cœli. The legend continues that the Pope immediately broke forth into hallelujahs for this sign that the plague was stayed, and, as it shortly afterward became less severe, a chapel was built at the summit of the mausoleum and dedicated to St. Michael; still later, above the whole was erected the colossal statue of the archangel sheathing his sword, which still stands to perpetuate the legend. Thus the greatest of Rome's ancient funeral monuments was made to bear testimony to this mediæval belief; the mausoleum of Hadrian became the castle of St. Angelo. A legend like this, claiming to date from the greatest of the early popes, and vouched for by such an imposing monument, had undoubtedly a marked effect upon the dominant theology throughout Europe, which was constantly developing a great body of thought regarding the agencies by which the Divine wrath might be averted.

First among these agencies, naturally, were evidences of devotion, especially gifts of land, money, or privileges to churches, monasteries, and shrines—the seats of fetiches which it was supposed had wrought cures or might work them. The whole evolution of modern history, not only ecclesiastical but civil, has been largely affected by the wealth transferred to the clergy at such periods. It was noted that in the fourteenth century, after the great plague, the Black Death, had passed, an immensely increased proportion of the landed and personal property of every European country was in the hands of the Church. Well did a great ecclesiastic remark that "pestilences are the harvests of the ministers of God."[2]

Other modes of propitiating the higher powers were penitential processions, the parading of images of the Virgin or of saints through plague-stricken towns, and fetiches innumerable. Very noted in the thirteenth and fourteenth centuries were the processions of the flagellants, trooping through various parts of Europe, scourging their naked bodies, shrieking the penitential psalms, and often running from wild excesses of devotion to the maddest orgies.

Sometimes, too, plagues were attributed to the wrath of lesser heavenly powers. Just as, in former times, the fury of "far-darting Apollo" was felt when his name was not respectfully treated by mortals, so, in 1680, the Church authorities at Rome discovered that the plague then raging resulted from the anger of St. Sebastian because no monument had been erected to him. Such a monument was therefore placed

2 For triumphant mention of St. Hilarion's filth, see the *Roman Breviary* for October 21st; and for details, see S. Hieronymus, *Vita S. Hilarionis Eremitæ,* in Migne, *Patrologia,* vol. xxiii. For Athanasius's reference to St. Anthony's filth, see works of St. Athanasius in *The Nicene and Post-Nicene Fathers,* second series, vol. iv, p. 209. For the filthiness of the other saints named, see citations from the *Lives of the Saints,* in Lecky's *History of European Morals,* vol. ii, pp. 117, 118. For Guy de Chauliac's observation on the filthiness of Carmelite monks and their great losses by pestilence, see Meryon, *History of Medicine,* vol, i, p. 257. For the mortality among the Carthusian monks in time of plague, see Mrs. Lecky's very interesting *Visit to the Grand Chartreuse,* in *The Nineteenth Century* for March, 1891. For the plague at Rome in 590, the legend regarding the fiery darts, mentioned by Pope Gregory himself, and that of the castle of St. Angelo, see Gregorovius, *Geschichte der Stadt Rom im Mittelalter,* vol. ii, pp. 26-35; also Story, *Castle of St. Angelo,* etc., chap. ii. For the remark that "pestilences are the harvest of the ministers of God," see reference to Charlevoix, in Southey, *History of Brazil* vol. ii, p. 254, cited in Buckle, vol. i, p. 130, note.

in the Church of St. Peter ad Vincula, and the plague ceased. So much for the endeavour to avert the wrath of the heavenly powers. On the other hand, theological reasoning no less subtle was used in thwarting the malice of Satan. This idea, too, came from far. In the sacred books of India and Persia, as well as in our own, we find the same theory of disease, leading to similar means of cure. Perhaps the most astounding among Christian survivals of this theory and its resultant practices was seen during the plague at Rome in 1522. In that year, at that centre of divine illumination, certain people, having reasoned upon the matter, came to the conclusion that this great scourge was the result of Satanic malice; and, in view of St. Paul's declaration that the ancient gods were devils, and of the theory that the ancient gods of Rome were the devils who had the most reason to punish that city for their dethronement, and that the great amphitheatre was the chosen haunt of these demon gods, an ox decorated with garlands, after the ancient heathen manner, was taken in procession to the Colosseum and solemnly sacrificed. Even this proved vain, and the Church authorities then ordered expiatory processions and ceremonies to propitiate the Almighty, the Virgin, and the saints, who had been offended by this temporary effort to bribe their enemies.

But this sort of theological reasoning developed an idea far more disastrous, and this was that Satan, in causing pestilences, used as his emissaries especially Jews and witches. The proof of this belief in the case of the Jews was seen in the fact that they escaped with a less percentage of disease than did the Christians in the great plague periods. This was doubtless due in some measure to their remarkable sanitary system, which had probably originated thousands of years before in Egypt, and had been handed down through Jewish lawgivers and statesmen. Certainly they observed more careful sanitary rules and more constant abstinence from dangerous foods than was usual among Christians; but the public at large could not understand so simple a cause, and jumped to the conclusion that their immunity resulted from protection by Satan, and that this protection was repaid and the pestilence caused by their wholesale poisoning of Christians. As a result of this mode of thought, attempts were made in all parts of Europe to propitiate the Almighty, to thwart Satan, and to stop the plague by torturing and murdering the Jews. Throughout Europe during great pestilences we hear of extensive burnings of this devoted people. In Bavaria, at the time of the Black Death, it is computed that twelve thousand Jews thus perished; in the small town of Erfurt the number is said to have been three thousand; in Strasburg, the Rue Brulée remains as a monument to the two thousand Jews burned there for poisoning the wells and causing the plague of 1348; at the royal castle of Chinon, near Tours, an immense trench was dug, filled with blazing wood, and in a single day one hundred and sixty Jews were burned. Everywhere in continental Europe this mad persecution went on; but it is a pleasure to say that one great churchman, Pope Clement VI, stood against this popular unreason, and, so far as he could bring his influence to bear on the maddened populace, exercised it in favour of mercy to these supposed enemies of the Almighty.[3]

Yet, as late as 1527, the people of Pavia, being threatened with plague, appealed to St. Bernardino of Feltro, who during his life had been a fierce enemy of the Jews, and they passed a decree promising that if the saint would avert the

[3] For an early conception in India of the Divinity acting through medicine, see *The Bhagavadgîtâ,* translated by Telang, p. 82, in Max Müller's *Sacred Books of the East.* For the necessity of religious means of securing knowledge of medicine, see the *Anugîta,* translated by Telang, in Max Müller's *Sacred Books of the East,* p. 388. For ancient Persian ideas of sickness as sent by the spirit of evil and to be cured by spells, but not excluding medicine and surgery, and for sickness generally as caused by the evil principle in demons, see the *Zend-Avesta,* Darmesteter's translation, introduction *passim,* but especially p. xciii. For diseases wrought by witchcraft, see the same, pp. 230, 293. On the preference of spells in healing over medicine and surgery, see *Zend-Avesta,* vol. i, pp. 85, 86. For healing by magic in ancient Greece, see, e. g., the cure of Ulysses in the *Odyssey,* "They stopped the black blood by a spell" (*Odyssey,* xix, 457). For medicine in Egypt as partly priestly and partly in the hands of physicians, see Rawlinson's *Herodotus,* vol. ii, p. 136, note. For ideas of curing of diseases by expulsion of demons still surviving among various tribes and nations of Asia, see J. G. Frazer, *The Golden Bough: a Study of Comparative Religion,* London, 1890, pp. 184-192. For the Flagellants and their processions at the time of the Black Death, see Lea, *History of the Inquisition,* New York, 1888, vol. ii, pp. 381 *et seq.* For the persecution of the Jews in time of pestilence, see ibid., p. 379 and following, with authorities in the notes. For the expulsion of the Jews from Padua, see the *Acta Sanctorum,* September, tom. vii, p. 893.

pestilence they would expel the Jews from the city. The saint apparently accepted the bargain, and in due time the Jews were expelled.

As to witches, the reasons for believing them the cause of pestilence also came from far. This belief, too, had been poured mainly from Oriental sources into our sacred books and thence into the early Church, and was strengthened by a whole line of Church authorities, fathers, doctors, and saints; but, above all, by the great bull, *Summis Desiderantes,* issued by Pope Innocent VIII, in 1484. This utterance from the seat of St. Peter infallibly committed the Church to the idea that witches are a great cause of disease, storms, and various ills which afflict humanity; and the Scripture on which the action recommended against witches in this papal bull, as well as in so many sermons and treatises for centuries afterward, was based, was the famous text, "Thou shalt not suffer a witch to live." This idea persisted long, and the evolution of it is among the most fearful things in human history.[4]

*　　*　　*

[4] On the plagues generally, see Hecker, *Epidemics of the Middle Ages, passim;* but especially Haeser, as above, 111. Band, pp. 1-202; also Sprengel, Baas, Isensee, *et al.* For brief statement showing the enormous loss of life in these plagues, see Littré, *Médecine et Médecins,* Paris, 1875, pp. 3 *et seq.* For a summary of the effects of the black plague throughout England, see Green's *Short History of the English People,* chap. v. For the mortality in the Paris hospitals, see Desmazes, *Supplices, Prisons et Graces en France,* Paris, 1866. For striking descriptions of plague-stricken cities, see the well-known passages in Thucydides, Boccaccio, De Foe, and, above all, Manzoni's *Promessi Sposi.* For examples of averting the plagues by processions, see Leopold Delisle, *Études sur la Condition de la Classe Agricole, etc., en Normandie au Moyen Age,* p. 630; also Fort, chap. xxiii. For the anger of St. Sebastian as a cause of the plague at Rome, and its cessation when a monument had been erected to him, see Paulus Diaconus, cited in Gregorovius, vol. ii, p. 165. For the sacrifice of an ox in the Colosseum to the ancient gods as a means of averting the plague of 1522, at Rome, see Gregorovius, vol. viii, p. 390. As to massacres of the Jews in order to avert the wrath of God in pestilence, see *L'École et la Science,* Paris, 1887, p. 178; also Hecker, and especially Hoeniger, *Gang und Verbreitung des Schwarzen Todes in Deutschland,* Berlin, 1880. For a long list of towns in which burnings of Jews took place for this imaginary cause, see pp. 7-11. As to absolute want of

Among the methods of this witch activity especially credited in central and southern Europe was the anointing of city walls and pavements with a diabolical unguent causing pestilence. In 1530 Michael Caddo was executed with fearful tortures for thus besmearing the pavements of Geneva. But far more dreadful was the torturing to death of a large body of people at Milan, in the following century, for producing the plague by anointing the walls; and a little later similar punishments for the same crime were administered in Toulouse and other cities. The case in Milan may be briefly summarized as showing the ideas on sanitary science of all classes, from highest to lowest, in the seventeenth century. That city was then under the control of Spain; and, its authorities having received notice from the Spanish Government that certain persons suspected of witchcraft had recently left Madrid, and had perhaps gone to Milan to anoint the walls, this communication was dwelt upon in the pulpits as another evidence of that Satanic malice which the Church alone had the means of resisting, and the people were thus excited and put upon the alert. One morning, in the year 1630, an old woman, looking out of her window, saw a man walking along the street and wiping his fingers upon the walls; she immediately called the attention of another old woman, and they agreed that this man must be one of the diabolical anointers. It was perfectly evident to a person under ordinary conditions that this unfortunate man was simply trying to remove from his fingers the ink gathered while writing from the ink-horn which he carried in his girdle; but this explanation was too simple to satisfy those

sanitary precautions, see Hecker, p. 292. As to condemnation by strong religionists of medical means in the plague, see Fort, p. 130. For a detailed account of the action of Popes Eugene IV, Innocent VIII, and other popes, against witchcraft, ascribing to it storms and diseases, and for the bull *Summis Desiderantes,* see the chapters on *Meteorology* and *Magic* in this series. The text of the bull is given in the *Malleus Maleficarum,* in Binsfeld, and in Roskoff, *Geschichte des Teufels,* Leipzig, 1869, vol. i, pp. 222-225, and a good summary and analysis of it in Soldan, *Geschichte der Hexenprocesse.* For a concise and admirable statement of the contents and effects of the bull, see Lea, *History of the Inquisition,* vol. iii, pp. 40 *et seq.;* and for the best statement known to me of the general subject, Prof. George L. Burr's paper on *The Literature of Witchcraft,* read before the American Historical Association at Washington, 1890.

who first observed him or those who afterward tried him: a mob was raised and he was thrown into prison. Being tortured, he at first did not know what to confess; but, on inquiring from the jailer and others, he learned what the charge was, and, on being again subjected to torture utterly beyond endurance, he confessed everything which was suggested to him; and, on being tortured again and again to give the names of his accomplices, he accused, at hazard, the first people in the city whom he thought of. These, being arrested and tortured beyond endurance, confessed and implicated a still greater number, until members of the foremost families were included in the charge. Again and again all these unfortunates were tortured beyond endurance. Under paganism, the rule regarding torture had been that it should not be carried beyond human endurance; and we therefore find Cicero ridiculing it as a means of detecting crime, because a stalwart criminal of strong nerves might resist it and go free, while a physically delicate man, though innocent, would be forced to confess. Hence it was that under paganism a limit was imposed to the torture which could be administered; but, when Christianity had become predominant throughout Europe, torture was developed with a cruelty never before known. There had been evolved a doctrine of "excepted cases"—these "excepted cases" being especially heresy and witchcraft; for by a very simple and logical process of theological reasoning it was held that Satan would give supernatural strength to his special devotees— that is, to heretics and witches—and therefore that, in dealing with them, there should be no limit to the torture. The result was in this particular case, as in tens of thousands besides, that the accused confessed everything which could be suggested to them, and often in the delirium of their agony confessed far more than all that the zeal of the prosecutors could suggest. Finally, a great number of worthy people were sentenced to the most cruel death which could be invented. The records of their trials and deaths are frightful. The treatise which in recent years has first brought to light in connected form an authentic account of the proceedings in this affair, and which gives at the end engravings of the accused subjected to horrible tortures on their way to the stake and at the place of execution itself, is one of the most fearful monuments of theological reasoning and human folly.

To cap the climax, after a poor apothecary had been tortured into a confession that he had made the magic ointment, and when he had been put to death with the most exquisite refinements of torture, his family were obliged to take another name, and were driven out from the city; his house was torn down, and on its site was erected "The Column of Infamy," which remained on this spot until, toward the end of the eighteenth century, a party of young radicals, probably influenced by the reading of Beccaria, sallied forth one night and leveled this pious monument to the ground.

Herein was seen the culmination and decline of the bull *Summis Desiderantes*. It had been issued by him whom a majority of the Christian world believes to be infallible in his teachings to the Church as regards faith and morals; yet here was a deliberate utterance in a matter of faith and morals which even children now know to be utterly untrue. Though Beccaria's book on *Crimes and Punishments,* with its declarations against torture, was placed by the Church authorities upon the *Index*, and though the faithful throughout the Christian world were forbidden to read it, even this could not prevent the victory of truth over this infallible utterance of Innocent VIII.[5]

As the seventeenth century went on, ingenuity in all parts of Europe seemed devoted to new developments of fetichism. A very curious monument of this evolution in Italy exists in the Royal Gallery of Paintings at Naples, where may be seen several pictures representing the measures taken to save the city from the plague during the seventeenth century, but especially from the plague of 1656. One enormous canvas gives a curious example of the theological doctrine of intercession between man and his Maker, spun out to its logical length. In the background is the plague-stricken city: in the foreground the people are praying to the city authorities to avert the plague; the city authorities are praying to the Carthusian monks; the monks are praying to St. Martin, St.

[5] . . . For the magic spreading of the plague at Milan, see Manzoni, *I Promessi Sposi* and *La Colonna Infame;* and for the origin of the charges, with all the details of the trial, see the *Processo Originale degli Untori,* Milan, 1839, *passim,* but especially the large folding plate at the end, exhibiting the tortures. For the after-history of the Column of Infamy, and for the placing of Beccaria's book on the *Index,* see Cantu, *Vita di Beccaria.* For the magic spreading of the plague in general, see Littré, pp. 492 and following.

Bruno, and St. Januarius; these three saints in their turn
are praying to the Virgin; the Virgin prays to Christ; and
Christ prays to the Almighty. Still another picture represents
the people, led by the priests, executing with horrible tortures
the Jews, heretics, and witches who were supposed to cause
the pestilence of 1656, while in the heavens the Virgin and
St. Januarius are interceding with Christ to sheathe his sword
and stop the plague.

In such an atmosphere of thought it is no wonder that
the death statistics were appalling. We hear of districts in
which not more than one in ten escaped, and some were entirely depopulated. Such appeals to fetich against pestilence
have continued in Naples down to our own time, the great
saving power being the liquefaction of the blood of St. Januarius. In 1856 the present writer saw this miracle performed in the gorgeous chapel of the saint forming part of
the Cathedral of Naples. The chapel was filled with devout
worshippers of every class, from the officials in court dress,
representing the Bourbon king, down to the lowest lazzaroni.
The reliquary of silver-gilt, shaped like a large human head,
and supposed to contain the skull of the saint, was first placed
upon the altar; next, two vials containing a dark substance
said to be his blood, having been taken from the wall, were
also placed upon the altar near the head. As the priests said
masses, they turned the vials from time to time, and the
liquefaction being somewhat delayed, the great crowd of
people burst out into more and more impassioned expostula-
tion and petitions to the saint. Just in front of the altar
were the lazzaroni who claimed to be descendants of the
saint's family, and these were especially importunate: at such
times they beg, they scold, they even threaten; they have
been known to abuse the saint roundly, and to tell him that,
if he did not care to show his favour to the city by liquefying
his blood, St. Cosmo and St. Damian were just as good saints
as he, and would no doubt be very glad to have the city devote itself to them. At last, on the occasion above referred
to, the priest, turning the vials suddenly, announced that the
saint had performed the miracle, and instantly priests, people,
choir, and organ burst forth into a great *Te Deum;* bells
rang, and cannon roared; a procession was formed, and the
shrine containing the saint's relics was carried through the
streets, the people prostrating themselves on both sides of the
way and throwing showers of rose leaves upon the shrine

and upon the path before it. The contents of these precious vials are an interesting relic indeed, for they represent to us vividly that period when men who were willing to go to the stake for their religious opinions thought it not wrong to save the souls of their fellow-men by pious mendacity and consecrated fraud. To the scientific eye this miracle is very simple: the vials contain, no doubt, one of those mixtures fusing at low temperature, which, while kept in its place within the cold stone walls of the church, remains solid, but upon being brought out into the hot, crowded chapel, and fondled by the warm hands of the priests, gradually softens and becomes liquid. It was curious to note, at the time above mentioned, that even the high functionaries representing the king looked at the miracle with awe: they evidently found "joy in believing," and one of them assured the present writer that the only thing which *could* cause it was the direct exercise of miraculous power.

It may be reassuring to persons contemplating a visit to that beautiful capital in these days, that, while this miracle still goes on, it is no longer the only thing relied upon to preserve the public health. An unbelieving generation, especially taught by the recent horrors of the cholera, has thought it wise to supplement the power of St. Januarius by the "Risanamento," begun mainly in 1885 and still going on. The drainage of the city has thus been greatly improved, the old wells closed, and pure water introduced from the mountains. Moreover, at the last outburst of cholera a few years since, a noble deed was done which by its moral effect exercised a widespread healing power. Upon hearing of this terrific outbreak of pestilence, King Humbert, though under the ban of the Church, broke from all the entreaties of his friends and family, went directly into the plague-stricken city, and there, in the streets, public places, and hospitals, encouraged the living, comforted the sick and dying, and took means to prevent a further spread of the pestilence. To the credit of the Church it should also be said that the Cardinal Archbishop San Felice joined him in this.

Miracle for miracle, the effect of this visit of the king seems to have surpassed anything that St. Januarius could do, for it gave confidence and courage which very soon showed their effects in diminishing the number of deaths. It would certainly appear that in this matter the king was more directly under Divine inspiration and guidance than was the Pope; for the fact that King Humbert went to Naples at the risk of his life, while Leo XIII remained in safety at the Vatican, impressed the Italian people in favour of the new *régime* and against the old as nothing else could have done.

In other parts of Italy the same progress is seen under the new Italian government. Venice, Genoa, Leghorn, and especially Rome, which under the sway of the popes was scandalously filthy, are now among the cleanest cities in Europe. What the relics of St. Januarius, St. Anthony, and a multitude of local fetiches throughout Italy were for ages utterly unable to do, has been accomplished by the development of the simplest sanitary principles.[6]

* * *

[2. Gradual Decay of Theological Views Regarding Sanitation]

[3. The Triumph of Sanitary Science]

[4. The Relation of Sanitary Science to Religion]

Chapter 15

From "Demoniacal Possession" to Insanity

1. Theological Ideas of Lunacy and Its Treatment

OF ALL THE TRIUMPHS won by science for humanity, few have been farther-reaching in good effects than the modern

[6] As to recourse to fetichism in Italy in time of plague, and the pictures showing the intercession of Januarius and other saints, I have relied on my own notes made at various visits to Naples. For the general subject, see Peter, *Études Napolitaines,* especially chapters v and vi. For detailed accounts of the liquefaction of St. Januarius's blood by eye-witnesses, one an eminent Catholic of the seventeenth century, and the other a distinguished Protestant of our own time, see Murray's *Handbook for South Italy and Naples,* description of the Cathedral of San Gennaro. For an interesting series of articles on the subject, see *The Catholic World* for September, October, and November, 1871. . . . See also the *Autobiography* of D'Ewes, London, 1845, vol. ii, p. 446; also, for various citations, the second volume of Buckle, *History of Civilization in England.*

treatment of the insane. But this is the result of a struggle long and severe between two great forces. On one side have stood the survivals of various superstitions, the metaphysics of various philosophies, the dogmatism of various theologies, the literal interpretation of various sacred books, and especially of our own—all compacted into a creed that insanity is mainly or largely demoniacal possession; on the other side has stood science, gradually accumulating proofs that insanity is always the result of physical disease.[1]

I purpose in this chapter to sketch, as briefly as I may, the history of this warfare, or rather of this evolution of truth out of error.

Nothing is more simple and natural, in the early stages of civilization, than belief in occult, self-conscious powers of evil. Troubles and calamities come upon man; his ignorance of physical laws forbids him to attribute them to physical causes; he therefore attributes them sometimes to the wrath of a good being, but more frequently to the malice of an evil being.

Especially is this the case with diseases. The real causes of disease are so intricate that they are reached only after ages of scientific labour; hence they, above all, have been attributed to the influence of evil spirits.[2]

---

[1] [White, of course, was unacquainted with Freud's work (*The Interpretation of Dreams* first appeared in 1899-1900), which undoubtedly would have caused him to modify this statement—and, indeed, the whole chapter. See further my Epilogue.—Ed.]

[2] On the general attribution of disease to demoniacal influence, see Sprenger, *History of Medicine, passim* (note, for a later attitude, vol. ii, pp. 150-170, 178); Calmeil, *De la Folie,* Paris, 1845, vol. i, pp. 104, 105; Esquirol, *Des Maladies Mentales,* Paris, 1838, vol. i, p. 482; also Tylor, *Primitive Culture.* For a very plain and honest statement of this view in our own sacred books, see Oort, Hooykaas, and Kuenen, *The Bible for Young People,* English translation, chap. v, p. 167, and following; also Farrar's *Life of Christ,* chap. xvii. For this idea in Greece and elsewhere, see Maury, *La Magie,* etc., vol. iii, p. 276, giving, among other citations, one from book v of the *Odyssey.* On the influence of Platonism, see Esquirol and others, as above—the main passage cited is from the *Phædo.* For the devotion of the early fathers and doctors to this idea, see citations from Eusebius, Lactantius, St. Jerome, St. Augustine, St. John Chrysostom, St. Gregory Nazianzen, in Tissot, *L'Imagination,* p. 369; also Jacob (i. e., Paul Lacroix), *Croyances Populaires,* p. 183. For St. Augustine, see also his

But, if ordinary diseases were likely to be attributed to diabolical agency, how much more diseases of the brain, and especially the more obscure of these! These, indeed, seemed to the vast majority of mankind possible only on the theory of Satanic intervention: any approach to a true theory of the connection between physical causes and mental results is one of the highest acquisitions of science.

Here and there, during the whole historic period, keen men had obtained an inkling of the truth; but to the vast multitude, down to the end of the seventeenth century, nothing was more clear than that insanity is, in many if not in most cases, demoniacal possession.

Yet at a very early date, in Greece and Rome, science had asserted itself, and a beginning had been made which seemed destined to bring a large fruitage of blessings.[3] In the fifth century before the Christian era, Hippocrates of Cos asserted the great truth that all madness is simply disease of the brain, thereby beginning a development of truth and mercy which lasted nearly a thousand years. In the first century after Christ, Aretæus carried these ideas yet further, observed the phenomena of insanity with great acuteness, and reached yet more valuable results. Near the beginning of the following century, Soranus went still further in the same path, giving new results of research, and strengthening scientific truth. Toward the end of the same century a new epoch was ushered in by Galen, under whom the same truth was developed yet further, and the path toward merciful treatment of the insane made yet more clear. In the third century Celius Aurelianus received this deposit of precious truth, elaborated it, and brought forth the great idea which, had theology, citing biblical texts, not banished it, would have saved fifteen centuries of cruelty—an idea not fully recognised again till near the beginning of the present century—the idea that insanity is brain disease, and that the

De Civitate Dei, lib. xxii, chap. viii, and his *Enarratio in Psal.,* cxxxv, 1. For the breaking away of the religious orders in Italy from the entire supremacy of this idea, see Bécavin, *L'École de Salerne,* Paris, 1888; also Daremberg, *Histoire de la Médecine.* Even so late as the Protestant Reformation, Martin Luther maintained (*Table Talk,* Hazlitt's translation, London, 1872, pp. 250-256) that "Satan produces all the maladies which afflict mankind."
[3] It is significant of this scientific attitude that the Greek word for superstition means, literally, fear of gods or demons.

treatment of it must be gentle and kind. In the sixth century Alexander of Tralles presented still more fruitful researches, and taught the world how to deal with *melancholia;* and, finally, in the seventh century, this great line of scientific men, working mainly under pagan auspices, was closed by Paul of Ægina, who under the protection of Caliph Omar made still further observations, but, above all, laid stress on the cure of madness as a disease, and on the absolute necessity of mild treatment.[4]

* * *

This evolution of divine truth was interrupted by theology. There set into the early Church a current of belief which was destined to bring all these noble acquisitions of science and religion to naught, and, during centuries, to inflict tortures, physical and mental, upon hundreds of thousands of innocent men and women—a belief which held its cruel sway for nearly eighteen centuries; and this belief was that madness was mainly or largely possession by the devil.

This idea of diabolic agency in mental disease had grown luxuriantly in all the Oriental sacred literatures. In the series of Assyrian mythological tablets in which we find those legends of the Creation, the Fall, the Flood, and other early conceptions from which the Hebrews so largely drew the accounts wrought into the book of Genesis, have been discovered the formulas for driving out the evil spirits which cause disease. In the Persian theology regarding the struggle of the great powers of good and evil this idea was developed to its highest point. From these and other ancient sources the Jews naturally received this addition to their earlier view: the Mocker of the Garden of Eden became Satan, with legions of evil angels at his command; and the theory of diabolic causes of mental disease took a firm place in our sacred books. Such cases in the Old Testament as the evil spirit in Saul, which we now see to have been simply melancholy—

[4] For authorities regarding this development of scientific truth and mercy in antiquity, see especially Krafft-Ebing, *Lehrbuch der Psychiatrie,* Stuttgart, 1888, p. 40 and the pages following; Trélat, *Recherches Historiques sur la Folie,* Paris, 1839; Semelaigne, *L'Aliénation mentale dans l'Antiquité,* Paris, 1869; Dagron, *Des Aliénés,* Paris, 1875; also Calmeil, *De la Folie,* Sprenger, and especially Isensée, *Geschichte der Medicin,* Berlin, 1840.

and, in the New Testament, the various accounts of the casting out of devils, through which is refracted the beautiful and simple story of that power by which Jesus of Nazareth soothed perturbed minds by his presence or quelled outbursts of madness by his words, give examples of this. In Greece, too, an idea akin to this found lodgment both in the popular belief and in the philosophy of Plato and Socrates; and though, as we have seen, the great leaders in medical science had taught with more or less distinctness that insanity is the result of physical disease, there was a strong popular tendency to attribute the more troublesome cases of it to hostile spiritual influence.[5]

From all these sources, but especially from our sacred books and the writings of Plato, this theory that mental disease is caused largely or mainly by Satanic influence passed on into the early Church. In the apostolic times no belief seems to have been more firmly settled. The early fathers and doctors in the following age universally accepted it, and the apologists generally spoke of the power of casting out devils as a leading proof of the divine origin of the Christian religion.

This belief took firm hold upon the strongest men. The case of St. Gregory the Great is typical. He was a pope of exceedingly broad mind for his time, and no one will think him unjustly reckoned one of the four Doctors of the Western Church. Yet he solemnly relates that a nun, having eaten some lettuce without making the sign of the cross, swallowed a devil, and that, when commanded by a holy man to come forth, the devil replied: "How am I to blame?

[5] For the exorcism against disease found at Nineveh, see G. Smith, Delitzsch's German translation, p. 34. For a very interesting passage regarding the representation of a diabolic personage on a Babylonian bronze, and for a very frank statement regarding the transmission of ideas regarding Satanic power to our sacred books, see Sayce, *Herodotus,* appendix ii, p. 393. It is, indeed, extremely doubtful whether Plato himself or his contemporaries knew anything of *evil* demons, this conception probably coming into the Greek world, as into the Latin, with the Oriental influences that began to prevail about the time of the birth of Christ; but to the early Christians a demon was a demon, and Plato's, good or bad, were pagan, and therefore devils. The Greek word "epilepsy" is itself a survival of the old belief, fossilized in a word, since its literal meaning refers to the *seizure* of the patient by evil spirits.

I was sitting on the lettuce, and this woman, not having made the sign of the cross, ate me along with it."[6]

As a result of this idea, the Christian Church at an early period in its existence virtually gave up the noble conquests of Greek and Roman science in this field, and originated, for persons supposed to be possessed, a regular discipline, developed out of dogmatic theology. But during the centuries before theology and ecclesiasticism had become fully dominant this discipline was, as a rule, gentle and useful. The afflicted, when not too violent, were generally admitted to the exercises of public worship, and a kindly system of cure was attempted, in which prominence was given to holy water, sanctified ointments, the breath or spittle of the priest, the touching of relics, visits to holy places, and submission to mild forms of exorcism. There can be no doubt that many of these things, when judiciously used in that spirit of love and gentleness and devotion inherited by the earlier disciples from "the Master," produced good effects in soothing disturbed minds and in aiding their cure.

Among the thousands of fetiches of various sorts then resorted to may be named, as typical, the Holy Handkerchief of Besançon. During many centuries multitudes came from far and near to touch it; for, it was argued, if touching the

[6] For a striking statement of the Jewish belief in diabolical interference, see Josephus, *De Bello Judaico*, vii, 6, iii; also his *Antiquities*, vol. viii, Whiston's translation. On the "devil cast out," in Mark ix, 17-29, as undoubtedly a case of epilepsy, see Cherullier, *Essai sur l'Épilepsie;* also Maury, art. *Démoniaque* in the *Encyclopédie Moderne*. In one text, at least, the popular belief is perfectly shown as confounding madness and possession: "He hath a devil, and is mad," John x, 20. Among the multitude of texts, those most relied upon were Matthew viii, 28, and Luke x, 17; and for the use of fetiches in driving out evil spirits, the account of the cures wrought by touching the garments of St. Paul in Acts xix, 12. On the general subject, see authorities already given, and as a typical passage Tertullian, *Ad. Scap.*, ii. For the very gross view taken by St. Basil, see Cudworth, *Intellectual System*, vol. ii, p. 648; also Archdeacon Farrar's *Life of Christ*. For the case related by St. Gregory the Great with comical details, see the *Exempla* of Archbishop Jacques de Vitry, edited by Prof. T. F. Crane, of Cornell University, p. 59, art. cxxx. For a curious presentation of Greek views, see Lélut, *Le Démon de Socrate*, Paris, 1856; and for the transmission of these to Christianity, see the same, p. 201 and following.

garments of St. Paul at Ephesus had cured the diseased, how much more might be expected of a handkerchief of the Lord himself!

With ideas of this sort was mingled a vague belief in medical treatment, and out of this mixture were evolved such prescriptions as the following:

"If an elf or a goblin come, smear his forehead with this salve, put it on his eyes, cense him with incense, and sign him frequently with the sign of the cross."

"For a fiend-sick man: When a devil possesses a man, or controls him from within with disease, a spew-drink of lupin, bishopswort, henbane, garlic. Pound these together, add ale and holy water."

And again: "A drink for a fiend-sick man, to be drunk out of a church bell: Githrife, cynoglossum, yarrow, lupin, flower-de-luce, fennel, lichen, lovage. Work up to a drink with clear ale, sing seven masses over it, add garlic and holy water, and let the possessed sing the *Beati Immaculati;* then let him drink the dose out of a church bell, and let the priest sing over him the *Domine Sancte Pater Omnipotens.*"[7]

Had this been the worst treatment of lunatics developed in the theological atmosphere of the Middle Ages, the world would have been spared some of the most terrible chapters in its history; but, unfortunately, the idea of the Satanic possession of lunatics led to attempts to punish the indwelling demon. As this theological theory and practice became more fully developed, and ecclesiasticism more powerful to enforce it, all mildness began to disappear; the admonitions to gentle treatment by the great pagan and Moslem physicians were forgotten, and the treatment of lunatics tended more and more toward severity: more and more generally it was felt that cruelty to madmen was punishment of the devil residing within or acting upon them.

A few strong churchmen and laymen made efforts to resist this tendency. As far back as the fourth century, Nemesius, Bishop of Emesa, accepted the truth as developed by pagan physicians, and aided them in strengthening it. In the seventh century, a Lombard code embodied a similar effort. In the eighth century, one of Charlemagne's capitularies seems to have had a like purpose. In the ninth century, that

---

[7] See Cockayne, *Leechdoms, Wort-cunning, and Star-Craft of Early England,* in the Rolls Series, vol. ii, p. 177; also pp. 355, 356. For the great value of priestly saliva, see W. W. Story's essays.

great churchman and statesman, Agobard, Archbishop of Lyons, superior to his time in this as in so many other things, tried to make right reason prevail in this field; and, near the beginning of the tenth century, Regino, Abbot of Prüm, in the diocese of Treves, insisted on treating possessions as disease. But all in vain; the current streaming most directly from sundry texts in the Christian sacred books, and swollen by theology, had become overwhelming.[8]

The first great tributary poured into this stream, as we approach the bloom of the Middle Ages, appears to have come from the brain of Michael Psellus. Mingling scriptural texts, Platonic philosophy, and theological statements by great doctors of the Church, with wild utterances obtained from lunatics, he gave forth, about the beginning of the twelfth century, a treatise on *The Work of Demons*. Sacred science was vastly enriched thereby in various ways; but two of his conclusions, the results of his most profound thought, enforced by theologians and popularized by preachers, soon took special hold upon the thinking portion of the people at large. The first of these, which he easily based upon Scripture and St. Basil, was that, since all demons suffer by material fire and brimstone, they must have material bodies; the second was that, since all demons are by nature cold, they gladly seek a genial warmth by entering the bodies of men and beasts.[9]

* * *

[8] For a very thorough and interesting statement on the general subject, see Kirchhoff, *Beziehungen des Dämonen- und Hexenwesens zur deutschen Irrenpflege,* in the *Allgemeine Zeitschrift für Psychiatrie,* Berlin, 1888, Bd. xliv, Heft 25. For Roman Catholic authority, see Addis and Arnold, *Catholic Dictionary,* article *Energumens.* For a brief and eloquent summary, see Krafft-Ebing, *Lehrbuch der Psychiatrie,* as above; and for a clear view of the transition from pagan mildness in the care of the insane to severity and cruelty under the Christian Church, see Maudsley, *The Pathology of Mind,* London, 1879, p. 523. See also Buchmann, *Die unfreie und die freie Kirche,* Breslau, 1873, p. 251. For other citations, see Kirchhoff, as above, pp. 334-336. For Bishop Nemesius, see Trélat, p. 48. For an account of Agobard's general position in regard to this and allied superstitions, see Reginald Lane Poole's *Illustrations of the History of Medieval Thought,* London, 1884.

[9] See Baas and Werner, cited by Kirchhoff, as above; also Lecky, *Rationalism in Europe,* vol. i, p. 68, and note, New York, 1884. As to Basil's belief in the corporeality of devils, see his *Commentary on Isaiah,* cap. i.

The first main weapon against the indwelling Satan continued to be the exorcism; but under the influence of inferences from Scripture farther and farther fetched, and of theological reasoning more and more subtle, it became something very different from the gentle procedure of earlier times, and some description of this great weapon at the time of its highest development will throw light on the laws which govern the growth of theological reasoning, as well as upon the main subject in hand.

A fundamental premise in the fully developed exorcism was that, according to sacred Scripture, a main characteristic of Satan is pride. Pride led him to rebel; for pride he was cast down; therefore the first thing to do, in driving him out of a lunatic, was to strike a fatal blow at his pride,—to disgust him.

This theory was carried out logically, to the letter. The treatises on the subject simply astound one by their wealth of blasphemous and obscene epithets which it was allowable for the exorcist to use in casting out devils. The *Treasury of Exorcisms* contains hundreds of pages packed with the vilest epithets which the worst imagination could invent for the purpose of overwhelming the indwelling Satan.[10]

Some of those decent enough to be printed in these degenerate days ran as follows:

"Thou lustful and stupid one, . . . thou lean sow, famine-stricken and most impure, . . . thou wrinkled beast, thou mangy beast, thou beast of all beasts and most beastly, . . . thou mad spirit, . . . thou bestial and foolish drunkard, . . . most greedy wolf, . . . most abominable whisperer, . . . thou sooty spirit from Tartarus! . . . I cast thee down, O

[10] *Thesaurus Exorcismorum atque Conjurationum terribilium, potentissimorum, efficacissimorum, cum* PRACTICA *probatissima: quibus spiritus maligni, Dæmones Maleficiaque omnia de Corporibus humanis obsessis, tanquam Flagellis Fustibusque fugantur, expelluntur,* . . . Cologne, 1626. Many of the books of the exorcists were put upon the various indexes of the Church, but this, the richest collection of all, and including nearly all those condemned, was not prohibited until 1709. Scarcely less startling manuals continued even later in use; and exorcisms adapted to every emergency may of course still be found in all the Benedictionals of the Church, even the latest. As an example, see the *Manuale Benedictionum* published by the Bishop of Passau in 1849, or the *Exorcismus in Satanam,* etc., issued in 1890 by the present Pope, and now on sale at the shop of the Propaganda in Rome.

Tartarean boor, into the infernal kitchen! . . . Loathsome cobbler, . . . dingy collier, . . . filthy sow (*scrofa stercorata*), . . . perfidious boar, . . . envious crocodile, . . . malodorous drudge, . . . wounded basilisk, . . . rust-coloured asp, . . . swollen toad, . . . entangled spider, . . . lousy swineherd (*porcarie pedicose*), . . . lowest of the low, . . . cudgelled ass," etc.

But, in addition to this attempt to disgust Satan's pride with blackguardism, there was another to scare him with tremendous words. For this purpose, thunderous names, from Hebrew and Greek, were imported, such as Acharon, Eheye, Schemhamphora, Tetragrammaton, Homöousion, Athanatos, Ischiros, Æcodes, and the like.[11]

Efforts were also made to drive him out with filthy and rank-smelling drugs; and, among those which can be mentioned in a printed article, we may name asafœtida, sulphur, squills, etc., which were to be burned under his nose.

Still further to plague him, pictures of the devil were to be spat upon, trampled under foot by people of low condition, and sprinkled with foul compounds.

But these were merely preliminaries to the exorcism proper. In this the most profound theological thought and sacred science of the period culminated.

Most of its forms were childish, but some rise to almost Miltonic grandeur. As an example of the latter, we may take the following:

"By the Apocalypse of Jesus Christ, which God hath given to make known unto his servants those things which are shortly to be; and hath signified, sending by his angel, . . . I exorcise you, ye angels of untold perversity!

"By the seven golden candlesticks, . . . and by one like unto the Son of man, standing in the midst of the candlesticks; by his voice, as the voice of many waters; . . . by his words, 'I am living, who was dead; and behold, I live forever and ever; and I have the keys of death and of hell,' I say unto you, Depart, O angels that show the way to eternal perdition!"

Besides these, were long litanies of billingsgate, cursing, and threatening. One of these "scourging" exorcisms runs partly as follows:

"May Agyos strike thee, as he did Egypt, with frogs!

[11] See the *Conjuratio* on p. 300 of the *Thesaurus*, and the general directions given on pp. 251, 252.

. . . May all the devils that are thy foes rush forth upon thee, and drag thee down to hell! . . . May . . . Tetragrammaton . . . drive thee forth and stone thee, as Israel did to Achan! . . . May the Holy One trample on thee and hang thee up in an infernal fork, as was done to the five kings of the Amorites! . . . May God set a nail to your skull, and pound it in with a hammer, as Jael did unto Sisera! . . . May . . . Sother . . . break thy head and cut off thy hands, as was done to the cursed Dagon! . . . May God hang thee in a hellish yoke, as seven men were hanged by the sons of Saul!" And so on, through five pages of close-printed Latin curses.[12]

Occasionally the demon is reasoned with, as follows: "O obstinate, accursed, fly! . . . why do you stop and hold back, when you know that your strength is lost on Christ? For it is hard for thee to kick against the pricks; and, verily, the longer it takes you to go, the worse it will go with you. Begone, then: take flight, thou venomous hisser, thou lying worm, thou begetter of vipers!"[13]

This procedure and its results were recognised as among the glories of the Church. As typical, we may mention an exorcism directed by a certain Bishop of Beauvais, which was so effective that five devils gave up possession of a sufferer and signed their names, each for himself and his subordinate imps, to an agreement that the possessed should be molested no more. So, too, the Jesuit fathers at Vienna, in 1583, gloried in the fact that in such a contest they had cast out twelve thousand six hundred and fifty-two living devils. The ecclesiastical annals of the Middle Ages, and, indeed, of a later period, abound in boasts of such "mighty works."[14]

Such was the result of a thousand years of theological reasoning, by the strongest minds in Europe, upon data partly given in Scripture and partly inherited from paganism, regarding Satan and his work among men.

[12] *Thesaurus Exorcismorum*, pp. 812-817.
[13] Ibid., p. 859.
[14] In my previous chapters, especially that on meteorology, I have quoted extensively from the original treatises, of which a very large collection is in my possession; but in this chapter I have mainly availed myself of the copious translations given by M. H. Dziewicki, in his excellent article in *The Nineteenth Century* for October, 1888, entitled *Exorcizo Te*. For valuable citations on the origin and spread of exorcism, see Lecky's *European Morals* (third English edition), vol. i, pp. 379-385.

Under the guidance of theology, always so severe against "science falsely so called," the world had come a long way indeed from the soothing treatment of the possessed by him who bore among the noblest of his titles that of "The Great Physician." The result was natural: the treatment of the insane fell more and more into the hands of the jailer, the torturer, and the executioner.

To go back for a moment to the beginnings of this unfortunate development. In spite of the earlier and more kindly tendency in the Church, the Synod of Ancyra, as early as 314 A.D., commanded the expulsion of possessed persons from the Church; the Visigothic Christians whipped them; and Charlemagne, in spite of some good enactments, imprisoned them. Men and women, whose distempered minds might have been restored to health by gentleness and skill, were driven into hopeless madness by noxious medicines and brutality. Some few were saved as mere lunatics —they were surrendered to general carelessness, and became simply a prey to ridicule and aimless brutality; but vast numbers were punished as tabernacles of Satan.

One of the least terrible of these punishments, and perhaps the most common of all, was that of scourging demons out of the body of a lunatic. This method commended itself even to the judgment of so thoughtful and kindly a personage as Sir Thomas More, and as late as the sixteenth century. But if the disease continued, as it naturally would after such treatment, the authorities frequently felt justified in driving out the demons by torture.[15]

Interesting monuments of this idea, so fruitful in evil, still exist. In the great cities of central Europe, "witch towers," where witches and demoniacs were tortured, and "fool towers," where the more gentle lunatics were imprisoned, may still be seen.

In the cathedrals we still see this idea fossilized. Devils and imps, struck into stone, clamber upon towers, prowl under cornices, peer out from bosses of foliage, perch upon capitals, nestle under benches, flame in windows. Above the great main entrance, the most common of all representations still shows Satan and his imps scowling, jeering, grinning,

[15] For prescription of the whipping-post by Sir Thomas More, see D. H. Tuke's *History of Insanity in the British Isles*, London, 1882, p. 41.

while taking possession of the souls of men and scourging them with serpents, or driving them with tridents, or dragging them with chains into the flaming mouth of hell. Even in the most hidden and sacred places of the mediæval cathedral we still find representations of Satanic power in which profanity and obscenity run riot. In these representations the painter and the glass-stainer vied with the sculptor. Among the early paintings on canvas a well-known example represents the devil in the shape of a dragon, perched near the head of a dying man, eager to seize his soul as it issues from his mouth, and only kept off by the efforts of the attendant priest. Typical are the colossal portrait of Satan, and the vivid picture of the devils cast out of the possessed and entering into the swine, as shown in the cathedral-windows of Strasburg. So, too, in the windows of Chartres Cathedral we see a saint healing a lunatic: the saint, with a long devil-scaring formula in Latin issuing from his mouth; and the lunatic, with a little detestable hobgoblin, horned, hoofed, and tailed, issuing from *his* mouth. These examples are but typical of myriads in cathedrals and abbeys and parish churches throughout Europe; and all served to impress upon the popular mind a horror of everything called diabolic, and a hatred of those charged with it. These sermons in stones preceded the printed book; they were a sculptured Bible, which preceded Luther's pictorial Bible.[16]

Satan and his imps were among the principal personages in every popular drama, and "Hell's Mouth" was a piece of stage scenery constantly brought into requisition. A miracle-play without a full display of the diabolic element in it

[16] I cite these instances out of a vast number which I have personally noted in visits to various cathedrals. For striking examples of mediæval grotesques, see Wright's *History of Caricature and the Grotesque,* London, 1875; Langlois's *Stalles de la Cathédrale de Rouen,* 1838; Adeline's *Les Sculptures Grotesques et Symboliques,* Rouen, 1878; Viollet le Duc, *Dictionnaire de l'Architecture;* Gailhabaud, *Sur l'Architecture,* etc. For a reproduction of an illuminated manuscript in which devils fly out of the mouths of the possessed under the influence of exorcisms, see Cahier and Martin, *Nouveaux Mélanges d'Archéologie* for 1874, p. 136; and for a demon emerging from a victim's mouth in a puff of smoke at the command of St. Francis Xavier, see *La Dévotion de Dix Vendredis,* etc., Plate xxxii.

would have stood a fair chance of being pelted from the stage.[17]

Not only the popular art but the popular legends embodied these ideas. The chroniclers delighted in them; the *Lives of the Saints* abounded in them; sermons enforced them from every pulpit. What wonder, then, that men and women had vivid dreams of Satanic influence, that dread of it was like dread of the plague, and that this terror spread the disease enormously, until we hear of convents, villages, and even large districts, ravaged by epidemics of diabolical possession![18]

* * *

One result of this idea was a mode of cure which especially aggravated and spread mental disease: the promotion of great religious processions. Troops of men and women, crying, howling, imploring saints, and beating themselves with whips, visited various sacred shrines, images, and places in the hope of driving off the powers of evil. The only result was an increase in the numbers of the diseased.

For hundreds of years this idea of diabolic possession was steadily developed. It was believed that devils entered into animals, and animals were accordingly exorcised, tried, tortured, convicted, and executed. The great St. Ambrose tells us that a priest, while saying mass, was troubled by the croaking of frogs in a neighboring marsh; that he exorcised

[17] See Wright, *History of Caricature and the Grotesque;* F. J. Mone, *Schauspiele des Mittelalters,* Carlsruhe, 1846; Dr. Karl Hase, *Miracle-Plays and Sacred Dramas,* Boston, 1880 (translation from the German). Examples of the miracle-plays may be found in Marriott's *Collection of English Miracle-Plays,* 1838; in Hone's *Ancient Mysteries;* in T. Sharpe's *Dissertation on the Pageants . . . anciently performed at Coventry,* Coventry, 1828; in the publications of the Shakespearean and other societies. See especially *The Harrowing of Hell,* a miracle-play, edited from the original now in the British Museum, by T. O. Halliwell, London, 1840. One of the items still preserved is a sum of money paid for keeping a fire burning in hell's mouth. Says Hase (as above, p. 42): "In wonderful satyrlike masquerade, in which neither horns, tail, nor hoofs were ever . . . wanting, the devil prosecuted on the stage his business of fetching souls," which left the mouths of the dying "in the form of small images."

[18] I shall discuss these epidemics of possession, which form a somewhat distinct class of phenomena, in the next chapter.

them, and so stopped their noise. St. Bernard, as the monkish chroniclers tell us, mounting the pulpit to preach in his abbey, was interrupted by a cloud of flies; straightway the saint uttered the sacred formula of excommunication, when the flies fell dead upon the pavement in heaps, and were cast out with shovels! A formula of exorcism attributed to a saint of the ninth century, which remained in use down to a recent period, especially declares insects injurious to crops to be possessed of evil spirits, and names, among the animals to be excommunicated or exorcised, mice, moles, and serpents. The use of exorcism against caterpillars and grasshoppers was also common. In the thirteenth century a Bishop of Lausanne, finding that the eels in Lake Leman troubled the fisherman, attempted to remove the difficulty by exorcism, and two centuries later one of his successors excommunicated all the May-bugs in the diocese. As late as 1731 there appears an entry on the Municipal Register of Thonon as follows: "*Resolved,* That this town join with other parishes of this province in obtaining from Rome an excommunication against the insects, and that it will contribute *pro rata* to the expenses of the same."

Did any one venture to deny that animals could be possessed by Satan, he was at once silenced by reference to the entrance of Satan into the serpent in the Garden of Eden, and to the casting of devils into swine by the Founder of Christianity himself.[19]

One part of this superstition most tenaciously held was the belief that a human being could be transformed into one of the lower animals. This became a fundamental point. The most dreaded of predatory animals in the Middle Ages were the wolves. Driven from the hills and forests in the winter by hunger, they not only devoured the flocks, but sometimes came into the villages and seized children. From time to time men and women whose brains were disordered dreamed that they had been changed into various animals, and especially into wolves. On their confessing this, and often implicating others, many executions of lunatics resulted; moreover, countless sane victims, suspected of the

[19] See Menabrea, *Procès au Moyen Age contre les Animaux,* Chambéry, 1846, pp. 31 and following; also Desmazes, *Supplices, Prisons et Grace en France,* pp. 89, 90, and 385-395. For a formula and ceremonies used in excommunicating insects, see Rydberg, pp. 75 and following.

same impossible crime, were forced by torture to confess it, and sent unpitied to the stake. The belief in such a transformation pervaded all Europe, and lasted long even in Protestant countries. Probably no article in the witch creed had more adherents in the fifteenth, sixteenth, and seventeenth centuries than this. Nearly every parish in Europe had its resultant horrors.

The reformed Church in all its branches fully accepted the doctrines of witchcraft and diabolic possession, and developed them still further. No one urged their fundamental ideas more fully than Luther. He did, indeed, reject portions of the witchcraft folly; but to the influence of devils he not only attributed his maladies, but his dreams, and nearly everything that thwarted or disturbed him. The flies which lighted upon his book, the rats which kept him awake at night, he believed to be devils; the resistance of the Archbishop of Mayence to his ideas, he attributed to Satan literally working in that prelate's heart; to his disciples he told stories of men who had been killed by rashly resisting the devil. Insanity, he was quite sure, was caused by Satan, and he exorcised sufferers. Against some he appears to have advised stronger remedies; and his horror of idiocy, as resulting from Satanic influence, was so great, that on one occasion he appears to have advised the killing of an idiot child, as being the direct offspring of Satan. Yet Luther was one of the most tender and loving of men; in the whole range of literature there is hardly anything more touching than his words and tributes to children. In enforcing his ideas regarding insanity, he laid stress especially upon the question of St. Paul as to the bewitching of the Galatians, and, regarding idiocy, on the account in Genesis of the birth of children whose fathers were "sons of God" and whose mothers were "daughters of men."

One idea of his was especially characteristic. The descent of Christ into hell was a frequent topic of discussion in the Reformed Church. Melanchthon, with his love of Greek studies, held that the purpose of the Saviour in making such a descent was to make himself known to the great and noble men of antiquity—Plato, Socrates, and the rest; but Luther insisted that his purpose was to conquer Satan in a hand-to-hand struggle.

This idea of diabolic influence pervaded his conversation,

his preaching, his writings, and spread thence to the Lutheran Church in general.

Calvin also held to the same theory, and, having more power with less kindness of heart than Luther, carried it out with yet greater harshness. Beza was especially severe against those who believed insanity to be a natural malady, and declared, "Such persons are refuted both by sacred and profane history."

Under the influence, then, of such infallible teachings, in the older Church and in the new, this superstition was developed more and more into cruelty; and as the biblical texts, popularized in the sculptures and windows and mural decorations of the great mediæval cathedrals, had done much to develop it among the people, so Luther's translation of the Bible, especially in the numerous editions of it illustrated with engravings, wrought with enormous power to spread and deepen it. In every peasant's cottage some one could spell out the story of the devil bearing Christ through the air and placing him upon the pinnacle of the Temple—of the woman with seven devils—of the devils cast into the swine. Every peasant's child could be made to understand the quaint pictures in the family Bible or the catechism which illustrated vividly all those texts. In the ideas thus deeply implanted, the men who in the seventeenth and eighteenth centuries struggled against this mass of folly and cruelty found the worst barrier to right reason.[20]

Such was the treatment of demoniacs developed by theology, and such the practice enforced by ecclesiasticism for more than a thousand years.

How an atmosphere was spread in which this belief began to dissolve away, how its main foundations were undermined by science, and how there came in gradually a reign of humanity, will now be related.

[20] For Luther, see, among the vast number of similar passages in his works, the *Table Talk,* Hazlitt's translation, pp. 251, 252. As to the grotesques in mediæval churches, the writer of this article, in visiting the town church of Wittenberg, noticed, just opposite the pulpit where Luther so often preached, a very spirited figure of an imp peering out upon the congregation. One can but suspect that this mediæval survival frequently suggested Luther's favourite topic during his sermons. For Beza, see his *Notes on the New Testament,* Matthew iv, 24.

2. Beginnings of a Healthful Scepticism

We have now seen the culmination of the old procedure regarding insanity, as it was developed under theology and enforced by ecclesiasticism; and we have noted how, under the influence of Luther and Calvin, the Reformation rather deepened than weakened the faith in the malice and power of a personal devil. Nor was this, in the Reformed churches any more than in the old, mere matter of theory. As in the early ages of Christianity, its priests especially appealed, in proof of the divine mission, to their power over the enemy of mankind in the bodies of men, so now the clergy of the rival creeds eagerly sought opportunities to establish the truth of their own and the falsehood of their opponents' doctrines by the visible casting out of devils. True, their methods differed somewhat: where the Catholic used holy water and consecrated wax, the Protestant was content with texts of Scripture and importunate prayer; but the supplementary physical annoyance of the indwelling demon did not greatly vary. Sharp was the competition for the unhappy objects of treatment. Each side, of course, stoutly denied all efficacy to its adversaries' efforts, urging that any seeming victory over Satan was due not to the defeat but to the collusion of the fiend. As, according to the Master himself, "no man can by Beelzebub cast out devils," the patient was now in greater need of relief than before; and more than one poor victim had to bear alternately Lutheran, Roman, and perhaps Calvinistic exorcism.[21]

*   *   *

The result of this widespread terror was naturally, therefore, a steady increase in mental disorders. A great modern authority tells us that, although modern civilization tends to increase insanity, the number of lunatics at present is far less than in the ages of faith and in the Reformation period. The treatment of the "possessed," as we find it laid down in standard treatises, sanctioned by orthodox churchmen and

[21] For instances of this competition, see Freytag, *Aus dem Jahrh. d. Reformation,* pp. 359-375. The Jesuit Stengel, in his *De judiciis divinis* (Ingolstadt, 1651), devotes a whole chapter to an exorcism, by the great Canisius, of a spirit that had baffled Protestant conjuration. Among the most jubilant Catholic satires of the time are those exulting in Luther's alleged failure as an exorcist.

jurists, accounts for this abundantly. One sort of treatment used for those accused of witchcraft will also serve to show this—the *"tortura insomniæ."* Of all things in brain-disease, calm and regular sleep is most certainly beneficial; yet, under this practice, these half-crazed creatures were prevented, night after night and day after day, from sleeping or even resting. In this way temporary delusion became chronic insanity, mild cases became violent, torture and death ensued, and the "ways of God to man" were justified.

* * *

Against one form of insanity both Catholics and Protestants were especially cruel. Nothing is more common in all times of religious excitement than strange personal hallucinations, involving the belief, by the insane patient, that he is a divine person. In the most striking representation of insanity that has ever been made, Kaulbach shows, at the centre of his wonderful group, a patient drawing attention to himself as the Saviour of the world.

Sometimes, when this form of disease took a milder hysterical character, the subject of it was treated with reverence, and even elevated to sainthood: such examples as St. Francis of Assisi and St. Catherine of Siena in Italy, St. Bridget in Sweden, St. Theresa in Spain, St. Mary Alacoque in France, and Louise Lateau in Belgium, are typical. But more frequently such cases shocked public feeling, and were treated with especial rigour: typical of this is the case of Simon Marin, who in his insanity believed himself to be the Son of God, and was on that account burned alive at Paris and his ashes scattered to the winds.[22]

The profundity of theologians and jurists constantly developed new theories as to the modes of diabolic entrance into the "possessed." One such theory was that Satan could be taken into the mouth with one's food—perhaps in the

[22] As to the frequency among the insane of this form of belief, see Calmeil, vol. ii, p. 257; also Maudsley, *Pathology of Mind*, pp. 201, 202, and 418-424; also Rambaud, *Histoire de la Civilisation en France,* vol. ii, p. 110. For the peculiar aberrations of the saints above named and other ecstatics, see Maudsley, as above, pp. 71, 72, and 149, 150. Maudsley's chapters on this and cognate subjects are certainly among the most valuable contributions to modern thought. For a discussion of the most recent case, see Warlomont, *Louise Lateau,* Paris, 1875.

form of an insect swallowed on a leaf of salad, and this was sanctioned by no less infallible an authority than Gregory the Great, Pope and Saint. Another theory was that Satan entered the body when the mouth was opened to breathe, and there are well-authenticated cases of doctors and divines who, when casting out evil spirits, took especial care lest the imp might jump into their own mouths from the mouth of the patient. Another theory was that the devil entered human beings during sleep; and at a comparatively recent period a King of Spain was wont to sleep between two monks, to keep off the devil.[23]

The monasteries were frequent sources of that form of mental disease which was supposed to be caused by bewitchment. From the earliest period it is evident that monastic life tended to develop insanity. Such cases as that of St. Anthony are typical of its effects upon the strongest minds; but it was especially the convents for women that became the great breeding-beds of this disease. Among the large numbers of women and girls thus assembled—many of them forced into monastic seclusion against their will, for the reason that their families could give them no dower—subjected to the unsatisfied longings, suspicions, bickerings, petty jealousies, envies, and hatreds, so inevitable in convent life—mental disease was not unlikely to be developed at any moment. Hysterical excitement in nunneries took shapes sometimes comical, but more generally tragical. Noteworthy is it that the last places where executions for witchcraft took place were mainly in the neighbourhood of great nunneries; and the last famous victim, of the myriads executed in Germany for this imaginary crime, was Sister Anna Renata Sänger, sub-prioress of a nunnery near Würzburg.[24]

[23] As to the devil's entering into the mouth while eating, see Calmeil, as above, vol. ii, pp. 105, 106. As to the dread of Dr. Borde lest the evil spirit, when exorcised, might enter his own body, see Tuke, as above, p. 28. As to the King of Spain, see the noted chapter in Buckle's *History of Civilization in England*.

[24] Among the multitude of authorities on this point, see Kirchhoff, as above, p. 337; and for a most striking picture of this dark side of convent life, drawn, indeed, by a devoted Roman Catholic, see Manzoni's *Promessi Sposi*. On Anna Renata there is a striking essay by the late Johannes Scherr, in his *Hammerschläge und Historien*. On the general subject of hysteria thus developed, see the writings of Carpenter and Tuke; and, as to its natural development in nunneries, see Maudsley, *Responsibility in Mental Disease,* p.

The same thing was seen among young women exposed to sundry fanatical Protestant preachers. Insanity, both temporary and permanent, was thus frequently developed among the Huguenots of France, and has been thus produced in America, from the days of the Salem persecution down to the "camp meetings" of the present time.

At various times, from the days of St. Agobard of Lyons in the ninth century to Pomponatius in the sixteenth, protests or suggestions, more or less timid, had been made by thoughtful men against this system. Medicine had made some advance toward a better view, but the theological torrent had generally overwhelmed all who supported a scientific treatment. At last, toward the end of the sixteenth century, two men made a beginning of a much more serious attack upon this venerable superstition. The revival of learning, and the impulse to thought on material matters given during the "age of discovery," undoubtedly produced an atmosphere which made the work of these men possible. In the year 1563, in the midst of demonstrations of demoniacal possession by the most eminent theologians and judges, who sat in their robes and looked wise, while women, shrieking, praying, and blaspheming, were put to the torture, a man arose who dared to protest effectively that some of the persons thus charged might be simply insane; and this man was John Wier, of Cleves.

His protest does not at this day strike us as particularly bold. In his books, *De Præstigiis Dæmonum* and *De Lamiis,* he did his best not to offend religious or theological susceptibilities; but he felt obliged to call attention to the mingled fraud and delusion of those who claimed to be bewitched, and to point out that it was often not their accusers, but the alleged witches themselves, who were really ailing, and to urge that these be brought first of all to a physician.

His book was at once attacked by the most eminent theologians. One of the greatest laymen of his time, Jean Bodin, also wrote with especial power against it, and by a plentiful use of scriptural texts gained to all appearance a complete victory: this superstition seemed thus fastened upon Europe for a thousand years more. But doubt was in the air, and, about a quarter of a century after the publication of Wier's

9. Especial attention will be paid to this in the chapter on *Diabolism and Hysteria.*

book there were published in France the essays of a man by no means so noble, but of far greater genius—Michel de Montaigne. The general scepticism which his work promoted among the French people did much to produce an atmosphere in which the belief in witchcraft and demoniacal possession must inevitably wither. But this process, though real, was hidden, and the victory still seemed on the theological side.

The development of the new truth and its struggle against the old error still went on. In Holland, Balthazar Bekker wrote his book against the worst forms of superstition, and attempted to help the scientific side by a text from the Second Epistle of St. Peter, showing that the devils had been confined by the Almighty, and therefore could not be doing on earth the work which was imputed to them. But Bekker's Protestant brethren drove him from his pulpit, and he narrowly escaped with his life.

The last struggles of a great superstition are very frequently the worst. So it proved in this case. In the first half of the seventeenth century the cruelties arising from the old doctrine were more numerous and severe than ever before. In Spain, Sweden, Italy, and, above all, in Germany, we see constant efforts to suppress the evolution of the new truth.

But in the midst of all this reactionary rage glimpses of right reason began to appear. It is significant that at this very time, when the old superstition was apparently everywhere triumphant, the declaration by Poulet that he and his brother and his cousin had, by smearing themselves with ointment, changed themselves into wolves and devoured children, brought no severe punishment upon them. The judges sent him to a mad-house. More and more, in spite of frantic efforts from the pulpit to save the superstition, great writers and jurists, especially in France, began to have glimpses of the truth and courage to uphold it. Malebranche spoke against the delusion; Séguier led the French courts to annul several decrees condemning sorcerers; the great chancellor, D'Aguesseau, declared to the Parliament of Paris that, if they wished to stop sorcery, they must stop talking about it—that sorcerers are more to be pitied than blamed.[25]

But just at this time, as the eighteenth century was approaching, the theological current was strengthened by a great ecclesiastic—the greatest theologian that France has produced,

[25] See Esquirol, *Des Maladies mentales,* vol. i, pp. 488, 489; vol. ii, p. 529.

whose influence upon religion and upon the mind of Louis XIV was enormous—Bossuet, Bishop of Meaux. There had been reason to expect that Bossuet would at least do something to mitigate the superstition; for his writings show that, in much which before his day had been ascribed to diabolic possession, he saw simple lunacy. Unfortunately, the same adherence to the literal interpretation of Scripture which led him to oppose every other scientific truth developed in his time, led him also to attack this: he delivered and published two great sermons, which, while showing some progress in the form of his belief, showed none the less that the fundamental idea of diabolic possession was still to be tenaciously held. What this idea was may be seen in one typical statement: he declared that "a single devil could turn the earth round as easily as we turn a marble."[26]

3. The Final Struggle and Victory of Science—Pinel

The theological current, thus re-enforced, seemed to become again irresistible; but it was only so in appearance. In spite of it, French scepticism continued to develop; signs of quiet change among the mass of thinking men were appearing more and more; and in 1672 came one of great significance, for, the Parliament of Rouen having doomed fourteen sorcerers to be burned, their execution was delayed for two years, evidently on account of scepticism among officials; and at length the great minister of Louis XIV, Colbert, issued an edict checking such trials, and ordering the convicted to be treated for madness.

Victory seemed now to incline to the standard of science, and in 1725 no less a personage than St. André, a court physician, dared to publish a work virtually showing "demoniacal possession" to be lunacy.

The French philosophy, from the time of its early development in the eighteenth century under Montesquieu and Voltaire, naturally strengthened the movement; the results of *post-mortem* examinations of the brains of the "possessed" confirmed it; and in 1768 we see it take form in a declaration

---

[26] See the two sermons, *Sur les Démons* (which are virtually but two forms of the same sermon), in Bossuet's works, edition of 1845, vol. iii, p. 236 *et seq.;* also Dziewicki, in *The Nineteenth Century* as above. On Bossuet's resistance to other scientific truths, especially in astronomy, geology, and political economy, see other chapters in this work.

by the Parliament of Paris, that possessed persons were to be considered as simply diseased.

Still, the old belief lingered on, its life flickering up from time to time in those parts of France most under ecclesiastical control, until in these last years of the nineteenth century a blow has been given it by the researches of Charcot and his compeers which will probably soon extinguish it. One evidence of Satanic intercourse with mankind especially, on which for many generations theologians had laid peculiar stress, and for which they had condemned scores of little girls and hundreds of old women to a most cruel death, was found to be nothing more than one of the many results of hysteria.[27]

In England the same warfare went on. John Locke had asserted the truth, but the theological view continued to control public opinion. Most prominent among those who exercised great power in its behalf was John Wesley, and the strength and beauty of his character made his influence in this respect all the more unfortunate. The same servitude to the mere letter of Scripture which led him to declare that "to give up witchcraft is to give up the Bible," controlled him in regard to insanity. He insisted, on the authority of the Old Testament, that bodily diseases are sometimes caused by devils, and, upon the authority of the New Testament, that the gods of the heathen are demons; he believed that dreams, while in some cases caused by bodily conditions and passions, are shown by Scripture to be also caused by occult powers of evil; he cites a physician to prove that "most lunatics are really demoniacs." In his great sermon on *Evil Angels*, he dwells upon this point especially; resists the idea that "possession" may be epilepsy, even though ordinary symptoms of epilepsy be present; protests against "giving up to infidels such proofs of an invisible world as are to be found in diabolic possession"; and evidently believes that some who have been made hysterical by his own preaching are "possessed of Satan." On all this, and much more to the same effect, he insisted with all the power given to him by his deep religious nature, his wonderful fa-

[27] For Colbert's influence, see Dagron, p. 8; also Rambaud, as above, vol. ii, p. 155. For St. André, see Lacroix, as above, pp. 189, 190. For Charcot's researches into the disease now known as *Meteorismus hystericus,* but which was formerly regarded in the ecclesiastical courts as an evidence of pregnancy through relations with Satan, see Snell, *Hexenprocesse und Geistesstörung*, München, 1891, chaps. xii and xiii.

miliarity with the Scriptures, his natural acumen, and his eloquence.

But here, too, science continued its work. The old belief was steadily undermined, an atmosphere favourable to the truth was more and more developed, and the act of Parliament, in 1735, which banished the crime of witchcraft from the statute book, was the beginning of the end.[28]

* * *

The first humane impulse of any considerable importance in this field seems to have been aroused in America. In the year 1751 certain members of the Society of Friends founded a small hospital for the insane, on better principles, in Pennsylvania. To use the language of its founders, it was intended "as a good work, acceptable to God." Twenty years later Virginia established a similar asylum, and gradually others appeared in other colonies.

But it was in France that mercy was to be put upon a scientific basis, and was to lead to practical results which were to convert the world to humanity. In this case, as in so many others, from France was spread and popularized not only the scepticism which destroyed the theological theory, but also the devotion which built up the new scientific theory and endowed the world with a new treasure of civilization.

In 1756 some physicians of the great hospital at Paris known as the Hôtel-Dieu protested that the cruelties prevailing in the treatment of the insane were aggravating the disease; and some protests followed from other quarters. Little effect was produced at first; but just before the French Revolution, Tenon, La Rochefoucauld-Liancourt, and others took up the subject, and in 1791 a commission was appointed to undertake a reform.

By great good fortune, the man selected to lead in the movement was one who had already thrown his heart into it—Jean Baptiste Pinel. In 1792 Pinel was made physician at Bicêtre, one of the most extensive lunatic asylums in France, and to the work there imposed upon him he gave all his

[28] For John Locke, see King's *Life of Locke,* pp. 326, 327. For Wesley, out of his almost innumerable writings bearing upon the subject, I may select the sermon on *Evil Angels,* and his *Letter to Dr. Middleton;* and in his collected works there are many striking statements and arguments, especially in vols. iii, vi, and ix. See also Tyerman's *Life of Wesley,* vol. ii, pp. 260 *et seq.*

powers. Little was heard of him at first. The most terrible scenes of the French Revolution were drawing nigh; but he laboured on, modestly and devotedly—apparently without a thought of the great political storm raging about him.

His first step was to discard utterly the whole theological doctrine of "possession," and especially the idea that insanity is the result of any subtle spiritual influence. He simply put in practice the theory that lunacy is the result of bodily disease.

It is a curious matter for reflection, that but for this sway of the destructive philosophy of the eighteenth century, and of the Terrorists during the French Revolution, Pinel's blessed work would in all probability have been thwarted, and he himself excommunicated for heresy and driven from his position. Doubtless the same efforts would have been put forth against him which the Church, a little earlier, had put forth against inoculation as a remedy for smallpox; but just at that time the great churchmen had other things to think of besides crushing this particular heretic: they were too much occupied in keeping their own heads from the guillotine to give attention to what was passing in the head of Pinel. He was allowed to work in peace, and in a short time the reign of diabolism at Bicêtre was ended. What the exorcisms and fetiches and prayers and processions, and drinking of holy water, and ringing of bells, had been unable to accomplish during eighteen hundred years, he achieved in a few months. His method was simple: for the brutality and cruelty which had prevailed up to that time, he substituted kindness and gentleness. The possessed were taken out of their dungeons, given sunny rooms, and allowed the liberty of pleasant ground for exercise; chains were thrown aside. At the same time, the mental power of each patient was developed by its fitting exercise, and disease was met with remedies sanctioned by experiment, observation, and reason. Thus was gained one of the greatest, though one of the least known, triumphs of modern science and humanity.

*   *   *

Chapter 16

From Diabolism to Hysteria

1. The Epidemics of "Possession"

IN THE FOREGOING CHAPTER I have sketched the triumph of science in destroying the idea that individual lunatics are "possessed by devils," in establishing the truth that insanity is physical disease, and in substituting for superstitious cruelties toward the insane a treatment mild, kindly, and based upon ascertained facts.

The Satan who had so long troubled individual men and women thus became extinct; henceforth his fossil remains only were preserved: they may still be found in the sculptures and storied windows of mediæval churches, in sundry liturgies, and in popular forms of speech.

But another Satan still lived—a Satan who wrought on a larger scale—who took possession of multitudes. For, after this triumph of the scientific method, there still remained a class of mental disorders which could not be treated in asylums, which were not yet fully explained by science, and which therefore gave arguments of much apparent strength to the supporters of the old theological view: these were the epidemics of "diabolic possession" which for so many centuries afflicted various parts of the world.

When obliged, then, to retreat from their old position in regard to individual cases of insanity, the more conservative theologians promptly referred to these epidemics as beyond the domain of science—as clear evidences of the power of Satan; and, as the basis of this view, they cited from the Old Testament frequent references to witchcraft, and, from the New Testament, St. Paul's question as to the possible bewitching of the Galatians, and the bewitching of the people of Samaria by Simon the Magician.

Naturally, such leaders had very many adherents in that class, so large in all times, who find that

> "To follow foolish precedents and wink
> With both our eyes, is easier than to think."[1]

[1] As to eminent physicians' finding a stumbling-block in hysterical mania, see Kirchhoff's article, p. 351, cited in previous chapter.

It must be owned that their case seemed strong. Though in all human history, so far as it is closely known, these phenomena had appeared, and though every classical scholar could recall the wild orgies of the priests, priestesses, and devotees of Dionysus and Cybele, and the epidemic of wild rage which took its name from some of these, the great fathers and doctors of the Church had left a complete answer to any scepticism based on these facts; they simply pointed to St. Paul's declaration that the gods of the heathen were devils; these examples, then, could be transformed into a powerful argument for diabolic possession.[2]

But it was more especially the epidemics of diabolism in mediæval and modern times which gave strength to the theological view, and from these I shall present a chain of typical examples.

As early as the eleventh century we find clear accounts of diabolical possession taking the form of epidemics of raving, jumping, dancing, and convulsions, the greater number of the sufferers being women and children. In a time so rude, accounts of these manifestations would rarely receive permanent record; but it is very significant that even at the beginning of the eleventh century we hear of them at the extremes of Europe—in northern Germany and in southern Italy. At various times during that century we get additional glimpses of these exhibitions, but it is not until the beginning of the thirteenth century that we have a renewal of them on a large scale. In 1237, at Erfurt, a jumping disease and dancing mania afflicted a hundred children, many of whom died in consequence; it spread through the whole region, and fifty years later we hear of it in Holland.

But it was the last quarter of the fourteenth century that saw its greatest manifestations. There was abundant cause for them. It was a time of oppression, famine, and pestilence: the crusading spirit, having run its course, had been succeeded by a wild, mystical fanaticism; the most frightful plague in human history—the Black Death—was depopulating whole regions—reducing cities to villages, and filling Europe with

[2] As to the Mænads, Corybantes, and the disease "Corybantism," see, for accessible and adequate statements, Smith's *Dictionary of Antiquities* and Lewis and Short's *Lexicon;* also reference in Hecker's *Essays upon the Black Death and the Dancing Mania.* For more complete discussion, see Semelaigne, *L'Aliénation mentale dans l'Antiquité,* Paris, 1869.

that strange mixture of devotion and dissipation which we always note during the prevalence of deadly epidemics on a large scale.

It was in this ferment of religious, moral, and social disease that there broke out in 1374, in the lower Rhine region, the greatest, perhaps, of all manifestations of "possession"— an epidemic of dancing, jumping, and wild raving.

The cures resorted to seemed on the whole to intensify the disease: the afflicted continued dancing for hours, until they fell in utter exhaustion. Some declared that they felt as if bathed in blood, some saw visions, some prophesied.

Into this mass of "possession" there was also clearly poured a current of scoundrelism which increased the disorder.

The immediate source of these manifestations seems to have been the wild revels of St. John's Day. In those revels sundry old heathen ceremonies had been perpetuated, but under a nominally Christian form: wild Bacchanalian dances had thus become a semi-religious ceremonial. The religious and social atmosphere was propitious to the development of the germs of diabolic influence vitalized in these orgies, and they were scattered far and wide through large tracts of the Netherlands and Germany, and especially through the whole region of the Rhine. At Cologne we hear of five hundred afflicted at once; at Metz of eleven hundred dancers in the streets; at Strasburg of yet more painful manifestations; and from these and other cities they spread through the villages and rural districts.

The great majority of the sufferers were women, but there were many men, and especially men whose occupations were sedentary. Remedies were tried upon a large scale—exorcisms first, but especially pilgrimages to the shrine of St. Vitus. The exorcisms accomplished so little that popular faith in them grew small, and the main effect of the pilgrimages seemed to be to increase the disorder by subjecting great crowds to the diabolic contagion. Yet another curative means was seen in the flagellant processions—vast crowds of men, women, and children who wandered through the country, screaming, praying, beating themselves with whips, imploring the Divine mercy and the intervention of St. Vitus. Most fearful of all the main attempts at cure were the persecutions of the Jews. A feeling had evidently spread among the people at large that the Almighty was filled with wrath at the toleration of his enemies, and might be propitiated by their destruction: in the principal cities and villages of Germany, then, the Jews were plundered, tortured, and murdered by tens of thousands. No doubt that, in all this, greed was united with fanaticism; but the argument of fanaticism was simple and cogent; the dart which pierced the breast of Israel at that time was winged and pointed from its own sacred books: the biblical argument was the same used in various ages to promote persecution; and this was, that the wrath of the Almighty was stirred against those who tolerated his enemies, and that because of this toleration the same curse had now come upon Europe which the prophet Samuel had denounced against Saul for showing mercy to the enemies of Jehovah.

It is but just to say that various popes and kings exerted themselves to check these cruelties. Although the argument of Samuel to Saul was used with frightful effect two hundred years later by a most conscientious pope in spurring on the rulers of France to extirpate the Huguenots, the papacy in the fourteenth century stood for mercy to the Jews. But even this intervention was long without effect; the tide of popular superstition had become too strong to be curbed even by the spiritual and temporal powers.[3]

Against this overwhelming current science for many generations could do nothing. Throughout the whole of the fifteenth century physicians appeared to shun the whole matter. Occasionally some more thoughtful man ventured to ascribe some phase of the disease to natural causes; but this was an unpopular doctrine, and evidently dangerous to those who developed it.

Yet, in the beginning of the sixteenth century, cases of "possession" on a large scale began to be brought within the scope of medical research, and the man who led in this evolution of medical science was Paracelsus. He it was who first

[3] See Wellhausen, article *Israel*, in the *Encyclopædia Britannica*, ninth edition; also the reprint of it in his *History of Israel*, London, 1885, p. 546. On the general subject of the demoniacal epidemics, see Isensee, *Geschichte der Medicin*, vol. i, pp. 260 *et seq.*; also Hecker's essay. As to the history of Saul, as a curious landmark in the general development of the subject, see *The Case of Saul, showing that his Disorder was a Real Spiritual Possession*, by Granville Sharp, London, 1807, *passim*. . . . For the general subject, with interesting details, see Laurent, *Études sur l'Histoire de l'Humanité*. See also Maury, *La Magie et l'Astrologie dans l'Antiquité et au Moyen Age*.

bade modern Europe think for a moment upon the idea that these diseases are inflicted neither by saints nor demons, and that the "dancing possession" is simply a form of disease, of which the cure may be effected by proper remedies and regimen.

Paracelsus appears to have escaped any serious interference: it took some time, perhaps, for the theological leaders to understand that he had "let a new idea loose upon the planet," but they soon understood it, and their course was simple. For about fifty years the new idea was well kept under; but in 1563 another physician, John Wier, of Cleves, revived it at much risk to his position and reputation.[4]

Although the new idea was thus resisted, it must have taken some hold upon thoughtful men, for we find that in the second half of the same century the St. Vitus's dance and forms of demoniacal possession akin to it gradually diminished in frequency and were sometimes treated as diseases. In the seventeenth century, so far as the north of Europe is concerned, these displays of "possession" on a great scale had almost entirely ceased; here and there cases appeared, but there was no longer the wild rage extending over great districts and afflicting thousands of people. Yet it was in this same seventeenth century, in the last expiring throes of this superstition, that it led to the worst acts of cruelty.[5]

While this Satanic influence had been exerted on so great a scale throughout northern Europe, a display strangely like it, yet strangely unlike it, had been going on in Italy. There, too, epidemics of dancing and jumping seized groups and communities; but they were attributed to a physical cause—the theory being that the bite of a tarantula in some way provoked a supernatural intervention, of which dancing was the accompaniment and cure.

In the middle of the sixteenth century Fracastoro made an evident impression on the leaders of Italian opinion by using medical means in the cure of the possessed; though it is worthy of note that the medicine which he applied successfully was such as we now know could not by any direct effects

[4] For Paracelsus, see Isensee, vol. i, chap. xi; also Pettigrew, *Superstitions connected with the History and Practice of Medicine and Surgery,* London, 1844, introductory chapter.
[5] As to this diminution of widespread epidemic at the end of the sixteenth century, see citations from Schenck von Grafenberg in Hecker, as above; also Horst.

of its own accomplish any cure: whatever effect it exerted was wrought upon the imagination of the suffered. This form of "possession," then, passed out of the supernatural domain, and became known as "tarantism." Though it continued much longer than the corresponding manifestations in northern Europe, by the beginning of the eighteenth century it had nearly disappeared; and, though special manifestations of it on a small scale still break out occasionally, its main survival is the "tarantella," which the traveller sees danced at Naples as a catchpenny assault upon his purse.[6]

* * *

In the sixteenth century the Protestant Reformation gave new force to witchcraft persecutions in Germany, the new Church endeavouring to show that in zeal and power she exceeded the old. But in France influential opinion seemed not so favourable to these forms of diabolical influence, especially after the publication of Montaigne's *Essays,* in 1580, had spread a sceptical atmosphere over many leading minds.

In 1588 occurred in France a case which indicates the growth of this sceptical tendency even in the higher regions of the French Church. In that year Martha Brossier, a country girl, was, it was claimed, possessed of the devil. The young woman was to all appearance under direct Satanic influence. She roamed about, begging that the demon might be cast out of her, and her imprecations and blasphemies brought consternation wherever she went. Myth-making began on a large scale; stories grew and sped. The Capuchin monks thundered from the pulpit throughout France regarding these proofs of the power of Satan: the alarm spread, until at last even jovial, sceptical King Henry IV was disquieted, and the reigning Pope was asked to take measures to ward off the evil.

Fortunately, there then sat in the episcopal chair of Angers a prelate who had apparently imbibed something of Montaigne's scepticism—Miron; and, when the case was brought before him, he submitted it to the most time-honoured of sacred tests. He first brought into the girl's presence two bowls, one containing holy water, the other ordinary spring water, but allowed her to draw a false inference regarding

[6] See Hecker's *Epidemics of the Middle Ages,* pp. 87-104; also extracts and observations in Carpenter's *Mental Physiology,* London, 1888, pp. 312-315; also Maudsley, *Pathology of Mind,* pp. 73 and following.

the contents of each: the result was that at the presentation of the holy water the devils were perfectly calm, but when tried with the ordinary water they threw Martha into convulsions.

The next experiment made by the shrewd bishop was to similar purpose. He commanded loudly that a book of exorcisms be brought, and, under a previous arrangement, his attendants brought him a copy of Virgil. No sooner had the bishop begun to read the first line of the *Æneid* than the devils threw Martha into convulsions. On another occasion a Latin dictionary, which she had reason to believe was a book of exorcisms, produced a similar effect.

Although the bishop was thereby led to pronounce the whole matter a mixture of insanity and imposture, the Capuchin monks denounced this view as godless. They insisted that these tests really proved the presence of Satan—showing his cunning in covering up the proofs of his existence. The people at large sided with their preachers, and Martha was taken to Paris, where various exorcisms were tried, and the Parisian mob became devoted to her as they had been twenty years before to the murderers of the Huguenots, as they became two centuries later to Robespierre, and as they more recently were to General Boulanger.

But Bishop Miron was not the only sceptic. The Cardinal de Gondi, Archbishop of Paris, charged the most eminent physicians of the city, and among them Riolan, to report upon the case. Various examinations were made, and the verdict was that Martha was simply a hysterical impostor. Thanks, then, to medical science, and to these two enlightened ecclesiastics who summoned its aid, what fifty or a hundred years earlier would have been the centre of a widespread epidemic of possession was isolated, and hindered from producing a national calamity.

* * *

The life of the early colonists in New England was such as to give rapid growth to the germs of the doctrine of possession brought from the mother country. Surrounded by the dark pine forests; having as their neighbours Indians, who were more than suspected of being children of Satan; harassed by wild beasts apparently sent by the powers of evil to torment the elect; with no varied literature to while away the long winter evenings; with few amusements save neighbourhood quarrels; dwelling intently on every text of Scripture which supported their gloomy theology, and adopting its most literal interpretation, it is not strange that they rapidly developed ideas regarding the darker side of nature.[7]

This fear of witchcraft received a powerful stimulus from the treatises of learned men. Such works, coming from Europe, which was at that time filled with the superstition, acted powerfully upon conscientious preachers, and were brought by them to bear upon the people at large. Naturally, then, throughout the latter half of the seventeenth century we find scattered cases of diabolic possession. At Boston, Springfield, Hartford, Groton, and other towns, cases occurred, and here and there we hear of death-sentences.

In the last quarter of the seventeenth century the fruit of these ideas began to ripen. In the year 1684 Increase Mather published his book, *Remarkable Providences,* laying stress upon diabolic possession and witchcraft. This book, having been sent over to England, exercised an influence there, and came back with the approval of no less a man than Richard Baxter: by this its power at home was increased.

In 1688 a poor family in Boston was afflicted by demons: four children, the eldest thirteen years of age, began leaping and barking like dogs or purring like cats, and complaining of being pricked, pinched, and cut; and, to help the matter, an old Irishwoman was tried and executed.

All this belief might have passed away like a troubled dream had it not become incarnate in a strong man. This man was Cotton Mather, the son of Increase Mather. Deeply religious, possessed of excellent abilities, a great scholar, anxious to promote the welfare of his flock in this world and in the next, he was far in advance of ecclesiastics generally on nearly all the main questions between science and theology. He came out of his earlier superstition regarding the divine origin of the Hebrew punctuation; he opposed the old theologic idea regarding the taking of interest for money; he favoured inoculation as a preventive of smallpox when a multitude of clergymen and laymen opposed it; he accepted the Newtonian astronomy despite the outcries against its "atheistic tendency"; he took ground against the time-honoured dogma that comets are "signs and wonders." He had,

[7] For the idea that America before the Pilgrims had been especially given over to Satan, see the literature of the early Puritan period, and especially the poetry of Wigglesworth, treated in Tyler's *History of American Literature,* vol. ii, p. 25 *et seq.*

indeed, some of the defects of his qualities, and among them pedantic vanity, pride of opinion, and love of power; but he was for his time remarkably liberal and undoubtedly sincere. He had thrown off a large part of his father's theology, but one part of it he could not throw off: he was one of the best biblical scholars of his time, and he could not break away from the fact that the sacred Scriptures explicitly recognise witchcraft and demoniacal possession as realities, and enjoin against witchcraft the penalty of death. Therefore it was that in 1689 he published his *Memorable Providences relating to Witchcrafts and Possessions*. The book, according to its title-page, was "recommended by the Ministers of Boston and Charleston," and its stories soon became the familiar reading of men, women, and children throughout New England.

Out of all these causes thus brought to bear upon public opinion began in 1692 a new outbreak of possession, which is one of the most instructive in history. The Rev. Samuel Parris was the minister of the church in Salem, and no pope ever had higher ideas of his own infallibility, no bishop a greater love of ceremony, no inquisitor a greater passion for prying and spying.[8]

Before long Mr. Parris had much upon his hands. Many of his hardy, independent parishioners disliked his ways. Quarrels arose. Some of the leading men of the congregation were pitted against him. The previous minister, George Burroughs, had left the germs of troubles and quarrels, and to these were now added new complications arising from the assumptions of Parris. There were innumerable wranglings and lawsuits; in fact, all the essential causes for Satanic interference which we saw at work in and about the monastery at Loudun, and especially the turmoil of a petty village where there is no intellectual activity, and where men and women find their chief substitute for it in squabbles, religious, legal, political, social, and personal.

In the darkened atmosphere thus charged with the germs of disease it was suddenly discovered that two young girls in the family of Mr. Parris were possessed of devils: they complained of being pinched, pricked, and cut, fell into strange spasms and made strange speeches—showing the signs of diabolic possession handed down in fireside legends or dwelt upon in popular witch literature—and especially such as had

[8] For curious examples of this, see Upham's *History of Salem Witchcraft*, vol. i.

lately been described by Cotton Mather in his book on *Memorable Providences*. The two girls, having been brought by Mr. Parris and others to tell who had bewitched them, first charged an old Indian woman, and the poor old Indian husband was led to join in the charge. This at once afforded new scope for the activity of Mr. Parris. Magnifying his office, he immediately began making a great stir in Salem and in the country round about. Two magistrates were summoned. With them came a crowd, and a court was held at the meeting-house. The scenes which then took place would have been the richest of farces had they not led to events so tragical. The possessed went into spasms at the approach of those charged with witchcraft, and when the poor old men and women attempted to attest their innocence they were overwhelmed with outcries by the possessed, quotations of Scripture by the ministers, and denunciations by the mob. One especially— Ann Putnam, a child of twelve years—showed great precocity and played a striking part in the performances. The mania spread to other children; and two or three married women also, seeing the great attention paid to the afflicted, and influenced by that epidemic of morbid imitation which science now recognises in all such cases, soon became similarly afflicted, and in their turn made charges against various persons. The Indian woman was flogged by her master, Mr. Parris, until she confessed relations with Satan; and others were forced or deluded into confession. These hysterical confessions, the results of unbearable torture, or the reminiscences of dreams, which had been prompted by the witch legends and sermons of the period, embraced such facts as flying through the air to witch gatherings, partaking of witch sacraments, signing a book presented by the devil, and submitting to Satanic baptism.

The possessed had begun with charging their possession upon poor and vagrant old women, but ere long, emboldened by their success, they attacked higher game, struck at some of the foremost people of the region, and did not cease until several of these were condemned to death, and every man, woman, and child brought under a reign of terror. Many fled outright, and one of the foremost citizens of Salem went constantly armed, and kept one of his horses saddled in the stable to flee if brought under accusation.

The hysterical ingenuity of the possessed women grew with their success. They insisted that they saw devils prompting the accused to defend themselves in court. Did one of the accused clasp her hands in despair, the possessed clasped theirs; did the accused, in appealing to Heaven, make any gesture, the possessed simultaneously imitated it; did the accused in weariness drop her head, the possessed dropped theirs, and declared that the witch was trying to break their necks. The court-room resounded with groans, shrieks, prayers, and curses; judges, jury, and people were aghast, and even the accused were sometimes thus led to believe in their own guilt.

Very striking in all these cases was the alloy of frenzy with trickery. In most of the madness there was method. Sundry witches charged by the possessed had been engaged in controversy with the Salem church people. Others of the accused had quarrelled with Mr. Parris. Still others had been engaged in old lawsuits against persons more or less connected with the girls. One of the most fearful charges, which cost the life of a noble and lovely woman, arose undoubtedly from her better style of dress and living. Old slumbering neighbourhood or personal quarrels bore in this way a strange fruitage of revenge; for the cardinal doctrine of a fanatic's creed is that his enemies are the enemies of God.

Any person daring to hint the slightest distrust of the proceedings was in danger of being immediately brought under accusation of a league with Satan. Husbands and children were thus brought to the gallows for daring to disbelieve these charges against their wives and mothers. Some of the clergy were accused for endeavouring to save members of their churches.[9]

One poor woman was charged with "giving a look toward the great meeting-house of Salem, and immediately a demon entered the house and tore down a part of it." This cause for the falling of a bit of poorly nailed wainscoting seemed perfectly satisfactory to Dr. Cotton Mather, as well as to the judge and jury, and she was hanged, protesting her innocence. Still another lady, belonging to one of the most respected families of the region, was charged with the crime of witchcraft. The children were fearfully afflicted whenever she appeared near them. It seemed never to occur to any one that

[9] This is admirably brought out by Upham, and the lawyerlike thoroughness with which he has examined all these hidden springs of the charges is one of the main things which render his book one of the most valuable contributions to the history and philosophy of demoniacal possession ever written.

a bitter old feud between the Rev. Mr. Parris and the family of the accused might have prejudiced the children and directed their attention toward the woman. No account was made of the fact that her life had been entirely blameless; and yet, in view of the wretched insufficiency of proof, the jury brought in a verdict of not guilty. As they brought in this verdict, all the children began to shriek and scream, until the court committed the monstrous wrong of causing her to be indicted anew. In order to warrant this, the judge referred to one perfectly natural and harmless expression made by the woman when under examination. The jury at last brought her in guilty. She was condemned; and, having been brought into the church heavily ironed, was solemnly excommunicated and delivered over to Satan by the minister. Some good sense still prevailed, and the Governor reprieved her; but ecclesiastical pressure and popular clamour were too powerful. The Governor was induced to recall his reprieve, and she was executed, protesting her innocence and praying for her enemies.[10]

Another typical case was presented. The Rev. Mr. Burroughs, against whom considerable ill will had been expressed, and whose petty parish quarrel with the powerful Putnam family had led to his dismissal from his ministry, was named by the possessed as one of those who plagued them, one of the most influential among the afflicted being Ann Putnam. Mr. Burroughs had led a blameless life, the main thing charged against him by the Putnams being that he insisted strenuously that his wife should not go about the parish talking of her own family matters. He was charged with afflicting the children, convicted, and executed. At the last moment he repeated the Lord's Prayer solemnly and fully, which it was supposed that no sorcerer could do, and this, together with his straightforward Christian utterances at the execution, shook the faith of many in the reality of diabolic possession.

Ere long it was known that one of the girls had acknowledged that she had belied some persons who had been executed, and especially Mr. Burroughs, and that she had begged forgiveness; but this for a time availed nothing. Persons who would not confess were tied up and put to a sort of torture which was effective in securing new revelations.

In the case of Giles Corey the horrors of the persecution

[10] See Drake, *The Witchcraft Delusion in New England*, vol. iii, pp. 34 *et seq.*

culminated. Seeing that his doom was certain, and wishing to preserve his family from attainder and their property from confiscation, he refused to plead. Though eighty years of age, he was therefore pressed to death, and when, in his last agonies, his tongue was pressed out of his mouth, the sheriff with his walking-stick thrust it back again.

Everything was made to contribute to the orthodox view of possession. On one occasion, when a cart conveying eight condemned persons to the place of execution stuck fast in the mire, some of the possessed declared that they saw the devil trying to prevent the punishment of his associates. Confessions of witchcraft abounded; but the way in which these confessions were obtained is touchingly exhibited in a statement afterward made by several women. In explaining the reasons why, when charged with afflicting sick persons, they made a false confession, they said:

". . . By reason of that suddain surprizal, we knowing ourselves altogether Innocent of that Crime, we were all exceedingly astonished and amazed, and consternated and affrighted even out of our Reason; and our nearest and dearest Relations, seeing us in that dreadful condition, and knowing our great danger, apprehending that there was no other way to save our lives, . . . out of tender . . . pitty perswaded us to confess what we did confess. And indeed that Confession, that it is said we made, was no other than what was suggested to us by some Gentlemen; they telling us, that we were Witches, and they knew it, and we knew it, and they knew that we knew it, which made us think that it was so; and our understanding, our reason, and our faculties almost gone, we were not capable of judging our condition; as also the hard measures they used with us, rendred us uncapable of making our Defence, but said anything and everything which they desired, and most of what we said, was in effect a consenting to what they said. . . ."[11]

Case after case, in which hysteria, fanaticism, cruelty, injustice, and trickery played their part, was followed up to the scaffold. In a short time twenty persons had been put to a cruel death, and the number of the accused grew larger and larger. The highest position and the noblest character formed no barrier. Daily the possessed became more bold, more tricky, and more wild. No plea availed anything. In behalf of

[11] See Calef, in Drake, vol. ii; also Upham.

several women, whose lives had been of the purest and gentlest, petitions were presented, but to no effect. A scriptural text was always ready to aid in the repression of mercy: it was remembered that "Satan himself is transformed into an angel of light," and above all resounded the Old Testament injunction, which had sent such multitudes in Europe to the torture-chamber and the stake, "Thou shalt not suffer a witch to live."

Such clergymen as Noyes, Parris, and Mather, aided by such judges as Stoughton and Hathorn, left nothing undone to stimulate these proceedings. The great Cotton Mather based upon this outbreak of disease thus treated his famous book, *Wonders of the Invisible World,* thanking God for the triumphs over Satan thus gained at Salem; and his book received the approbation of the Governor of the Province, the President of Harvard College, and various eminent theologians in Europe as well as in America.

But, despite such efforts as these, observation, and thought upon observation, which form the beginning of all true science, brought in a new order of things. The people began to fall away. Justice Bradstreet, having committed thirty or forty persons, became aroused to the absurdity of the whole matter; the minister of Andover had the good sense to resist the theological view; even so high a personage as Lady Phips, the wife of the Governor, began to show lenity.

Each of these was, in consequence of this disbelief, charged with collusion with Satan; but such charges seemed now to lose their force.

In the midst of all this delusion and terrorism stood Cotton Mather firm as ever. His efforts to uphold the declining superstition were heroic. But he at last went one step too far. Being himself possessed of a mania for myth-making and wonder-mongering, and having described a case of witchcraft with possibly greater exaggeration than usual, he was confronted by Robert Calef. Calef was a Boston merchant, who appears to have united the good sense of a man of business to considerable shrewdness in observation, power in thought, and love for truth; and he began writing to Mather and others, to show the weak points in the system. Mather, indignant that a person so much his inferior dared dissent from his opinion, at first affected to despise Calef; but, as Calef pressed him more and more closely, Mather denounced him, calling him among other things "A Coal from Hell." All to no purpose:

Calef fastened still more firmly upon the flanks of the great theologian. Thought and reason now began to resume their sway.

The possessed having accused certain men held in very high respect, doubts began to dawn upon the community at large. Here was the repetition of that which had set men thinking in the German bishoprics when those under trial for witchcraft there had at last, in their desperation or madness, charged the very bishops and the judges upon the bench with sorcery. The party of reason grew stronger. The Rev. Mr. Parris was soon put upon the defensive: for some of the possessed began to confess that they had accused people wrongfully. Herculean efforts were made by certain of the clergy and devout laity to support the declining belief, but the more thoughtful turned more and more against it; jurymen prominent in convictions solemnly retracted their verdicts and publicly craved pardon of God and man. Most striking of all was the case of Justice Sewall. A man of the highest character, he had in view of authority deduced from Scripture and the principles laid down by the great English judges, unhesitatingly condemned the accused; but reason now dawned upon him. He looked back and saw the baselessness of the whole proceedings, and made a public statement of his errors. His diary contains many passages showing deep contrition, and ever afterward, to the end of his life, he was wont, on one day in the year, to enter into solitude, and there remain all the day long in fasting, prayer, and penitence.

Chief-Justice Stoughton never yielded. To the last he lamented the "evil spirit of unbelief" which was thwarting the glorious work of freeing New England from demons.

The church of Salem solemnly revoked the excommunications of the condemned and drove Mr. Parris from the pastorate. Cotton Mather passed his last years in groaning over the decline of the faith and the ingratitude of a people for whom he had done so much. Very significant is one of his complaints, since it shows the evolution of a more scientific mode of thought abroad as well as at home: he laments in his diary that English publishers gladly printed Calef's book, but would no longer publish his own, and he declares this "an attack upon the glory of the Lord."

*   *   *

[2. Beginnings of Helpful Scepticism]

[3. Theological "Restatements"—Final Triumph of the Scientific View and Methods]

Chapter 17

From Babel to Comparative Philology

1. The Sacred Theory in Its First Form

AMONG THE SCIENCES which have served as entering wedges into the heavy mass of ecclesiastical orthodoxy—to cleave it, disintegrate it, and let the light of Christianity into it—none perhaps has done a more striking work than Comparative Philology. In one very important respect the history of this science differs from that of any other; for it is the only one whose conclusions theologians have at last fully adopted as the result of their own studies. This adoption teaches a great lesson, since, while it has destroyed theological views cherished during many centuries, and obliged the Church to accept theories directly contrary to the plain letter of our sacred books, the result is clearly seen to have helped Christianity rather than to have hurt it. It has certainly done much to clear our religious foundations of the dogmatic rust which was eating into their structure.

How this result was reached, and why the Church has so fully accepted it, I shall endeavour to show in the present chapter.

At a very early period in the evolution of civilization men began to ask questions regarding language; and the answers to these questions were naturally embodied in the myths, legends, and chronicles of their sacred books.

Among the foremost of these questions were three: "Whence came language?" "Which was the first language?" "How came the diversity of language?"

The answer to the first of these was very simple: each people naturally held that language was given it directly or indirectly by some special or national deity of its own; thus, to the Chaldeans by Oannes, to the Egyptians by Thoth, to the Hebrews by Jahveh.

The Hebrew answer is embodied in the great poem which

opens our sacred books. Jahveh talks with Adam and is perfectly understood; the serpent talks with Eve and is perfectly understood; Jahveh brings the animals before Adam, who bestows on each its name. Language, then, was God-given and complete. Of the fact that every language is the result of a growth process there was evidently, among the compilers of our sacred books, no suspicion.

The answer to the second of these questions was no less simple. As, very generally, each nation believed its own chief divinity to be "a god above all gods,"—as each believed itself "a chosen people,"—as each believed its own sacred city the actual centre of the earth, so each believed its own language to be the first—the original of all. This answer was from the first taken for granted by each "chosen people," and especially by the Hebrews: throughout their whole history, whether the Almighty talks with Adam in the Garden or writes the commandments on Mount Sinai, he uses the same language—the Hebrew.

The answer to the third of these questions, that regarding the diversity of languages, was much more difficult. Naturally, explanations of this diversity frequently gave rise to legends somewhat complicated.

The "law of wills and causes," formulated by Comte, was exemplified here as in so many other cases. That law is, that, when men do not know the natural causes of things, they simply attribute them to wills like their own; thus they obtain a theory which provisionally takes the place of science, and this theory forms a basis for theology.

Examples of this recur to any thinking reader of history. Before the simpler laws of astronomy were known, the sun was supposed to be trundled out into the heavens every day and the stars hung up in the firmament every night by the right hand of the Almighty. Before the laws of comets were known, they were thought to be missiles hurled by an angry God at a wicked world. Before the real cause of lightning was known, it was supposed to be the work of a good God in his wrath, or of evil spirits in their malice. Before the laws of meteorology were known, it was thought that rains were caused by the Almighty or his angels opening "the windows of heaven" to let down upon the earth "the waters that be above the firmament." Before the laws governing physical health were known, diseases were supposed to result from the direct interposition of the Almighty or of Satan. Before the laws governing mental health were known, insanity was generally thought to be diabolic possession. All these early conceptions were naturally embodied in the sacred books of the world, and especially in our own.[1]

So, in this case, to account for the diversity of tongues, the direct intervention of the Divine Will was brought in. As this diversity was felt to be an inconvenience, it was attributed to the will of a Divine Being in anger. To explain this anger, it was held that it must have been provoked by human sin.

Out of this conception explanatory myths and legends grew as thickly and naturally as elms along water-courses; of these the earliest form known to us is found in the Chaldean accounts, and nowhere more clearly than in the legend of the Tower of Babel.

The inscriptions recently found among the ruins of Assyria have thrown a bright light into this and other scriptural myths and legends: the deciphering of the characters in these inscriptions by Grotefend, and the reading of the texts by George Smith, Oppert, Sayce, and others, have given us these traditions more nearly in their original form than they appear in our own Scriptures.

The Hebrew story of Babel, like so many other legends in the sacred books of the world, combined various elements. By a play upon words, such as the history of myths and legends frequently shows, it wrought into one fabric the earlier explanations of the diversities of human speech and of the great ruined tower at Babylon. The name Babel (*bab-el*) means "Gate of God" or "Gate of the Gods." All modern scholars of note agree that this was the real significance of the name; but the Hebrew verb which signifies *to confound* resembles somewhat the word Babel, so that out of this resemblance, by one of the most common processes in myth formation, came to the Hebrew mind an indisputable proof that the tower was connected with the confusion of tongues, and this became part of our theological heritage.

In our sacred books the account runs as follows:

[1] Any one who wishes to realize the mediæval view of the direct personal attention of the Almighty to the universe, can perhaps do so most easily by looking over the engravings in the well-known *Nuremberg Chronicle,* representing him in the work of each of the six days, and resting afterward.

"And the whole earth was of one language, and of one speech.

"And it came to pass, as they journeyed from the east, that they found a plain in the land of Shinar; and they dwelt there.

"And they said one to another, Go to, let us make brick, and burn them thoroughly. And they had brick for stone, and slime had they for mortar.

"And they said, Go to, let us build us a city, and a tower, whose top may reach unto heaven; and let us make a name, lest we be scattered abroad upon the face of the whole earth.

"And the Lord came down to see the city and the tower, which the children of men builded.

"And the Lord said, Behold, the people is one, and they have all one language; and this they begin to do: and now nothing will be restrained from them, which they have imagined to do.

"Go to, let us go down, and there confound their language, that they may not understand one another's speech.

"So the Lord scattered them abroad from thence upon the face of all the earth: and they left off to build the city.

"Therefore is the name of it called Babel; because the Lord did there confound the language of all the earth: and from thence did the Lord scatter them abroad upon the face of all the earth." (Genesis xi, 1-9.)

Thus far the legend had been but slightly changed from the earlier Chaldean form in which it has been found in the Assyrian inscriptions. Its character is very simple: to use the words of Prof. Sayce, "It takes us back to the age when the gods were believed to dwell in the visible sky, and when man, therefore, did his best to rear his altars as near them as possible." And this eminent divine might have added that it takes us back also to a time when it was thought that Jehovah, in order to see the tower fully, was obliged to come down from his seat above the firmament.

As to the real reasons for the building of the towers which formed so striking a feature in Chaldean architecture—any one of which may easily have given rise to the explanatory myth which found its way into our sacred books—there seems a substantial agreement among leading scholars that they were erected primarily as parts of temples, but largely for the purpose of astronomical observations, to which the Chaldeans were so devoted, and to which their country, with its level surface and clear atmosphere, was so well adapted. As to the real cause of the ruin of such structures, one of the inscribed cylinders discovered in recent times, speaking of a tower which most of the archæologists identify with the Tower of Babel, reads as follows:

"The building named the Stages of the Seven Spheres, which was the Tower of Borsippa, had been built by a former king. He had completed forty-two cubits, but he did not finish its head. During the lapse of time, it had become ruined; they had not taken care of the exit of the waters, so that rain and wet had penetrated into the brickwork; the casing of burned brick had swollen out, and the terraces of crude brick are scattered in heaps."

We can well understand how easily "the gods, assisted by the winds," as stated in the Chaldean legend, could overthrow a tower thus built.

It may be instructive to compare with the explanatory myth developed first by the Chaldeans, and in a slightly different form by the Hebrews, various other legends to explain the same diversity of tongues. The Hindu legend of the confusion of tongues is as follows:

"There grew in the centre of the earth the wonderful 'world tree,' or 'knowledge tree.' It was so tall that it reached almost to heaven. It said in its heart, 'I shall hold my head in heaven and spread my branches over all the earth, and gather all men together under my shadow, and protect them, and prevent them from separating.' But Brahma, to punish the pride of the tree, cut off its branches and cast them down on the earth, when they sprang up as wata trees, and made differences of belief and speech and customs to prevail on the earth, to disperse men upon its surface."

Still more striking is a Mexican legend: according to this, the giant Xelhua built the great Pyramid of Cholula, in order to reach heaven, until the gods, angry at his audacity, threw fire upon the building and broke it down, whereupon every separate family received a language of its own.

Such explanatory myths grew or spread widely over the earth. A well-known form of the legend, more like the Chaldean than the Hebrew later form, appeared among the Greeks. According to this, the Aloidæ piled Mount Ossa upon Olympus and Pelion upon Ossa, in their efforts to reach heaven and dethrone Jupiter.

Still another form of it entered the thoughts of Plato. He

held that in the golden age men and beasts all spoke the same language, but that Zeus confounded their speech because men were proud and demanded eternal youth and immortality.[2]

But naturally the version of the legend which most affected Christendom was that modification of the Chaldean form developed among the Jews and embodied in their sacred books. To a thinking man in these days it is very instructive. The coming down of the Almighty from heaven to see the tower and put an end to it by dispersing its builders, points to the time when his dwelling was supposed to be just above the firmament or solid vault above the earth: the time when he

[2] For the identification of the Tower of Babel with the "Birs Nimrad" amid the ruins of the city of Borsippa, see Rawlinson; also Schrader, *The Cuneiform Inscriptions and the Old Testament,* London, 1885, pp. 106-112 and following; and especially George Smith, *Assyrian Discoveries,* p. 59. For some of these inscriptions discovered and read by George Smith, see his *Chaldean Account of Genesis,* New York, 1876, pp. 160-162. For the statement regarding the origin of the word Babel, see Ersch and Gruber, article *Babylon;* also the Rev. Prof. A. H. Sayce, in the latest edition of the *Encyclopædia Britannica;* also Colenso, *Pentateuch Examined,* part iv, p. 302; also John Fiske, *Myths and Mythmakers,* p. 72; also Lenormant, *Histoire Ancienne de l'Orient,* Paris, 1881, vol. i, pp. 115 *et seq.* As to the character and purpose of the great tower of the Temple of Belus, see Smith's *Bible Dictionary,* article *Babel,* quoting Diodorus; also Rawlinson, especially in *Journal of the Asiatic Society* for 1861; also Sayce, *Religion of the Ancient Babylonians* (Hibbert Lectures for 1887), London, 1877, chap. ii and elsewhere, especially pp. 96, 397, 407; also Max Duncker, *History of Antiquity,* Abbott's translation, vol. ii, chaps. ii and iii. For similar legends in other parts of the world, see Delitzsch; also Humboldt, *American Researches;* also Brinton, *Myths of the New World;* also Colenso, as above. The Tower of Cholula is well known, having been described by Humboldt and Lord Kingsborough. For superb engravings showing the view of Babel as developed by the theological imagination, see Kircher, *Turris Babel,* Amsterdam, 1679. For the Law of Wills and Causes, with deductions from it well stated, see Beattie Crozier, *Civilization and Progress,* London, 1888, pp. 112, 178, 179, 273. For Plato, see the *Politicus,* p. 272, ed. Stephani, cited in Ersch and Gruber, article *Babylon.* For a good general statement, see *Bible Myths,* New York, 1883, chap. iii. For Aristotle's strange want of interest in any classification of the varieties of human speech, see Max Müller, *Lectures on the Science of Language,* London, 1864, series i, chap. iv, pp. 123-125.

410 / History of the Warfare of Science with Theology

exercised his beneficent activity in such acts as opening "the
windows of heaven" to give down rain upon the earth; in
bringing out the sun every day and hanging up the stars every
night to give light to the earth; in hurling comets, to give
warning; in placing his bow in the cloud, to give hope; in
coming down in the cool of the evening to walk and talk
with the man he had made; in making coats of skins for
Adam and Eve; in enjoying the odour of flesh which Noah
burned for him; in eating with Abraham under the oaks of
Mamre; in wrestling with Jacob; and in writing with his own
finger on the stone tables for Moses.

So came the answer to the third question regarding language; and all three answers, embodied in our sacred books
and implanted in the Jewish mind, supplied to the Christian
Church the germs of a theological development of philology.
These germs developed rapidly in the warm atmosphere of
devotion and ignorance of natural law which pervaded the
early Church, and there grew a great orthodox theory of language, which was held throughout Christendom, "always,
everywhere, and by all," for nearly two thousand years, and
to which, until the present century, all science has been
obliged, under pains and penalties, to conform.

There did, indeed, come into human thought at an early
period some suggestions of the modern scientific view of
philology. Lucretius had proposed a theory, inadequate indeed, but still pointing toward the truth, as follows: "Nature
impelled man to try the various sounds of the tongue, and
so struck out the names of things, much in the same way
as the inability to speak is seen in its turn to drive children
to the use of gestures." But, among the early fathers of the
Church, the only one who seems to have caught an echo of
this utterance was St. Gregory of Nyssa: as a rule, all the
other great founders of Christian theology, as far as they expressed themselves on the subject, took the view that the
original language spoken by the Almighty and given by him
to men was Hebrew, and that from this all other languages
were derived at the destruction of the Tower of Babel. This
doctrine was especially upheld by Origen, St. Jerome, and
St. Augustine. Origen taught that "the language given at the
first through Adam, the Hebrew, remained among that portion of mankind which was assigned not to any angel, but
continued the portion of God himself." St. Augustine declared
that, when the other races were divided by their own peculiar

languages, Heber's family preserved that language which is not unreasonably believed to have been the common language of the race, and that on this account it was henceforth called Hebrew. St. Jerome wrote, "The whole of antiquity affirms that Hebrew, in which the Old Testament is written, was the beginning of all human speech."

Amid such great authorities as these even Gregory of Nyssa struggled in vain. He seems to have taken the matter very earnestly, and to have used not only argument but ridicule. He insists that God does not speak Hebrew, and that the tongue used by Moses was not even a pure dialect of one of the languages resulting from "the confusion." He makes man the inventor of speech, and resorts to raillery: speaking against his opponent Eunomius, he says that, "passing in silence his base and abject garrulity," he will "note a few things which are thrown into the midst of his useless or wordy discourse, where he represents God teaching words and names to our first parents, sitting before them like some pedagogue or grammar master." But, naturally, the great authority of Origen, Jerome, and Augustine prevailed; the view suggested by Lucretius, and again by St. Gregory of Nyssa, died out; and "always, everywhere, and by all," in the Church, the doctrine was received that the language spoken by the Almighty was Hebrew,—that it was taught by him to Adam,—and that all other languages on the face of the earth originated from it at the dispersion attending the destruction of the Tower of Babel.[3]

This idea threw out roots and branches in every direction,

[3] For Lucretius's statement, see the *De Rerum Natura,* lib. v, Munro's edition, with translation, Cambridge, 1886, vol. iii, p. 141. For the opinion of Gregory of Nyssa, see Benfey, *Geschichte der Sprachwissenschaft in Deutschland,* München, 1869, p. 179; and for the passage cited, see Gregory of Nyssa in his *Contra Eunomium,* xii, in Migne's *Patr. Græca,* vol. ii, p. 1043. For St. Jerome, see his *Epistle XVIII,* in Migne's *Patr. Lat.,* vol. xxii, p. 365. For citation from St. Augustine, see the *City of God,* Dods's translation, Edinburgh, 1871, vol. ii, p. 122. For citation from Origen, see his *Homily XI,* cited by Guichard in preface to *L'Harmonie Étymologique,* Paris, 1631, lib. xvi, chap. xi. For absolutely convincing proofs that the Jews derived the Babel and other legends of their sacred books from the Chaldeans, see George Smith, *Chaldean Account of Genesis, passim;* but especially for a most candid though evidently somewhat reluctant summing up, see p. 291.

and so developed ever into new and strong forms. As all scholars now know, the vowel points in the Hebrew language were not adopted until at some period between the second and tenth centuries; but in the mediæval Church they soon came to be considered as part of the great miracle—as the work of the right hand of the Almighty; and never until the eighteenth century was there any doubt allowed as to the divine origin of these rabbinical additions to the text. To hesitate in believing that these points were dotted virtually by the very hand of God himself came to be considered a fearful heresy.

The series of battles between theology and science in the field of comparative philology opened just on this point, apparently so insignificant: the direct divine inspiration of the rabbinical punctuation. The first to impugn this divine origin of these vocal points and accents appears to have been a Spanish monk, Raymundus Martinus, in his *Pugio Fidei,* or Poniard of the Faith, which he put forth in the thirteenth century. But he and his doctrine disappeared beneath the waves of the orthodox ocean, and apparently left no trace. For nearly three hundred years longer the full sacred theory held its ground; but about the opening of the sixteenth century another glimpse of the truth was given by a Jew, Elias Levita, and this seems to have had some little effect, at least in keeping the germ of scientific truth alive.

The Reformation, with its renewal of the literal study of the Scriptures, and its transfer of all infallibility from the Church and the papacy to the letter of the sacred books, intensified for a time the devotion of Christendom to this sacred theory of language. The belief was strongly held that the writers of the Bible were merely pens in the hand of God (*Dei calami*); hence the conclusion that not only the sense but the words, letters, and even the punctuation proceeded from the Holy Spirit. Only on this one question of the origin of the Hebrew points was there any controversy, and this waxed hot. It began to be especially noted that these vowel points in the Hebrew Bible did not exist in the synagogue rolls, were not mentioned in the Talmud, and seemed unknown to St. Jerome; and on these grounds some earnest men ventured to think them no part of the original revelation to Adam. Zwingli, so much before most of the Reformers in other respects, was equally so in this. While not doubting the divine origin and preservation of the Hebrew language as a whole, he denied the antiquity of the vocal points, demonstrated their unessential character, and pointed out the fact that St. Jerome makes no mention of them. His denial was long the refuge of those who shared this heresy.

But the full orthodox theory remained established among the vast majority both of Catholics and Protestants. The attitude of the former is well illustrated in the imposing work of the canon Marini, which appeared at Venice in 1593, under the title of *Noah's Ark: A New Treasury of the Sacred Tongue*. The huge folios begin with the declaration that the Hebrew tongue was "divinely inspired at the very beginning of the world," and the doctrine is steadily maintained that this divine inspiration extended not only to the letters but to the punctuation.

Not before the seventeenth century was well under way do we find a thorough scholar bold enough to gainsay this preposterous doctrine. This new assailant was Capellus, Professor of Hebrew at Saumur; but he dared not put forth his argument in France: he was obliged to publish it in Holland, and even there such obstacles were thrown in his way that it was ten years before he published another treatise of importance.

The work of Capellus was received as settling the question by very many open-minded scholars, among whom was Hugo Grotius. But many theologians felt this view to be a blow at the sanctity and integrity of the sacred text; and in 1648 the great scholar, John Buxtorf the younger, rose to defend the orthodox citadel: in his *Anticritica* he brought all his stores of knowledge to uphold the doctrine that the rabbinical points and accents had been jotted down by the right hand of God.

The controversy waxed hot: scholars like Voss and Brian Walton supported Capellus; Wasmuth and many others of note were as fierce against him. The Swiss Protestants were especially violent on the orthodox side; their formula consensus of 1675 declared the vowel points to be inspired, and three years later the Calvinists of Geneva, by a special canon, forbade that any minister should be received into their jurisdiction until he publicly confessed that the Hebrew text, as it to-day exists in the Masoretic copies, is, both as to the consonants and vowel points, divine and authentic.

While in Holland so great a man as Hugo Grotius supported the view of Capellus, and while in France the eminent Catholic scholar Richard Simon, and many others, Catholic and Protestant, took similar ground against this divine origin of the Hebrew punctuation, there was arrayed against them a body apparently overwhelming. In France, Bossuet, the greatest theologian that France has ever produced, did his best to crush Simon. In Germany, Wasmuth, professor first at Rostock and afterward at Kiel, hurled his *Vindiciæ* at the innovators. Yet at this very moment the battle was clearly won; the arguments of Capellus were irrefragable, and, despite the commands of bishops, the outcries of theologians, and the sneering of critics, his application of strictly scientific observation and reasoning carried the day.

Yet a casual observer, long after the fate of the battle was really settled, might have supposed that it was still in doubt. As is not unusual in theologic controversies, attempts were made to galvanize the dead doctrine into an appearance of life. Famous among these attempts was that made as late as the beginning of the eighteenth century by two Bremen theologians, Hase and Iken. They put forth a compilation in two huge folios simultaneously at Leyden and Amsterdam, prominent in which work is the treatise on *The Integrity of Scripture,* by Johann Andreas Danzius, Professor of Oriental Languages and Senior Member of the Philosophical Faculty of Jena, and, to preface it, there was a formal and fulsome approval by three eminent professors of theology at Leyden. With great fervour the author pointed out that "religion itself depends absolutely on the infallible inspiration, both verbal and literal, of the Scripture text"; and with impassioned eloquence he assailed the blasphemers who dared question the divine origin of the Hebrew points. But this was really the last great effort. That the case was lost was seen by the fact that Danzius felt obliged to use other missiles than arguments, and especially to call his opponents hard names. From this period the old sacred theory as to the origin of the Hebrew points may be considered as dead and buried.

[2. The Sacred Theory of Language in Its Second Form]

3. Breaking Down of the Theological View

*   *   *

The reason why the Church has so fully accepted the conclusions of science which have destroyed the sacred theory is instructive. The study of languages has been, since the

Revival of Learning and the Reformation, a favourite study with the whole Western Church, Catholic and Protestant. The importance of understanding the ancient tongues in which our sacred books are preserved first stimulated the study, and Church missionary efforts have contributed nobly to supply the material for extending it, and for the application of that comparative method which, in philology as in other sciences, has been so fruitful. Hence it is that so many leading theologians have come to know at first hand the truths given by this science, and to recognise its fundamental principles. What the conclusions which they, as well as all other scholars in this field, have been absolutely forced to accept, I shall now endeavour to show.

The beginnings of a scientific theory seemed weak indeed, but they were none the less effective. As far back as 1661, Hottinger, professor at Heidelberg, came into the chorus of theologians like a great bell in a chime; but like a bell whose opening tone is harmonious and whose closing tone is discordant. For while, at the beginning, Hottinger cites a formidable list of great scholars who had held the sacred theory of the origin of language, he goes on to note a closer resemblance to the Hebrew in some languages than in others, and explains this by declaring that the confusion of tongues was of two sorts, total and partial: the Arabic and Chaldaic he thinks underwent only a partial confusion; the Egyptian, Persian, and all the European languages a total one. Here comes in the discord; here gently sounds forth from the great chorus a new note—that idea of grouping and classifying languages which at a later day was to destroy utterly the whole sacred theory.

But the great chorus resounded on, as we have seen, from shore to shore, until the closing years of the seventeenth century; then arose men who silenced it forever. The first leader who threw the weight of his knowledge, thought, and authority against it was Leibnitz. He declared, "There is as much reason for supposing Hebrew to have been the primitive language of mankind as there is for adopting the view of Goropius, who published a work at Antwerp in 1580 to prove that Dutch was the language spoken in paradise." In a letter to Tenzel, Leibnitz wrote, "To call Hebrew the primitive language is like calling the branches of a tree primitive branches, or like imagining that in some country hewn trunks could grow instead of trees." He also asked, "If the primeval language existed even up to the time of Moses, whence came the Egyptian language?"

But the efficiency of Leibnitz did not end with mere suggestions. He applied the inductive method to linguistic study, made great efforts to have vocabularies collected and grammars drawn up wherever missionaries and travellers came in contact with new races, and thus succeeded in giving the initial impulse to at least three notable collections—that of Catharine the Great, of Russia; that of the Spanish Jesuit, Lorenzo Hervas; and, at a later period, the *Mithridates* of Adelung. The interest of the Empress Catharine in her collection of linguistic materials was very strong, and her influence is seen in the fact that Washington, to please her, requested governors and generals to send in materials from various parts of the United States and the Territories. The work of Hervas extended over the period from 1735 to 1809: a missionary in America, he enlarged his catalogue of languages to six volumes, which were published in Spanish in 1800, and contained specimens of more than three hundred languages, with the grammars of more than forty. It should be said to his credit that Hervas dared point out with especial care the limits of the Semitic family of languages, and declared, as a result of his enormous studies, that the various languages of mankind could not have been derived from the Hebrew.

While such work was done in Catholic Spain, Protestant Germany was honoured by the work of Adelung. It contained the Lord's Prayer in nearly five hundred languages and dialects, and the comparison of these, early in the nineteenth century, helped to end the sway of theological philology.

But the period which intervened between Leibnitz and this modern development was a period of philological chaos. It began mainly with the doubts which Leibnitz had forced upon Europe, and ended only with the beginning of the study of Sanskrit in the latter half of the eighteenth century, and with the comparisons made by means of the collections of Catharine, Hervas, and Adelung at the beginning of the nineteenth. The old theory that Hebrew was the original language had gone to pieces; but nothing had taken its place as a finality. Great authorities, like Buddeus, were still cited in behalf of the narrower belief; but everywhere researches, unorganized though they were, tended to destroy it. The story of Babel continued indeed throughout the whole eighteenth century to hinder or warp scientific investigation, and a very curious illustration of this fact is seen in the book of Lord Nelme on *The Origin and Elements of Language*. He declares that connected with the confusion was the cleaving of America from Europe, and he regards the most terrible chapters in the book of Job as intended for a description of the Flood, which in all probability Job had from Noah himself. Again, Rowland Jones tried to prove that Celtic was the primitive tongue, and that it passed through Babel unharmed. Still another effect was made by a Breton to prove that all languages took their rise in the language of Brittany. All was chaos. There was much wrangling, but little earnest controversy. Here and there theologians were calling out frantically, beseeching the Church to save the old doctrine as "essential to the truth of Scripture"; here and there other divines began to foreshadow the inevitable compromise which has always been thus vainly attempted in the history of every science. But it was soon seen by thinking men that no concessions as yet spoken of by theologians were sufficient. In the latter half of the century came the bloom period of the French philosophers and encyclopedists, of the English deists, of such German thinkers as Herder, Kant, and Lessing; and while here and there some writer on the theological side, like Perrin, amused thinking men by his flounderings in this great chaos, all remained without form and void.[4]

* * *

4. Triumph of the New Science

Such was that chaos of thought into which the discovery

[4] For Hottinger, see the preface to his *Etymologicum Orientale,* Frankfort, 1661. For Leibnitz, Catharine the Great, Hervas, and Adelung, see Max Müller, as above, from whom I have quoted very fully; see also Benfey, *Geschichte der Sprachwissenschaft,* etc., p. 269. Benfey declares that the Catalogue of Hervas is even now a mine for the philologist. For the first two citations from Leibnitz, as well as for a statement of his importance in the history of languages, see Max Müller as above, pp. 135, 136. For the third quotation, Leibnitz, *Opera,* Geneva, 1768, vi, part ii, p. 232. For Nelme, see his *Origin and Elements of Language,* London, 1772, pp. 85-100. For Rowland Jones, see *The Origin of Language and Nations,* London, 1764, and preface. For the origin of languages in Brittany, see Le Brignant, Paris, 1787. For Herder and Lessing, see Canon Farrar's treatise; on Lessing, see Sayce, as above. As to Perrin, see his essay *Sur l'Origine et l'Antiquité des Langues,* London, 1767.

of Sanskrit suddenly threw its great light. Well does one of the foremost modern philologists say that this "was the electric spark which caused the floating elements to crystallize into regular forms." Among the first to bring the knowledge of Sanskrit to Europe were the Jesuit missionaries, whose services to the material basis of the science of comparative philology had already been so great; and the importance of the new discovery was soon seen among all scholars, whether orthodox or scientific. In 1784 the Asiatic Society at Calcutta was founded, and with it began Sanskrit philology. Scholars like Sir William Jones, Carey, Wilkins, Foster, Colebrooke, did noble work in the new field. A new spirit brooded over that chaos, and a great new orb of science was evolved.

The little group of scholars who gave themselves up to these researches, though almost without exception reverent Christians, were recognised at once by theologians as mortal foes of the whole sacred theory of language. Not only was the dogma of the multiplication of languages at the Tower of Babel swept out of sight by the new discovery, but the still more vital dogma of the divine origin of language, never before endangered, was felt to be in peril, since the evidence became overwhelming that so many varieties had been produced by a process of natural growth.

Heroic efforts were therefore made, in the supposed interest of Scripture, to discredit the new learning. Even such a man as Dugald Stewart declared that the discovery of Sanskrit was altogether fraudulent, and endeavoured to prove that the Brahmans had made it up from the vocabulary and grammar of Greek and Latin. Others exercised their ingenuity in picking the new discovery to pieces, and still others attributed it all to the machinations of Satan.

On the other hand, the more thoughtful men in the Church endeavoured to save something from the wreck of the old system by a compromise. They attempted to prove that Hebrew is at least a cognate tongue with the original speech of mankind, if not the original speech itself; but here they were confronted by the authority they dreaded most—the great Christian scholar, Sir William Jones himself. His words were: "I can only declare my belief that the language of Noah is irretrievably lost. After diligent search I can not find a single word used in common by the Arabian, Indian, and

Tartar families, before the intermixture of dialects occasioned by the Mohammedan conquests."

So, too, in Germany came full acknowledgment of the new truth, and from a Roman Catholic, Frederick Schlegel. He accepted the discoveries in the old language and literature of India as final: he saw the significance of these discoveries as regards philology, and grouped the languages of India, Persia, Greece, Italy, and Germany under the name afterward so universally accepted—Indo-Germanic.

It now began to be felt more and more, even among the most devoted churchmen, that the old theological dogmas regarding the origin of language, as held "always, everywhere, and by all," were wrong, and that Lucretius and sturdy old Gregory of Nyssa might be right.

But this was not the only wreck. During ages the great men in the Church had been calling upon the world to admire the amazing exploit of Adam in naming the animals which Jehovah had brought before him, and to accept the history of language in the light of this exploit. The early fathers, the mediæval doctors, the great divines of the Reformation period, Catholic and Protestant, had united in this universal chorus. Clement of Alexandria declared Adam's naming of the animals proof of a prophetic gift. St. John Chrysostom insisted that it was an evidence of consummate intelligence. Eusebius held that the phrase "That was the name thereof" implied that each name embodied the real character and description of the animal concerned.

This view was echoed by a multitude of divines in the seventeenth and eighteenth centuries. Typical among these was the great Dr. South, who, in his sermon on *The State of Man before the Fall,* declared that "Adam came into the world a philosopher, which sufficiently appears by his writing the nature of things upon their names."

In the chorus of modern English divines there appeared one of eminence who declared against this theory: Dr. Shuckford, chaplain in ordinary to his Majesty George II, in the preface to his work on *The Creation and Fall of Man,* pronounced the whole theory "romantic and irrational." He goes on to say: "The original of our speaking was from God; not that God put into Adam's mouth the very sounds which he designed he should use as the names of things; but God made Adam with the powers of a man; he had the use of an understanding to form notions in his mind of the things about him, and he had the power to utter sounds which should be to himself the names of things according as he might think fit to call them."

This echo of Gregory of Nyssa was for many years of little avail. Historians of philosophy still began with Adam, because only a philosopher could have named all created things. There was, indeed, one difficulty which had much troubled some theologians: this was, that fishes were not specially mentioned among the animals brought by Jehovah before Adam for naming. To meet this difficulty there was much argument, and some theologians laid stress on the difficulty of bringing fishes from the sea to the Garden of Eden to receive their names; but naturally other theologians replied that the almighty power which created the fishes could have easily brought them into the garden, one by one, even from the uttermost parts of the sea. This point, therefore, seems to have been left in abeyance.[5]

It had continued, then, the universal belief in the Church that the names of all created things, except possibly fishes, were given by Adam and in Hebrew; but all this theory was whelmed in ruin when it was found that there were other and indeed earlier names for the same animals than those in the Hebrew language; and especially was this enforced on thinking men when the Egyptian discoveries began to reveal the pictures of animals with their names in hieroglyphics at a period earlier than that agreed on by all the sacred chronologists as the date of the Creation.

[5] For the dangers of "the little system of the history of the world," see Sayce, as above. On Dugald Stewart's contention, see Max Müller, *Lectures on Language,* pp. 167, 168. For Sir William Jones, see his *Works,* London, 1807, vol. i, p. 199. For Schlegel, see Max Müller, as above. For an enormous list of great theologians, from the fathers down, who dwelt on the divine inspiration and wonderful gifts of Adam on this subject, see Canon Farrar, *Language and Languages.* The citation from Clement of Alexandria is *Strom.,* i, p. 335. See also Chrysostom, *Hom. XIV in Genesin;* also Eusebius, *Præp. Evang. XI,* p. 6. For the two quotations above given from Shuckford, see *The Creation and Fall of Man,* London, 1763, preface, p. lxxxiii; also his *Sacred and Profane History of the World,* 1753; revised edition by Wheeler, London, 1858. For the argument regarding the difficulty of bringing the fishes to be named into the Garden of Eden, see Massey, *Origin and Progress of Letters,* London, 1763, pp. 14-19.

Still another part of the sacred theory now received its death-blow. Closely allied with the question of the origin of language was that of the origin of letters. The earlier writers had held that letters were also a divine gift to Adam; but as we go on in the eighteenth century we find theological opinion inclining to the belief that this gift was reserved for Moses. This, as we have seen, was the view of St. John Chrysostom; and an eminent English divine early in the eighteenth century, John Johnson, Vicar of Kent, echoed it in the declaration concerning the alphabet, that "Moses first learned it from God by means of the lettering on the tables of the law." But here a difficulty arose—the biblical statement that God commanded Moses to "write in a book" his decree concerning Amalek before he went up into Sinai. With this the good vicar grapples manfully. He supposes that God had previously concealed the tables of stone in Mount Horeb, and that Moses, "when he kept Jethro's sheep thereabout, had free access to these tables, and perused them at discretion, though he was not permitted to carry them down with him." Our reconciler then asks for what other reason could God have kept Moses up in the mountain forty days at a time, except to teach him to write; and says, "It seems highly probable that the angel gave him the alphabet of the Hebrew, or in some other way unknown to us became his guide."

But this theory of letters was soon to be doomed like the other parts of the sacred theory. Studies in Comparative Philology, based upon researches in India, began to be re-enforced by facts regarding the inscriptions in Egypt, the cuneiform inscriptions of Assyria, the legends of Chaldea, and the folklore of China—where it was found in the sacred books that the animals were named by Fohi, and with such wisdom and insight that every name disclosed the nature of the corresponding animal.

But, although the old theory was doomed, heroic efforts were still made to support it. In 1788 James Beattie, in all the glory of his Oxford doctorate and royal pension, made a vigorous onslaught, declaring the new system of philology to be "degrading to our nature," and that the theory of the natural development of language is simply due to the beauty of Lucretius' poetry. But his main weapon was ridicule, and in this he showed himself a master. He tells the world, "The following paraphrase has nothing of the elegance of Horace or Lucretius, but seems to have all the elegance that so ridiculous a doctrine deserves":

> "When men out of the earth of old
> A dumb and beastly vermin crawled;
> For acorns, first, and holes of shelter,
> They tooth and nail, and helter skelter,
> Fought fist to fist; then with a club
> Each learned his brother brute to drub;
> Till, more experienced grown, these cattle
> Forged fit accoutrements for battle.
> At last (Lucretius says and Creech)
> They set their wits to work on *speech:*
> And that their thoughts might all have marks
> To make them known, these learnèd clerks
> Left off the trade of cracking crowns,
> And manufactured verbs and nouns."

But a far more powerful theologian entered the field in England to save the sacred theory of language—Dr. Adam Clarke. He was no less severe against Philology than against Geology. In 1804, as President of the Manchester Philological Society, he delivered an address in which he declared that, while men of all sects were eligible to membership, "he who rejects the establishment of what we believe to be a divine revelation, he who would disturb the peace of the quiet, and by doubtful disputations unhinge the minds of the simple and unreflecting, and endeavour to turn the unwary out of the way of peace and rational subordination, can have no seat among the members of this institution." The first sentence in this declaration gives food for reflection, for it is the same confusion of two ideas which has been at the root of so much interference of theology with science for the last two thousand years. Adam Clarke speaks of those "who reject the establishment of what *'we believe'* to be a divine revelation." Thus comes in that customary begging of the question —the substitution, as the real significance of Scripture, of *"what we believe"* for what *is*.

The intended result, too, of this ecclesiastical sentence was simple enough. It was that great men like Sir William Jones, Colebrooke, and their compeers, must not be heard in the Manchester Philological Society in discussion with Dr. Adam Clarke on questions regarding Sanskrit and other matters regarding which they knew all that was then known, and Dr. Clarke knew nothing.

But even Clarke was forced to yield to the scientific current. Thirty years later, in his *Commentary on the Old Testament,* he pitched the claims of the sacred theory on a much lower key. He says: "Mankind was of one language, in all likelihood the Hebrew. . . . The proper names and other significations given in the Scripture seem incontestable evidence that the Hebrew language was the original language of the earth,— the language in which God spoke to man, and in which he gave the revelation of his will to Moses and the prophets." Here are signs that this great champion is growing weaker in the faith: in the citations made it will be observed he no longer says *"is,"* but *"seems"*; and finally we have him saying, "What the first language was is almost useless to inquire, as it is impossible to arrive at any satisfactory information on this point."

In France, during the first half of the nineteenth century, yet more heavy artillery was wheeled into place, in order to make a last desperate defence of the sacred theory. The leaders in this effort were the three great Ultramontanes, De Maistre, De Bonald, and Lamennais. Condillac's contention that "languages were gradually and insensibly acquired, and that every man had his share of the general result," they attacked with reasoning based upon premises drawn from the book of Genesis. De Maistre especially excelled in ridiculing the philosophic or scientific theory. Lamennais, who afterward became so vexatious a thorn in the side of the Church, insisted, at this earlier period, that "man can no more think without words than see without light." And then, by that sort of mystical play upon words so well known in the higher ranges of theologic reasoning, he clinches his argument by saying, "The Word is truly and in every sense 'the light which lighteth every man that cometh into the world.' "

But even such champions as these could not stay the progress of thought. While they seemed to be carrying everything before them in France, researches in philology made at such centres of thought as the Sorbonne and the College of France were undermining their last great fortress. Curious indeed is it to find that the Sorbonne, the stronghold of theology through so many centuries, was now made in the nineteenth century the arsenal and stronghold of the new ideas. But the most striking result of the new tendency in France was seen when the greatest of the three champions, Lamennais himself, though offered the highest Church preferment, and even a cardinal's hat, braved the papal anathema, and went over to the scientific side.[6]

*　　*　　*

While at the middle of the nineteenth century the theory of the origin and development of language was upon the continent considered as settled, and a well-ordered science had there emerged from the old chaos, Great Britain still held back, in spite of the fact that the most important contributors to the science were of British origin. Leaders in every English church and sect vied with each other, either in denouncing the encroachments of the science of language or in explaining them away.

But a new epoch had come, and in a way least expected. Perhaps the most notable effort in bringing it in was made by Dr. Wiseman, afterward Cardinal Archbishop of Westminster. His is one of the best examples of a method which has been used with considerable effect during the latest stages of nearly all the controversies between theology and science. It consists in stating, with much fairness, the conclusions of the scientific authorities, and then in persuading one's self and trying to persuade others that the Church has always accepted them and accepts them now as "additional proofs of the truth of Scripture." A little juggling with words, a little amalgamation of texts, a little judicious suppression, a little imaginative deduction, a little unctuous phrasing, and the thing is done. One great service this eminent and kindly Catholic champion undoubtedly rendered: by this acknowledgment, so widely spread in his published lectures, he made it impossible

[6] For Johnson's work, showing how Moses learned the alphabet, see the *Collection of Discourses* by Rev. John Johnson, A.M., Vicar of Kent, London, 1728, p. 42, and the preface. For Beattie, see his *Theory of Language,* London, 1788, p. 98; also pp. 100, 101. For Adam Clarke, see, for the speech cited, his *Miscellaneous Works,* London, 1837; for the passage from his *Commentary,* see the London edition of 1836, vol. i, p. 93; for the other passage, see *Introduction to Bibliographical Miscellany,* quoted in article, *Origin of Language and Alphabetical Characters,* in *Methodist Magazine,* vol. xv, p. 214. For De Bonald, see his *Recherches Philosophiques,* part iii, chap. ii, *De l'Origine du Langage,* in his *Œuvres Complètes,* Paris, 1859, pp. 64-78, *passim.* For Joseph de Maistre, see his *Œuvres,* Bruxelles, 1852, vol. i, *Les Soirées de Saint Petersbourg,* deuxième entretien, *passim.* For Lamennais, see his *Œuvres Complètes,* Paris, 1836-'37, tome ii, pp. 78-81, chap. xv of *Essai sur l'Indifférence en Matière de Religion.*

for Catholics or Protestants longer to resist the main conclusions of science. Henceforward we only have efforts to save
theological appearances, and these only by men whose zeal
outran their discretion.

*   *   *

5. Summary

*   *   *

It may, indeed, be now fairly said that the thinking leaders
of theology have come to accept the conclusions of science
regarding the origin of language, as against the old explanations by myth and legend. The result has been a blessing both
to science and to religion. No harm has been done to religion;
what has been done is to release it from the clog of theories
which thinking men saw could no longer be maintained. No
matter what has become of the naming of the animals by
Adam, of the origin of the name Babel, of the fear of the
Almighty lest men might climb up into his realm above the
firmament, and of the confusion of tongues and the dispersion
of nations; the essentials of Christianity, as taught by its
blessed Founder, have simply been freed, by Comparative
Philology, from one more great incubus, and have therefore
been left to work with more power upon the hearts and minds
of mankind.

Nor has any harm been done to the Bible. On the contrary,
this divine revelation through science has made it all the more
precious to us. In these myths and legends caught from earlier
civilizations we see an evolution of the most important religious and moral truths for our race. Myth, legend, and parable seem, in obedience to a divine law, the necessary setting
for these truths, as they are successively evolved, ever in
higher and higher forms. What matters it, then, that we have
come to know that the accounts of Creation, the Fall, the
Deluge, and much else in our sacred books, were remem-
brances of lore obtained from the Chaldeans? What matters
it that the beautiful story of Joseph is found to be in part derived from an Egyptian romance, of which the hieroglyphs
may still be seen? What matters it that the story of David and
Goliath is poetry; and that Samson, like so many men of
strength in other religions, is probably a sun-myth? What matters it that the inculcation of high duty in the childhood of the
world is embodied in such quaint stories as those of Jonah
and Balaam? The more we realize these facts, the richer be-

comes that great body of literature brought together within the covers of the Bible. What matters it that those who incorporated the Creation lore of Babylonia and other Oriental nations into the sacred books of the Hebrews, mixed it with their own conceptions and deductions? What matters it that Darwin changed the whole aspect of our Creation myths; that Lyell and his compeers placed the Hebrew story of Creation and of the Deluge of Noah among legends; that Copernicus put an end to the standing still of the sun for Joshua; that Halley, in promulgating his law of comets, put an end to the doctrine of "signs and wonders"; that Pinel, in showing that all insanity is physical disease, relegated to the realm of mythology the witch of Endor and all stories of demoniacal possession; that the Rev. Dr. Schaff, and a multitude of recent Christian travellers in Palestine, have put into the realm of legend the story of Lot's wife transformed into a pillar of salt; that the anthropologists, by showing how man has risen everywhere from low and brutal beginnings, have destroyed the whole theological theory of "the fall of man"? Our great body of sacred literature is thereby only made more and more valuable to us: more and more we see how long and patiently the forces in the universe which make for righteousness have been acting in and upon mankind through the only agencies fitted for such work in the earliest ages of the world —through myth, legend, parable, and poem.

[Chapter 18

From the Dead Sea Legends to Comparative Mythology]

[1. The Growth of Explanatory Transformation Myths]

[2. Mediæval Growth of the Dead Sea Legends]

[3. Post-Reformation Culmination of the Dead Sea Legends—Beginnings of a Healthful Scepticism]

[4. Theological Efforts at Compromise—Triumph of the Scientific View]

[Chapter 19

From Leviticus to Political Economy]

[1. Origin and Progress of Hostility to Loans at Interest]

[2. Retreat of the Church, Protestant and Catholic]

Chapter 20

From the Divine Oracles to the Higher Criticism

1. The Older Interpretation

THE GREAT SACRED BOOKS of the world are the most precious of human possessions. They embody the deepest searchings into the most vital problems of humanity in all its stages: the naïve guesses of the world's childhood, the opening conceptions of its youth, the more fully rounded beliefs of its maturity.

These books, no matter how unhistorical in parts and at times, are profoundly true. They mirror the evolution of man's loftiest aspirations, hopes, loves, consolations, and enthusiasms; his hates and fears; his views of his origin and destiny; his theories of his rights and duties; and these not merely in their lights but in their shadows. Therefore it is that they contain the germs of truths most necessary in the evolution of humanity, and give to these germs the environment and sustenance which best insure their growth and strength.

With wide differences in origin and character, this sacred literature has been developed and has exercised its influence in obedience to certain general laws. First of these in time, if not in importance, is that which governs its origin: in all civilizations we find that the Divine Spirit working in the mind of man shapes his sacred books first of all out of the chaos of myth and legend; and of these books, when life is thus breathed into them, the fittest survive.

So broad and dense is this atmosphere of myth and legend enveloping them that it lingers about them after they have been brought forth full-orbed; and, sometimes, from it are even produced secondary mythical and legendary concretions —satellites about these greater orbs of early thought. Of these secondary growths one may be mentioned as showing how rich in myth-making material was the atmosphere which enveloped our own earlier sacred literature.

In the third century before Christ there began to be elaborated among the Jewish scholars of Alexandria, then the great centre of human thought, a Greek translation of the main books constituting the Old Testament. Nothing could be more natural at that place and time than such a translation; yet the growth of explanatory myth and legend around it was none the less luxuriant. There was indeed a twofold growth. Among the Jews favourable to the new version a legend rose which justified it. This legend in its first stage was to the effect that the Ptolemy then on the Egyptian throne had, at the request of his chief librarian, sent to Jerusalem for translators; that the Jewish high priest Eleazar had sent to the king a most precious copy of the Scriptures from the temple at Jerusalem, and six most venerable, devout, and learned scholars from each of the twelve tribes of Israel; that the number of translators thus correspond with the mysterious seventy-two appellations of God; and that the combined efforts of these seventy-two men produced a marvellously perfect translation.

But in that atmosphere of myth and marvel the legend continued to grow, and soon we have it blooming forth yet more gorgeously in the statement that King Ptolemy ordered each of the seventy-two to make by himself a full translation of the entire Old Testament, and shut up each translator in a separate cell on the island of Pharos, secluding him there until the work was done; that the work of each was completed in exactly seventy-two days; and that when, at the end of the seventy-two days, the seventy-two translations were compared, each was found exactly like all the others. This showed clearly Jehovah's *approval*.

But out of all this myth and legend there was also evolved an account of a very different sort. The Jews who remained faithful to the traditions of their race regarded this Greek version as a profanation, and therefore there grew up the legend that on the completion of the work there was darkness over the whole earth during three days. This showed clearly Jehovah's *disapproval*.

These well-known legends, which arose within what—as compared with any previous time—was an exceedingly enlightened period, and which were steadfastly believed by a vast multitude of Jews and Christians for ages, are but single examples among scores which show how inevitably such traditions regarding sacred books are developed in the earlier stages of civilization, when men explain everything by miracle and nothing by law.[1]

As the second of these laws governing the evolution of sacred literature may be mentioned that which we have constantly seen so effective in the growth of theological ideas —that to which Comte gave the name of the *Law of Wills and Causes*. Obedient to this, man attributes to the Supreme Being a physical, intellectual, and moral structure like his own; hence it is that the votary of each of the great world religions ascribes to its sacred books what he considers absolute perfection: he imagines them to be what he himself would give the world, were he himself infinitely good, wise, and powerful.

A very simple analogy might indeed show him that even a literature emanating from an all-wise, beneficent, and powerful author might not seem perfect when judged by a human standard; for he has only to look about him in the world to find that the work which he attributes to an all-wise, all-beneficent, and all-powerful Creator is by no means free from evil and wrong.

But this analogy long escapes him, and the exponent of each great religion proves to his own satisfaction, and to the

[1] For the legend regarding the Septuagint, especially as developed by the letters of Pseudo-Aristeas, and for quaint citations from the fathers regarding it, see *The History of the Seventy-two Interpretators, from the Greek of Aristeas*, translated by Mr. Lewis, London, 1715; also Clement of Alexandria, in the *Ante-Nicene Christian Library*, Edinburgh, 1867, p. 448. For interesting summaries showing the growth of the story, see Drummond, *Philo Judæus and the Growth of the Alexandrian Philosophy*, London, 1888, vol. i, pp. 231 *et. seq.;* also Renan, *Histoire du Peuple Israel*, vol. iv, chap. iv; also, for Philo Judæus's part in developing the legend, see Rev. Dr. Sanday's *Bampton Lectures* for 1893, on *Inspiration*, pp. 86, 87.

edification of his fellows, that their own sacred literature is absolutely accurate in statement, infinitely profound in meaning, and miraculously perfect in form. From these premises also he arrives at the conclusion that his own sacred literature is unique; that no other sacred book can have emanated from a divine source; and that all others claiming to be sacred are impostures.

Still another law governing the evolution of sacred literature in every great world religion is that when the books which compose it are once selected and grouped they come to be regarded as a final creation from which nothing can be taken away, and of which even error in form, if sanctioned by tradition, may not be changed.

The working of this law has recently been seen on a large scale.

A few years since, a body of chosen scholars, universally acknowledged to be the most fit for the work, undertook, at the call of English-speaking Christendom, to revise the authorized English version of the Bible.

Beautiful as was that old version, there was abundant reason for a revision. The progress of biblical scholarship had revealed multitudes of imperfections and not a few gross errors in the work of the early translators, and these, if uncorrected, were sure to bring the sacred volume into discredit.

Nothing could be more reverent than the spirit of the revisers, and the nineteenth century has known few historical events of more significant and touching beauty than the participation in the holy communion by all these scholars—prelates, presbyters, ministers, and laymen of churches most widely differing in belief and observance—kneeling side by side at the little altar in Westminster Abbey.

Nor could any work have been more conservative and cautious than theirs; as far as possible they preserved the old matter and form with scrupulous care.

Yet their work was no sooner done than it was bitterly attacked and widely condemned; to this day it is largely regarded with dislike. In Great Britain, in America, in Australia, the old version, with its glaring misconceptions, mistranslations, and interpolations, is still read in preference to the new; the great body of English-speaking Christians clearly preferring the accustomed form of words given by the seventeenth-century translators, rather than a nearer approach to the exact teaching of the Holy Ghost.

Still another law is, that when once a group of sacred books has been evolved—even though the group really be a great library of most dissimilar works, ranging in matter from the hundredth Psalm to the Song of Songs, and in manner from the sublimity of Isaiah to the offhand story-telling of Jonah—all come to be thought one inseparable mass of inter-penetrating parts; every statement in each fitting exactly and miraculously into each statement in every other; and each and every one, and all together, literally true to fact, and at the same time full of hidden meanings.

The working of these and other laws governing the evolution of sacred literature is very clearly seen in the great rabbinical schools which flourished at Jerusalem, Tiberias, and elsewhere, after the return of the Jews from the Babylonian captivity, and especially as we approach the time of Christ. These schools developed a subtlety in the study of the Old Testament which seems almost preternatural. The resultant system was mainly a jugglery with words, phrases, and numbers, which finally became a "sacred science," with various recognised departments, in which interpretation was carried on sometimes by attaching a numerical value to letters; sometimes by interchange of letters from differently arranged alphabets; sometimes by the making of new texts out of the initial letters of the old; and with ever-increasing subtlety.

Such efforts as these culminated fitly in the rabbinical declaration that each passage in the law has seventy distinct meanings, and that God himself gives three hours every day to their study.

After this the Jewish world was prepared for anything, and it does not surprise us to find such discoveries in the domain of ethical culture as the doctrine that, for inflicting the forty stripes save one upon those who broke the law, the lash should be braided of ox-hide and ass-hide; and, as warrant for this construction of the lash, the text, "The ox knoweth his owner, and the ass his master's crib, but Israel doth not know"; and, as the logic connecting text and lash, the statement that Jehovah evidently intended to command that "the men who know not shall be beaten by those animals whose knowledge shames them."

By such methods also were revealed such historical treasures as that Og, King of Bashan, escaped the deluge by wading after Noah's ark.

There were, indeed, noble exceptions to this kind of teaching. It can not be forgotten that Rabbi Hillel formulated the golden rule, which had before him been given to the extreme Orient by Confucius, and which afterward received a yet more beautiful and positive emphasis from Jesus of Nazareth; but the seven rules of interpretation laid down by Hillel were multiplied and refined by men like Rabbi Ismael and Rabbi Eleazar until they justified every absurd subtlety.[2]

An eminent scholar has said that while the letter of Scripture became ossified in Palestine, it became volatilized at Alexandria; and the truth of this remark was proved by the Alexandrian Jewish theologians just before the beginning of our era.

This, too, was in obedience to a law of development, which is, that when literal interpretation clashes with increasing knowledge or with progress in moral feeling, theologians take refuge in mystic meanings—a law which we see working in all great religions, from the Brahmans finding hidden senses in the Vedas, to Plato and the Stoics finding them in the Greek myths; and from the Sofi reading new meanings into the Koran, to eminent Christian divines of the nineteenth century giving a non-natural sense to some of the plainest statements in the Bible.

Nothing is more natural than all this. When naïve statements of sacred writers, in accord with the ethics of early ages, make Brahma perform atrocities which would disgrace a pirate; and Jupiter take part in adventures worthy of Don Juan; and Jahveh practise trickery, cruelty, and high-handed injustice which would bring any civilized mortal into the criminal courts, the invention of allegory is the one means of saving the divine authority as soon as men reach higher planes of civilization.

The great early master in this evolution of allegory, for the satisfaction of Jews and Christians, was Philo: by him its use

[2] For a multitude of amusing examples of rabbinical interpretations, see an article in *Blackwood's Magazine* for November, 1882. For a more general discussion, see Archdeacon Farrar's *History of Interpretation,* lect. i and ii, and Rev. Prof. H. P. Smith's *Inspiration and Inerrancy,* Cincinnati, 1893, especially chap. iv; also Reuss, *History of the New Testament,* English translation, pp. 527, 528.

came in as never before. The four streams of the garden of Eden thus become the four virtues; Abraham's country and kindred, from which he was commanded to depart, the human body and its members; the five cities of Sodom, the five senses; the Euphrates, correction of manners. By Philo and his compeers even the most insignificant words and phrases, and those especially, were held to conceal the most precious meanings.

A perfectly natural and logical result of this view was reached when Philo, saturated as he was with Greek culture and nourished on pious traditions of the utterances at Delphi and Dodona, spoke reverently of the Jewish Scriptures as *"oracles."* Oracles they became: as oracles they appeared in the early history of the Christian Church; and oracles they remained for centuries: eternal life or death, infinite happiness or agony, as well as ordinary justice in this world, being made to depend on shifting interpretations of a long series of dark and doubtful utterances—interpretations frequently given by men who might have been prophets and apostles, but who had become simply oracle-mongers.

Pressing these oracles into the service of science, Philo became the forerunner of that long series of theologians who, from Augustine and Cosmas to Mr. Gladstone, have attempted to extract from scriptural myth and legend profound contributions to natural science. Thus he taught that the golden candlesticks in the tabernacle symbolized the planets, the high priest's robe the universe, and the bells upon it the harmony of earth and water—whatever that may mean. So Cosmas taught, a thousand years later, that the table of shewbread in the tabernacle showed forth the form and construction of the world; and Mr. Gladstone hinted, more than a thousand years later still, that Neptune's trident had a mysterious connection with the Christian doctrine of the Trinity.[3]

[3] For Philo Judæus, see Yonge's translation, Bohn's edition; see also Sanday, *Inspiration,* pp. 78-85. For admirable general remarks on this period in the history of exegesis, see Bartlett, *Bampton Lectures,* 1888, p. 29. For efforts in general to save the credit of myths by allegorical interpretation, and for those of Philo in particular, see Drummond, *Philo Judæus,* London, 1888, vol. i, pp. 18, 19, and notes. For interesting samples of Alexandrian exegesis and for Philo's application of the term "oracle" to the Jewish Scriptures, see Farrar, *History of Interpretation,* p. 147 and note. For his discovery of symbols of the universe in the furniture of the tabernacle, see Drummond, as above, vol. i, pp. 269 *et seq.*

These methods, as applied to the Old Testament, had appeared at times in the New; in spite of the resistance of Tertullian and Irenæus, they were transmitted to the Church; and in the works of the early fathers they bloomed forth luxuriantly.

Justin Martyr and Clement of Alexandria vigorously extended them. Typical of Justin's method is his finding, in a very simple reference by Isaiah to Damascus, Samaria, and Assyria, a clear prophecy of the three wise men of the East who brought gifts to the infant Saviour; and in the bells on the priest's robe a prefiguration of the twelve apostles. Any difficulty arising from the fact that the number of bells is not specified in Scripture, Justin overcame by insisting that David referred to this prefiguration in the nineteenth Psalm: "Their sound is gone out through all the earth, and their words to the end of the world."

Working in this vein, Clement of Alexandria found in the form, dimensions, and colour of the Jewish tabernacle a whole wealth of interpretation—the altar of incense representing the earth placed at the centre of the universe; the high priest's robe the visible world; the jewels on the priest's robe the zodiac; and Abraham's three days' journey to Mount Moriah the three stages of the soul in its progress toward the knowledge of God. Interpreting the New Testament, he lessened any difficulties involved in the miracle of the barley loaves and fishes by suggesting that what it really means is that Jesus gave mankind a preparatory training for the gospel by means of the law and philosophy; because, as he says, barley, like the law, ripens sooner than wheat, which represents the gospel; and because, just as fishes grow in the waves of the ocean, so philosophy grew in the waves of the Gentile world.

Out of reasonings like these, those who followed, especially Cosmas, developed, as we have seen, a complete theological science of geography and astronomy.[4]

For the general subject, admirably discussed from a historical point of view, see the Rev. Edwin Hatch, D. D., *The Influence of Greek Ideas and Usages upon the Christian Church*, Hibbert Lectures for 1888, chap. iii. For Cosmas, see my chapter on *Geography* and *Astronomy*. For Mr. Gladstone's view of the connection between Neptune's trident and the doctrine of the Trinity, see his *Juventus Mundi*.

[4] For Justin, see the *Dialogue with Trypho*, chaps. xlii, lxxvi, and lxxxiii. For Clement of Alexandria, see his *Miscellanies*, book v,

But the instrument in exegesis which was used with most cogent force was the occult significance of certain numbers. The Chaldean and Egyptian researches of our own time have revealed the main source of this line of thought; the speculations of Plato upon it are well known; but among the Jews and in the early Church it grew into something far beyond the wildest imaginings of the priests of Memphis and Babylon.

Philo had found for the elucidation of Scripture especially deep meanings in the numbers four, six, and seven; but other interpreters soon surpassed him. At the very outset this occult power was used in ascertaining the canonical books of Scripture. Josephus argued that, since there were twenty-two letters in the Hebrew alphabet, there must be twenty-two sacred books in the Old Testament; other Jewish authorities thought that there should be twenty-four books, on account of the twenty-four watches in the temple. St. Jerome wavered between the argument based upon the twenty-two letters in the Hebrew alphabet and that suggested by the twenty-four elders in the Apocalypse. Hilary of Poitiers argued that there must be twenty-four books, on account of the twenty-four letters in the Greek alphabet. Origen found an argument for the existence of exactly four gospels in the existence of just four elements. Irenæus insisted that there could be neither more nor fewer than four gospels, since the earth has four quarters, the air four winds, and the cherubim four faces; and he denounced those who declined to accept this reasoning as "vain, ignorant, and audacious."[5]

But during the first half of the third century came one who exercised a still stronger influence in this direction—a great man who, while rendering precious services, did more than

---

chaps. vi and xi, and book vii, chap. xvi, and especially Hatch, *Hibbert Lectures,* as above, pp. 76, 77. As to the loose views of the canon held by these two fathers and others of their time, see Ladd, *Doctrine of the Sacred Scriptures,* vol. ii, pp. 86, 88; also Diestel, *Geschichte des alten Testaments.*

[5] For Jerome and Origen, see notes on pages following. For Irenæus, see Irenæus, *Adversus Hæres.,* lib. iii, cap. xi, § 8. For the general subject, see Sanday, *Inspiration,* p. 115; also Farrar and H. P. Smith as above. For a recent very full and very curious statement from a Roman Catholic authority regarding views cherished in the older Church as to the symbolism of numbers, see Detzel, *Christliche Iconographie,* Freiburg im Breisgau, 1894, Band i, *Einleitung,* p. 4.

any other to fasten upon the Church a system which has been one of its heaviest burdens for more than sixteen hundred years: this was Origen. Yet his purpose was noble and his work based on profound thought. He had to meet the leading philosophers of the pagan world, to reply to their arguments against the Old Testament, and especially to break the force of their taunts against its imputation of human form, limitations, passions, weaknesses, and even immoralities to the Almighty.

Starting with a mistaken translation of a verse in the book of Proverbs, Origen presented as a basis for his main structure the idea of a threefold sense of Scripture: the literal, the moral, and the mystic—corresponding to the Platonic conception of the threefold nature of man. As results of this we have such masterpieces as his proof, from the fifth verse of chapter xxv of Job, that the stars are living beings, and from the well-known passage in the nineteenth chapter of St. Matthew his warrant for self-mutilation. But his great triumphs were in the allegorical method. By its use the Bible was speedily made an oracle indeed, or, rather, a book of riddles. A list of kings in the Old Testament thus becomes an enumeration of sins; the waterpots of stone, "containing two or three firkins apiece," at the marriage of Cana, signify the literal, moral, and spiritual sense of Scripture; the ass upon which the Saviour rode on his triumphal entry into Jerusalem becomes the Old Testament, the foal the New Testament, and the two apostles who went to loose them the moral and mystical senses; blind Bartimeus throwing off his coat while hastening to Jesus, opens a whole treasury of oracular meanings.

The genius and power of Origen made a great impression on the strong thinkers who followed him. St. Jerome called him "the greatest master in the Church since the apostles," and Athanasius was hardly less emphatic.

The structure thus begun was continued by leading theologians during the centuries following: St. Hilary of Poitiers— "the Athanasius of Gaul"—produced some wonderful results of this method; but St. Jerome, inspired by the example of the man whom he so greatly admired, went beyond him. A triumph of his exegesis is seen in his statement that the Shunamite damsel who was selected to cherish David in his old age signified heavenly wisdom.

The great mind of St. Augustine was drawn largely into this kind of creation, and nothing marks more clearly the vast change which had come over the world than the fact that this greatest of the early Christian thinkers turned from the broader paths opened by Plato and Aristotle into that opened by Clement of Alexandria.

In the mystic power of numbers to reveal the sense of Scripture Augustine found especial delight. He tells us that there is deep meaning in sundry scriptural uses of the number forty, and especially as the number of days required for fasting. Forty, he reminds us, is four times ten. Now, four, he says, is the number especially representing time, the day and the year being each divided into four parts; while ten, being made up of three and seven, represents knowledge of the Creator and creature, three referring to the three persons in the triune Creator, and seven referring to the three elements, heart, soul, and mind, taken in connection with the four elements, fire, air, earth, and water, which go to make up the creature. Therefore this number ten, representing knowledge, being multiplied by four, representing time, admonishes us to live during time according to knowledge—that is, to fast for forty days.

Referring to such misty methods as these, which lead the reader to ask himself whether he is sleeping or waking, St. Augustine remarks that "ignorance of numbers prevents us from understanding such things in Scripture." But perhaps the most amazing example is to be seen in his notes on the hundred and fifty and three fishes which, according to St. John's Gospel, were caught by St. Peter and the other apostles. Some points in his long development of this subject may be selected to show what the older theological method could be made to do for a great mind. He tells us that the hundred and fifty and three fishes embody a mystery; that the number ten, evidently as the number of the commandments, indicates the law; but, as the law without the spirit only kills, we must add the seven gifts of the spirit, and we thus have the number seventeen, which signifies the old and new dispensations; then, if we add together every several number which seventeen contains from one to seventeen inclusive, the result is a hundred and fifty and three—the number of the fishes.

With this sort of reasoning he finds profound meanings in the number of furlongs mentioned in the sixth chapter of St. John. Referring to the fact that the disciples had rowed about "twenty-five or thirty furlongs," he declares that "twenty-five typifies the law, because it is five times five, but the law was imperfect before the gospel came; now perfection is comprised in six, since God in six days perfected the world, hence five is multiplied by six that the law may be perfected by the gospel, and six times five is thirty."

But Augustine's exploits in exegesis were not all based on numerals; he is sometimes equally profound in other modes. Thus he tells us that the condemnation of the serpent to eat dust typifies the sin of curiosity, since in eating dust he "penetrates the obscure and shadowy"; and that Noah's ark was "pitched within and without with pitch" to show the safety of the Church from the leaking in of heresy.

Still another exploit—one at which the Church might well have stood aghast—was his statement that the drunkenness of Noah prefigured the suffering and death of Christ. It is but just to say that he was not the original author of this interpretation: it had been presented long before by St. Cyprian. But this was far from Augustine's worst. Perhaps no interpretation of Scripture has ever led to more cruel and persistent oppression, torture, and bloodshed than his reading into one of the most beautiful parables of Jesus of Nazareth—into the words "Compel them to come in"—a warrant for religious persecution: of all unintended blasphemies since the world began, possibly the most appalling.

Another strong man follows to fasten these methods on the Church: St. Gregory the Great. In his renowned work on the book of Job, the *Magna Moralia,* given to the world at the end of the sixth century, he lays great stress on the deep mystical meanings of the statement that Job had seven sons. He thinks the seven sons typify the twelve apostles, for "the apostles were selected through the sevenfold grace of the Spirit; moreover, twelve is produced from seven—that is, the two parts of seven, four and three, when multiplied together give twelve." He also finds deep significance in the number of the apostles; this number being evidently determined by a multiplication of the number of persons in the Trinity by the number of quarters of the globe. Still, to do him justice, it must be said that in some parts of his exegesis the strong sense which was one of his most striking characteristics crops out in a way very refreshing. Thus, referring to a passage in the first chapter of Job, regarding the oxen which were ploughing and the asses which were feeding beside them, he tells us pithily that these typify two classes of Christians: the oxen, the energetic Christians who do the work of the Church; the asses, the lazy Christians who merely feed.[6]

Thus began the vast theological structure of oracular interpretation applied to the Bible. As we have seen, the men who prepared the ground for it were the rabbis of Palestine and the Hellenized Jews of Alexandria; and the four great men who laid its foundation courses were Origen, St. Augustine, St. Jerome, and St. Gregory.

During the ten centuries following the last of these men this structure continued to rise steadily above the plain meanings of Scripture. The Christian world rejoiced in it, and the few great thinkers who dared bring the truth to bear upon it were rejected. It did indeed seem at one period in the early Church that a better system might be developed. The School of Antioch, especially as represented by Chrysostom, appeared likely to lead in this better way, but the dominant forces were too strong; the passion for myth and marvel prevailed over the love of real knowledge, and the reasonings of Chrysostom and his compeers were neglected.[7]

In the ninth century came another effort to present the claims of right reason. The first man prominent in this was St. Agobard, Bishop of Lyons, whom an eminent historian has well called the clearest head of his time. With the same insight which penetrated the fallacies and follies of image worship, belief in witchcraft persecution, the ordeal, and the judicial duel, he saw the futility of this vast fabric of interpretation, protested against the idea that the Divine Spirit

[6] For Origen, see the *De Principiis*, book iv, chaps. i-vii *et seq.*, Crombie's translation; also the *Contra Celsum*, vol. vi, p. 70; vol. vii, p. 20, etc.; also various citations in Farrar. For Hilary, see his *Tractatus super Psalmos*, cap. ix, li, etc., in Migne, vol. ix, and *De Trinitate*, lib. ii, cap. ii. For Jerome's interpretation of the text relating to the Shunamite woman, see Epist. lii, in Migne, vol. xxii, pp. 527, 528. For Augustine's use of numbers, see the *De Doctrina Christiana*, lib. ii, cap. xvi; and for the explanation of the draught of fishes, see Augustine in, *In Johan. Evangel.*, tractat. cxxii; and on the twenty-five to thirty furlongs, ibid., tract. xxv, cap. 6; and for the significance of the serpent eating dust, *De Gen.*, lib. ii, c. 18. For the view that the drunkenness of Noah prefigured the suffering of Christ, as held by SS. Cyprian and Augustine, see Farrar, as above, pp. 181, 238. For St. Gregory, see the *Magna Moralia*, lib. i, cap. xiv.

[7] For the work of the School of Antioch, and especially of Chrysostom, see the eloquent tribute to it by Farrar, as above.

extended its inspiration to the mere words of Scripture, and asked a question which has resounded through every generation since: "If you once begin such a system, who can measure the absurdity which will follow?"

During the same century another opponent of this dominant system appeared: John Scotus Erigena. He contended that "reason and authority come alike from the one source of Divine Wisdom"; that the fathers, great as their authority is, often contradict each other; and that, in last resort, reason must be called in to decide between them.

But the evolution of unreason continued: Agobard was unheeded, and Erigena placed under the ban by two councils—his work being condemned by a synod as a *"Commentum Diaboli."* Four centuries later Honorius III ordered it to be burned, as "teeming with the venom of hereditary depravity"; and finally, after eight centuries, Pope Gregory XIII placed it on the Index, where, with so many other works which have done good service to humanity, it remains to this day. Nor did Abélard, who, three centuries after Agobard and Erigena, made an attempt in some respects like theirs, have any better success: his fate at the hands of St. Bernard and the Council of Sens the world knows by heart. Far more consonant with the spirit of the universal Church was the teaching in the twelfth century of the great Hugo of St. Victor, conveyed in these ominous words, "Learn first what is to be believed" (*Disce primo quod credendum est*), meaning thereby that one should first accept doctrines, and then find texts to confirm them.

These principles being dominant, the accretions to the enormous fabric of interpretation went steadily on. Typical is the fact that the Venerable Bede contributed to it the doctrine that, in the text mentioning Elkanah and his two wives, Elkanah means Christ and the two wives the Synagogue and the Church. Even such men as Alfred the Great and St. Thomas Aquinas were added to the forces at work in building above the sacred books this prodigious structure of sophistry.

Perhaps nothing shows more clearly the tenacity of the old system of interpretation than the sermons of Savonarola. During the last decade of the fifteenth century, just at the close of the mediæval period, he was engaged in a life-and-death struggle at Florence. No man ever preached more powerfully the gospel of righteousness; none ever laid more stress on conduct; even Luther was not more zealous for reform or more careless of tradition; and yet we find the great Florentine apostle and martyr absolutely tied fast to the old system of allegorical interpretation. The autograph notes of his sermons, still preserved in his cell at San Marco, show this abundantly. Thus we find him attaching to the creation of grasses and plants on the third day an allegorical connection with the "multitude of the elect" and with the "sound doctrines of the Church"; and to the creation of land animals on the sixth day a similar relation to "the Jewish people" and to "Christians given up to things earthly."[8]

The revival of learning in the fifteenth century seemed likely to undermine this older structure.

Then it was that Lorenzo Valla brought to bear on biblical research, for the first time, the spirit of modern criticism. By truly scientific methods he proved the famous "Letter of Christ to Abgarus" a forgery; the "Donation of Constantine," one of the great foundations of the ecclesiastical power in temporal things, a fraud; and the "Apostles' Creed" a creation which post-dated the apostles by several centuries. Of even more permanent influence was his work upon the New Testament, in which he initiated the modern method of comparing manuscripts to find what the sacred text really is. At an earlier or later period he would doubtless have paid for his temerity with his life; fortunately, just at that time the ruling pontiff and his contemporaries cared much for literature and little for orthodoxy, and from their palaces he could bid defiance to the Inquisition.

While Valla thus initiated biblical criticism south of the

[8] For Agobard, see the *Liber adversus Fredigisum,* cap. xii; also Reuter's *Relig. Aufklärung im Mittelalter,* vol. i, p. 24; also Poole, *Illustrations of the History of Medieval Thought,* London, 1884, pp. 38 *et seq.* For Erigena, see his *De Divisione Naturæ,* lib. iv. cap. v; also i, cap. lxvi-lxxi; and for general account, see Ueberweg, *History of Philosophy,* New York, 1871, vol. i, pp. 358 *et seq.;* and for the treatment of his work by the Church, see the edition of the *Index* under Leo XIII, 1881. For Abélard, see the *Sic et Non,* Prologue, Migne, vol. clxxviii; and on the general subject, Milman, *Latin Christianity,* vol. iii, pp. 371-377. For Hugo of St. Victor, see *Erudit. Didask.,* lib. vii, vi, 4, in Migne, clxxvi. For Savonarola's interpretations, see various references to his preaching in Villari's *Life of Savonarola,* English translation, London, 1890, and especially the exceedingly interesting table in the appendix to vol. i, chap. vii.

Alps, a much greater man began a more fruitful work in northern Europe. Erasmus, with his edition of the New Testament, stands at the source of that great stream of modern research and thought which is doing so much to undermine and dissolve away the vast fabric of patristic and scholastic interpretation.

Yet his efforts to purify the scriptural text seemed at first to encounter insurmountable difficulties, and one of these may stimulate reflection. He had found, what some others had found before him, that the famous verse in the fifth chapter of the First Epistle General of St. John, regarding the "three witnesses," was an interpolation. Careful research through all the really important early manuscripts showed that it appeared in none of them. Even after the Bible had been corrected, in the eleventh and twelfth centuries, by Lanfranc, Archbishop of Canterbury, and by Nicholas, cardinal and librarian of the Roman Church, "in accordance with the orthodox faith," the passage was still wanting in the more authoritative Latin manuscripts. There was not the slightest tenable ground for believing in the authenticity of the text; on the contrary, it has been demonstrated that, after a universal silence of the orthodox fathers of the Church, of the ancient versions of the Scriptures, and of all really important manuscripts, the verse first appeared in a Confession of Faith drawn up by an obscure zealot toward the end of the fifth century. In a very mild exercise, then, of critical judgment, Erasmus omitted this text from the first two editions of his Greek Testament as evidently spurious. A storm arose at once. In England, Lee, afterward Archbishop of York; in Spain, Stunica, one of the editors of the Complutensian Polyglot; and in France, Budé, Syndic of the Sorbonne, together with a vast army of monks in England and on the Continent, attacked him ferociously. He was condemned by the University of Paris, and various propositions of his were declared to be heretical and impious. Fortunately, the worst persecutors could not reach him; otherwise they might have treated him as they treated his disciple, Berquin, whom in 1529 they burned at Paris.

The fate of this spurious text throws light into the workings of human nature in its relations to sacred literature. Although Luther omitted it from his translation of the New Testament, and kept it out of every copy published during his lifetime, and although at a later period the most eminent

Christian scholars showed that it had no right to a place in the Bible, it was, after Luther's death, replaced in the German translation, and has been incorporated into all important editions of it, save one, since the beginning of the seventeenth century. So essential was it found in maintaining the dominant theology that, despite the fact that Sir Isaac Newton, Richard Porson, the nineteenth-century revisers, and all other eminent authorities have rejected it, the Anglican Church still retains it in its Lectionary, and the Scotch Church continues to use it in the Westminster Catechism, as a main support of the doctrine of the Trinity.

Nor were other new truths presented by Erasmus better received. His statement that "some of the epistles ascribed to St. Paul are certainly not his," which is to-day universally acknowledged as a truism, also aroused a storm. For generations, then, his work seemed vain.

On the coming in of the Reformation the great structure of belief in the literal and historical correctness of every statement in the Scriptures, in the profound allegorical meanings of the simplest texts, and even in the divine origin of the vowel punctuation, towered more loftily and grew more rapidly than ever before. The Reformers, having cast off the authority of the Pope and of the universal Church, fell back all the more upon the infallibility of the sacred books. The attitude of Luther toward this great subject was characteristic. As a rule, he adhered tenaciously to the literal interpretation of the Scriptures; his argument against Copernicus is a fair example of his reasoning in this respect; but, with the strong good sense which characterized him, he from time to time broke away from the received belief. Thus, he took the liberty of understanding certain passages in the Old Testament in a different sense from that given them by the New Testament, and declared St. Paul's allegorical use of the story of Sarah and Hagar "too unsound to stand the test." He also emphatically denied that the Epistle to the Hebrews was written by St. Paul, and he did this in the exercise of a critical judgment upon internal evidence. His utterance as to the Epistle of St. James became famous. He announced to the Church: "I do not esteem this an apostolic epistle; I will not have it in my Bible among the canonical books," and he summed up his opinion in his well-known allusion to it as "an epistle of straw."

Emboldened by him, the gentle spirit of Melanchthon,

while usually taking the Bible very literally, at times revolted; but this was not due to any want of loyalty to the old method of interpretation: whenever the wildest and most absurd system of exegesis seemed necessary to support any part of the reformed doctrine, Luther and Melanchthon unflinchingly developed it. Both of them held firmly to the old dictum of Hugo of St. Victor, which, as we have seen, was virtually that one must first accept the doctrine, and then find scriptural warrant for it. Very striking examples of this were afforded in the interpretation by Luther and Melanchthon of certain alleged marvels of their time, and one out of several of these may be taken as typical of their methods.

In 1523 Luther and Melanchthon jointly published a work under the title *Der Papstesel*—interpreting the significance of a strange, ass-like monster which, according to a popular story, had been found floating in the Tiber some time before. This book was illustrated by startling pictures, and both text and pictures were devoted to proving that this monster was "a sign from God," indicating the doom of the papacy. This treatise by the two great founders of German Protestantism pointed out that the ass's head signified the Pope himself; "for," said they, "as well as an ass's head is suited to a human body, so well is the Pope suited to be head over the Church." This argument was clinched by a reference to Exodus. The right hand of the monster, said to be like an elephant's foot, they made to signify the spiritual rule of the Pope, since "with it he tramples upon all the weak": this they proved from the book of Daniel and the Second Epistle to Timothy. The monster's left hand, which was like the hand of a man, they declared to mean the Pope's secular rule, and they found passages to support this view in Daniel and St. Luke. The right foot, which was like the foot of an ox, they declared to typify the servants of the spiritual power; and proved this by a citation from St. Matthew. The left foot, like a griffin's claw, they made to typify the servants of the temporal power of the Pope, and the highly developed breasts and various other members, cardinals, bishops, priests, and monks, "whose life is eating, drinking, and unchastity": to prove this they cited passages from Second Timothy and Philippians. The alleged fish-scales on the arms, legs, and neck of the monster they made to typify secular princes and lords; "since," as they said, "in St. Matthew and Job the sea typifies the world, and fishes men." The old man's head at the base of the monster's spine they interpreted to mean "the abolition and end of the papacy," and proved this from Hebrews and Daniel. The dragon which opens his mouth in the rear and vomits fire, "refers to the terrible, virulent bulls and books which the Pope and his minions are now vomiting forth into the world." The two great Reformers then went on to insist that, since this monster was found at Rome, it could refer to no person but the Pope; "for," they said, "God always sends his signs in the places where their meaning applies." Finally, they assured the world that the monster in general clearly signified that the papacy was then near its end. To this development of interpretation Luther and Melanchthon especially devoted themselves; the latter by revising this exposition of the prodigy, and the former by making additions to a new edition.

Such was the success of this kind of interpretation that Luther, hearing that a monstrous calf had been found at Freiburg, published a treatise upon it—showing, by citations from the books of Exodus, Kings, the Psalms, Isaiah, Daniel, and the Gospel of St. John, that this new monster was the especial work of the devil, but full of meaning in regard to the questions at issue between the Reformers and the older Church.

The other main branch of the Reformed Church appeared for a time to establish a better system. Calvin's strong logic seemed at one period likely to tear his adherents away from the older method; but the evolution of scholasticism continued, and the influence of the German reformers prevailed. At every theological centre came an amazing development of interpretation. Eminent Lutheran divines in the seventeenth century, like Gerhard, Calovius, Cocceius, and multitudes of others, wrote scores of quartos to further this system, and the other branch of the Protestant Church emulated their example. The pregnant dictum of St. Augustine—"Greater is the authority of Scripture than all human capacity"—was steadily insisted upon, and, toward the close of the seventeenth century, Voetius, the renowned professor at Utrecht, declared, "Not a word is contained in the Holy Scriptures which is not in the strictest sense inspired, the very punctuation not excepted"; and this declaration was echoed back from multitudes of pulpits, theological chairs, synods, and councils. Unfortunately, it was very difficult to find what the "authority of Scripture" really was. To the greater number of Protestant ecclesiastics it meant the authority of any meaning in the text which they had the wit to invent and the power to enforce.

To increase this vast confusion, came, in the older branch of the Church, the idea of the divine inspiration of the Latin translation of the Bible ascribed to St. Jerome—the Vulgate. It was insisted by leading Catholic authorities that this was as completely a product of divine inspiration as was the Hebrew original. Strong men arose to insist even that, where the Hebrew and the Latin differed, the Hebrew should be altered to fit Jerome's mistranslation, as the latter, having been made under the new dispensation, must be better than that made under the old. Even so great a man as Cardinal Bellarmine exerted himself in vain against this new tide of unreason.[9]

[9] For Valla, see various sources already named; and for an especially interesting account, Symonds's *Renaissance in Italy, The Revival of Learning,* pp. 260-269; and for the opinion of the best contemporary judge, see Erasmus, *Opera,* Leyden, 1703, tom. iii, p. 98. For Erasmus and his opponents, see *Life of Erasmus,* by Butler, London, 1825, pp. 179-182; but especially, for the general subject, Bishop Creighton's *History of the Papacy during the Reformation.* For the attack by Budé and the Sorbonne and the burning of Berquin, see Drummond, *Life and Character of Erasmus,* vol. ii, pp. 220-223; also pp. 230-239. As to the text of the Three Witnesses, see Gibbon, *Decline and Fall of the Roman Empire,* chap. xxxvii, notes 116-118; also Dean Milman's note thereupon. For a full and learned statement of the evidence against the verse, see Porson's *Letters to Travis,* London, 1790, in which an elaborate discussion of all the MSS. is given. See also Jowett in *Essays and Reviews,* p. 307. For a very full and impartial history of the long controversy over this passage, see Charles Butler's *Horæ Biblicæ,* reprinted in Jared Sparks's *Theological Essays and Tracts,* vol. ii. For Luther's ideas of interpretation, see his *Sämmtliche Schriften,* Walch edition, vol. i, p. 1199, vol. ii, p. 1758, vol. viii, p. 2140; for some of his more free views, vol. xiv, p. 472, vol. vi, p. 121, vol. xi, p. 1448, vol. xii, p. 830; also Tholuck, *Doctrine of Inspiration,* Boston, 1867, citing the *Colloquia,* Frankfort, 1571, vol. ii, p. 102; also the *Vorreden zu der deutschen Bibelübersetzung,* in Walch's edition, as above, vol. xiv, especially pp. 94, 98, and 146-150. As to Melanchthon, see especially his *Loci Communes,* 1521; and as to the enormous growth of commentaries in the generations immediately following, see Charles Beard, *Hibbert Lectures* for 1883, on the Reformation, especially the admirable chapter on *Protestant Scholasticism;* also Archdeacon Farrar, *History of Interpretation.* For the *Papstesel,* etc., see Luther's *Sämmtliche Schriften,* edit. Walch, vol. xiv, pp. 2403 *et seq.;* also

Nor was a fanatical adhesion to the mere letter of the sacred text confined to western Europe. About the middle of the seventeenth century, in the reign of Alexis, father of Peter the Great, Nikon, Patriarch of the Russian Greek Church, attempted to correct the Slavonic Scriptures and service-books. They were full of interpolations due to ignorance, carelessness, or zeal, and in order to remedy this state of the texts Nikon procured a number of the best Greek and Slavonic manuscripts, set the leading and most devout scholars he could find at work upon them, and caused Russian Church councils in 1655 and 1666 to promulgate the books thus corrected.

But the same feelings which have wrought so strongly against our nineteenth-century revision of the Bible acted even more forcibly against that revision in the seventeenth century. Straightway great masses of the people, led by monks and parish priests, rose in revolt. The fact that the revisers had written in the New Testament the name of Jesus correctly, instead of following the old wrong orthography, aroused the wildest fanaticism. The monks of the great convent of Solovetsk, when the new books were sent them, cried in terror: "Woe, woe! what have you done with the Son of God?" They then shut their gates, defying patriarch, council, and Czar, until, after a struggle lasting seven years, their

---

Melanchthon's *Opera,* edit. Bretschneider, vol. xx, pp. 665 *et seq.* In the White Library of Cornell University will be found an original edition of the book, with engravings of the monster. For the *Mönchkalb,* see Luther's works as above, vol. xix, pp. 2416 *et seq.* For the spirit of Calvin in interpretation, see Farrar, and especially H. P. Smith, D. D., *Inspiration and Inerrancy,* chap. iv, and the very brilliant essay forming chap. iii of the same work, by L. J. Evans, pp. 66 and 67, note. For the attitude of the older Church toward the Vulgate, see Pallavicini, *Histoire du Concile de Trente,* Montrouge, 1844, tome i, pp. 19, 20; but especially Symonds, *The Catholic Reaction,* vol. i, pp. 226 *et seq.* As to a demand for a revision of the Hebrew Bible to correct its differences from the Vulgate, see Emanuel Deutsch's *Literary Remains,* New York, 1874, p. 9. For the work and spirit of Calovius and other commentators immediately following the Reformation, see Farrar, as above; also Beard, Schaff, and Hertzog, *Geschichte des alten Testaments in der christlichen Kirche,* pp. 527 *et seq.* As to extreme views of Voetius and others, see Tholuck, as above. For the *Formula Consensus Helvetica,* which in 1675 affirmed the inspiration of the vowel points, see Schaff, *Creeds.*

monastery was besieged and taken by an imperial army. Hence arose the great sect of the "Old Believers," lasting to this day, and fanatically devoted to the corrupt readings of the old text.[10]

Strange to say, on the development of Scripture interpretation, largely in accordance with the old methods, wrought, about the beginning of the eighteenth century, Sir Isaac Newton.

It is hard to believe that from the mind which produced the *Principia,* and which broke through the many time-honoured beliefs regarding the dates and formation of scriptural books, could have come his discussions regarding the prophecies; still, at various points even in this work, his power appears. From internal evidence he not only discarded the text of the Three Witnesses, but he decided that the Pentateuch must have been made up from several books; that Genesis was not written until the reign of Saul; that the books of Kings and Chronicles were probably collected by Ezra; and, in a curious anticipation of modern criticism, that the book of Psalms and the prophecies of Isaiah and Daniel were each written by various authors at various dates. But the old belief in prophecy as prediction was too strong for him, and we find him applying his great powers to the relation of the details given by the prophets and in the Apocalypse to the history of mankind since unrolled, and tracing from every statement in prophetic literature its exact fulfilment even in the most minute particulars.

[10] The present writer, visiting Moscow in the spring of 1894, was presented by Count Leo Tolstoi to one of the most eminent and influential members of the sect of "Old Believers," which dates from the reform of Nikon. Nothing could exceed the fervor with which this venerable man, standing in the chapel of his superb villa, expatiated upon the horrors of making the sign of the cross with three fingers instead of with two. His argument was that the *two* fingers, as used by the "Old Believers," typify the divine and human nature of our Lord, and hence that the use of them is strictly correct; whereas signing with *three* fingers, representing the blessed Trinity, is "virtually to crucify all three persons of the Godhead afresh." Not less cogent were his arguments regarding the immense value of the old text of Scripture as compared with the new. For the revolt against Nikon and his reforms, see Rambaud, *History of Russia,* vol. i, pp. 414-416; also Wallace, *Russia,* vol. ii, pp. 307-309; also Leroy-Beaulieu, *L'Empire des Tsars,* vol. iii, livre iii.

By the beginning of the eighteenth century the structure of scriptural interpretation had become enormous. It seemed destined to hide forever the real character of our sacred literature and to obscure the great light which Christianity had brought into the world. The Church, Eastern and Western, Catholic and Protestant, was content to sit in its shadow, and the great divines of all branches of the Church reared every sort of fantastic buttress to strengthen or adorn it. It seemed to be founded for eternity; and yet, at this very time when it appeared the strongest, a current of thought was rapidly dissolving away its foundations, and preparing that wreck and ruin of the whole fabric which is now, at the close of the nineteenth century, going on so rapidly.[11]

*   *   *

2. Beginnings of Scientific Interpretation

At the base of the vast structure of the older scriptural interpretation were certain ideas regarding the first five books of the Old Testament. It was taken for granted that they had been dictated by the Almighty to Moses about fifteen hundred years before our era; that some parts of them, indeed, had been written by the corporeal finger of Jehovah, and that all parts gave not merely his thoughts but his exact phraseology. It was also held, virtually by the universal Church, that while every narrative or statement in these books is a precise statement of historical or scientific fact, yet that the entire text contains vast hidden meanings. Such was the rule: the exceptions made by a few interpreters here and there only confirmed it. Even the indifference of St. Jerome to the doctrine of Mosaic authorship did not prevent its ripening into a dogma.

*   *   *

About the middle of the twelfth century came, so far as the world now knows, the first gainsayer of this general theory. Then it was that Aben Ezra, the greatest biblical scholar of the Middle Ages, ventured very discreetly to call attention to certain points in the Pentateuch incompatible with the

[11] For Newton's boldness in textual criticism, compared with his credulity as to the literal fulfilment of prophecy, see his *Observations upon the Prophecies of Daniel and the Apocalypse of St. John,* in his works, edited by Horsley, London, 1785, vol. v, pp. 297-491.

belief that the whole of it had been written by Moses and handed down in its original form. His opinion was based upon the well-known texts which have turned all really eminent biblical scholars in the nineteenth century from the old view by showing the Mosaic authorship of the five books in their present form to be clearly disproved by the books themselves; and, among these texts, accounts of Moses' own death and burial, as well as statements based on names, events, and conditions which only came into being ages after the time of Moses.

But Aben Ezra had evidently no aspirations for martyrdom; he fathered the idea upon a rabbi of a previous generation, and, having veiled his statement in an enigma, added the caution, "Let him who understands hold his tongue."[12]

For about four centuries the learned world followed the prudent rabbi's advice, and then two noted scholars, one of them a Protestant, the other a Catholic, revived his idea. The first of these, Carlstadt, insisted that the authorship of the Pentateuch was unknown and unknowable; the other, Andreas Maes, expressed his opinion in terms which would not now offend the most orthodox, that the Pentateuch had been edited by Ezra, and had received in the process sundry divinely inspired words and phrases to clear the meaning. Both these innovators were dealt with promptly: Carlstadt was, for this and other troublesome ideas, suppressed with the applause of the Protestant Church; and the book of Maes was placed by the older Church on the *Index*.

But as we now look back over the Revival of Learning, the Age of Discovery, and the Reformation, we can see clearly that powerful as the older Church then was, and powerful as the Reformed Church was to be, there was at work something far more mighty than either or than both; and this was a great law of nature—the law of evolution through differ-

12 For the texts referred to by Aben Ezra as incompatible with the Mosaic authorship of the Pentateuch, see Meyer, *Geschichte der Exegese,* vol. i, pp. 85-88; and for a pithy short account, Moore's introduction to *The Genesis of Genesis,* by B. W. Bacon, Hartford, 1893, p. 23; also Curtiss, as above [in the *Bibliotheca Sacra* for January, 1884]. For a full exhibition of the absolute incompatibility of these texts with the Mosaic authorship, etc., see *The Higher Criticism of the Pentateuch,* by C. A. Briggs, D. D., New York, 1893, especially chapter iv; also Robertson Smith, art. *Bible,* in *Encycl. Brit.*

entiation. Obedient to this law there now began to arise, both within the Church and without it, a new body of scholars— not so much theologians as searchers for truth by scientific methods. Some, like Cusa, were ecclesiastics; some, like Valla, Erasmus, and the Scaligers, were not such in any real sense; but whether in holy orders, really, nominally, or not at all, they were, first of all, literary and scientific investigators.

During the sixteenth century a strong impulse was given to more thorough research by several very remarkable triumphs of the critical method as developed by this new class of men, and two of these ought here to receive attention on account of their influence upon the whole after course of human thought.

For many centuries the Decretals bearing the great name of Isidore had been cherished as among the most valued muniments of the Church. They contained what claimed to be a mass of canons, letters of popes, decrees of councils, and the like, from the days of the apostles down to the eighth century —all supporting at important points the doctrine, the discipline, the ceremonial, and various high claims of the Church and its hierarchy.

But in the fifteenth century that sturdy German thinker, Cardinal Nicholas of Cusa, insisted on examining these documents and on applying to them the same thorough research and patient thought which led him, even before Copernicus, to detect the error of the Ptolemaic astronomy.

As a result, he avowed his scepticism regarding this pious literature; other close thinkers followed him in investigating it, and it was soon found a tissue of absurd anachronisms, with endless clashing and confusion of events and persons.

For a time heroic attempts were made by Church authorities to cover up these facts. Scholars revealing them were frowned upon, even persecuted, and their works placed upon the *Index;* scholars explaining them away—the "apologists" or "reconcilers" of that day—were rewarded with Church preferment, one of them securing for a very feeble treatise a cardinal's hat. But all in vain; these writings were at length acknowledged by all scholars of note, Catholic and Protestant, to be mainly a mass of devoutly cunning forgeries.

While the eyes of scholars were thus opened as never before to the skill of early Church zealots in forging documents useful to ecclesiasticism, another discovery revealed their equal skill in forging documents useful to theology.

For more than a thousand years great stress had been laid by theologians upon the writings ascribed to Dionysius the Areopagite, the Athenian convert of St. Paul. Claiming to come from one so near the great apostle, they were prized as a most precious supplement to Holy Writ. A belief was developed that when St. Paul had returned to earth, after having been "caught up to the third heaven," he had revealed to Dionysius the things he had seen. Hence it was that the varied pictures given in these writings of the heavenly hierarchy and the angelic ministers of the Almighty took strong hold upon the imagination of the universal Church: their theological statements sank deeply into the hearts and minds of the Mystics of the twelfth century and the Platonists of the fifteenth; and the ten epistles they contained, addressed to St. John, to Titus, to Polycarp, and others of the earliest period, were considered treasures of sacred history. An Emperor of the East had sent these writings to an Emperor of the West as the most precious of imperial gifts. Scotus Erigena had translated them; St. Thomas Aquinas had expounded them; Dante had glorified them; Albert the Great had claimed that they were virtually given by St. Paul and inspired by the Holy Ghost. Their authenticity was taken for granted by fathers, doctors, popes, councils, and the universal Church.

But now, in the glow of the Renascence, all this treasure was found to be but dross. Investigators in the old Church and in the new joined in proving that the great mass of it was spurious. To say nothing of other evidences, it failed to stand the simplest of all tests, for these writings constantly presupposed institutions and referred to events of much later date than the time of Dionysius; they were at length acknowledged by all authorities worthy of the name, Catholic as well as Protestant, to be simply—like the Isidorian Decretals— pious frauds.

Thus arose an atmosphere of criticism very different from the atmosphere of literary docility and acquiescence of the "Ages of Faith"; thus it came that great scholars in all parts of Europe began to realize, as never before, the part which theological skill and ecclesiastical zeal had taken in the development of spurious sacred literature; thus was stimulated a new energy in research into all ancient documents, no matter what their claims.

To strengthen this feeling and to intensify the stimulating qualities of this new atmosphere came, as we have seen, the researches and revelations of Valla regarding the forged *Letter of Christ to Abgarus,* the fraudulent *Donation of Constantine,* and the late date of the Apostles' Creed; and, to give this feeling direction toward the Hebrew and Christian sacred books, came the example of Erasmus.[13]

Naturally, then, in this new atmosphere the bolder scholars of Europe soon began to push more vigorously the researches begun centuries before by Aben Ezra, and the next efforts of these men were seen about the middle of the seventeenth century when Hobbes, in his *Leviathan,* and La Peyrère, in his *Preadamites,* took them up and developed them still further. The result came speedily. Hobbes, for this and other sins, was put under the ban, even by the political party which sorely needed him, and was regarded generally as an outcast; while La Peyrère, for this and other heresies, was thrown into prison by the Grand Vicar of Mechlin, and kept there until he fully retracted: his book was refuted by seven theologians within a year after its appearance, and within a generation thirty-six elaborate answers to it had appeared: the Parliament of Paris ordered it to be burned by the hangman.

In 1670 came an utterance vastly more important, by a man far greater than any of these—the *Tractatus Theologico-Politicus* of Spinoza. Reverently but firmly he went much more deeply into the subject. Suggesting new arguments and recasting the old, he summed up all with judicial fairness, and showed that Moses could not have been the author

[13] For very fair statements regarding the great forged documents of the Middle Ages, see Addis and Arnold, *Catholic Dictionary,* articles *Dionysius the Areopagite* and *False Decretals,* and in the latter the curious acknowledgment that the mass of pseudo-Isidorian Decretals "is what we now call a forgery."

For the derivation of Dionysius's ideas from St. Paul, and for the idea of inspiration attributed to him, see Albertus Magnus, *Opera Omnia,* vol. xiii, early chapters and chap. vi. For very interesting details on this general subject, see Döllinger, *Das Papstthum,* chap. ii; also his *Fables respecting the Popes of the Middle Ages,* translation by Plummer and H. B. Smith, part i, chap. v. Of the exposure of these works, see Farrar, as above, pp. 254, 255; also Beard, *Hibbert Lectures,* pp. 4, 354. For the False Decretals, see Milman, *History of Latin Christianity,* vol. ii, pp. 373 *et seq.* For the great work of the pseudo-Dionysius, see ibid., vol. iii, p. 352, and vol. vi, pp. 402 *et seq.,* and Canon Westcott's article on *Dionysius the Areopagite* in vol. v of the *Contemporary Review;* also the chapter on *Astronomy* in this work.

of the Pentateuch in the form then existing; that there had been glosses and revisions; that the biblical books had grown up as a literature; that, though great truths are to be found in them, and they are to be regarded as a divine revelation, the old claims of inerrancy for them can not be maintained; that in studying them men had been misled by mistaking human conceptions for divine meanings; that, while prophets have been inspired, the prophetic faculty has not been the dowry of the Jewish people alone; that to look for exact knowledge of natural and spiritual phenomena in the sacred books is an utter mistake; and that the narratives of the Old and New Testaments, while they surpass those of profane history, differ among themselves not only in literary merit, but in the value of the doctrines they inculcate. As to the authorship of the Pentateuch, he arrived at the conclusion that it was written long after Moses, but that Moses may have written some books from which it was compiled—as, for example, those which are mentioned in the Scriptures, the *Book of the Wars of God,* the *Book of the Covenant,* and the like—and that the many repetitions and contradictions in the various books show a lack of careful editing as well as a variety of original sources. Spinoza then went on to throw light into some other books of the Old and New Testaments, and added two general statements which have proved exceedingly serviceable, for they contain the germs of all modern broad churchmanship; and the first of them gave the formula which was destined in our own time to save to the Anglican Church a large number of her noblest sons: this was, that "sacred Scripture *contains* the Word of God, and in so far as it contains it is incorruptible"; the second was, that "error in speculative doctrine is not impious."

Though published in various editions, the book seemed to produce little effect upon the world at that time; but its result to Spinoza himself was none the less serious. Though so deeply religious that Novalis spoke of him as "a God-intoxicated man," and Schleiermacher called him a "saint," he had been, for the earlier expression of some of the opinions it contained, abhorred as a heretic both by Jews and Christians: from the synagogue he was cut off by a public curse, and by the Church he was now regarded as in some sort a forerunner of Antichrist. For all this, he showed no resentment, but devoted himself quietly to his studies, and to the simple manual labour by which he supported himself; declined all proffered honours, among them a professorship at Heidelberg; found pleasure only in the society of a few friends as gentle and affectionate as himself; and died contentedly, without seeing any widespread effect of his doctrine other than the prevailing abhorrence of himself.

Perhaps in all the seventeenth century there was no man whom Jesus of Nazareth would have more deeply loved, and no life which he would have more warmly approved; yet down to a very recent period this hatred for Spinoza has continued. When, about 1880, it was proposed to erect a monument to him at Amsterdam, discourses were given in churches and synagogues prophesying the wrath of Heaven upon the city for such a profanation; and when the monument was finished, the police were obliged to exert themselves to prevent injury to the statue and to the eminent scholars who unveiled it.

But the ideas of Spinoza at last secured recognition. They had sunk deeply into the hearts and minds of various leaders of thought, and, most important of all, into the heart and mind of Lessing; he brought them to bear in his treatise on the *Education of the World,* as well as in his drama, *Nathan the Wise,* and both these works have spoken with power to every generation since.

In France, also, came the same healthful evolution of thought. For generations scholars had known that multitudes of errors had crept into the sacred text. Robert Stephens had found over two thousand variations in the oldest manuscripts of the Old Testament, and in 1633 Jean Morin, a priest of the Oratory, pointed out clearly many of the most glaring of these. Seventeen years later, in spite of the most earnest Protestant efforts to suppress his work, Cappellus gave forth his *Critica Sacra,* demonstrating not only that the vowel pointing of Scripture was not divinely inspired, but that the Hebrew text itself, from which the modern translations were made, is full of errors due to the carelessness, ignorance, and doctrinal zeal of early scribes, and that there had clearly been no miraculous preservation of the "original autographs" of the sacred books.

While orthodox France was under the uneasiness and alarm thus caused, appeared a *Critical History of the Old Testament* by Richard Simon, a priest of the Oratory. He was a thoroughly religious man and an acute scholar, whose whole purpose was to develop truths which he believed healthful to the Church and to mankind. But he denied that Moses was the author of the Pentateuch, and exhibited the internal evidence, now so well known, that the books were composed much later by various persons, and edited later still. He also showed that other parts of the Old Testament had been compiled from older sources, and attacked the time-honoured theory that Hebrew was the primitive language of mankind. The whole character of his book was such that in these days it would pass, on the whole, as conservative and orthodox; it had been approved by the censor in 1678, and printed, when the table of contents and a page of the preface were shown to Bossuet. The great bishop and theologian was instantly aroused; he pronounced the work "a mass of impieties and a bulwark of irreligion"; his biographer tells us that, although it was Holy Thursday, the bishop, in spite of the solemnity of the day, hastened at once to the Chancellor Le Tellier, and secured an order to stop the publication of the book and to burn the whole edition of it. Fortunately, a few copies were rescued, and a few years later the work found a new publisher in Holland; yet not until there had been attached to it, evidently by some Protestant divine of authority, an essay warning the reader against its dangerous doctrines. Two years later a translation was published in England.

This first work of Simon was followed by others, in which he sought, in the interest of scriptural truth, to throw a new and purer light upon our sacred literature; but Bossuet proved implacable. Although unable to suppress all of Simon's works, he was able to drive him from the Oratory, and to bring him into disrepute among the very men who ought to have been proud of him as Frenchmen and thankful to him as Christians.

But other scholars of eminence were now working in this field, and chief among them Le Clerc. Virtually driven out of Geneva, he took refuge at Amsterdam, and there published a series of works upon the Hebrew language, the interpretation of Scripture, and the like. In these he combated the prevalent idea that Hebrew was the primitive tongue, expressed the opinion that in the plural form of the word used in Genesis for God, "Elohim," there is a trace of Chaldean polytheism, and, in his discussion on the serpent who tempted Eve, curiously anticipated modern geological and zoölogical ideas by quietly confessing his inability to see how depriving the serpent of feet and compelling him to go on his belly could be punishment—since all this was natural to the animal. He also ventured quasi-scientific explanations of the confusion of tongues at Babel, the destruction of Sodom, the conversion of Lot's wife into a pillar of salt, and the dividing of the Red Sea. As to the Pentateuch in general, he completely rejected the idea that it was written by Moses. But his most permanent gift to the thinking world was his answer to those who insisted upon the reference by Christ and his apostles to Moses as the author of the Pentateuch. The answer became a formula which has proved effective from his day to ours: "Our Lord and his apostles did not come into this world to teach criticism to the Jews, and hence spoke according to the common opinion."

Against all these scholars came a theological storm, but it raged most pitilessly against Le Clerc. Such renowned theologians as Carpzov in Germany, Witsius in Holland, and Huet in France berated him unmercifully and overwhelmed him with assertions which still fill us with wonder. . . . Carpzov showed that Protestantism could not be outdone by Catholicism when he declared, in the face of all modern knowledge, that not only the matter but the exact form and words of the Bible had been divinely transmitted to the modern world free from all error.

At this Le Clerc stood aghast, and finally stammered out a sort of half recantation.[14]

14 For Carlstadt, and Luther's dealings with him on various accounts, see Meyer, *Geschichte der Exegese,* vol. ii, pp. 373, 397. As to the value of Maes's work in general, see Meyer, vol. ii, p. 125; and as to the sort of work in question, ibid., vol. iii, p. 245, note. For Carlstadt, see also Farrar, *History of Interpretation,* and Moore's introduction, as above. For Hobbes's view that the Pentateuch was written long after Moses's day, see the *Leviathan,* vol. iii, p. 33. For La Peyrère's view, see especially his *Præ-Adamitæ,* lib. iv, chap. ii, also lib. ii, *passim;* also Lecky, *Rationalism in Europe,* vol. i, p. 294; also interesting points in Bayle's *Dictionary.* For Spinoza's view, see the *Tractatus Theologico-Politicus,* chaps. ii and iii, and for the persecution, see the various biographies. Details regarding the demonstration against the unveiling of his statue were given to the present writer at the time by Berthold Auerbach, who took part in the ceremony. For Morinus and Cappellus, see Farrar, as above, p. 387 and note. For Richard Simon, see his *Histoire Critique de l'Ancien Testament,* liv. i, chaps. ii, iii, iv, v, and xiii. For his denial of the prevailing theory regarding Hebrew, see liv. i, chap. xiv. For Morinus (Morin) and his work,

During the eighteenth century constant additions were made to the enormous structure of orthodox scriptural interpretation, some of them gaining the applause of the Christian world then, though nearly all are utterly discredited now. But in 1753 appeared two contributions of permanent influence, though differing vastly in value. In the comparative estimate of these two works the world has seen a remarkable reversal of public opinion.

The first of these was Bishop Lowth's *Prelections upon the Sacred Poetry of the Hebrews*. In this was well brought out that characteristic of Hebrew poetry to which it owes so much of its peculiar charm—its parallelism.

The second of these books was Astruc's *Conjectures on the Original Memoirs which Moses used in composing the Book of Genesis*. In this was for the first time clearly revealed the fact that, amid various fragments of old writings, at least two main narratives enter into the composition of Genesis; that in the first of these is generally used as an appellation of the Almighty the word "Elohim," and in the second the word "Yahveh" (Jehovah); that each narrative has characteristics of its own, in thought and expression, which distinguish it from the other; that, by separating these, two clear and distinct narratives may be obtained, each consistent with itself, and that thus, and thus alone, can be explained the repetitions, discrepancies, and contradictions in Genesis which so long baffled the ingenuity of commentators, espe-

---

see the *Biog. Univ.* and *Nouvelle Biog. Générale;* also Curtiss. For Bossuet's opposition to Simon, see the *Histoire de Bossuet* in the *Œuvres de Bossuet,* Paris, 1846, tome xii, pp. 330, 331; also t. x, p. 738; also sundry attacks in various volumes. It is interesting to note that among the chief instigators of the persecution were the Port-Royalists, upon whose persecution afterward by the Jesuits so much sympathy has been lavished by the Protestant world. For Le Clerc, see especially his *Pentateuchus,* Prolegom., dissertat. i; also *Com. in Genes.,* cap. vi-viii. For a translation of selected passages on the points noted, see *Twelve Dissertations out of Monsieur Le Clerc's Genesis, done out of Latin by Mr. Brown,* London, 1696; also Le Clerc's *Sentiments de Quelques Theologiens de Hollande, passim;* also his work on *Inspiration,* English translation, Boston, 1820, pp. 47-50, also 57-67. For Witsius and Carpzov, see Curtiss, as above. For some subordinate points in the earlier growth of the opinion at present dominant, see Briggs, *The Higher Criticism of the Hexateuch,* New York, 1893, chap. iv.

cially the two accounts of the creation, so utterly inconsistent with each other.

Interesting as was Lowth's book, this work by Astruc was, as the thinking world now acknowledges, infinitely more important; it was, indeed, the most valuable single contribution ever made to biblical study. But such was not the judgment of the world *then*. While Lowth's book was covered with honour and its author promoted from the bishopric of St. David's to that of London, and even offered the primacy, Astruc and his book were covered with reproach. Though, as an orthodox Catholic, he had mainly desired to reassert the authorship of Moses against the argument of Spinoza, he received no thanks on that account. Theologians of all creeds sneered at him as a doctor of medicine who had blundered beyond his province; his fellow-Catholics in France bitterly denounced him as a heretic; and in Germany the great Protestant theologian, Michaelis, who had edited and exalted Lowth's work, poured contempt over Astruc as an ignoramus.

The case of Astruc is one of the many which show the wonderful power of the older theological reasoning to close the strongest minds against the clearest truths. The fact which he discovered is now as definitely established as any in the whole range of literature or science. It has become as clear as the day, and yet for two thousand years the minds of professional theologians, Jewish and Christian, were unable to detect it. Not until this eminent physician applied to the subject a mind trained in making scientific distinctions was it given to the world.

It was, of course, not possible even for so eminent a scholar as Michaelis to pooh-pooh down a discovery so pregnant; and, curiously enough, it was one of Michaelis's own scholars, Eichhorn, who did the main work in bringing the new truth to bear upon the world. He, with others, developed out of it the theory that Genesis, and indeed the Pentateuch, is made up entirely of fragments of old writings, mainly disjointed. But they did far more than this: they impressed upon the thinking part of Christendom the fact that the Bible is not a *book,* but a *literature;* that the style is not supernatural and unique, but simply the Oriental style of the lands and times in which its various parts were written; and that these must be studied in the light of the modes of thought and statement and the literary habits generally of Oriental peoples. From Eichhorn's time the process which, by historical, philological, and textual research, brings out the truth regarding this literature has been known as "the higher criticism."

He was a deeply religious man, and the mainspring of his efforts was the desire to bring back to the Church the educated classes, who had been repelled by the stiff Lutheran orthodoxy; but this only increased hostility to him. Opposition met him in Germany at every turn; and in England, Lloyd, Regius Professor of Hebrew at Cambridge, who sought patronage for a translation of Eichhorn's work, was met generally with contempt and frequently with insult.

Throughout Catholic Germany it was even worse. In 1774 Isenbiehl, a priest at Mayence who had distinguished himself as a Greek and Hebrew scholar, happened to question the usual interpretation of the passage in Isaiah which refers to the virgin-born Immanuel, and showed then—what every competent critic knows now—that it had reference to events looked for in older Jewish history. The censorship and faculty of theology attacked him at once and brought him before the elector. Luckily, this potentate was one of the old easy-going prince-bishops, and contented himself with telling the priest that, though his contention was perhaps true, he "must remain in the old paths, and avoid everything likely to make trouble."

But at the elector's death, soon afterward, the theologians renewed the attack, threw Isenbiehl out of his professorship and degraded him. One insult deserves mention for its ingenuity. It was declared that he—the successful and brilliant professor—showed by the obnoxious interpretation that he had not yet rightly learned the Scriptures; he was therefore sent back to the benches of the theological school, and made to take his seat among the ingenuous youth who were conning the rudiments of theology.

At this he made a new statement, so carefully guarded that it disarmed many of his enemies, and his high scholarship soon won for him a new professorship of Greek—the condition being that he should cease writing upon Scripture. But a crafty bookseller having republished his former book, and having protected himself by keeping the place and date of publication secret, a new storm fell upon the author; he was again removed from his professorship and thrown into prison; his book was forbidden, and all copies of it in that part of Germany were confiscated.

In 1778, having escaped from prison, he sought refuge with another of the minor rulers who in blissful unconsciousness were doing their worst while awaiting the French Revolution, but was at once delivered up to the Mayence authorities and again thrown into prison.

The Pope, Pius VI, now intervened with a brief on Isenbiehl's book, declaring it "horrible, false, perverse, destructive, tainted with heresy," and excommunicating all who should read it. At this, Isenbiehl, declaring that he had written it in the hope of doing a service to the Church, recanted, and vegetated in obscurity until his death in 1818.

But, despite theological faculties, prince-bishops, and even popes, the new current of thought increased in strength and volume, and into it at the end of the eighteenth century came important contributions from two sources widely separated and most dissimilar.

The first of these, which gave a stimulus not yet exhausted, was the work of Herder. By a remarkable intuition he had anticipated some of those ideas of an evolutionary process in nature and in literature which first gained full recognition nearly three quarters of a century after him; but his greatest service in the field of biblical study was his work, at once profound and brilliant, *The Spirit of Hebrew Poetry*. In this field he eclipsed Bishop Lowth. Among other things of importance, he showed that the Psalms were by different authors and of different periods—the bloom of a great poetic literature. Until his time no one had so clearly done justice to their sublimity and beauty; but most striking of all was his discussion of Solomon's Song. For over twenty centuries it had been customary to attribute to it mystical meanings. If here and there some man saw the truth, he was careful, like Aben Ezra, to speak with bated breath.

The penalty for any more honest interpretation was seen, among Protestants, when Calvin and Beza persecuted Castellio, covered him with obloquy, and finally drove him to starvation and death, for throwing light upon the real character of the Song of Songs; and among Catholics it was seen when Philip II allowed the pious and gifted Luis de Leon, for a similar offense, to be thrown into a dungeon of the Inquisition and kept there for five years, until his health was utterly shattered and his spirit so broken that he consented to publish a new commentary on the song, "as theological and obscure as the most orthodox could desire."

Here, too, we have an example of the efficiency of the older biblical theology in fettering the stronger minds and in stupefying the weaker. Just as the book of Genesis had to wait over two thousand years for a physician to reveal the simplest fact regarding its structure, so the Song of Songs had to wait even longer for a poet to reveal not only its beauty but its character. Commentators innumerable had interpreted it; St. Bernard had preached over eighty sermons on its first two chapters; Palestrina had set its most erotic parts to sacred music; Jews and Gentiles, Catholics and Protestants, from Origen to Aben Ezra and from Luther to Bossuet, had uncovered its deep meanings and had demonstrated it to be anything and everything save that which it really is. Among scores of these strange imaginations it was declared to represent the love of Jehovah for Israel; the love of Christ for the Church; the praises of the Blessed Virgin; the union of the soul with the body; sacred history from the Exodus to the Messiah; Church history from the Crucifixion to the Reformation; and some of the more acute Protestant divines found in it references even to the religious wars in Germany and to the Peace of Passau. In these days it seems hard to imagine how really competent reasoners could thus argue without laughing in each other's faces, after the manner of Cicero's augurs. Herder showed Solomon's Song to be what the whole thinking world now knows it to be—simply an Oriental love-poem.

But his frankness brought him into trouble: he was bitterly assailed. Neither his noble character nor his genius availed him. Obliged to flee from one pastorate to another, he at last found a happy refuge at Weimar in the society of Goethe, Wieland, and Jean Paul, and thence he exercised a powerful influence in removing noxious and parasitic growths from religious thought.

It would hardly be possible to imagine a man more different from Herder than was the other of the two who most influenced biblical interpretation at the end of the eighteenth century. This was Alexander Geddes—a Roman Catholic priest and a Scotchman. Having at an early period attracted much attention by his scholarship, and having received the very rare distinction, for a Catholic, of a doctorate from the

University of Aberdeen, he began publishing in 1792 a new translation of the Old Testament, and followed this in 1800 with a volume of critical remarks. In these he supported mainly three views: first, that the Pentateuch in its present form could not have been written by Moses; secondly, that it was the work of various hands; and, thirdly, that it could not have been written before the time of David. Although there was a fringe of doubtful theories about them, these main conclusions, supported as they were by deep research and cogent reasoning, are now recognised as of great value. But such was not the orthodox opinion then. Though a man of sincere piety, who throughout his entire life remained firm in the faith of his fathers, he and his work were at once condemned: he was suspended by the Catholic authorities as a misbeliever, denounced by Protestants as an infidel, and taunted by both as "a would-be corrector of the Holy Ghost." Of course, by this taunt was meant nothing more than that he dissented from sundry ideas inherited from less enlightened times by the men who just then happened to wield ecclesiastical power.

But not all the opposition to him could check the evolution of his thought. A line of great men followed in these paths opened by Astruc and Eichhorn, and broadened by Herder and Geddes. Of these was De Wette, whose various works, especially his *Introduction to the Old Testament,* gave a new impulse early in the nineteenth century to fruitful thought throughout Christendom. In these writings, while showing how largely myths and legends had entered into the Hebrew sacred books, he threw especial light into the books Deuteronomy and Chronicles. The former he showed to be, in the main, a late priestly summary of law, and the latter a very late priestly recast of early history. He had, indeed, to pay a penalty for thus aiding the world in its march toward more truth, for he was driven out of Germany, and obliged to take refuge in a Swiss professorship; while Theodore Parker, who published an English translation of his work, was, for this and similar sins, virtually rejected by what claimed to be the most liberal of all Christian bodies in the United States.

But contributions to the new thought continued from quarters whence least was expected. Gesenius, by his Hebrew Grammar, and Ewald, by his historical studies, greatly advanced it.

To them and to all like them during the middle years of the nineteenth century was sturdily opposed the colossus of orthodoxy—Hengstenberg. In him was combined the haughtiness of a Prussian drill-sergeant, the zeal of a Spanish inquisitor, and the flippant brutality of a French orthodox journalist. Behind him stood the gifted but erratic Frederick William IV—a man admirably fitted for a professorship of æsthetics, but whom an inscrutable fate had made King of Prussia. Both these rulers in the German Israel arrayed all possible opposition against the great scholars labouring in the new paths; but this opposition was vain: the succession of acute and honest scholars continued: Vatke, Bleek, Reuss, Graf, Kayser, Hupfeld, Delitzsch, Kuenen, and others wrought on in Germany and Holland, steadily developing the new truth.

Especially to be mentioned among these is Hupfeld, who published in 1853 his treatise on *The Sources of Genesis*. Accepting the *Conjectures* which Astruc had published just a hundred years before, he established what has ever since been recognised by the leading biblical commentators as the true basis of work upon the Pentateuch—the fact that *three* true documents are combined in Genesis, each with its own characteristics. He, too, had to pay a price for letting more light upon the world. A determined attempt was made to punish him. Though deeply religious in his nature and aspirations, he was denounced in 1865 to the Prussian Government as guilty of irreverence; but, to the credit of his noble and true colleagues who trod in the more orthodox paths—men like Tholuck and Julius Müller—the theological faculty of the University of Halle protested against this persecuting effort, and it was brought to naught.

The demonstrations of Hupfeld gave new life to biblical scholarship in all lands. More and more clear became the evidence that throughout the Pentateuch, and indeed in other parts of our sacred books, there had been a fusion of various ideas, a confounding of various epochs, and a compilation of various documents. Thus was opened a new field of thought and work: in sifting out this literature; in rearranging it; and in bringing it into proper connection with the history of the Jewish race and of humanity.

Astruc and Hupfeld having thus found a key to the true character of the "Mosaic" Scriptures, a second key was found which opened the way to the secret of order in all this chaos.

For many generations one thing had especially puzzled commentators and given rise to masses of futile "reconciliation":
this was the patent fact that such men as Samuel, David,
Elijah, Isaiah, and indeed the whole Jewish people down to
the Exile, showed in all their utterances and actions that they
were utterly ignorant of that vast system of ceremonial law
which, according to the accounts attributed to Moses and
other parts of our sacred books, was in full force during their
time and during nearly a thousand years before the Exile. It
was held "always, everywhere, and by all," that in the Old
Testament the chronological order of revelation was: first,
the law; secondly, the Psalms; thirdly, the prophets. This belief continued unchallenged during more than two thousand
years, and until after the middle of the nineteenth century.

Yet, as far back as 1835, Vatke at Berlin had, in his *Religion of the Old Testament,* expressed his conviction that this
belief was unfounded. Reasoning that Jewish thought must
have been subject to the laws of development which govern
other systems, he arrived at the conclusion that the legisla-
tion ascribed to Moses, and especially the elaborate para-
phernalia and composite ceremonies of the ritual, could not
have come into being at a period so rude as that depicted in
the "Mosaic" accounts.

Although Vatke wrapped this statement in a mist of Hege-
lian metaphysics, a sufficient number of watchmen on the
walls of the Prussian Zion saw its meaning, and an alarm was
given. The chroniclers tell us that "fear of failing in the examinations, through knowing too much, kept students away
from Vatke's lectures." Naturally, while Hengstenberg and
Frederick William IV were commanding the forces of orthodoxy, Vatke thought it wise to be silent.

Still, the new idea was in the air; indeed, it had been
divined about a year earlier, on the other side of the Rhine,
by a scholar well known as acute and thoughtful—Reuss, of
Strasburg. Unfortunately, he too was overawed, and he re-
frained from publishing his thought during more than forty
years. But his ideas were caught by some of his most gifted
scholars; and, of these, Graf and Kayser developed them and
had the courage to publish them.

At the same period this new master key was found and
applied by a greater man than any of these—by Kuenen, of
Holland; and thus it was that three eminent scholars, working in different parts of Europe and on different lines, in

spite of all obstacles, joined in enforcing upon the thinking world the conviction that the complete Levitical law had been established not at the beginning, but at the end, of the Jewish nation—mainly, indeed, after the Jewish nation as an independent political body had ceased to exist; that this code had not been revealed in the childhood of Israel, but that it had come into being in a perfectly natural way during Israel's final decay—during the period when heroes and prophets had been succeeded by priests. Thus was the historical and psychological evolution of Jewish institutions brought into harmony with the natural development of human thought; elaborate ceremonial institutions being shown to have come after the ruder beginnings of religious development instead of before them. Thus came a new impulse to research, and the fruitage was abundant; the older theological interpretation, with its insoluble puzzles, yielded on all sides.

The lead in the new epoch thus opened was taken by Kuenen. Starting with strong prepossessions in favour of the older thought, and even with violent utterances against some of the supporters of the new view, he was borne on by his love of truth, until his great work, *The Religion of Israel,* published in 1869, attracted the attention of thinking scholars throughout the world by its arguments in favour of the upward movement. From him now came a third master key to the mystery; for he showed that the true opening point for research into the history and literature of Israel is to be found in the utterances of the great prophets of the eighth century before our era. Starting from these, he opened new paths into the periods preceding and following them. Recognising the fact that the religion of Israel was, like other great world religions, a development of higher ideas out of lower, he led men to bring deeper thinking and wider research into the great problem. With ample learning and irresistible logic he proved that Old Testament history is largely mingled with myth and legend; that not only were the laws attributed to Moses in the main a far later development, but that much of their historical setting was an afterthought; also that Old Testament prophecy was never supernaturally predictive, and least of all predictive of events recorded in the New Testament. Thus it was that his genius gave to the thinking world a new point of view, and a masterly exhibition of the true method of study. Justly has one of the most eminent divines of the contemporary Anglican Church indorsed the statement of another eminent scholar, that "Kuenen stood upon his watch-tower, as it were the conscience of Old Testament science"; that his work is characterized "not merely by fine scholarship, critical insight, historical sense, and a religious nature, but also by an incorruptible conscientiousness, and a majestic devotion to the quest of truth."

Thus was established the science of biblical criticism. And now the question was, whether the Church of northern Germany would accept this great gift—the fruit of centuries of devoted toil and self-sacrifice—and take the lead of Christendom in and by it.

The great curse of Theology and Ecclesiasticism has always been their tendency to sacrifice large interests to small— Charity to Creed, Unity to Uniformity, Fact to Tradition, Ethics to Dogma. And now there were symptoms throughout the governing bodies of the Reformed churches indicating a determination to sacrifice leadership in this new thought to ease in orthodoxy. Every revelation of new knowledge encountered outcry, opposition, and repression; and, what was worse, the ill-judged declarations of some unwise workers in the critical field were seized upon and used to discredit all fruitful research. Fortunately, a man now appeared who both met all this opposition successfully, and put aside all the half truths or specious untruths urged by minor critics whose zeal outran their discretion. This was a great constructive scholar—not a destroyer, but a builder—Wellhausen. Reverently, but honestly and courageously, with clearness, fulness, and convicting force, he summed up the conquests of scientific criticism as bearing on Hebrew history and literature. These conquests had reduced the vast structures which theologians had during ages been erecting over the sacred text to shapeless ruin and rubbish: this rubbish he removed, and brought out from beneath it the reality. He showed Jewish history as an evolution obedient to laws at work in all ages, and Jewish literature as a growth out of individual, tribal, and national life. Thus was our sacred history and literature given a beauty and high use which had long been foreign to them. Thereby was a vast service rendered immediately to Germany, and eventually to all mankind; and this service was greatest of all in the domain of religion.[15]

[15] For Lowth, see the Rev. T. K. Cheyne, D. D., Professor of the Interpretation of the Holy Scripture in the University of Oxford, *Founders of Old Testament Criticism*, London, 1893, pp. 3, 4. For

Astruc's very high character as a medical authority, see the *Dictionnaire des Sciences Médicales,* Paris, 1820; it is significant that at first he concealed his authorship of the *Conjectures.* For a brief statement, see Cheyne; also Moore's introduction to Bacon's *Genesis of Genesis;* but for a statement remarkably full and interesting, and based on knowledge at first hand of Astruc's very rare book, see Curtiss, as above. For Michaelis and Eichhorn, see Meyer, *Geschichte der Exegese;* also Cheyne and Moore. For Isenbiehl, see Reusch, in *Allg. deutsche Biographie.* The texts cited against him were Isaiah vii, 14, and Matt. i, 22, 23. For Herder, see various historians of literature and writers on exegesis, and especially Pfleiderer, *Development of Theology in Germany,* chap. ii. For his influence, as well as that of Lessing, see Beard's *Hibbert Lectures,* chap. x. For a brief comparison of Lowth's work with that of Herder, see Farrar, *History of Interpretation,* p. 377. For examples of interpretations of the Song of Songs, see Farrar, as above, p. 33. For Castellio (Châtillon), his anticipation of Herder's view of Solomon's Song, and his persecution by Calvin and Beza, which drove him to starvation and death, see Lecky, *Rationalism,* etc., vol. ii, pp. 46-48; also Bayle's *Dictionary,* article *Castalio;* also Montaigne's *Essais,* liv. i, chap. xxxiv; and especially the new life of him by Buisson. For the persecution of Luis de Leon for a similar offence, see Ticknor, *History of Spanish Literature,* vol. ii, pp. 41, 42, and note. For a remarkably frank acceptance of the consequences flowing from Herder's view of it, see Sanday, *Inspiration,* pp. 211, 405. For Geddes, see Cheyne, as above. For De Wette and contemporaries, see Meyer, Cheyne, Pfleiderer, and others, as above. For Theodore Parker, see his various biographies, *passim.* For Reuss, Graf, and Kuenen, see Cheyne, as above; and for the citations referred to, see the Rev. Dr. Driver, Regius Professor of Hebrew at Oxford, in *The Academy,* October 27, 1894; also a note to Wellhausen's article *Pentateuch,* in the *Encyclopædia Britannica.* For a generous yet weighty tribute to Kuenen's method, see Pfleiderer, as above, book iii, chap. ii. For the view of leading Christian critics on the book of Chronicles, see especially Driver, *Introduction to the Literature of the Old Testament,* pp. 495 *et seq.*; also Wellhausen, as above; also Hooykaas, Oort, and Kuenen, *Bible for Learners.* For many of the foregoing, see also the writings of Prof. W. Robertson Smith; also Beard's *Hibbert Lectures,* chap. x. For Hupfeld and his discovery, see Cheyne, *Founders,* etc., as above, chap. vii; also Moore's *Introduction.* For a justly indignant judgment of Hengstenberg and his school, see Canon Farrar, as above, p. 417, note; and for a few words throwing a bright light into his character and career, see C. A. Briggs, D. D., *Authority of Holy Scripture,* p. 93. For Wellhausen, see Pfleiderer, as above, book iii, chap. ii. For an excellent popular statement of the general results of German criticism, see

3. The Continued Growth of Scientific Interpretation

The science of biblical criticism was, as we have seen, first developed mainly in Germany and Holland. Many considerations there, as elsewhere, combined to deter men from opening new paths to truth: not even in those countries were these the paths to preferment; but there, at least, the sturdy Teutonic love of truth for truth's sake, strengthened by the Kantian ethics, found no such obstacles as in other parts of Europe.[16] Fair investigation of biblical subjects had not there been extirpated, as in Italy and Spain; nor had it been forced into channels which led nowhither, as in France and southern Germany; nor were men who might otherwise have pursued it dazzled and drawn away from it by the multitude of splendid prizes for plausibility, for sophistry, or for silence displayed before the ecclesiastical vision in England. In the frugal homes of North German and Dutch professors and pastors high thinking on these great subjects went steadily on, and the "liberty of teaching," which is the glory of the northern Continental universities, while it did not secure honest thinkers against vexations, did at least protect them against the persecutions which in other countries would have thwarted their studies and starved their families.[17]

In England the admission of the new current of thought was apparently impossible. The traditional system of biblical interpretation seemed established on British soil forever. It was knit into the whole fabric of thought and observance; it was protected by the most justly esteemed hierarchy the world has ever seen; it was intrenched behind the bishops' palaces, the cathedral stalls, the professors' chairs, the country parsonages—all these, as a rule, the seats of high endeavour and beautiful culture. The older thought held a controlling voice in the senate of the nation; it was dear to the hearts of all classes; it was superbly endowed; every strong thinker seemed to hold a brief, or to be in receipt of a retaining fee for it.

J. T. Sunderland, *The Bible: Its Origin, Growth, and Character,* New York and London, 1893.

[16] [White, it must be remembered, was writing in the hey-day of German scholarship, the nineteenth century; he had not experienced the perversion of "The sturdy Teutonic love of truth" under the Nazis.—Ed.]

[17] As to the influence of Kant on honest thought in Germany, see Pfleiderer, as above, chap. i.

As to preferment in the Church, there was a cynical aphorism current, "He may hold anything who will hold his tongue."[18]

*   *   *

At the centre of biblical teaching at Oxford sat Pusey, Regius Professor of Hebrew, a scholar who had himself remained for a time at a German university, and who early in life had imbibed just enough of the German spirit to expose him to suspicion and even to attack. One charge against him at that time shows curiously what was then expected of a man perfectly sound in the older Anglican theology. He had ventured to defend holy writ with the argument that there were fishes actually existing which could have swallowed the prophet Jonah. The argument proved unfortunate. He was attacked on the scriptural ground that the fish which swallowed Jonah was created for that express purpose. He, like others, fell back under the charm of the old system: his ideas gave force to the reaction: in the quiet of his study, which, especially after the death of his son became a hermitage, he relapsed into patristic and mediæval conceptions of Christianity, enforcing them from the pulpit and in his published works. He now virtually accepted the famous dictum of Hugo of St. Victor—that one is first to find what is to be believed, and then to search the Scriptures for proofs of it. His devotion to the main features of the older interpretation was seen at its strongest in his utterances regarding the book of Daniel. Just as Cardinal Bellarmine had insisted that the doctrine of the Incarnation depends upon the retention of the Ptolemaic astronomy; just as Danzius had insisted that the very continuance of religion depends on the divine origin of the Hebrew punctuation; just as Peter Martyr had made everything sacred depend on the literal acceptance of Genesis; just as Bishop Warburton had insisted that Christianity absolutely depends upon a right interpretation of the prophecies regarding Antichrist; just as John Wesley had insisted that the truth of the Bible depends on the reality of witchcraft; just as, at

[18] For an eloquent and at the same time profound statement of the evils flowing from the "moral terrorism" and "intellectual tyranny" at Oxford at the period referred to, see quotations in Pfleiderer, *Development of Theology*, p. 371.

For the alloy of interested motives among English church dignitaries, see the pungent criticism of Bishop Hampden by Canon Liddon, in his *Life of Pusey*, vol. i, p. 363.

a later period, Bishop Wilberforce insisted that the doctrine of the Incarnation depends on the "Mosaic" statements regarding the origin of man; and just as Canon Liddon insisted that Christianity itself depends on a literal belief in Noah's flood, in the transformation of Lot's wife, and in the sojourn of Jonah in the whale: so did Pusey then virtually insist that Christianity must stand or fall with the early date of the book of Daniel. Happily, though the Ptolemaic astronomy, and witchcraft, and the Genesis creation myths, and the Adam, Noah, Lot, and Jonah legends, and the divine origin of the Hebrew punctuation, and the prophecies regarding Antichrist, and the early date of the book of Daniel have now been relegated to the limbo of outworn beliefs, Christianity has but come forth the stronger.

Nothing seemed less likely than that such a vast intrenched camp as that of which Oxford was the centre could be carried by an effort proceeding from a few isolated German and Dutch scholars. Yet it was the unexpected which occurred; and it is instructive to note that, even at the period when the champions of the older thought were to all appearance impregnably intrenched in England, a way had been opened into their citadel, and that the most effective agents in preparing it were really the very men in the universities and cathedral chapters who had most distinguished themselves by uncompromising and intolerant orthodoxy.

A rapid survey of the history of general literary criticism at that epoch will reveal this fact fully. During the last decade of the seventeenth century there had taken place the famous controversy over the *Letters of Phalaris,* in which, against Charles Boyle and his supporters at Oxford, was pitted Richard Bentley at Cambridge, who insisted that the letters were spurious. In the series of battles royal which followed, although Boyle, aided by Atterbury, afterward so noted for his mingled ecclesiastical and political intrigues, had gained a temporary triumph by wit and humour, Bentley's final attack had proved irresistible. Drawing from the stores of his wonderfully wide and minute knowledge, he showed that the letters could not have been written in the time of Phalaris— proving this by an exhibition of their style, which could not then have been in use, of their reference to events which had not then taken place, and of a mass of considerations which no one but a scholar almost miraculously gifted could have marshalled so fully. The controversy had attracted attention not only in England but throughout Europe. With Bentley's reply it had ended. In spite of public applause at Atterbury's wit, scholars throughout the world acknowledged Bentley's victory: he was recognised as the foremost classical scholar of his time; the mastership of Trinity, which he accepted, and the Bristol bishopric, which he rejected, were his formal reward.

Although, in his new position as head of the greatest college in England, he went to extreme lengths on the orthodox side in biblical theology, consenting even to support the doctrine that the Hebrew punctuation was divinely inspired, this was as nothing compared with the influence of the system of criticism which he introduced into English studies of classical literature in preparing the way for the application of a similar system to *all* literature, whether called sacred or profane.

Up to that period there had really been no adequate criticism of ancient literature. Whatever name had been attached to any ancient writing was usually accepted as the name of the author: what texts should be imputed to an author was settled generally on authority. But with Bentley began a new epoch. His acute intellect and exquisite touch revealed clearly to English scholars the new science of criticism, and familiarized the minds of thinking men with the idea that the texts of ancient literature must be submitted to this science. Henceforward a new spirit reigned among the best classical scholars, prophetic of more and more light in the greater field of sacred literature. Scholars, of whom Porson was chief, followed out this method, and though at times, as in Porson's own case, they were warned off, with much loss and damage, from the application of it to the sacred text, they kept alive the better tradition.

A hundred years after Bentley's main efforts appeared in Germany another epoch-making book—Wolf's *Introduction to Homer*. In this was broached the theory that the *Iliad* and *Odyssey* are not the works of a single great poet, but are made up of ballad literature wrought into unity by more or less skilful editing. In spite of various changes and phases of opinion on this subject since Wolf's day, he dealt a killing blow at the idea that classical works are necessarily to be taken at what may be termed their face value.

More and more clearly it was seen that the ideas of early copyists, and even of early possessors of masterpieces in ancient literature, were entirely different from those to which the modern world is accustomed. It was seen that manipulations and interpolations in the text by copyists and possessors had long been considered not merely venial sins, but matters of right, and that even the issuing of whole books under assumed names had been practised freely.

In 1811 a light akin to that thrown by Bentley and Wolf upon ancient literature was thrown by Niebuhr upon ancient history. In his *History of Rome* the application of scientific principles to the examination of historical sources was for the first time exhibited largely and brilliantly. Up to that period the time-honoured utterances of ancient authorities had been, as a rule, accepted as final: no breaking away, even from the most absurd of them, was looked upon with favour, and any one presuming to go behind them was regarded as troublesome and even as dangerous.

Through this sacred conventionalism Niebuhr broke fearlessly, and, though at times overcritical, he struck from the early history of Rome a vast mass of accretions, and gave to the world a residue infinitely more valuable than the original amalgam of myth, legend, and chronicle.

His methods were especially brought to bear on students' history by one of the truest men and noblest scholars that the English race has produced—Arnold of Rugby—and, in spite of the inevitable heavy conservatism, were allowed to do their work in the field of ancient history as well as in that of ancient classical literature.

The place of myth in history thus became more and more understood, and historical foundations, at least so far as *secular* history was concerned, were henceforth dealt with in a scientific spirit. The extension of this new treatment to *all* ancient literature and history was now simply a matter of time.

Such an extension had already begun; for in 1829 had appeared Milman's *History of the Jews*. In this work came a further evolution of the truths and methods suggested by Bentley, Wolf, and Niebuhr, and their application to sacred history was made strikingly evident. Milman, though a clergyman, treated the history of the chosen people in the light of modern knowledge of Oriental and especially of Semitic peoples. He exhibited sundry great biblical personages of the wandering days of Israel as sheiks or emirs or Bedouin chieftains; and the tribes of Israel as obedient then to the same general laws, customs, and ideas governing wandering tribes in the same region now. He dealt with conflicting sources somewhat in the spirit of Bentley, and with the mythical, legendary, and miraculous somewhat in the spirit of Niebuhr. This treatment of the history of the Jews, simply as the development of an Oriental tribe, raised great opposition. Such champions of orthodoxy as Bishop Mant and Dr. Faussett straightway took the field, and with such effect that the *Family Library,* a very valuable series in which Milman's history appeared, was put under the ban, and its further publication stopped. For years Milman, though a man of exquisite literary and lofty historical gifts, as well as of most honourable character, was debarred from preferment and outstripped by ecclesiastics vastly inferior to him in everything save worldly wisdom; for years he was passed in the race for honours by divines who were content either to hold briefs for all the contemporary unreason which happened to be popular, or to keep their mouths shut altogether. This opposition to him extended to his works. For many years they were sneered at, decried, and kept from the public as far as possible.

Fortunately, the progress of events lifted him, before the closing years of his life, above all this opposition. As Dean of St. Paul's he really outranked the contemporary archbishops: he lived to see his main ideas accepted, and his *History of Latin Christianity* received as certainly one of the most valuable, and no less certainly the most attractive, of all Church histories ever written.

The two great English histories of Greece—that by Thirlwall, which was finished, and that by Grote, which was begun, in the middle years of the nineteenth century—came in to strengthen this new development. By application of the critical method to historical sources, by pointing out more and more fully the inevitable part played by myth and legend in early chronicles, by displaying more and more clearly the ease with which interpolations of texts, falsifications of statements, and attributions to pretended authors were made, they paved the way still further toward a just and fruitful study of sacred literature.[19]

19 For Mr. Gladstone's opinion, see his *Church and State,* and Macaulay's review of it. For Pusey, see Mozley, Ward, Newman's *Apologia,* Dean Church, etc., and especially his *Life,* by Liddon. Very characteristic touches are given in vol. i, showing the origin of many of his opinions (see letter on p. 184). For the scandalous treatment of Mr. Everett by the clerical mob at Oxford, see a rather jaunty account of the preparations and of the whole

Down to the middle of the nineteenth century the traditionally orthodox side of English scholarship, while it had not been able to maintain any effective quarantine against Continental criticism of classical literature, had been able to keep up barriers fairly strong against Continental discussions of sacred literature. But in the second half of the nineteenth century these barriers were broken at many points, and, the stream of German thought being united with the current of devotion to truth in England, there appeared early in 1860 a modest volume entitled *Essays and Reviews*. This work discussed sundry of the older theological positions which had been rendered untenable by modern research, and brought to bear upon them the views of the newer school of biblical interpretation. The authors were, as a rule, scholars in the prime of life, holding influential positions in the universities and public schools. They were seven—the first being Dr. Temple, a successor of Arnold at Rugby; and the others, the Rev. Dr. Rowland Williams, Prof. Baden Powell, the Rev. H. B. Wilson, Mr. C. W. Goodwin, the Rev. Mark Pattison, and the Rev. Prof. Jowett—the only one of the seven not in holy orders being Goodwin. All the articles were important, though the first, by Temple, on *The Education of the World,* and the last, by Jowett, on *The Interpretation of Scripture,* being the most moderate, served most effectually as entering wedges into the old tradition.

---

performance in a letter written at the time from Oxford by the late Dean Church, in *The Life and Letters of Dean Church,* London, 1894, pp. 40, 41. For a brief but excellent summary of the character and services of Everett, see J. F. Rhodes's *History of the United States from the Compromise of 1850,* New York, 1893, vol. i, pp. 291 *et seq.* For a succinct and brilliant history of the Bentley-Boyle controversy, see Macaulay's article on *Bentley* in the *Encyclopædia Britannica*; also Beard's *Hibbert Lectures* for 1893, pp. 344, 345; also *Dissertation* in Bentley's works, edited by Dyce, London, 1836, vol. i, especially the preface. For Wolf, see his *Prolegomena ad Homerum,* Halle, 1795; for its effects, see the admirable brief statement in Beard, as above, p. 345. For Niebuhr, see his *Roman History,* translated by Hare and Thirlwall, London, 1828; also Beard, as above. For Milman's view, see, as a specimen, his *History of the Jews,* last edition, especially pp. 15-27. For a noble tribute to his character, see the preface to Lecky's *History of European Morals.* For Thirlwall, see his *History of Greece, passim*; also his letters; also his *Charge of the Bishop of St. David's,* 1863.

At first no great attention was paid to the book, the only notice being the usual attempts in sundry clerical newspapers to pooh-pooh it. But in October, 1860, appeared in the *Westminster Review* an article exulting in the work as an evidence that the new critical method had at last penetrated the Church of England. The opportunity for defending the Church was at once seized by no less a personage than Bishop Wilberforce, of Oxford, the same who a few months before had secured a fame more lasting than enviable by his attacks on Darwin and the evolutionary theory. His first onslaught was made in a charge to his clergy. This he followed up with an article in the *Quarterly Review,* very explosive in its rhetoric, much like that which he had devoted in the same periodical to Darwin. The bishop declared that the work tended "toward infidelity, if not to atheism"; that the writers had been "guilty of criminal levity"; that, with the exception of the essay by Dr. Temple, their writings were "full of sophistries and scepticisms." He was especially bitter against Prof. Jowett's dictum, "Interpret the Scripture like any other book"; he insisted that Mr. Goodwin's treatment of the Mosaic account of the origin of man "sweeps away the whole basis of inspiration and leaves no place for the Incarnation"; and through the article were scattered such rhetorical adornments as the words "infidel," "atheistic," "false," and "wanton." It at once attracted wide attention, but its most immediate effect was to make the fortune of *Essays and Reviews,* which was straightway demanded on every hand, went through edition after edition, and became a power in the land. At this a panic began, and with the usual results of panic—much folly and some cruelty. Addresses from clergy and laity, many of them frantic with rage and fear, poured in upon the bishops, begging them to save Christianity and the Church: a storm of abuse arose: the seven essayists were stigmatized as "the seven extinguishers of the seven lamps of the Apocalypse," "the seven champions *not* of Christendom." As a result of all this pressure, Sumner, Archbishop of Canterbury, one of the last of the old, kindly, bewigged pluralists of the Georgian period, headed a declaration, which was signed by the Archbishop of York and a long list of bishops, expressing pain at the appearance of the book, but doubts as to the possibility of any effective dealing with it. This letter only made matters worse. The orthodox decried it as timid, and the liberals denounced it as irregular. The same influences were exerted in the sister island, and the

Protestant archbishops in Ireland issued a joint letter warning the faithful against the "disingenuousness" of the book. Everything seemed to increase the ferment. A meeting of clergy and laity having been held at Oxford in the matter of electing a Professor of Sanscrit, the older orthodox party, having made every effort to defeat the eminent scholar Max Müller, and all in vain, found relief after defeat in new denunciations of *Essays and Reviews.*

Of the two prelates who might have been expected to breast the storm, Tait, Bishop of London, afterward Archbishop of Canterbury, bent to it for a period, though he soon recovered himself and did good service; the other, Thirlwall, Bishop of St. David's, bided his time, and, when the proper moment came, struck most effective blows for truth and justice.

Tait, large-minded and shrewd, one of the most statesman-like of prelates, at first endeavoured to detach Temple and Jowett from their associates; but, though Temple was broken down with a load of care, and especially by the fact that he had upon his shoulders the school at Rugby, whose patrons had become alarmed at his connection with the book, he showed a most refreshing courage and manliness. A passage from his letters to the Bishop of London runs as follows: "With regard to my own conduct I can only say that nothing on earth will induce me to do what you propose. I do not judge for others, but in me it would be base and untrue." On another occasion Dr. Temple, when pressed in the interest of the institution of learning under his care to detach himself from his associates in writing the book, declared to a meeting of the masters of the school that, if any statements were made to the effect that he disapproved of the other writers in the volume, he should probably find it his duty to contradict them. Another of these letters to the Bishop of London contains sundry passages of great force. One is as follows: "Many years ago you urged us from the university pulpit to undertake the critical study of the Bible. You said that it was a dangerous study, but indispensable. You described its difficulties, and those who listened must have felt a confidence (as I assuredly did, for I was there) that if they took your advice and entered on the task, you, at any rate, would never join in treating them unjustly if their study had brought with it the difficulties you described. Such a study, so full of difficulties, imperatively demands freedom for its condition. To tell a man to study, and yet bid him, under heavy penalties, come to the same conclusions with those who have not studied, is to mock him. If the conclusions are prescribed, the study is precluded." And again, what, as coming from a man who has since held two of the most important bishoprics in the English Church, is of great importance: "What can be a grosser superstition than the theory of literal inspiration? But because that has a regular footing it is to be treated as a good man's mistake, while the courage to speak the truth about the first chapter of Genesis is a wanton piece of wickedness."

The storm howled on. In the Convocation of Canterbury it was especially violent. In the Lower House Archdeacon Denison insisted on the greatest severity, as he said, "for the sake of the young who are tainted, and corrupted, and thrust almost to hell by the action of this book." At another time the same eminent churchman declared: "Of all books in any language which I ever laid my hands on, this is incomparably the worst; it contains all the poison which is to be found in Tom Paine's *Age of Reason,* while it has the additional disadvantage of having been written by clergymen."

Hysterical as all this was, the Upper House was little more self-contained. Both Tait and Thirlwall, trying to make some headway against the swelling tide, were for a time beaten back by Wilberforce, who insisted on the duty of the Church to clear itself publicly from complicity with men who, as he said, "gave up God's Word, Creation, redemption, and the work of the Holy Ghost."

The matter was brought to a curious issue by two prosecutions—one against the Rev. Dr. Williams by the Bishop of Salisbury, the other against the Rev. Mr. Wilson by one of his clerical brethren. The first result was that both these authors were sentenced to suspension from their offices for a year. At this the two condemned clergymen appealed to the Queen in Council. Upon the judicial committee to try the case in last resort sat the lord chancellor, the two archbishops, and the Bishop of London; and one occurrence now brought into especial relief the power of the older theological reasoning and ecclesiastical zeal to close the minds of the best of men to the simplest principles of right and justice. Among the men of his time most deservedly honoured for lofty character, thorough scholarship, and keen perception of right and justice was Dr. Pusey. No one doubted then, and no one doubts now, that he would have gone to the stake sooner than knowingly countenance wrong or injustice; and yet we find him at this time writing a series of long and earnest letters to the Bishop of London, who, as a judge, was hearing this case, which involved the livelihood and even the good name of the men on trial, pointing out to the bishop the evil consequences which must follow should the authors of *Essays and Reviews* be acquitted, and virtually beseeching the judges, on grounds of expediency, to convict them. Happily, Bishop Tait was too just a man to be thrown off his bearings by appeals such as this.

The decision of the court, as finally rendered by the Lord chancellor, virtually declared it to be no part of the duty of the tribunal to pronounce any opinion upon the book; that the court only had to do with certain extracts which had been presented. Among these was one adduced in support of a charge against Mr. Wilson—that he denied the doctrine of eternal punishment. On this the court decided that it did "not find in the formularies of the English Church any such distinct declaration upon the subject as to require it to punish the expression of a hope by a clergyman that even the ultimate pardon of the wicked who are condemned in the day of judgment may be consistent with the will of Almighty God." While the archbishops dissented from this judgment, Bishop Tait united in it with the lord chancellor and the lay judges.

And now the panic broke out more severely than ever. Confusion became worse confounded. The earnest-minded insisted that the tribunal had virtually approved *Essays and Reviews*; the cynical remarked that it had "dismissed hell with costs." An alliance was made at once between the more zealous High and Low Church men, and Oxford became its headquarters: Dr. Pusey and Archdeacon Denison were among the leaders, and an impassioned declaration was posted to every clergyman in England and Ireland, with a letter begging him, "for the love of God," to sign it. Thus it was that in a very short time eleven thousand signatures were obtained. Besides this, deputations claiming to represent one hundred and thirty-seven thousand laymen waited on the archbishops to thank them for dissenting from the judgment. The Convocation of Canterbury also plunged into the fray, Bishop Wilberforce being the champion of the older orthodoxy, and Bishop Tait of the new. Caustic was the speech made by Bishop Thirlwall, in which he declared that he considered the eleven thousand names, headed by that of Pusey, attached to the Oxford declaration "in the light of a row of figures preceded by a decimal point, so that, however far the series may be advanced, it never can rise to the value of a single unit."

In spite of all that could be done, the act of condemnation was carried in Convocation.

The last main echo of this whole struggle against the newer mode of interpretation was heard when the chancellor, referring to the matter in the House of Lords, characterized the ecclesiastical act as "simply a series of well-lubricated terms —a sentence so oily and saponaceous that no one can grasp it; like an eel, it slips through your fingers, and is simply nothing."

The word "saponaceous" necessarily elicited a bitter retort from Bishop Wilberforce; but perhaps the most valuable judgment on the whole matter was rendered by Bishop Tait, who declared, "These things have so effectually frightened the clergy that I think there is scarcely a bishop on the bench, unless it be the Bishop of St. David's [Thirlwall], that is not useless for the purpose of preventing the widespread alienation of intelligent men."

During the whole controversy, and for some time afterward, the press was burdened with replies, ponderous and pithy, lurid and vapid, vitriolic and unctuous, but in the main bearing the inevitable characteristics of pleas for inherited opinions stimulated by ample endowments.

The authors of the book seemed for a time likely to be swept out of the Church. One of the least daring but most prominent, finding himself apparently forsaken, seemed, though a man of very tough fibre, about to die of a broken heart; but sturdy English sense at last prevailed. The storm passed, and afterward came the still, small voice. Really sound thinkers throughout England, especially those who held no briefs for conventional orthodoxy, recognised the service rendered by the book. It was found that, after all, there existed even among churchmen a great mass of public opinion in favour of giving a full hearing to the reverent expression of honest thought, and inclined to distrust any cause which subjected fair play to zeal.

The authors of the work not only remained in the Church of England, but some of them have since represented the broader views, though not always with their early courage, in the highest and most influential positions in the Anglican Church.[20]

[20] For the origin of *Essays and Reviews*, see *Edinburgh Review*, April, 1861, p. 463. For the reception of the book, see the *West-*

minster Review, October, 1860. For the attack on it by Bishop Wilberforce, see his article in the *Quarterly Review*, January, 1861; for additional facts, *Edinburgh Review*, April, 1861, pp. 461 *et seq.* For action on the book by Convocation, see *Dublin Review*, May, 1861, citing Jelf *et al.*; also Davidson's *Life of Archbishop Tait*, vol, i, chap. xii. For the Archiepiscopal Letter, see *Dublin Review*, as above; also *Life of Bishop Wilberforce*, by his son, London, 1882, vol. iii, pp. 4, 5; it is there stated that Wilberforce drew up the letter. For curious inside views of the *Essays and Reviews* controversy, including the course of Bishop Hampden, Tait, *et al.*, see *Life of Bishop Wilberforce*, by his son, as above, pp. 3-11; also pp. 141-149. For the denunciation of the present Bishop of London (Temple) as a "leper," etc., see ibid., pp. 319, 320. For general treatment of Temple, see *Fraser's Magazine*, December, 1869. For very interesting correspondence, see Davidson's *Life of Archbishop Tait*, as above. For Archdeacon Denison's speeches, see ibid., vol. i, p. 302. For Dr. Pusey's letter to Bishop Tait, urging conviction of the Essayists and Reviewers, ibid., p. 314. For the striking letters of Dr. Temple, ibid., pp. 290 *et seq.*; also *The Life and Letters of Dean Stanley*. For replies, see *Charge of the Bishop of Oxford*, 1863; also *Replies to Essays and Reviews*, Parker, London, with preface by Wilberforce; also *Aids to Faith*, edited by the Bishop of Gloucester, London, 1861; also those by Jelf, Burgon, *et al.* For the legal proceedings, see *Quarterly Review*, April, 1864; also Davidson, as above. For Bishop Thirlwall's speech, see *Chronicle of Convocation*, quoted in *Life of Tait*, vol. i, p. 320. For Tait's tribute to Thirlwall, see *Life of Tait*, vol. i, p. 325. For a remarkably able review, and in most charming form, of the ideas of Bishop Wilberforce and Lord Chancellor Westbury, see H. D. Traill, *The New Lucian*, first dialogue. For the cynical phrase referred to, see Nash, *Life of Lord Westbury*, vol. ii, p. 78, where the noted epitaph is given, as follows:

"RICHARD BARON WESTBURY,
Lord High Chancellor of England.
He was an eminent Christian,
An energetic and merciful Statesman,
And a still more eminent and merciful Judge.
During his three years' tenure of office
He abolished the ancient method of conveying land,
The time-honoured institution of the Insolvents' Court,
And
The Eternity of Punishment.
Toward the close of his earthly career,
In the Judicial Committee of the Privy Council,
He dismissed Hell with costs
And took away from Orthodox members of the
Church of England
Their last hope of everlasting damnation."

[4. The Closing Struggle]

5. Victory of the Scientific and Literary Methods

While this struggle for the new truth was going on in various fields, aid appeared from a quarter whence it was least expected. The great discoveries by Botta and Layard in Assyria were supplemented by the researches of Rawlinson, George Smith, Oppert, Sayce, Sarzec, Pinches, and others, and thus it was revealed more clearly than ever before that as far back as the time assigned in Genesis to the creation a great civilization was flourishing in Mesopotamia; that long ages, probably two thousand years, before the scriptural date assigned to the migration of Abraham from Ur of the Chaldees, this Chaldean civilization had bloomed forth in art, science, and literature; that the ancient inscriptions recovered from the sites of this and kindred civilizations presented the Hebrew sacred myths and legends in earlier forms—forms long antedating those given in the Hebrew Scriptures; and that the accounts of the Creation, the Tree of Life in Eden, the institution and even the name of the Sabbath, the Deluge, the Tower of Babel, and much else in the Pentateuch, were simply an evolution out of earlier Chaldean myths and legends. So perfect was the proof of this that the most eminent scholars in the foremost seats of Christian learning were obliged to acknowledge it.[21]

[21] As to the revelation of the vast antiquity of Chaldean civilization, and especially regarding the Nabonidos inscription, see *Records of the Past*, vol. i, new series, first article, and especially pp. 5, 6, where a translation of that inscription is given; also Hommel, *Geschichte Babyloniens und Assyriens*, introduction, in which, on page 12, an engraving of the Sargon cylinder is given; also, on general subject, especially pp. 166 *et seq.*, 309 *et seq.*; also Meyer, *Geschichte des Alterthums*, pp. 161-163; also Maspero and Sayce, *Dawn of Civilization*, p. 599 and note.

For the earlier Chaldean forms of the Hebrew Creation accounts, Tree of Life in Eden, Hebrew Sabbath, both the institution and the name, and various other points of similar interest, see George Smith, *Chaldean Account of Genesis*, throughout the work, especially p. 308 and chaps. xvi, xvii; also Jensen, *Die Kosmologie der Babylonier;* also Schrader, *The Cuneiform Inscriptions and the Old Testament;* also Lenormant, *Origines de l'Histoire;* also Sayce, *The Assyrian Story of Creation*, in *Records of the Past*, new series, vol.

The more general conclusions which were thus given to biblical criticism were all the more impressive from the fact that they had been revealed by various groups of earnest Christian scholars working on different lines, by different methods, and in various parts of the world. Very honourable was the full and frank testimony to these results given in 1885 by the Rev. Francis Brown, a professor in the Presbyterian Theological Seminary at New York. In his admirable though brief book on Assyriology, starting with the declaration that "it is a great pity to be afraid of facts," he showed how Assyrian research testifies in many ways to the historical value of the Bible record; but at the same time he freely allowed to Chaldean history an antiquity fatal to the sacred chronology of the Hebrews. He also cast aside a mass of doubtful apologetics, and dealt frankly with the fact that very many of the early narratives in Genesis belong to the common stock of ancient tradition, and, mentioning as an example the cuneiform inscriptions which record a story of the Accadian king Sargon—how "he was born in retirement, placed by his mother in a basket of rushes, launched on a river, rescued and brought up by a stranger, after which he became king"— he did not hesitate to remind his readers that Sargon lived a thousand years and more before Moses; that this story was told of him several hundred years before Moses was born; and that it was told of various other important personages of antiquity. The professor dealt just as honestly with the inscriptions which show sundry statements in the book of Daniel to be unhistorical; candidly making admissions which but a short time before would have filled orthodoxy with horror.

A few years later came another testimony even more striking. Early in the last decade of the nineteenth century it was noised abroad that the Rev. Professor Sayce, of Oxford, the most eminent Assyriologist and Egyptologist of Great Britain, was about to publish a work in which what is known as the "higher criticism" was to be vigorously and probably destructively dealt with in the light afforded by recent research among the monuments of Assyria and Egypt. The book was looked for with eager expectation by the supporters of the traditional view of Scripture; but, when it appeared, the exul-

---

i. For a general statement as to earlier sources of much in the Hebrew sacred origins, see Huxley, *Essays on Controverted Questions,* English edition, p. 525.

tation of the traditionalists was speedily changed to dismay. For Prof. Sayce, while showing some severity toward sundry minor assumptions and assertions of biblical critics, confirmed all their more important conclusions which properly fell within his province. While his readers soon realized that these assumptions and assertions of overzealous critics no more disproved the main results of biblical criticism than the wild guesses of Kepler disproved the theory of Copernicus, or the discoveries of Galileo, or even the great laws which bear Kepler's own name, they found new mines sprung under some of the most lofty fortresses of the old dogmatic theology. A few of the statements of this champion of orthodoxy may be noted. He allowed that the week of seven days and the Sabbath rest are of Babylonian origin; indeed, that the very word "Sabbath" is Babylonian; that there are two narratives of Creation on the Babylonian tablets, wonderfully like the two leading Hebrew narratives in Genesis, and that the latter were undoubtedly drawn from the former; that the "garden of Eden" and its mystical tree were known to the inhabitants of Chaldea in pre-Semitic days; that the beliefs that woman was created out of man, and that man by sin fell from a state of innocence, are drawn from very ancient Chaldean-Babylonian texts; that Assyriology confirms the belief that the book Genesis is a compilation; that portions of it are by no means so old as the time of Moses; that the expression in our sacred book, "The Lord smelled a sweet savour" at the sacrifice made by Noah, is "identical with that of the Babylonian poet"; that "it is impossible to believe that the language of the latter was not known to the biblical writer"; and that the story of Joseph and Potiphar's wife was drawn in part from the old Egyptian tale of *The Two Brothers*. Finally, after a multitude of other concessions, Prof. Sayce allowed that the book of Jonah, so far from being the work of the prophet himself, can not have been written until the Assyrian Empire was a thing of the past; that the book of Daniel contains serious mistakes; that the so-called historical chapters of that book so conflict with the monuments that the author can not have been a contemporary of Nebuchadnezzar and Cyrus; that "the story of Belshazzar's fall is not historical"; that the Belshazzar referred to in it as king, and as the son of Nebuchadnezzar, was not the son of Nebuchadnezzar, and was never king; that "King Darius the Mede," who plays so great a part in the story, never existed; that the book associates persons and events really many years apart, and that it must have been written at a period far later than the time assigned in it for its own origin.

As to the book of Ezra, he tells us that we are confronted by a chronological inconsistency which no amount of ingenuity can explain away. He also acknowledges that the book of Esther "contains many exaggerations and improbabilities, and is simply founded upon one of those same historical tales of which the Persian chronicles seem to have been full." Great was the dissatisfaction of the traditionalists with their expected champion; well might they repeat the words of Balak to Balaam, "I called thee to curse mine enemies, and, behold, thou hast altogether blessed them.[22]

No less fruitful have been modern researches in Egypt.

[22] For Prof. Brown's discussion, see his *Assyriology, its Use and Abuse in Old Testament Study*, New York, 1885, *passim*. For Prof. Sayce's views, see *The Higher Criticism and the Monuments*, third edition, London, 1894, and especially his own curious anticipation, in the first lines of the preface, that he must fail to satisfy either side. For the declaration that the "higher critic" with all his offences is no worse than the orthodox "apologist," see p. 21. For the important admission that the same criterion must be applied in researches into our own sacred books as into others, and even into the mediæval chronicles, see p. 26. For justification of critical scepticism regarding the history given in the book of Daniel, see pp. 27, 28, also chap. xi. For very full and explicit statements, with proofs, that the "Sabbath," both in name and nature, was derived by the Hebrews from the Chaldeans, see pp. 74 *et seq*. For a very full and fair acknowledgment of the "Babylonian element in Genesis," see chap. iii, including the statement regarding the expression in our sacred book, "The Lord smelled a sweet savour," at the sacrifice made by Noah, etc., on p. 119. For an excellent summary of the work, see Dr. Driver's article in the *Contemporary Review* for March, 1894. For a pungent but well-deserved rebuke of Prof. Sayce's recent attempts to propitiate pious subscribers to his archæological fund, see Prof. A. A. Bevan, in the *Contemporary Review* for December, 1895. For the inscription on the Assyrian tablets relating in detail the exposure of King Sargon in a basket of rushes, his rescue and rule, see George Smith, *Chaldean Account of Genesis*, Sayce's edition, London, 1880, pp. 319, 320. For the frequent recurrence of the Sargon and Moses legend in ancient folklore, see Maspero and Sayce, *Dawn of History*, p. 598 and note. For various other points of similar interest, see ibid., *passim*, especially chaps. xvi and xvii; also Jensen, *Die Kosmologie der Babylonier*, and Schrader, *The Cuneiform Inscriptions and the Old Testament;* also Lenormant, *Origines de l'Histoire*.

While, on one hand, they have revealed a very considerable number of geographical and archæological facts proving the good faith of the narratives entering into the books attributed to Moses, and have thus made our early sacred literature all the more valuable, they have at the same time revealed the limitations of the sacred authors and compilers. They have brought to light facts utterly disproving the sacred Hebrew date of creation and the main framework of the early biblical chronology; they have shown the suggestive correspondence between the ten antediluvian patriarchs in Genesis and the ten early dynasties of the Egyptian gods, and have placed by the side of these the ten antediluvian kings of Chaldean tradition, the ten heroes of Armenia, the ten primeval kings of Persian sacred tradition, the ten "fathers" of Hindu sacred tradition, and multitudes of other tens, throwing much light on the manner in which the sacred chronicles of ancient nations were generally developed.

These scholars have also found that the legends of the plagues of Egypt are in the main but natural exaggerations of what occurs every year; as, for example, the changing of the water of the Nile into blood—evidently suggested by the phenomena exhibited every summer, when, as various eminent scholars, and, most recent of all, Maspero and Sayce, tell us, "about the middle of July, in eight or ten days the river turns from grayish blue to dark red, occasionally of so intense a colour as to look like newly shed blood." These modern researches have also shown that some of the most important features in the legends can not possibly be reconciled with the records of the monuments; for example, that the Pharaoh of the Exodus was certainly not overwhelmed in the Red Sea. As to the supernatural features of the Hebrew relations with Egypt, even the most devoted apologists have become discreetly silent.

Egyptologists have also translated for us the old Nile story of *The Two Brothers,* and have shown, as we have already seen, that one of the most striking parts of our sacred Joseph legend was drawn from it; they have been obliged to admit that the story of the exposure of Moses in the basket of rushes, his rescue, and his subsequent greatness, had been previously told, long before Moses's time, not only of King Sargon, but of various other great personages of the ancient world; they have published plans of Egyptian temples and copies of the sculptures upon their walls, revealing the earlier origin of

some of the most striking features of the worship and ceremonial claimed to have been revealed especially to the Hebrews; they have found in the *Egyptian Book of the Dead,*
and in various inscriptions of the Nile temples and tombs,
earlier sources of much in the ethics so long claimed to have
been revealed only to the chosen people in the Book of the
Covenant, in the ten commandments, and elsewhere; they
have given to the world copies of the Egyptian texts showing
that the theology of the Nile was one of various fruitful
sources of later ideas, statements, and practices regarding the
brazen serpent, the golden calf, trinities, miraculous conceptions, incarnations, resurrections, ascensions, and the like, and
that Egyptian sacro-scientific ideas contributed to early Jewish
and Christian sacred literature statements, beliefs, and even
phrases regarding the Creation, astronomy, geography, magic,
medicine, diabolical influences, with a multitude of other
ideas, which we also find coming into early Judaism in greater
or less degree from Chaldean and Persian sources.

But Egyptology, while thus aiding to sweep away the former conception of our sacred books, has aided biblical criticism in making them far more precious; for it has shown
them to be a part of that living growth of sacred literature
whose roots are in all the great civilizations of the past, and
through whose trunk and branches are flowing the currents
which are to infuse a higher religious and ethical life into the
civilizations of the future.[23]

[23] For general statements of agreements and disagreements between
biblical accounts and the revelations of the Egyptian monuments,
see Sayce, *The Higher Criticism and the Monuments,* especially
chap. iv. For discrepancies between the Hebrew sacred accounts of
Jewish relations with Egypt and the revelations of modern Egyptian research, see Sharpe, *History of Egypt;* Flinders Petrie, *History
of Egypt;* and especially Maspero and Sayce, *The Dawn of Civilization in Egypt and Chaldea,* London, published by the Society for
Promoting Christian Knowledge, 1894. For the statement regarding the Nile, that about the middle of July "in eight or ten days it
turns from grayish blue to dark red, occasionally of so intense a
colour as to look like newly shed blood," see Maspero and Sayce,
as above, p. 23. For the relation of the Joseph legend to the *Tale
of Two Brothers,* see Sharpe and others cited. For examples of
exposure of various great personages of antiquity in their childhood, see G. Smith, *Chaldean Account of Genesis,* Sayce's edition,
p. 320. For the relation of the *Book of the Dead,* etc., to Hebrew
ethics, see a striking passage in Huxley's essay on *The Evolution*

But while archæologists thus influenced enlightened opinion, another body of scholars rendered services of a different sort—the centre of their enterprise being the University of Oxford. By their efforts was presented to the English-speaking world a series of translations of the sacred books of the East, which showed the relations of the more Eastern sacred literature to our own, and proved that in the religions of the world the ideas which have come as the greatest blessings to mankind are not of sudden revelation or creation, but of slow evolution out of a remote past.

The facts thus shown did not at first elicit much gratitude

---

of Theology, also others cited in this chapter. As to trinities in Egypt and Chaldea, see Maspero and Sayce, especially pp. 104-106, 175, and 659-663. For miraculous conception and birth of sons of Ra, ibid., pp. 388, 389. For ascension of Ra into heaven, ibid., pp. 167, 168; for resurrections, see ibid., p. 695, also representations in Lepsius, Prisse d'Avennes, et al.; and for striking resemblance between Egyptian and Hebrew ritual and worship, and especially the ark, cherubim, ephod, Urim and Thummim, and wave offerings, see the same, passim. For a very full exhibition of the whole subject, see Renan, Histoire du Peuple Israel, vol. i, chap. xi. For Egyptian and Chaldean ideas in astronomy, out of which Hebrew ideas of "the firmament," "pillars of heaven," etc., were developed, see text and engravings in Maspero and Sayce, pp. 17 and 543. For creation of man out of clay by a divine being in Egypt, see Maspero and Sayce, p. 154; for a similar idea in Chaldea, see ibid., p. 545; and for the creation of the universe by a word, ibid., pp. 146, 147. For Egyptian and Chaldean ideas on magic and medicine, dread of evil spirits, etc., anticipating those of the Hebrew Scriptures, see Maspero and Sayce, as above, pp. 212-214, 217, 636; and for extension of these to neighbouring nations, pp. 782, 783. For visions and use of dreams as oracles, ibid., p. 641 and elsewhere. See also, on these and other resemblances, Lenormant, Origines de l'Histoire, vol. i, passim; see also George Smith and Sayce, as above, chaps. xvi and xvii, for resemblances especially striking, combining to show how simple was the evolution of many Hebrew sacred legends and ideas out of those of earlier civilizations. For an especially interesting presentation of the reasons why Egyptian ideas of immortality were not seized upon by the Jews, see the Rev. Barham Zincke's work upon Egypt. For the sacrificial vessels, temple rites, etc., see the bas-reliefs figured by Lepsius, Prisse d'Avennes, Mariette, Maspero, et al. For a striking summary by a brilliant scholar and divine of the Anglican Church, see Mahaffy, Prolegomena to Anc. Hist., cited in Sunderland The Bible, New York, 1893, p. 21, note.

from supporters of traditional theology, and perhaps few things brought more obloquy on Renan, for a time, than his statement that "the influence of Persia is the most powerful to which Israel was submitted." Whether this was an over-statement or not, it was soon seen to contain much truth. Not only was it made clear by study of the Zend Avesta that the Old and New Testament ideas regarding Satanic and demoniacal modes of action were largely due to Persian sources, but it was also shown that the idea of immortality was mainly developed in the Hebrew mind during the close relations of the Jews with the Persians. Nor was this all. In the Zend Avesta were found in earlier form sundry myths and legends which, judging from their frequent appearance in early religions, grow naturally about the history of the adored teachers of our race. Typical among these was the Temptation of Zoroaster.

It is a fact very significant and full of promise that the first large, frank, and explicit revelation regarding this whole subject in form available for the general thinking public was given to the English-speaking world by an eminent Christian divine and scholar, the Rev. Dr. Mills. Having already shown himself by his translations a most competent authority on the subject, he in 1894 called attention, in a review widely read, to "the now undoubted and long since suspected fact that it pleased the Divine Power to reveal some of the important articles of our Catholic creed first to the Zoroastrians, and through their literature to the Jews and ourselves." Among these beliefs Dr. Mills traced out very conclusively many Jewish doctrines regarding the attributes of God, and all, virtually, regarding the attributes of Satan. There, too, he found accounts of the Miraculous Conception, Virgin Birth, and Temptation of Zoroaster. As to the last, Dr. Mills presented a series of striking coincidences with our own later account. As to its main features, he showed that there had been developed among the Persians, many centuries before the Christian era, the legend of a vain effort of the arch-demon, one seat of whose power was the summit of Mount Arezura, to tempt Zoroaster to worship him,—of an argument between tempter and tempted,—and of Zoroaster's refusal; and the doctor continued: "No Persian subject in the streets of Jerusalem, soon after or long after the Return, could have failed to know this striking myth." Dr. Mills then went on to show that, among the Jews, "the doctrine of immortality was scarcely mooted before the later Isaiah—that is, before the captivity—while

the Zoroastrian scriptures are one mass of spiritualism, referring all results to the heavenly or to the infernal worlds."
He concludes by saying that, as regards the Old and New Testaments, "the humble, and to a certain extent prior, religion of the Mazda worshippers was useful in giving point and beauty to many loose conceptions among the Jewish religious teachers, and in introducing many ideas which were entirely new, while as to the doctrines of immortality and resurrection —the most important of all—it positively determined belief."[24]

Even more extensive were the revelations made by scientific criticism applied to the sacred literature of southern and eastern Asia. The resemblances of sundry fundamental narratives and ideas in our own sacred books with those of Buddhism were especially suggestive.

Here, too, had been a long preparatory history. The discoveries in Sanscrit philology made in the latter half of the eighteenth century and the first half of the nineteenth, by Sir William Jones, Carey, Wilkins, Foster, Colebrooke, and others, had met at first with some opposition from theologians. The declaration by Dugald Stewart that the discovery of Sanscrit was fraudulent, and its vocabulary and grammar patched

[24] For the passages in the *Vendidad* of special importance as regards the Temptation myth, see *Fargard*, xix, 18, 20, 26, also 140, 147. Very striking is the account of the Temptation in the Pehlavi version of the *Vendidad*. The devil is represented as saying to Zaratusht (Zoroaster): "I had the worship of thy ancestors; do thou also worship me." I am indebted to Prof. E. P. Evans, formerly of the University of Michigan, but now of Munich, for a translation of the original text from Spiegel's edition. For a good account, see also Haug, *Essays on the Sacred Language, etc., of the Parsees,* edited by West, London, 1884, pp. 252 *et seq.*; see also Mills's and Darmesteter's work in *Sacred Books of the East.* For Dr. Mills's article referred to, see his *Zoroaster and the Bible,* in *The Nineteenth Century,* January, 1894. For the citation from Renan, see his *Histoire du Peuple Israel,* tome xiv, chap. iv; see also, for Persian ideas of heaven, hell, and resurrection, Haug, as above, pp. 310 *et seq.* For an interesting *résumé* of Zoroastrianism, see Laing, *A Modern Zoroastrian,* chap. xiii, London, eighth edition, 1893. For the Buddhist version of the judgment of Solomon etc., see Fausböll, *Buddhist Birth Stories,* translated by Rhys Davids, London, 1880, vol. i, p. 14, and following. For very full statements regarding the influence of Persian ideas upon the Jews during the captivity, see Kohut, *Ueber die jüdische Angelologie und Daemonologie in ihren Abhängigkeit vom Parsismus,* Leipzig, 1866.

together out of Greek and Latin, showed the feeling of the older race of biblical students. But researches went on. Bopp, Burnouf, Lassen, Weber, Whitney, Max Müller, and others continued the work during the nineteenth century. More and more evident became the sources from which many ideas and narratives in our own sacred books had been developed. Studies in the sacred books of Brahmanism, and in the institutions of Buddhism, the most widespread of all religions, its devotees outnumbering those of all branches of the Christian Church together, proved especially fruitful in facts relating to general sacred literature and early European religious ideas.

Noteworthy in the progress of this knowledge was the work of Fathers Huc and Gabet. In 1839 the former of these, a French Lazarist priest, set out on a mission to China. Having prepared himself at Macao by eighteen months of hard study, and having arrayed himself like a native, even to the wearing of the queue and the staining of his skin, he visited Peking and penetrated Mongolia. Five years later, taking Gabet with him, both disguised as Lamas, he began his long and toilsome journey to the chief seats of Buddhism in Thibet, and, after two years of fearful dangers and sufferings, accomplished it. Driven out finally by the Chinese, Huc returned to Europe in 1852, having made one of the most heroic, self-denying, and, as it turned out, one of the most valuable efforts in all the noble annals of Christian missions. His accounts of these journeys, written in a style simple, clear, and interesting, at once attracted attention throughout the world. But far more important than any services he had rendered to the Church he served was the influence of his book upon the general opinions of thinking men; for he completed a series of revelations made by earlier, less gifted, and less devoted travellers, and brought to the notice of the world the amazing similarity of the ideas, institutions, observances, ceremonies, and ritual, and even the ecclesiastical costumes of the Buddhists to those of his own Church.

Buddhism was thus shown with its hierarchy, in which the Grand Lama, an infallible representative of the Most High, is surrounded by its minor Lamas, much like cardinals; with its bishops wearing mitres, its celibate priests with shaven crown, cope, dalmatic, and censer; its cathedrals with clergy gathered in the choir; its vast monasteries filled with monks and nuns vowed to poverty, chastity, and obedience; its church arrangements, with shrines of saints and angels; its use of images, pictures, and illuminated missals; its service, with a striking general resemblance to the Mass; antiphonal choirs; intoning of prayers; recital of creeds; repetition of litanies; processions; mystic rites and incense; the offering and adoration of bread upon an altar lighted by candles; the drinking from a chalice by the priest; prayers and offerings for the dead; benediction with outstretched hands; fasts, confessions, and doctrine of purgatory—all this and more was now clearly revealed. The good father was evidently staggered by these amazing facts; but his robust faith soon gave him an explanation: he suggested that Satan, in anticipation of Christianity, had revealed to Buddhism this divinely constituted order of things. This naïve explanation did not commend itself to his superiors in the Roman Church. In the days of St. Augustine or of St. Thomas Aquinas it would doubtless have been received much more kindly; but in the days of Cardinal Antonelli this was hardly to be expected: the Roman authorities, seeing the danger of such plain revelations in the nineteenth century, even when coupled with such devout explanations, put the book under the ban, though not before it had been spread throughout the world in various translations. Father Huc was sent on no more missions.

* * *

As the Buddhist scriptures were more fully examined, there were disclosed interesting anticipations of statements in later sacred books. The miraculous conception of Buddha and his virgin birth, like that of Horus in Egypt and of Krishna in India; the previous annunciation to his mother Maja; his birth during a journey by her; the star appearing in the east, and the angels chanting in the heavens at his birth; his temptation— all these and a multitude of other statements were full of suggestions to larger thought regarding the development of sacred literature in general. Even the eminent Roman Catholic missionary Bishop Bigandet was obliged to confess, in his scholarly life of Buddha, these striking similarities between the Buddhist scriptures and those which it was his mission to expound, though by this honest statement his own further promotion was rendered impossible. Fausböll also found the story of the judgment of Solomon imbedded in Buddhist folklore; and Sir Edwin Arnold, by his poem, *The Light of Asia,* spread far and wide a knowledge of the anticipation in Buddhism of some ideas which down to a recent period were considered distinctively Christian. Imperfect as the revelations thus made of an evolution of religious beliefs, institutions, and literature still are, they have not been without an important bearing upon the newer conception of our own sacred books: more and more manifest has become the interdependence of all human development; more and more clear the truth that Christianity, as a great fact in man's history, is not dependent for its life upon any parasitic growths of myth and legend, no matter how beautiful they may be.[25]

No less important was the closer research into the New Testament during the latter part of the nineteenth century. To go into the subject in detail would be beyond the scope of this work, but a few of the main truths which it brought before the world may be here summarized.[26]

By the new race of Christian scholars it has been clearly shown that the first three Gospels, which, down to the close of the last century, were so constantly declared to be three independent testimonies agreeing as to the events recorded, are neither independent of each other nor in that sort of agreement which was formerly asserted. All biblical scholars of any standing, even the most conservative, have come to admit that all three took their rise in the same original sources,

[25] For Huc and Gabet, see *Souvenirs d'un Voyage dans la Tartarie, le Thibet, et la Chine*, English translation by Hazlitt, London, 1851; also supplementary work by Huc. For Bishop Bigandet, see his *Life of Buddha, passim*. As authority for the fact that his book was condemned at Rome and his own promotion prevented, the present writer has the bishop's own statement. For notices of similarities between Buddhist and Christian institutions, ritual, etc., see Rhys Davids's *Buddhism*, London, 1894, *passim;* also Lillie, *Buddhism and Christianity*, especially chaps. ii and xi. It is somewhat difficult to understand how a scholar so eminent as Mr. Rhys Davids should have allowed the Society for Promoting Christian Knowledge, which published his book, to eliminate all the interesting details regarding the birth of Buddha, and to give so fully everything that seemed to tell against the Roman Catholic Church; *cf.* p. 27 with p. 246 *et seq.* For more thorough presentation of the development of features in Buddhism and Brahmanism which anticipate those of Christianity, see Schroeder, *Indiens Literatur und Cultur,* Leipsic, 1887, especially *Vorlesung XXVII* and following. . . .

[26] For a brief but thorough statement of the work of Strauss, Baur, and the earlier cruder efforts in New Testament exegesis, see Pfleiderer, as already cited, book ii, chap. i; and for the later work on *Supernatural Religion* and Lightfoot's answer, ibid., book iv, chap. ii.

growing by the accretions sure to come as time went on—accretions sometimes useful and often beautiful, but in no inconsiderable degree ideas and even narratives inherited from older religions: it is also fully acknowledged that to this growth process are due certain contradictions which can not otherwise be explained. As to the fourth Gospel, exquisitely beautiful as large portions of it are, there has been growing steadily and irresistibly the conviction, even among the most devout scholars, that it has no right to the name, and does not really give the ideas of St. John, but that it represents a mixture of Greek philosophy with Jewish theology, and that its final form, which one of the most eminent among recent Christian scholars has characterized as "an unhistorical product of abstract reflection," is mainly due to some gifted representative or representatives of the Alexandrian school. Bitter as the resistance to this view has been, it has during the last years of the nineteenth century won its way more and more to acknowledgment. A careful examination made in 1893 by a competent Christian scholar showed facts which are best given in his own words, as follows: "In the period of thirty years ending in 1860, of the fifty great authorities in this line, *four to one* were in favour of the Johannine authorship. Of those who in that period had advocated this traditional position, one quarter—and certainly the very greatest—finally changed their position to the side of a late date and non-Johannine authorship. Of those who have come into this field of scholarship since about 1860, some forty men of the first class, two thirds reject the traditional theory wholly or very largely. Of those who have contributed important articles to the discussion from about 1880 to 1890, about *two to one* reject the Johannine authorship of the Gospel in its present shape—that is to say, while forty years ago great scholars were *four to one in favour of,* they are now *two to one against,* the claim that the apostle John wrote this Gospel as we have it. Again, one half of those on the conservative side to-day—scholars like Weiss, Beyschlag, Sanday, and Reynolds—admit the existence of a dogmatic intent and an ideal element in this Gospel, so that we do not have Jesus's thought in his exact words, but only in substance."[27]

[27] For the citations given regarding the development of thought in relation to the fourth Gospel, see Crooker, *The New Bible and its Uses,* Boston, 1893, pp. 29, 30. For the characterization of St. John's Gospel above referred to, see Robertson Smith in the *Encyc.*

In 1881 came an event of great importance as regards the development of a more frank and open dealing with scriptural criticism. In that year appeared the Revised Version of the New Testament. It was exceedingly cautious and conservative; but it had the vast merit of being absolutely conscientious. One thing showed, in a striking way, ethical progress in theological methods. Although all but one of the English revisers represented Trinitarian bodies, they rejected the two great proof texts which had so long been accounted essential bulwarks of Trinitarian doctrine. Thus disappeared at last from the Epistle of St. John the text of the Three Witnesses, which had for centuries held its place in spite of its absence from all the earlier important manuscripts, and of its rejection in later times by Erasmus, Luther, Isaac Newton, Porson, and a long line of the greatest biblical scholars. And with this was thrown out the other like unto it in spurious origin and zealous intent, that interpolation of the word "God" in the sixteenth verse of the third chapter of the First Epistle to Timothy, which had for ages served as a warrant for condemning some of the noblest of Christians, even such men as Newton and Milton and Locke and Priestley and Channing.

Indeed, so honest were the revisers that they substituted the correct reading of Luke ii, 33, in place of the time-honoured corruption in the King James version which had been thought necessary to safeguard the dogma of the virgin birth of Jesus of Nazareth. Thus came the true reading, "*His father* and his mother," instead of the old piously fraudulent words "*Joseph* and his mother."

An even more important service to the new and better growth of Christianity was the virtual setting aside of the last twelve verses of the Gospel according to St. Mark; for among these stood that sentence which has cost the world more innocent blood than any other—the words "He that believeth not shall be damned." From this source had logi-

---

Brit., 9th edit., art. *Bible*, p. 642. For a very careful and candid summary of the reasons which are gradually leading the more eminent among the newer scholars to give up the Johannine authorship of the fourth Gospel, see Schürer, in the *Contemporary Review* for September, 1891. American readers, regarding this and the whole series of subjects of which this forms a part, may most profitably study the Rev. Dr. Cone's *Gospel Criticism and Historic Christianity*, one of the most lucid and judicial of recent works in this field.

cally grown the idea that the intellectual rejection of this or that dogma which dominant theology had happened at any given time to pronounce essential, since such rejection must bring punishment infinite in agony and duration, is a crime to be prevented at any cost of finite cruelty. Still another service rendered to humanity by the revisers was in substituting a new and correct rendering for the old reading of the famous text regarding the inspiration of Scripture, which had for ages done so much to make our sacred books a fetich. By this more correct reading the revisers gave a new charter to liberty in biblical research.[28]

Most valuable, too, have been studies during the latter part of the nineteenth century upon the formation of the canon of Scripture. The result of these has been to substitute something far better for that conception of our biblical literature, as forming one book handed out of the clouds by the Almighty, which had been so long practically the accepted view among

[28] The texts referred to as most beneficially changed by the revisers are I John v, 7, and I Timothy iii, 16. Mention may also be made of the fact that the American revision gave up the Trinitarian version of Romans ix, 5, and that even their more conservative British brethren, while leaving it in the text, discredited it in the margin.

Though the revisers thought it better not to suppress altogether the last twelve verses of St. Mark's Gospel they softened the word "damned" to "condemned," and separated them from the main Gospel, adding a note stating that "the two oldest Greek manuscripts, and some other authorities, omit from verse nine to the end"; and that "some other authorities have a different ending to this Gospel."

The resistance of staunch high churchmen of the older type even to so mild a reform as the first change above noted may be exemplified by a story told of Philpotts, Bishop of Exeter, about the middle of the nineteenth century. A kindly clergyman reading the invitation to the holy communion, and thinking that so affectionate a call was disfigured by the harsh phrase "eateth and drinketh to his own damnation," ventured timidly to substitute the word "condemnation." Thereupon the bishop, who was kneeling with the rest of the congregation, threw up his head and roared *"damnation!"* The story is given in T. A. Trollope's *What I Remember,* vol. i, p. 444. American churchmen may well rejoice that the fathers of the American branch of the Anglican Church were wise enough and Christian enough to omit from their Prayer Book this damnatory clause as well as the Commination Service and the Athanasian Creed.

probably the majority of Christians. Reverent scholars have demonstrated our sacred literature to be a growth in obedience to simple laws natural and historical; they have shown how some books of the Old Testament were accepted as sacred, centuries before our era, and how others gradually gained sanctity, in some cases only fully acquiring it long after the establishment of the Christian Church. The same slow growth has also been shown in the New Testament canon. It has been demonstrated that the selection of the books composing it, and their separation from the vast mass of spurious gospels, epistles, and apocalyptic literature was a gradual process, and, indeed, that the rejection of some books and the acceptance of others was accidental, if anything is accidental.

So, too, scientific biblical research has, as we have seen, been obliged to admit the existence of much mythical and legendary matter, as a setting for the great truths not only of the Old Testament but of the New. It has also shown, by the comparative study of literatures, the process by which some books were compiled and recompiled, adorned with beautiful utterances, strengthened or weakened by alterations and interpolations expressing the views of the possessors or transcribers, and attributed to personages who could not possibly have written them. The presentation of these things has greatly weakened that sway of mere dogma which has so obscured the simple teachings of Christ himself; for it has shown that the more we know of our sacred books, the less certain we become as to the authenticity of "proof texts," and it has disengaged more and more, as the only valuable residuum, like the mass of gold at the bottom of the crucible, the personality, spirit, teaching, and ideals of the blessed Founder of Christianity. More and more, too, the new scholarship has developed the conception of the New Testament as, like the Old, the growth of literature in obedience to law—a conception which in all probability will give it its strongest hold on the coming centuries. In making this revelation Christian scholarship has by no means done work mainly destructive. It has, indeed, swept away a mass of noxious growths, but it has at the same time cleared the ground for a better growth of Christianity—a growth through which already pulsates the current of a nobler life. It has forever destroyed the contention of scholars like those of the eighteenth century who saw, in the multitude of irreconcilable discrepancies between various biblical statements, merely evidences of priestcraft and intentional fraud.

The new scholarship has shown that even such absolute contradictions as those between the accounts of the early life of Jesus by Matthew and Luke, and between the date of the crucifixion and details of the resurrection in the first three Gospels and in the fourth, and other discrepancies hardly less serious, do not destroy the historical character of the narrative. Even the hopelessly conflicting genealogies of the Saviour and the evidently mythical accretions about the simple facts of his birth and life are thus full of interest when taken as a natural literary development in obedience to the deepest religious feeling.[29]

*   *   *

6. Reconstructive Force of Scientific Criticism

For all this dissolving away of traditional opinions regarding our sacred literature, there has been a cause far more general and powerful than any which has been given, for it is a cause surrounding and permeating all. This is simply the atmosphere of thought engendered by the development of all sciences during the last three centuries.

Vast masses of myth, legend, marvel, and dogmatic assertion, coming into this atmosphere, have been dissolved and are now dissolving quietly away like icebergs drifted into the Gulf Stream. In earlier days, when some critic in advance of his time insisted that Moses could not have written an account embracing the circumstances of his own death, it was sufficient to answer that Moses was a prophet; if attention was called to the fact that the great early prophets, by all which they did and did not do, showed that there could not have existed in their time any "Levitical code," a sufficient answer was "mystery"; and if the discrepancy was noted be-

[29] Among the newer English works on the canon of Scripture, especially as regards the Old Testament, see Ryle in work cited. As to the evidences of frequent mutilations of the New Testament text, as well as of frequent charge of changing texts made against each other by early Christian writers, see Reuss, *History of the New Testament*, vol. ii, § 362. For a reverent and honest treatment of some of the discrepancies and contradictions which are absolutely irreconcilable, see Crooker, as above, appendix; also Cone, *Gospel Criticism and Historic Christianity,* especially chap. iii; also Matthew Arnold, *Literature and Dogma,* and *God and the Bible,* especially chap. vi; and for a brief but full showing of them in a judicial and kindly spirit, see Laing, *Problems of the Future,* chap. ix, on *The Historical Element in the Gospels.*

tween the two accounts of creation in Genesis, or between the genealogies or the dates of the crucifixion in the Gospels, the cogent reply was "infidelity." But the thinking world has at last been borne by the general development of a scientific atmosphere beyond that kind of refutation.

If, in the atmosphere generated by the earlier developed sciences, the older growths of biblical interpretation have drooped and withered and are evidently perishing, new and better growths have arisen with roots running down into the newer sciences. Comparative Anthropology in general, by showing that various early stages of belief and observance, once supposed to be derived from direct revelation from heaven to the Hebrews, are still found as arrested developments among various savage and barbarous tribes; Comparative Mythology and Folklore, by showing that ideas and beliefs regarding the Supreme Power in the universe are progressive, and not less in Judea than in other parts of the world; Comparative Religion and Literature, by searching out and laying side by side those main facts in the upward struggle of humanity which show that the Israelites, like other gifted peoples, rose gradually, through ghost worship, fetichism, and polytheism, to higher theological levels; and that, as they thus rose, their conceptions and statements regarding the God they worshipped became nobler and better—all these sciences are giving a new solution to those problems which dogmatic theology has so long laboured in vain to solve. While researches in these sciences have established the fact that accounts formerly supposed to be special revelations to Jews and Christians are but repetitions of widespread legends dating from far earlier civilizations, and that beliefs formerly thought fundamental to Judaism and Christianity are simply based on ancient myths, they have also begun to impress upon the intellect and conscience of the thinking world the fact that the religious and moral truths thus disengaged from the old masses of myth and legend are all the more venerable and authoritative, and that all individual or national life of any value must be vitalized by them.[30]

[30] For plaintive lamentations over the influence of this atmosphere of scientific thought upon the most eminent contemporary Christian scholars, see the *Christus Comprobator*, by the Bishop of Gloucester and Bristol, London, 1893, and the article in the *Contemporary Review* for May, 1892, by the Bishop of Colchester, *passim*. For some less known examples of sacred myths and legends

If, then, modern science in general has acted powerfully to dissolve away the theories and dogmas of the older theologic interpretation, it has also been active in a reconstruction and recrystallization of truth; and very powerful in this reconstruction have been the evolution doctrines which have grown out of the thought and work of men like Darwin and Spencer.

In the light thus obtained the sacred text has been transformed: out of the old chaos has come order; out of the old welter of hopelessly conflicting statements in religion and morals has come, in obedience to this new conception of development, the idea of a sacred literature which mirrors the most striking evolution of morals and religion in the history of our race. Of all the sacred writings of the world, it shows us our own as the most beautiful and the most precious; exhibiting to us the most complete religious development to which humanity has attained, and holding before us the loftiest ideals which our race has known. Thus it is that, with the keys furnished by this new race of biblical scholars, the way has been opened to treasures of thought which have been inaccessible to theologians for two thousand years.

As to the Divine Power in the universe: these interpreters have shown how, beginning with the tribal god of the Hebrews—one among many jealous, fitful, unseen, local sovereigns of Asia Minor—the higher races have been borne on to the idea of the just Ruler of the whole earth, as revealed by the later and greater prophets of Israel, and finally to the belief in the Universal Father, as best revealed in the New Testament. As to man: beginning with men after Jehovah's own heart—cruel, treacherous, revengeful—we are borne on to an ideal of men who do right for right's sake; who search and speak the truth for truth's sake; who love others as themselves. As to the world at large: the races dominant in religion and morals have been lifted from the idea of a "chosen people" stimulated and abetted by their tribal god in every sort of cruelty and injustice, to the conception of a vast community in which the fatherhood of God overarches all, and the brotherhood of man permeates all.

Thus, at last, out of the old conception of our Bible as a collection of oracles—a mass of entangling utterances, fruitful in wrangling interpretations, which have given to the

---

inherited from ancient civilizations, see Lenormant, *Les Origines de l'Histoire, passim,* but especially chaps. ii, iv, v, vi; see also Goldziher.

world long and weary ages of "hatred, malice, and all uncharitableness"; of fetichism, subtlety, and pomp; of tyranny, bloodshed, and solemnly constituted imposture; of everything which the Lord Jesus Christ most abhorred—has been gradually developed through the centuries, by the labours, sacrifices, and even the martyrdom of a long succession of men of God, the conception of it as a sacred literature—a growth only possible under that divine light which the various orbs of science have done so much to bring into the mind and heart and soul of man—a revelation, not of the Fall of Man, but of the Ascent of Man—an exposition, not of temporary dogmas and observances, but of the Eternal Law of Righteousness—the one upward path for individuals and for nations. No longer an oracle, good for the "lower orders" to accept, but to be quietly sneered at by "the enlightened" —no longer a fetich, whose defenders must become persecutors, or reconcilers, or "apologists"; but a most fruitful fact, which religion and science may accept as a source of strength to both.

Epilogue

by Bruce Mazlish

THE WARFARE of science with theology in Christendom appears to be over. The autonomy of scientific thought has been vindicated, and theology, on the whole, no longer sits in judgment where science offers explanations. Concerning this subject, then, White's *History* tells us of things past.

What, however, of things to come? Of the events which have occurred since White wrote his book? Through what vicissitudes has science made its way since the end of the nineteenth century? This would make another history by itself. And what adventures lie in store for it? This would comprise a more serious form of science fiction. In our epilogue, we shall not seek to give full and weighty answers to these questions, but only to raise them in slightly more specific terms. In short, what follows are merely some brief reflections, provoked by White's work, on the relationship of scientific thought to social forces.

(1)

In considering the battle of science with theology described by White, it would be a grave error to mistake a local victory for a lasting and conclusive triumph. To begin with, the theological spirit can take many forms besides the Christian; it can manifest itself as other "theologies"—Mohammedan, Buddhist, Hindu, or tribal worship. Then, too, the fight between science and theology forms only one part of a larger conflict: the clash of science with *any* non-scientific authority. Today, this non-scientific authority may be equated mainly with the power of the state.

Let us first consider the "other theologies." If we accept the fact that the scientific revolution is a revolution primarily in ways of thinking—in a conceptual framework—then we must also accept the fact that "underdeveloped," i.e., non-industrial and scientific, nations have to pass through more or less the same intellectual change as the Western world. Science means a new world-view. Techniques and industrial processes can, undoubtedly, be learned *mechanically* (al-

502

though even this learning imposes its own conditions); science—at least creative science—cannot. We need only think of modern science, with its abstract concepts of space, time, causality, indeterminacy, relativity, etc., against a background of, say, primitive tribal religions in parts of Africa to see the disparity involved. And the case is not all that different with the so-called advanced religions: the *Koran,* to take a random example, is not *necessarily* any more compatible with scientific ways of thinking than Mau Mau practices. Arab scientists may have to struggle against their mullahs as much as Africans against their witch doctors.[1]

Naturally, these struggles have differed or will differ from the one described by White: for example, they undoubtedly take different shapes in relation to the different "theologies" involved. They can also be dramatically affected by the changed context of the modern world. In this regard, one thing seems clear. Whatever the pressures from mullahs and witch doctors, the combination in most nations of internal economic needs and external military powers—and here I neglect all the other tremendous complexities which may be involved—can give extraordinary support to the move toward science. In fact, it is exactly the tie to state authority which can bring rapid success to science in its fight against local versions of theology. We shall see later on what new dangers are posed for science in this "Popular Front" of knowledge.

For the moment, we wish to return to the warfare of science and theology per se, and to remark that the relations of these two forces really comprise part of a larger inquiry. In lieu of a better name, we can call this inquiry the sociology of knowledge (briefly, this may be defined as the attempt to replace classic epistemology—Hume and Kant—with an inquiry into the social-cultural conditions surrounding man's ways of acquiring knowledge).

Let us specify a few areas of research. As a matter of historical interest, we should like to know how and why modern science arose. For example, why did it arise only in the West, and in the period coming after the Renaissance? Why did China—an advanced country at the time of the

[1] See, for example, the recent musical play, *Kwamina,* libretto by Robert Alan Aurthur, for a dramatic portrayal of the clash between the forces of witch doctorship and modern medicine.

Renaissance—not break through to modern science? Why did the Arabs not carry through with their brilliant work of the Middle Ages? Was Western science largely a concomitant of commercial and industrial growth, i.e., owing to economic factors (as the Marxists would have it)? Rooted in a special relationship to the artisan work of the Christian Middle Ages? Connected in some special sense with the coming of Protestantism? These, and a host of similar questions, bestir the minds of some of our present-day historians of science.[2]

As a matter of contemporary, rather than historical, interest, we should like to know the conditions favoring scientific thought—its sociology—so that we may foster (or, if we oppose it, impede) its growth, whether in developed nations —England, for example—or in underdeveloped countries.

[2] On these questions, general surveys are A. C. Crombie, *Medieval and Early Modern Science,* 2 Vols., (New York, 1959); Herbert Butterfield, *The Origins of Modern Science* (New York, 1952); and A. R. Hall, *The Scientific Revolution, 1500-1800* (Boston, 1954). On Chinese science, see Joseph Needham, *Science and Civilisation in China,* 3 Vols. (Cambridge, 1954-1959). On Arabic scientific thought, there is no adequate single short work; see, however, A. Mieli, *La science arabe et son rôle dans l'evolution scientifique mondiale* (Leiden, 1938). The relationship of science and economics is discussed in G. N. Clark, *Science and Social Welfare in the Age of Newton* (Oxford, 1937) and in B. Hessen, "The Social and Economic Roots of Newton's Principia," *Science at the Crossroads* (London, 1931). For the so-called artisan work of the Middle Ages, see L. Olschki, *Geschichte der neusprachlichen wissenschaftlichen Literatur,* 3 Vols. (1919-1927). On Puritanism and science, consult Robert Merton, *Science, Technology and Society in Seventeenth Century England* (Bruges, 1938), as an example of some of the early work on this subject. Further materials are to be found in Merton's essays, "Puritanism, Pietism and Science," and "Science and Economy of 17th Century England," in his *Social Theory and Social Structure* (Glencoe, Illinois, 1949) and in Dorothy Stimson, "Puritanism and the New Philosophy in Seventeenth-Century England," *Bulletin of the Institute of the History of Medicine* (May, 1935), pp. 321-334. A contrary view as to the role of Puritanism in the scientific revolution emerges from the various articles in *The Royal Society: Its Origins and Founders,* edited by Sir Harold Hartley (London, 1960), especially the article by Douglas McKie, "The Origins and Foundation of the Royal Society of London."

The value of history to this contemporary concern is that history may serve as a laboratory of sorts, in which a number of variables can be observed. (Caution, of course, is required; the number of variables may be legion, and we may not be able to "vary" the variables in any really satisfactory way.) Looked at in this way, the subject of White's *History*—the conflict of science and theology in Christendom—takes its place as one piece in a large puzzle.

(2)

If, in our reflections on White's book, we backtrack for a moment, we can observe the full measure of the vindication of scientific thought from Western theological authority in a special case not dealt with by him: the so-called Freudian revolution.

Before Freud, the human ego had already received two "traumatic" shocks: the Copernican and the Darwinian. Copernicus had removed man's abode—the earth—from its central place in the cosmos; and we have seen the delayed shock effect of this displacement break out in the trial of Galileo. Darwin, in his turn, had removed the nimbus of unique creation surrounding man and shown him an image of himself in unbroken continuity with the rest of the animal world. The repercussions of this new disillusionment were still evident as late as the famous Scopes trial in 1925, where Darrow and Bryan acted out a modern passion play.

Then, standing on the shoulders of Darwin, Freud removed what may be the final veil shrouding man's "naturalness." He looked at man as "a natural object, amenable to the same objective, disinterested approach as previously used by man on the non-human materials of nature." The result was to eliminate the dichotomy, not only between man and the other animals, as Darwin had done, but between civilized man and the primitive; normal man and the pervert; adult man and the child. Man was now at one with the universe—but in a scientific instead of religious sense.

Freud's challenge to religion, however, was not left merely implicit. He carried the fight directly to the enemy. Religion, he claimed, was an illusion; almost a neurosis. It was a way of evading reality. Starting with animism (and totemism), early man had risen to the lofty illusions of the great world religions, and Freud dealt with the psychic mechanisms involved in this evolution in various of his writings.[3] In man's evolution, Freud suggested in the *New Introductory Lectures in Psychoanalysis,* religion is really a "parallel to the neurosis which the civilized individual must pass through on his way from childhood to maturity."

It is interesting, in this connection, to compare Freud and White. The latter, as we have seen, is perhaps most seriously outdated—and understandably so—in his chapter on "From 'Demoniacal Possession' to Insanity," where he ascribes all lunacy to physical disease. Although the two men have much in common—they both start from a shared basis in comparative myth and legend, and, for both, religion is an evolution, marking various stages of the human psyche—there remains, of course, a major difference: White makes no attempt to explore the mechanism of the psyche, while Freud does. From this difference, too, springs another major distinction: while White separates theology from religion, in favor of the latter, Freud treats them both as part of a unified phenomenon.

As a result of this last difference, whereas White conceives of man's nature as partly spiritual, Freud conceives of it as cultural; and, further, as subject to "mechanistic" explanation. In the Freudian scheme, as part of man's total culture, religion has no sanctity shielding it from scientific inquiry. Science alone aims at a correspondence with reality and can tell us what is true. The truth it tells us is that religion is an illusion, masquerading as a truth about ourselves and the universe. As such, Freud tells us in the *New Introductory Lectures,* "religion alone is a really serious enemy" to science. Then, in words that remind us of the main theme of White's *History,* he suggests, "The struggle between the scientific spirit and the religious *Weltanschauung* is not yet at an end; it is still going on under our very eyes today."

To go into detail about Freud's work is not to our purpose in these reflections. Suffice it to say that he believed it time for man "to put childish vanities away" and to evolve into maturity by putting religion behind him. A large part of Freud's work, in fact, is a major offensive in the struggle between science and religion.

The extraordinary thing is that, in spite of the gauntlet

[3] In addition to the *New Introductory Lectures on Psychoanalysis,* see *Totem and Taboo, The Future of an Illusion,* and *Moses and Monotheism.*

so defiantly thrown down, there has been no pitched battle between psychoanalysis and the churches. Without forgetting some of the early resistance to Freud's work—on the part of scholars and ordinary people, universities and medical schools —we can only marvel at its pacific reception. In spite of touching man at his quickest point—his psyche, or soul— psychoanalysis has not called forth the vituperation and the violent condemnation occasioned by the Copernican solar hypothesis or the Darwinian theory of evolution. There has been no combat to match the Galileo or Scopes trials. If anything, the various churches have quietly appropriated for themselves some of the Freudian revelations, and have added psychiatric counseling to their spiritual admonitions.[4]

No greater testimonial could be given to the conclusion that the churches have learned, through bitter experience, not to contest science on scientific grounds. There has been almost no effort, therefore, by non-professionals to refute psychoanalysis in terms of its clinical evidence. The couch and the analyst's office have been treated with almost as much respect as the test tube and the laboratory: their results are beyond the pale of non-scientific discussion.

This is not to say that the churches have accepted the Freudian *Weltanschauung* (to treat Freudianism, for the moment, as one; Freud himself denied that it was), or that they have abandoned their own beliefs. It is simply to say that the churches now accept the empirical findings of science, and restrict themselves largely to pronouncing, with more or less vigor, on the moral and spiritual aspects of the effect of science upon society.

Why this specific reaction to Freudianism and this general reaction to science? I suspect that, on the first point, Freudianism, one major reason is simply that the fight concerning Scripture is over. Aside from fundamentalists—now relatively few in number—the "Higher Criticism" of the Bible enjoys general, though perhaps unspoken, acceptance. Far too many people, *especially* in the theological schools and the pulpits, where a good deal of knowledge on the subject prevails, have an uneasy conscience as to the "revealed" aspect of the sacred books: the odor, "human, all too human," pervades the atmosphere of both the Old and New

[4] Interestingly enough, the real opposition on the part of non-scientific authority to Freudian inquiry has come in the Soviet Union.

Testaments.[5] Looked at from this viewpoint, Freudian science does not so much attack the holy books as help us better to understand them as great and wonderful expressions of the human spirit.[6]

As to the second point—the general reaction to science by the churches—the explanation here, I believe, is simply that religion has been superseded as a power and an authority by Leviathan: the State. This, however, is to introduce a new subject, one which we must treat separately from the settlement White has described so effectively as occurring between science and theology.

(3)

The Thirty Years' War is as good a place as any to notice the displacement of religious authority by state interests. Starting in 1618 as primarily a war between Protestant and Catholic factions, it ended in 1648 with France, a Catholic nation, on the side of the original Protestant powers, against Catholic Austria: the reason, pure reasons of state. The Treaty of Westphalia in 1648 marks in a dramatic way, then, the transition from religion as the dominant power in moving men to the newer secular concerns of *homo politicus*.[7]

In the realm of ideas, too, the churches appear to have abandoned their authority in the seventeenth century. The last real pretence of religion to judge the legitimacy of political power by appeal to divine origin was effectively ended by the corrosive thought of investigators like Hobbes and Locke, who took up the work of Machiavelli and made political philosophy henceforward a purely secular matter. Economics was also removed from the aegis of religious authority, and such items as price and the taking of interest

[5] It must be mentioned, of course, that one can admit the direct human authorship of the sacred texts while yet maintaining that the authors have been touched by the hand of God working through other means than revelation.
[6] Throughout this section, I have been accepting the term "science" as a correct description for Freud's researches. For a discussion as to the legitimacy of this use, see, for example, some of the essays in *Psychoanalysis, Scientific Method and Philosophy. A Symposium* edited by Sidney Hook (New York, 1959).
[7] An echo of this transition would seem to be the Puritan Revolution in England from 1640 to 1660, which, starting largely as a combined religious-constitutional quarrel, ended in a *politique* fashion.

became matters of economic calculation rather than of ethical judgment; beginning with the practitioners of "political arithmetic" and of physiocracy, this development found its fulfillment in Adam Smith.

Thus, by the eighteenth century the emancipation of the social sciences from the tutelage of religion is as much an accomplished fact as is the freeing of natural science; and while White perhaps has emphasized the latter, he has also contributed to telling the tale of the former.[8]

The removal of religious authority did not necessarily mean the autonomy of science—natural or social—from any and all non-scientific authority. After the last throes of religious presumption in scientific matters—the Darwinian controversy—there arose, or better still remained, as we have already suggested, another claimant to outside authority: the State. The latter's relationship to science involves a long history, and takes its rise from about the same period as that in which White's warfare of science and theology flared at its mightiest.

Indeed, the theme of science in the *service* of the state is announced right from the beginning of the modern period. Thus, for example, Leonardo da Vinci placed his knowledge at the feet of Ludovico Sforza, lord of Milan, in a boastful letter which talked, not of painting skills, but of expertise in building bridges and fortresses, constructing tunnels and mines, and flinging projectiles. Surprisingly enough, the great and independent Galileo, in an effort to secure a position at the court of the Grand Duke of Tuscany, wrote the same sort of boastful fawning letter. Promising "such inventions as no other prince can match, for of these I have a great many and am certain I can find more as occasion presents itself," Galileo candidly admits that "Great and remarkable things are mine, but I can only serve (or rather, be put to work by) princes; for it is they who carry on wars, build and defend fortresses, and in their royal diversions make those great expenditures which neither I nor other private persons may."

The purse strings—these are what the state controls.

---

[8] The classic account of the emancipation of economics from religion is, of course, R. H. Tawney, *Religion and the Rise of Capitalism* (New York, 1947). Tawney, incidentally, seems to suggest that the autonomy of economic science from ethical judgment—not necessarily the same as clerical judgment—is not wholly a good thing.

Private persons may serve as patrons for Spenser's poems or Shakespeare's plays, but only the rulers can effectively and continuously subsidize scientific research. And this holds, even in a period when almost all scientific research was an individual matter.

Of course, what is emerging in the seventeenth century onwards is only a tendency to state control of science: the relations of states to science were not simple and uniform, and varied widely from example to example. We see some of the problems nicely illuminated by the divergent histories of the early Royal Society and the *Académie des Sciences*. In the English case, the Society, though under the royal namesake and implied patronage of the King, Charles II, received almost no government support. Reflecting English traditions of self-government and local initiative, the Society's members financed their own experiments—Boyle, for example, had all sorts of air pumps and other equipment built at his own expense—and paid for the publication of their *Philosophical Transactions* by hawking public subscriptions. Nevertheless, the government did turn to the Society and command it to undertake certain investigations—for example, related to navigation or to hydraulics—in the service of state needs.[9]

In France, the state needs were directly linked to the *Académie des Sciences*. The motive which inspired Colbert to establish and support a scientific academy was purely utilitarian: the Academy took its place with his forced growth of the state tapestry-weaving industry. The French state recruited the scientists—for example, hiring foreigners like the Dutchman, Christian Huygens, the Academy's first President—and paid them extremely high salaries. In return, the King and his Minister expected the scientists to work on problems which would directly benefit the power position of the state.

Enough has been said here, it is hoped, to suggest that the relationship of state subsidy to science has varied, as might be expected, according to traditions of government between two poles: a loose form of sponsored research and a tight form of state control and financial support. A history of this entire relationship awaits the writing. It seems more than

[9] See, for example, Robert Merton, "Science and Economy of 17th Century England," in *Social Theory and Social Structure* (Glencoe, Illinois, 1949).

likely such a study will show that, while the really great discoveries continue to be made by isolated figures—Newton, Darwin, Freud, Einstein—the steady direction of the bulk of modern science has been toward sponsored research— whether by private industry or directly by the state; and increasingly by the latter, who alone can pay for the gigantic tools and equipment needed: 200" telescopes, cyclotrons, nuclear reactors, and giant computers.

The question, however, of who pays for science, while important in itself, is not *necessarily* the same as who controls—or seeks to control—science. Thus, it does not matter whether a religious body or the English navy financed the voyage of the *Beagle* which ultimately resulted in Darwin's theory of evolution: it is a question of which authority claims to sit in judgment on the findings. Though it is true that one way of exercising this judgment is to refuse money or equipment to unpopular scientists, the more important issues arise over scientific findings and theories already produced and propounded.

Once again, we can appeal to Galileo for a formulation of the problem. In his *Letter to the Grand Duchess Christina* he attacked theological authorities who "decide on controversies in professions which they have neither studied nor practiced," in terms which have an uncanny applicability to political authorities today: "Why, this would be as if an absolute despot, being neither a physician nor an architect but knowing himself free to command, should undertake to administer medicines and erect buildings according to his whim—at grave peril of his poor patients' lives and the speedy collapse of his edifices."[10]

Surely, the name of Stalin leaps immediately to our modern attention. Neither a physician nor an architect—yet, he pontificated about the budding of plants and the building of edifices. Hitler, too, had his say about these matters: with perhaps more knowledge of architecture, he designed state opera houses; but with equally little knowledge of the natural sciences, he banned the theories of Einstein, a Jew. One wonders even, to bring the matter closer to home, whether the Oppenheimer case in America would not fit into roughly the same category: of decisions—and punishments—by poli-

---

[10] The translation used here is by Stillman Drake, who has edited *Discoveries and Opinions of Galileo* (Doubleday Anchor, 1957), p. 193.

tical authorities who "decide on controversies in professions which they have neither studied nor practiced."

In the cases just cited, the authority has been the state, not the church. Yet the challenge to the autonomy of scientific thought is the same. The historian of this warfare will have to devote a chapter to the vicissitudes of science under Nazi Germany, and long chapters and sections to the relationship of Soviet Marxism and Natural Science, wherein prominent attention will be given to the experience of Freudianism and the doctrines of Lysenko. One wonders, too, what sad examples may have to be cited from the trials and tribulations of science in the more democratic countries.

Our task here, of course, is not to write that history. (Indeed, as we have been repeatedly saying, our only purpose in this epilogue is to propose certain reflections.) One comment—or hazardous prophecy—however, seems in order. It is, to paraphrase Lenin's supposed comment of "He who wills the end, wills the means," "He who wishes the power offered by modern science must will the means to that power: free and autonomous scientific inquiry." Willy-nilly, I believe, and *in the long run,* the modern state must and will learn that the only people to pass judgment on scientific matters are scientists. Undoubtedly, before the lesson is learned, there will be many unfortunate episodes—most of them trivial, a few of Galileo-like proportions—in many countries. However, a study of the relationship of Soviet Marxist state power with Russian scientists would appear to validate this view: after the sad spectacle of Stalin—Galileo's twentieth-century "absolute despot"—and his imposition of non-scientific authority over scientific matters, a new era appears to have dawned (at least in relation to the natural sciences).[11] What can be more revealing than the following recent statement of Khrushchev, in reference to the controversy over the "grass-arable" system of crop rotation versus rotation with beans and corn?

> You, Comrade Vlasuk, do not understand what the party is, and have a bad understanding of the duties of a member of the party. You say that Comrade Khrushchev said this and

[11] The best work in this area is David Joravsky, *Soviet Marxism and Natural Science, 1917-1932* (New York, 1961), with a sequel promised.

at—am I to be the highest judge on the question of agri-cultural science? You are the president of the Ukrainian Academy of Agricultural Sciences, and I am the secretary of the Central Committee (of the Soviet Communist Party). It is you who must help me, not I who should help you. I may make mistakes. And you, if you are an honest scientist, must say: "Comrade Khrushchev, you do not understand this question quite correctly." If you explain to me how to understand it correctly, I shall thank you.[12]

Then Khrushchev added, "Mere bootlicking is unscientific." How Galileo would have glowed with pleasure if Pope Urban VIII had addressed these words to him in 1632!

The story just told ought not to suggest, however, that non-scientific authority, in the Soviet or anywhere, has withdrawn or will withdraw completely from scientific matters. Quite the contrary. The present-day non-scientific authority, in this case, the state, like the clerical organizations before it, may have accepted the autonomy of science on scientific grounds; it hardly needs saying that the state is increasingly involved, however, with the moral, social, and political implications of scientific work. Thus, problems of fluoridation and fall-out, birth control and selective breeding, nuclear energy and climatic control are very much to the fore, and here the data of science are mere starting points for policy decisions taken largely on non-scientific grounds.

On this last matter—a huge and important topic—we shall restrict ourselves to only one reflection: that perhaps policy decisions, on non-scientific grounds, are the only ones possible. Certainly, this is the situation at the moment; and it will remain so unless we develop more certain human sciences. Whether we can develop such human sciences is itself a major question today: the complexity of the materials, the nature of values, etc., all raise truly formidable obstacles. And whether, if we did create such human sciences, society would accept them, leads us even further into the unpredictable future. Who knows what Galileo of the coming centuries will be needed to establish the autonomy of a "science" of man and society? But all this is to abandon the plain dress of the historian for the flowing robes of the prophet.

[12] This story is reported in the New York Herald Tribune, Dec. 26, 1961.

(4)

Let us be more pedestrian, and return to the present. Science may, broadly speaking, have triumphed completely on its own terrain. It may, in fact, be partially successful in imposing its general view—the scientific approach—as the *Weltanschauung* of the modern world. The scientist may be the culture hero of our time. But the exceptions to the scientific influence are large and numerous; and it would be presumptuous to overlook them.

If myths about Adam and chosen people no longer enthrall as they formerly did, there are new, powerful myths about race or class which have taken their place.[13] Against the myth of the master race, the dry findings of biological science seem to have had little effect; and even an advanced scientific society, such as the United States, in many parts of the country, appears little better in this regard than certain other outposts of Western civilization in, say, Africa. If the belief in witches on brooms has faded, paranoic "witch-hunts" have only shortly dropped out of fashion in the Soviet Union, the number two nation in scientific progress, and even in America there have been recent spasms and twitchings in the political arena. And if modern scientists perfect polio vaccines and perform extraordinary operations, there are still Billy Grahams producing miracle healings (even using such modern wonders as TV) and Christian Scientists increasing their numbers. (There is a rather wonderful irony in the first American space explorer, Alan B. Shepard, Jr., being a Christian Scientist.)

Nor is the challenge to science which started perhaps with Rousseau's *Discourse on the Arts and Sciences,* wherein he condemned progress in science and technology as leading to moral degradation, by any means over. The annoyed reaction of many of the nineteenth-century Romantics to the depersonalization of the universe—and worse, of man—is echoed by so recent a figure as D. H. Lawrence, who rejected petulantly the scientific explanation of the nature of the moon with the cry: "It's no use telling me it's a dead rock in the sky! I *know* it's not"; and even more recently by the

13 On myth, see, for example, Ernst Cassirer, *The Myth of the State* (New Haven, 1946), and the collection of essays by various authors, *Race and Science* (New York, 1961).

controversy revolving around the so-called Two Cultures.[14] There are still, then, many in contemporary society—even of the "advanced" nations—who reject either the products or the outlook—or both—of modern science.

The only fitting conclusion to White's book, therefore, would seem to be the following: the warfare of science with theology in Christendom which he describes so well is simply part of a continuing conflict—a conflict which takes its rise from the contradictory nature of man: rational and irrational, creator of his own conditions and conditioned by forces seemingly beyond his control. The tension generated by these warring elements is not a mere transient phase of man's existence: as long as he remains human, it will be his problem—and his glory. When it ceases, we will no longer be recording history, which by definition deals with human beings. Only then will White's book be classic in the sense of talking of a dead past; until then, it is classic in the sense of being a vital contribution to man's ever-contemporary quest for knowledge and control of the universe and of himself—in short, the quest for scientific understanding.

[14] For the relationship of the new science to literature see Basil Willey, *The Seventeenth Century Background* (Doubleday Anchor, 1953), especially Chapter XII, "On Wordsworth and the Locke Tradition." For the two cultures, see C. P. Snow, *The Two Cultures and the Scientific Revolution* (New York, 1959); I am also indebted to Snow for the story about D. H. Lawrence, cited by him in another place. It should be evident, I hope, that to remark on the "romantic" reaction to science is not to deny this reaction *any* value; from the literary point of view, a certain type of scientific thought may be antithetical to imaginative writing.

Index

Aaron, 351
Abelard, 440, 441n.
Aben Ezra, 449, 462
Abraham, 155, 433
Abraham, St., 352
Academie des Sciences, 510
Academy of Science, Vienna, 81
Acosta, Emanuel, 297-298, 306-307
    cited, 301n.
Acosta, Joseph, 121, 298-299, 308, 310, 345
Adam, 77, 92, 405
Adams, John, 284, 285n.
Adams, W. E., cited, 108n.
Adams, W. H. D., cited, 333n.
Addison, 175
Adelung, on philology, 416
Ælfric, 250n.
Æsculapius, 155, 291
Agassiz, Louis, 90, 91, 243
Agnus Dei, 262, 263n., 269, 315
Agobard, Archbishop, 270, 439
    theory of insanity, 370, 383
    cited, 270n., 441n.
Agrippa, Cornelius, of Nettesheim, 273
d'Aguesseau, on sorcery, 384
d'Ailly, Cardinal, 115, 251
Albert the Great, 452
    on comets, 158, 161
    on Aristotle, 250
    on storms, 258
    cited, 158n., 453n.
Alby, Council of, 329
Alcuin, 320
Alexander I, Pope, 262
Alexander III, Pope, 321
Alexander of Tralles, on insanity, 366
Alexandria, 428, 432
    school of, 292
Alexis, Czar, 447
Alfred the Great, 440

Allegory, in Scripture, 432-438
Alliez, Abbé, cited, 289n.
Almamon, 319
Almeida, on Xavier, 302
Aloidae, legend of, 408
Amabile, cited, 148n.
Ambrose, St., 55n., 62, 245
America, 430
    opposition, to Darwinism, 93
        to inoculation, 340
    witchcraft in, 387, 396-403
American Historical Society, 14n.
Amsterdam, 455
Amulets, demand for, 315
Analysis, spectrum, 66
Anatomy, study opposed, 316, 317, 331, 333-339
Anaximander, on evolution, 63, 74, 75
Anaximenes, on evolution, 63, 75
Ancyra, Synod of, 374
Anesthetics, opposition to, 339-346
Anfossi, 151
Angelis, Father Augustin de, 270
Angels, hierarchy of, 119
Angelus, the, 166
Angoulême, Duchesse d', 266
Animals, theology and, 78, 376-377
Anthony, St., of Egypt, 325, 352, 382
Anthony, St., of Padua, 327, 363
Anthropology, 221-237, 499
Anugîta, cited, 356n.
Apian, Peter, 121, 168
Apocalypse, 127, 351
Apollonia, St., 325
Apostles' Creed, 60, 316, 336, 441
Arabic medicine, 319
    language, 415
Arago, cited, 171n., 266n.
Arbuthnot, 284

FREE PRESS PAPERBACKS

A Series of Paperbound Books in the Social and Natural Sciences, Philosophy, and the Humanities

These books, chosen for their intellectual importance and editorial excellence, are printed on good quality book paper, in large and readable type, and are Smyth-sewn for enduring use. Free Press Paperbacks conform in every significant way to the high editorial and production standards maintained in the higher-priced, case-bound books published by The Free Press.

**Many of these books are available in their original cloth bindings.
A complete catalogue of all Free Press titles will be sent on request**